THE
PUBLIC
ARTS

GILBERT SELDES

SIMON AND SCHUSTER · NEW YORK

1956

First Printing

LIBRARY OF CONGRESS CATALOG CARD NUMBER: 56-7488
MANUFACTURED IN THE UNITED STATES OF AMERICA
BY H. WOLFF BOOK MFG. CO., INC., NEW YORK, N. Y.

To Edward R. Murrow and Jimmy Durante

DEAR JIMMY AND ED:

I don't know whether you know one another, but I'm sure you don't need me to introduce you. Part of the good fortune of my life has been knowing both of you fairly well, and I dedicate this book to each of you, separately, in affection.

Professionally I dedicate it to you together because the two fields in which you work are parts of one field, each essential to the other. I wasn't prophetic enough to see this when I wrote The 7 Lively Arts in praise of the gaiety and vigor of our popular entertainments, and I wasn't detached enough to see this when I wrote in The Great Audience a rather ominous warning that these same popular arts which are also the mass media might be used to keep us complacent and perpetually immature. It would be silly for me to make excuses now for failing to see that the lively arts and the mass media are two aspects of the same phenomenon, which I now call "the public arts." When I wrote my first book the engineers were still thinking of radio as a method of private communication and the revolution in American life which began when Station KDKA broadcast the results of the Harding-Cox election was a year away. So I wrote about the pleasures the lively arts were creating. I had less excuse for the stingy way I treated the same pleasures in The Great Audience, but, like many other people, I was obsessed at the time with the questions the mass media were raising and my book was out of balance. I didn't see that, while the Murrows and the Durantes worked on opposite sides of the street, it was the same street, that each needed the other, and the audience needed both.

This connection between the things you two are doing, so obvious on the surface and so far-reaching in its effects, is the connecting link between my various approaches to our contemporary popular arts and the problems they bring up. You will not take me too seriously if I say I've been working toward my own "unified field theory." To it you supplied the clue, and although I didn't set out to write a book in order to dedicate it to you, I discovered, halfway through, that whole sections were organizing themselves around you, so that the book dedicated itself, leaving to me only the pleasure of telling you why.

The name I have given to the field in which you both work—the public arts—has the merit of brevity and reminds us that none of us can be entirely a private person any more. We may not be too conscious of duties to our fellow men, but we are all damnably aware of what our fellow men, at home and abroad, can do to us. We enjoy a good laugh and the next moment see rising into the sky the great symbol of our time, the mushroom cloud, and I think we are not to be blamed if our laughter is not so light and quick as it was twenty-five years ago. Neither we nor the arts we practice and enjoy exist in a vacuum. They have changed and we have changed and, more than either, the world around us has changed so profoundly that we hardly seem to breathe the same air we breathed a generation ago. Indeed, the composition of the air as we know it today tells the whole story; for the jet plane and the H-bomb on one side and, on the other, the TV signal crossing a continent, promising to cross the five oceans if the plane and the bomb will only give us a little time—these are the new elements in the air, and we breathe them in with oxygen and nitrogen as if our existence depended on them, our security and our happiness.

To a great extent they do. And our dependence, for our pleasures and for our ideas on the popular arts, on the movies and radio and television particularly, gives another significance to the word "public." You represent institutions as powerful in shaping our lives as our schools, our politics, our system of government—and anything that affects the entire public is by nature compelled to serve the public. You represent the whole business which can justify itself only if it deserves well of the people and the people have the right to make sure that the service is well rendered. The right and, I think, the duty. The 165,000,000 of us, "we, the people," have sovereign rights over you. The world is too complex, and living in the world is too hazardous, for any instrument affecting all of us to be allowed to get out of our control.

In such a world it isn't hard to define your service to us: life would be less good without you, and if one of you makes life more pleasurable, the other makes it more understandable, which is also a kind of pleasure, and the most important thing is that you should, as you do, interact. For the comedian creates an audience and hands it over to the news analyst, and when that audience has met statesmen and philosophers and demagogues and poets it returns to the comedian, living more fully, using more of its faculties. Am I describing an ideal situation? I am describing a situation that is on the way to becoming real, and it is the task of broadcasters and citizens and statesmen to make sure that the process is not interrupted or reversed. That it can be reversed, that the comedian may prevent the audience from going to the news analyst, is a gloomy foreboding which I have often felt and which, I fear, I have induced in others. It is still my considered judgment that this can happen, that we may create two audiences—a vast one for the entertainers, a tiny one for the communicators—and this would mean that the public arts had failed in their duty to a democratic people. This can happen, it may happen; and every intelligent man and woman ought to be aware of the possibility. A critic or a statesman who pretends that the danger doesn't exist is simply irresponsible. He is like a health officer who will not send out warnings of an epidemic because it would make him unpopular. An epidemic of bad morals or bad taste can be almost as dangerous as an outbreak of typhus, and this is what I felt during the writing of The Great Audience, *the tone of which was ominous. But, as you will see, I have now returned to my first discovery about all the popular arts —that nothing is final about them. Competition for public favor may lead to degradation, but it must lead to change, and as long as change occurs we need never be without hope.*

You have seen many changes, and you have not only seen but have yourselves been conspicuous examples of another phenomenon: the persistence of the first-rate. Against the superstition that the public always prefers the mediocre stands the eminent fact that in the fiercely competitive race for public favor the consistent winners have almost all been the best in their class. The consistent ones, the ones that "stay up there." The great public is as apt to fall for a phony as the critics are (and the philosophers and the artists), but give people adequate time to become acquainted with the special quality of one man's work as compared to another's and in the long run they will make the better man the winner, with place and show for the rest. There are a few neglected geniuses, to be sure, but the real danger is that the public arts will succumb to their own routines, that experiments will become fewer and fewer, that new things will be only superficially different from the old and good things will not be allowed time enough to take hold, to root themselves, to live. These arts are dreadfully at the mercy of time. In the older ones the chance for a revival remains: a Melville can be brought back from near oblivion and a change in taste can restore to favor a Berlioz or a Delacroix. But in the expensive mass arts we are all out for instantaneous success; we have no time for that kind of slow excellence which we will eventually admire but which now has something harsh and rebarbative about it, so we cannot give it our instant applause. Productions that are instantly successful may be the very best, but they do not always have the germ of new life in them; they are only the perfection of what has gone before. To continue growing, we need some special strength, and it is found often enough in unexpected and even unexplored places.

This is a long letter of dedication, and if it concerns myself and my side of our mutual interest more than yours, remember that you get your due inside the book.

Only one thing more: I have to ask you to take what I have written about you as a tribute to your fellow workers as well. This is not an encyclopedia of entertainment, and I have omitted many talented people in the first rank of popularity, and even some of the first order of excellence, in the confidence that your two names will represent and symbolize the satisfactions as well as the perplexities we always encounter in the public arts.

G. S.

CONTENTS

THE
PUBLIC
ARTS

1

THE REVOLUTION

This book is fundamentally the story of a revolution. For convenience, the beginning of that revolution can be placed in the late summer of 1929, when millions of Americans, with more money to spend on recreation than they had ever had before, spent nothing because they were staying home to be entertained by the *Amos 'n' Andy* radio program.

That revolution is still going on, affecting our lives in a hundred different ways, providing us with new forms of entertainment which are at the same time new instruments of communication, their power so great that they impose on us the positive obligation to control and direct them. Like all fundamental changes in society, this revolution has many aspects. The one I am concerned with is the transformation of those entertainments which once could properly be called "the lively arts" into "the public arts," and it is a pleasant paradox that this transformation begins with the arrival of entertainment, via radio, into the privacy of the home. Until that moment entertainment had been individual; from that moment it began to be universal. It had been needed and it became indispensable, as much a part of the American household as the telephone and, when radio developed into television, more cherished than the motorcar. When payments lapsed in installment buying, the TV set was the last item to be sacrificed. It had become what entertainment had never been before—a free and continuous and integrated part of the daily home life of an entire nation.

We can measure the extent of the revolution by a little exercise of the imagination. Think of a prosperous merchant in 1910 coming home to hear from his wife that the servants would all leave unless they had a small orchestra and a comedian to entertain them at their work. And then quickly think of a cook being told today that she couldn't have a radio in the kitchen.

There had been omens of change for many years. The appetite for entertainment had been growing, and the machinery for duplicating the printed page, the phonograph record and eventually the motion-picture film brought quantity production into the field. But the comic strip and the popular fiction magazine and the recorded recitation or ragtime tune were read and heard individually, and the motion picture, seen by hundreds of thousands in theaters scattered over the entire country, still had the quality of earlier entertainment. People went to the movie house when they had the time and the money, or let their children go as a reward for good behavior. Going to the movies became a habit—but one still had to go and to pay. A fully realized form of entertainment in an egalitarian democracy had to be so inexpensive as to appear to be free and had to be enjoyed by millions of people at the same time.

The American people became aware of radio as an instrument of communication when Station KDKA in Pittsburgh announced the election of Harding in 1920. A few years later it was so far on its way to becoming the first universal entertainment that churches postponed midweek gatherings and movie houses delayed their evening shows long enough for people to listen to the Amos 'n' Andy program at home or, in many places, announced that the program would be heard before the beginning of Bible class or the feature picture. That change—from radio as a carrier of news and ideas to radio as a virtually endless entertainment—is another aspect of the revolution.

One factor in radio's conquest of the American people was the publicity it acquired. People who had no receivers read about the stunts and triumphs of the new invention and began to hear names of people and odd phrases like "I'se regusted" in the conversations around them. In that respect the movies had done at least as well. As far back as 1916 Charlie Chaplin and Mary Pickford ran a headline race to be the first to sign a million-dollar contract. The fan magazine and the clubs of idolaters came into being and were not matched in radio until the crooner began to enchant the bobby-soxer. The movies anticipated radio also in side effects—in providing models of behavior. It was never proved that they turned children into delinquents, but when Clark Gable removed his shirt in a movie and showed his bare skin the sale of undershirts dropped so low that manufacturers begged the star to let himself be seen in one in a later picture, and when two stars toasted each other in pink champagne the stock of this wine was immediately exhausted. These trifles were symptomatic. The movies reached one of their summits of extravagance during the 1920s and reflected and also exaggerated a kind of opulent standard of life, so that ideals of excellence and of ways of living were affected by what we saw on the screen.

This is one of the distinctive marks by which we recognize the public arts. And because other arts of high quality are not so marked, they are outside the scope of this book. The pleasurable art of the musical show, more beautifully practiced here than anywhere else in the world, has only the slightest public effect, and on the whole it seems to me that all our music (except when it is broadcast) is in the same class. The phenomenon of "rock 'n' roll" has, to be sure, been observed by the law. State police have kept their eyes on roadhouses where the young enthusiasts for this music congregate, but only to make sure that illegal liquor is not added to the excitement of the songs. On the other hand, the suspicion that the "comic" horror book is an active contributor to juvenile delinquency would bring it directly into my field and would be, in contrast to the arts treated here, the only one that has no charm, no skill, no merit of any kind, imposing itself on public attention by its unredeemed vulgarity, the suspicion of its viciousness, and its unquestioned popularity. As the only positive question it brings up—the question of censorship—rises also in connection with television and the movies, I have preferred to treat it there. Whether the horror book actually is a contributor to juvenile delinquency is not a question I can usefully discuss.

All the other greatly popular entertainments have style and wit and intelligence—not all of them in the same degree, to be sure. All of them are interesting to the adult mind. And one of them has, at different times, given promise of becoming the single really new art of our time. The story of the movies is not conclusive; on the other hand, it is not ended.

Certainly it is the proper place to begin.

2

THE LOVELY ART: MOVEMENT

Twenty-five years after the movies began to talk, a reputation began to solidify into a phrase: "the one incontestable genius of the screen." It was applied to Charlie Chaplin. It became familiar and irritating, like the parentheses in *Time*: Charles ("The Incontestable") Chaplin.

He might himself have noted that the phrase grew common just at the time when political and religious boycotts had ruined one of his best pictures; he might have been pleased that the same estimate was put on record by Samuel Goldwyn, who sympathized little with those ideas which eventually forced Chaplin into exile from the United States. Not by Mr. Goldwyn, but by many others, the phrase was only a prelude to an attack on his private life. Irony is not a prime constituent in Chaplin's temperament, and he would have found small satisfaction in the added circumstance that the tribute was usually based on those silent or semi-silent pictures which are now museum pieces. There can be, however, a low compensation in being reduced to a cliché, for these same museum pieces, especially the full-length features, make a sizable fortune for Chaplin when reissued with musical accompaniment, and, although avarice is not so marked a trait in him as his detractors assert, he is entitled to one satisfaction: the proceeds from the reissue of *City Lights*, after a boycott had killed *Monsieur Verdoux*, made it possible for Chaplin to finance *Limelight*. It is now difficult for many people to think of him as an artist; they have been told by critics and headline-writers and occasionally by Chaplin himself that he is a political figure. I make my guess that in the fullness of time he will return to his original place—pre-eminently the creative genius of the popular arts.

One other figure moves forward on the screen of our memory: Greta Garbo. Enigmatical as Chaplin is plain, reserved as he is aggressive, she is parallel and opposite to him in this also: as he is the great genius who fully expressed himself on the screen, she haunts us as the image of unfulfilled, eternally possible, unrealized greatness. If Hollywood had a collective conscience, a sense of something like guilt would fall upon it whenever her name was mentioned, but perhaps not of actual guilt because there is no proof that film was the only right medium for Garbo, that she had talent greater than the screen ever used. What she did have was not always well used; between her own temperament, as perceived by her directors, and the needs of her studio, many pictures were spoiled and many others were left undone. It is as if professionally she died young, her talents still scattered, never in a single picture completely focused, matured, beyond criticism—but having left on us an impression of matchless grandeur waiting for the perfect moment, the perfect movie, to reveal itself. In any long-range view of the movies, these two images, of Garbo and Chaplin, zoom toward us until they fill almost the entire screen of our memory. But this distorts the picture, because if we focus sharply on them alone, everything in the background will be fuzzy and the contours blurred. To get a clear and comprehensive view we must think not so much of what these two individuals were, but rather what they witnessed—not so much what they did for the movies as what the movies made it possible for them to do.

I want to take a long view of the movies and I know that it is bound to be distorted by nostalgia, by my own commitment to them, from their earliest days, as a lovely art. To prevent myself from losing perspective entirely, I am going to put in the foreground a close view of the movies as they were in a recent year, at a moment of crisis: the last full year before the coming of the wide screen and three-dimensional effects—the year 1952. The pictures in the running for the Academy Awards included *Come Back, Little Sheba* and *The Member of the Wedding*; most of the lists of the best pictures of that year mentioned *The Quiet Man*, Chaplin's *Limelight*, and *High Noon*; still current were *Five Fingers* and

The Fourposter; just gone was *Cry, the Beloved Country.* Omitting all importations, even from England, these pictures carry with them a distinct sense of quality, and I note that a certain response to quality can be counted on, for one of the shrewdest and most intelligent satirical comedies of the past twenty years, *Born Yesterday,* and a tragic picture with an intensely personal outlook on life, *A Streetcar Named Desire,* were among the five pictures of 1951 which had grossed over $4,000,000 in two years —the others being spectacles and musicals. The continuing slogan of the industry is that "movies are better than ever," which does not prove that they are good enough; but even the critical can feel that the best movies are extremely good. And in light entertainment that lacks prestige but gives delight to the judicious, the level is also good; the average in 1952 was a little low only because the studios had discovered that they must finance themselves with Technicolored spectacles and proceeded to make more of them than the available talents could justify. Goaded by television, the movie industry showed more vigor than it had for many years, and even before the new lenses and new screens arrived, signs of strength and willpower were visible.

This sense of present goodness in the movies has to be kept in the foreground by anyone who thinks about the glories of the past. A mawkish lament is not the proper tribute to the silent picture. The right tribute is enough: the silents put their stamp on and gave their character to the movie with sound, and so, in the process of change, they were the decisive creative element in television as entertainment.

Looking back not on what has been recorded, by myself and others, about the old movies, but on a kind of composite reel that forms in the memory, I find at first a feeling of dismay, a doubt whether they were as wonderful as they seemed ten years after they had vanished. They should have left a multitude of enduring images, not Chaplin and Garbo alone. They did, of course; the flash of genius around these two blinds us momentarily and it takes a little time to see Mabel Normand, all mischief and delight, and William S. Hart with his cold eyes, and Buster Keaton and Mary Pickford and the Keystone Cops and Harold Lloyd and Theda Bara and Valentino and Pola Negri. But even when we have enumerated all these and a hundred more who were in some degree world images, we know that something still eludes us. These men and women we admired, but the movies we loved.

This profound affection, universal and enduring, is unique in human experience. Fortunate people love what they do, their work or their play. A few love the arts they come to know well, as people genuinely love music; they love the novels of one writer, they become addicts of a special kind of fiction and would rather read a bad mystery story than none at all. But all these are private and special forms of love, whereas the love felt for the movies by one generation after another among all the peoples of the world was instant and whole, it was for everything the movies were, it was love of the essential and almost indefinable thing the movies offered. Nothing like this emotion has been inspired by radio or by television, and I think it would be interesting if the reasons were discovered because we might learn something valid about human nature in the process. I shall not try to do the work, which would require a team of researchers: a psychologist, an aesthetician, a sociologist, and a banker, for instance. I make my guess after observing the variations in the visual art as practiced first by the silent movies, then by movies with sound, and finally by television. I would like to think that the movies are universally loved precisely because they are a subtle and complex form of art, but I cannot prove this, so I settle for another explanation: the movies are loved because they are the first form of fiction presented visually in which the way of telling the story anticipates all the needs of the spectator before he is aware of them—in a sense, the way the story is told does all the work for the spectator and gives him the highly satisfactory sense of exercising a divine power. How that is done is another matter; at the moment, I would like to trace the course of this true love between the people of the world and the movies—which was more than a love affair and gave the lie to the old axiom, because it *did* run smooth.

It began with the sense of wonder when the workers walked out of the Lumiere factory and were made immortal on film.* And wonder remained in spite of all the stupidities and corruptions visited upon the screen. It was the shock of recognition, not between men of genius, but between common men and their fellows; from the beginning and for many years the wonder and delight of the movies was that they moved, and the spasmodic jerks of the first movies were just enough different from the human gait to give the last essential element—the movies were true to life, but they were not life itself.

The first French film strip was an actuality; the first American strip to scandalize the country was a piece of fiction, a kiss lasting something less

* The strip still exists. I saw it in Canada in 1952.

than a minute; before the movies were out of their teens, they were delinquent—a championship prize fight was re-enacted and offered as the original event, as a few years later a movie purporting to be a record of Theodore Roosevelt's explorations was shown (with Lew Dockstader impersonating the President). But the true line of development was held, and *The Great Train Robbery* (a compendium of the cinematic art as it existed in 1903) led the way to *The Birth of a Nation* in 1915. By that time the dominant types had been established: the picture of sentimental drama, as with Mary Pickford; the Western with Broncho Billy and Tom Mix; the slapstick comedy with the Keystone Cops; the sex picture with Theda Bara. Bathing beauties and the star system and inflated salaries and censorship and lengthy features, including the imported *Quo Vadis* in nine reels, and, in big cities, downtown "showcase" houses with elaborate "presentations"—there were even attempts at color and synchronized sound. By 1916 the movies had completed their first cycle, the experimental one, and set all their patterns; during the next ten years they consolidated their position. In a chronology of the movies prepared by the authoritative *Motion Picture Herald*, all but two of the notable events between 1916 and 1926 are concerned with mergers, real estate, circuits, patents, and the like. The two exceptions are the appearance of Valentino and the personal scandals of 1922 which brought Will Hays to Hollywood and so laid the groundwork for "self"-censorship.

In this period, also, the industry developed most of its more interesting faults. Its cardinal sin—the creation of the movie personality with or without talent—was forced upon it by the public. The instinct of the front office was to identify the stars with the studio, so we had the Biograph Girl and the Gaumont Girl and the Keystone Bathing Beauties, but the public kept writing in for the names and eventually we had them —and the fan magazine was around the corner. Soon another factor had been added: money. We have suffered the inflation that followed two wars, but a million dollars a year is still a lot of money; the first two people in the United States whose publicized wages were a million a year were Chaplin and Mary Pickford—and they got theirs when dollars were gold. No elaborate press-agentry was needed to make movie millionaires famous, and when, presently, stars began to have love affairs and after love affairs scandals, and when murder and mystery were piled upon all this, the appetite of the American for intimacy with the stars seemed natural and proper. We have lavished our affections and money on artificially created personalities who have given far less in return than some of the gods of the movies.

The fan magazine and the star system fed each other, and together they had their effect on all phases of the movie business. Stories were bought and altered to fit stars who either could render no character but their own on the screen or became identified wtih one kind of personality and were afraid (with ample reason) that their loyal fans would not want to see them in another image. The really loyal fan—the founder of clubs to promote the success of one star by the process of tearing down all others, the fan who later turned to crooners and cryers—would not let Mary Pickford play a man's mistress because that would make Mary immoral; the process of identification of actress with character was virtually complete. The consequence was that even the few players who could create characters were restricted; the only ones allowed to show any range were of the second order of stardom and almost always in the higher age-brackets. Economically, one consequence was that a studio might lose a million dollars if its efforts failed to put over a star; another was the guarantee demanded by the big showcase theaters that no less than two stars would appear in any picture they contracted to exhibit. Socially, the star system created a strange society in Beverly Hills and other suburbs of Hollywood—a hard-working, technically expert group of men and women, professionally insecure and isolated from the people to whom their work was sold, proving that they were men and women of the world by buying modern paintings.

The stars of Hollywood were not always respectable, and some of them discovered that the adoration of the public could be turned to cruelty and hate. Mabel Normand, who was never accused of any crime, saw her pictures banned because she had been a friend of the director William Desmond Taylor, the mystery of whose murder in 1922 has never been solved. Fatty Arbuckle couldn't get work for years after he had been declared innocent of a charge of murder. The movie fans assumed the right of eminent domain over the lives of the stars, telling them what to do and what not to do, and would tolerate no variations. Morally, the public was actually not so savage as the few conspicuous cases made it appear; it was led by groups of active propagandists, and when women's clubs, with churchly backing either real or implied, started to destroy a Hollywood star they usually succeeded because there was no organized resistance.

In a sense, the fan made the movies. The fan saw five pictures a week, the fan created publicity, the fan demanded glamour, the fan supported those sub-standard pictures which might otherwise have dragged studios into the red. The fans were possessive lovers and it was natural that they should insist on knowing everything about those they loved; for they had taken the movie and its people into their hearts, and in the heart there can be no secrets.

In the great fan magazines there was always a department called "The Question Man" who told the color of Bessie Love's hair and the size of Wally Reid's shoes and whatever else anyone asked him. One thing no one asked was why the movies were so loved, what the art was that so enraptured the world.

That art has been discussed a thousand times and I do not propose even to summarize all that has been written and said on the subject because my present interest is in what the movie-goer *felt* about the movies. The inner quality of the moving picture, its essence, created the special kind of love which, so far as I know, has never been universally felt for any other kind of entertainment. The Marx Brothers were admired on the stage and so were a score of Hamlets in the past generation; the Marx Brothers and Hamlet on the screen excited a different emotion, and the difference rose not from the material, obviously, but from the medium. And the movies themselves, using every subject from the Crucifixion to the Ku Klux Klan, from Dante's *Inferno* to Mickey Mouse, and every style of acting from the pure theatricality of Bernhardt to the pure cinematics of Margaret O'Brien, created, when taken together, the special thing that made people love "the movies" more than they loved any single movie or any special kind of movie or any person in the movies.

I am convinced that the "illusion of reality" or the "illusion of movement" is only a secondary element, although it is the most striking one, in creating the total movie effect. Several other things affect the average movie-goer more. The first is that in the movies the camera not only sees for the audience, it selects what is to be seen and, in a way, pays attention for the audience.* The most striking example is the closeup by which the audience is prevented from thinking about anything except the object shown, but this is only a particular instance of the general effect. When the camera swings from the right side of a room to the left,

* This was noted as early as 1916 by the psychologist Hugo Muensterberg.

END OF AN ERA

The day I arrived in Hollywood in 1952, the Chateau Elysée was sold, its name changed to Fifield Manor, its destiny to be a home for old people, if they are rich, with this special inducement: if you take a lifelong lease, you can be buried right from the Manor! Wafted by I know not what agency to the trilling birds (recorded) of Forest Lawn, you can, when dead, have not a care left on earth.

This could, of course, have happened to many an ancient (thirty years old) edifice in Hollywood, but that it happened to the Chateau seemed to put a dot—almost an exclamation mark—at the end of an era. The Chateau, which looked like an amalgam of half a dozen notable piles on the Loire, was built by some investors about thirty years ago, one of them being Mrs. Thomas Ince, widow of the great rival to Griffith, with money she received after his sudden death. It had still some beautiful, and some overrun, grounds around it, and tennis courts and fountains. In it nearly every one of the old Hollywood hierarchy had lived or visited. Around it, on the hills, are dozens of large, usually Spanish or half-Spanish villas, perched dubiously at the end of twisting roads, but with good views. Near by is De Mille Drive, where I last saw W. C. Fields in a house that had six game rooms, each one leading, at a slight angle, to another. The Chateau and all that surrounds it were symbols of a Hollywood supremely confident, gone a little crazy with wealth and fame, without a care in its lovely head.

The movie-makers in the next generation made money and promptly moved away from this source of their money. Then scandal hit them, then sound came in, and the wild foolish days were over. The new hotels are like hotels anywhere, the new houses are big and in good taste; everybody owns paintings (often called "originals"). Drop a tear for the Chateau.

it is doing what the audience in a theater would do when an actor suddenly crossed the stage or another came in through the door. But this is only a beginning. The camera naturally corresponds to the way we look *at* or look *for* things, by performing the physical movement for us. It corresponds also to our *interest*. We come into a room in which a party is going on; we aren't sure whether we know many people there; we don't know whether the lover with whom we had a quarrel last night has arrived—and if so, whether the quarrel has been forgotten; actually all our doubts are resolved before we have moved two steps into the room and with only the smallest movements, left to right, of our eyes. But the camera does what the mind and the heart do, as well as what the eyes do: it moves rapidly over the groups of people, it picks out the one or two whom we have known before, it searches for the loved one, it lingers on the expression that tells us whether we are forgiven. The eye can see across a room, but the mind and the heart need more than the eye can give: intensity and concentration. It is the *mind*, not the eye, that creates long shots and medium shots and closeups; and the well-handled camera satisfies us by being true to our thoughts and, when it acts for the heart, to our desires. The great Russian director Serge Eisenstein has provided a perfect example of the opposite use of the camera—to prevent us from seeing too much. Imagine, he says, that we see a woman, her face contorted with terror. The next shot can make us clench our hands with empathic fright or it can make us laugh, for the next shot can be a snarling lion about to leap or a little mouse scurrying away. And the effect would not be at all the same if we had seen woman plus mouse (or lion) together in the first placc because we would have had no curiosity as to the cause of her emotion and no suspense.

As long as the camera acts in these ways for us, we have the feeling, as we watch the screen, that we aren't missing anything; a good director, in addition, makes us want to see something in a particular way—close to, the middle distance, far away—and gratifies this desire just in time; so we get in double measure the sense of satisfaction. *And the way the movies tell their stories satisfies us as much as the stories they tell.* These stories may be myths, they may correspond to our most infantile desires, they may be false to the realities of existence, and they may satisfy us because the movies themselves have made us incapable of asking for anything else—all these things *may* be; the certainty is that the way the movies are told is a separate gratification, as legitimate in its essence as that of any other art.

The art closest to the movies (and by extension to television) is music because in each the element of time is so significant. In each the full effect of what we hear or see *at this moment* depends on what has gone before and will in turn produce a further effect on what is to come. In its simplest form, the note we hear is part of a sequence of notes which create the melody, and the woman's face we see at the window connects with the detective we have just seen looking for this woman and with the other man who will presently draw down the blind; and the length of time we see each of these shots and their grouping together create the rhythm of the picture, corresponding to the duration of and accent on the notes in music which create their time signature.

The annihilation of ordinary time is one of the most extraordinary effects the movies can produce. Parallel to the invention of perspective in painting, the invention of cutting in the movies is a landmark in the history of art. For cutting is the essential element in creating a second time-span for the spectator: he lives in his own sense of duration, knowing that sixty minutes and no less make an hour, and at the same time he lives by the durations of the movie, in which it may take half an hour to show the events of ten minutes or a lifetime may be condensed into three hours. We have all seen the way this is done, and, as a simple matter of courtesy, the example chosen should be put together from the works of David Wark Griffith, who was the master of this technique and who combined it with his love of the last-minute rescue in truly classic terms.

You begin with the grizzled pioneer or veteran, alone in his cabin with the child he has rescued; around the cabin the Indians are circling; you go back to the interior of the cabin and our hero feeding the child, and the next time you see the Indians, they are closer. From a hill a scout observes the event and sets out for Fort Dodge. The next time we go into the interior of the cabin, nothing much happens, but the following shot may show us the scout forty miles advanced on his journey; then the Indians coming closer; then the cavalry troop starting. The approach of the Indians to the cabin is mercilessly slowed up and the coming of the cavalry enormously accelerated—but we should not be able to accept either one without the right tempo of cutting. As the climax approaches, the cutter has three elements at his disposal: the cabin, the Indians, the cavalry; and he can show them in irregular order, turning the screw as tight as he likes by showing us cabin-Indians and again cabin-Indians before he cuts to cavalry. As long as he keeps the situation clearly before us, as long as we are afraid that the cavalry will not arrive in time, there is no limit to the combinations he can use. (Cabin-cavalry-cabin is the only one that destroys the situation.) The cutter controls also and varies the duration of each of the three elements on the screen, and the cameraman has given him one further variation, for he has caught the cavalry or the Indians head-on or from strange angles and the terrain through which the cavalry passes has given him gorges and slopes and fordings and notches to exploit. Still another effect is produced by the solid silent cube of the cabin, the circular movement of the Indians, and the diagonal of the cavalry. So, as he plays a trick with time, the cutter is also using space and form, and a kind of architectural inner structure in the movie begins to make itself felt.

In this handling of parallel action Griffith was breaking out of one literary tradition and into another. He said that he was in debt to Dickens for the idea of the flashback, but he did not seem to know that when he sent his Indians and cavalry into action he was actually suppressing Dickens's favorite device. When Martin Chuzzlewit and Mark Tapley have been launched into the wilds of New York, we leave them there; "Meanwhile," says Dickens, in effect, "what was happening in London?" There is no "meanwhile" in the movies; we live in London and in New York at the same time; and in one way this is close to the choppy effect of certain Elizabethan plays where in Act One we may watch three or four scenes of plots and subplots, with different and unrelated characters, and have no idea of their connection, so that the scenes may all be taking place at the same time. With Shakespeare we begin to get a more orderly presentation, we get the connections more clearly. In the movies the bridges between events are evident, we know that scene five is the dance to which all the characters in scene two have been invited or that scene nine is a hallucination in the mind of one person whom we met in scene eight. That is how future and past are identified for us. But when we need to see everything that is happening in the movies' "now," events interpenetrate and we see "now" simultaneously in three different places. (I use the quotation marks because the movies' present tense is not that of radio and television, as I shall explain.)

The flashback is an awkward device for the movies, especially when it becomes like the Greek messenger reporting offstage events—but the events are onstage. It is the man telling how he landed the big fish yesterday while we see him landing the fish, apparently today. It has its uses, to be sure. One of the best flashbacks in history (which I have never seen on film) is the story of the Crucifixion as told by Pontius Pilate in Anatole France's story, "The Procurator of Judea"—for the irony to come through, we must hear the report of the event twenty years after it happened. But in general the instinct of the great directors has made them limit the flashback to the dream, to maniacal ravings, to confessions (as brilliantly done in *Double Indemnity*) and other such exceptional frameworks—and without the narrator talking to us.

One reason for this is that the flashback imposes one past on another. The movie's present tense is not quite the present. It lies somewhere between the past of fiction and the immediate present of broadcasting. The novel says: "He walked" and television says: "Look, I am walking." Perhaps the movies say: "He was walking." In the novel you can even say: "She had been gone six hours before he had noticed it" and it is awkward to use the present tense except as a stunt; whereas in radio and television it is almost impossible to throw anything into the past. Jack Benny tried it by pretending that what you see now (Sunday night) is really last Thursday's rehearsal for Sunday night, so the announcer said he would now take us to Benny's house last Thursday—but the *now* overpowered everything else. The sense that radio and television are happening right now persists even when they present an episode from history or a costume play, and the few films made for television which are first-rate keep some of this quality. This sense rises in part from our knowing that current events, personality-and-panel shows, a large amount of vaudeville, and most of the more important dramatic shows are "live"—and the miracle of the instantaneous is constantly in the back of our minds.

Another source of the feeling of presentness lies, I suspect, in the way we receive broadcasts in sound and sight; they present themselves, so to speak, before us. The movie is something we know was made some time ago, and this affects our time-relation to it in the opposite way. And it is not merely the time; the place counts, too. We go out to a movie house, finding not the theater, but only its shadow; we get a sense that what we see is something recalled, and if the recollection is clear and emotionally strong, we have great movies; whereas when we see something in television, coming to us at home, it isn't recalled at all, it never happened before this moment. And if this happening is feeble and unworthy, the very sense of actuality damns the program, making it an embarrassment precisely because it is so real.

So we can accept the commonplace that the movies satisfy subconscious longings and repeat racial myths. But we must add the satisfactions that come from the essentials of the movie art. The way the camera sees for us, the way time is related to our desires and fears, the way past and present are interstructured all bring the movie close to our instinctive, not our intellectual, life.

The moment sound arrived, the freedom of the cutter-director was limited by the necessities of the writer. A totally new art of the movies came into being.

It was a far more intricate art because it had to reconcile the flowing images of the silent picture with the broken sequences of dialogue; it had to use picture and cutting to address the subconscious and at the same time let speech address itself to the mind. That mistakes were made in the beginning is not remarkable; the miracle is that a satisfactory art of the sound picture was developed—and the irony of cinematic fate is that this art, in turn, had to be sacrificed to the demands of wide-screen pictures.

3

THE LOVELY ART: SOUND

For a year or so, around 1952, it looked as if we should have to write a second obituary for the movies. After the gadget of sound, the gadget of space had come in—and we knew there could be no salvation in gadgetry.

The recollection of our doubts and despairs of a generation ago helped us. The first three years of sound had indeed been full of false starts, but only three years after Al Jolson said "Hey, Mom, listen to this" in *The Jazz Singer*, the gangster cycle arrived and took the movie away from dialogue and made it a movie again.

By that time the United States had entered into the first acute phase of the Great Depression. The effect on the movies was unexpected. Bad times had come to the Warner Brothers studio prematurely and led them to take the desperate chance on sound films; by the time the whole country was hit, the theaters which were wired for sound were doing so well that bankers were willing to lend money for equipment; the silent film was abandoned and the way ahead was clear by 1932. The movie business followed the rest of the United States into bankruptcy, but it came out completely up-to-date in machinery and methods.

Richard Griffith, of the Museum of Modern Art, has contributed a brilliant summary of these years to the fat and useful book *The Film Till Now*. I follow his outline (with a point of divergence noted below).

Soon after talk came in we had *Hallelujah*, made by King Vidor, remarkable in this, that it was substantially a silent film with sound made to fit the action; there followed a brief foray into polite drama (very talky), then the gangster pictures arrived with *Little Caesar* and *Public Enemy*. The cycle lasted hardly more than a year (most people imagine it lasted ten), and before it had ended, a series of "confessional" movies appeared, about streetwalkers and courtesans, all doing their work out of the best of motives, almost all received back into good society after their work was done. They are all forgotten now except, possibly, Garbo's *Susan Lennox*, which is more realistic. Mr. Griffith thinks that the acceptance by Americans of the honest whore, plying her trade only to buy food for the children or provide a good doctor for a loved one, is a reflection of the economic situation—"an echo of despair" as experienced by untrained women in the third year of a depression when trained men could not find work to do.

After the gangster film and the confessional for women, the next phase was social criticism. The subjects were varied: the newspaper business, banking, unethical lawyers, grafting judges, chain-gang prisoners, sharecroppers, and even the exploitation of the American Indian. Lighter satires appeared before the New Deal swept in; some of the more serious ones were made earlier but not released until 1933. The reservation I have about Hollywood's way of reflecting the most shocking economic event of our time is this: that from the end of 1929 to the beginning of 1933 no significant film actually dealing with the Depression was made and the only reference to the depression one calls to mind is *One More Spring*, based on a book by Robert Nathan, which showed how whimsical, how positively darling, life was in the Hoovervilles of Central Park.

Before the next cycle set in, something happened to Hollywood. In desperation, Paramount had decided to make a movie starring Mae West, no matter what "the Code" might say. Her first two films each grossed a couple of million dollars and saved the day for the studio (which reorganized under new laws). Mae West had appeared in a play called *Sex* and had been in jail for offenses against the civic morality of New York; she made no concessions in her movies, and her big, bosomy presence on the screen was a frank invitation, promising mutual pleasure. Mr. Griffith thinks the middle class in America were disturbed by irreverent movies telling the audience that "romantic love was hypocrisy, a biological joke" perhaps. But I recall no signs of bourgeois resentment against Miss West, no rejection of her invitation to come up and see her some time. The people who were disturbed were women, dismayed by this buxom apparition with whom they had no desire to compete, or no capacity. They banded together and got action. The Production Code was rewritten under Catholic auspices and enforced by Joseph I. Breen, a distinguished layman of that church, and Protestant and Jewish groups supported the movement.

This isn't the place for me to rehash the absurdities of the Code and the mean devices to which intelligent men had to resort in order to circumvent it. At the end of twenty years a grain of sense has entered into the day-by-day enforcement of the rules and, led by Samuel Goldwyn, a few producers have been bold enough to say that the rules themselves need to be overhauled. They were reminded that the rules represent not the opinions and tastes and judgments of the men who wrote them down, but the laws of God, and there the matter rested until, by a pleasant twist, certain Catholic dignitaries began to attack the enforcement of the Code, the leniency in borderline cases, and the Johnston office found itself on the defensive—its enemy not the immoralists, the atheists, and the would-be pornographers, but the very fount and origin of the Code itself. This attack coincided with a Congressional investigation into the relation between films and juvenile delinquency, forcing Hollywood to defend itself on two fronts and to make delicate moral and intellectual distinctions—an art in which it had never excelled.

The enforcement of the Code in the 1930s sent the producers scurrying to history and to family novelists (Dickens and Barrie among them) and to "the fantasy of good will created by the middle-class writers and principally enunciated in *The Saturday Evening Post*" leading to the Kelland-Capra combination and *Mr. Deeds Goes to Town*. It was Capra, too, who directed Claudette Colbert and Clark Gable in *It Happened One Night*, based on a story by another *Post* writer, Samuel Hopkins Adams, the most famous and next to the best of the light comedies to which the name "screwball" was then applied. The best (and also the first comedy in color) was *Nothing Sacred*, into which Ben Hecht put a lot of satire which William Wellman brought out, particularly in the dashing performance by Carole Lombard, who, like Mabel Normand before her and Lucille Ball after her, combined a dazzling sexuality and an uninhibited appetite for knockabout farce. Perhaps her nearest rival, who was once identified in *Life* as the "ideal mistress" of the American man, was Myrna Loy, and she did her best work in *The Thin Man*, where she played the wife of the detective (William Powell).

I have myself been so often reproached for being serious about the movies that I hesitate to reproach others for the same (honorable) attitude; but when these comedies are said to reflect the insecure and frustrated lives of their heroes and heroines and their popularity is taken as indicating some deep disappointment or disturbance in American life, I retreat. I will not use a complicated explanation when a simple one covers the available facts. The simple explanation for the lighthearted nonsense of some two dozen hugely attractive pictures is that the producers (meaning, in this instance, everyone who had to do with making the pictures) correctly sensed the relief that the whole country felt in the first half-year of the New Deal. It was not that a frightened people wanted to forget, it was not that they pretended to be gay—they *were* gay! And they didn't want to escape from their gaiety. They were confident and could make fun of themselves. Mr. Griffith and Mr. Lewis Jacobs, whom he quotes, believe that "bewilderment and dissatisfaction in a 'crazy' world" were reflected in satiric comedies in which the protagonists lead "aimless lives . . . redeemed by gaiety and good will . . . [and] find in marriage an adventure which blots out the insufficiency of the world outside it." It is true that the cycle continued to 1937 at least and the exuberance of the New Deal's first year had evaporated, but neither the movie-makers nor the movie-goers needed so desperately to "escape from a meaningless existence into an imaginary world dominated by personal relationships . . . the private world of marriage [where they] can reconstruct the phantasies which substitute for a meaningful relation to the world."

A rude word comes to mind, but I suppress it. I cannot, of course, prove that all this is overelaborate; for all I know, this is sound psychological analysis. And if my "common sense" rejects it, I have no one-hundred-per-cent conviction that my common sense is infallible. It still seems to me that other circumstances can account for most of the facts, for the way the pictures were made and the way they were received. Briefly—condensing a fuller analysis I made in *The Great Audience*—I suggest this: the Code made the man-and-mistress relationship unusable for comedy because it insisted (against all human experience) that this connection corrupts the soul and *inevitably* ends in disaster—a prison sentence, a dreadful death, and, if possible, both. The turn given to sex by *The Thin Man* was a recognition of the simple fact that even when a man and a woman are married to each other, they may enjoy sleeping together. This revolutionary idea was introduced into the movies by Woody Van Dyke, who asked his writers (Frances Goodrich and Albert Hackett) to give him several scenes between Powell and Myrna Loy, and these were so deftly done that no one could think of them as evasions of the Code. The Code says that "the treatment of bedrooms must be governed by good taste and delicacy" and explains further that "certain places are so closely associated with sexual life or with sexual sin that their use must be carefully limited." Perhaps that is why the cohabitation between Nick and his wife took place in a lower berth (not too closely associated with sexual life, not entirely dissociated from sexual sin). That such a relationship between man and wife was "a substitute for a meaningful relation to the world" is possible, but in the history of mankind it has also and often been found a pretty good thing in itself.

The missing factor in the "frustration-substitution" analysis of these comedies is the simple fact that under the New Deal the intellectuals and the people were reconciled. For a time the average man did not mistrust education and the trained mind; for a time the writer-artist-intellectual forgot his contempt of the "common" man. In that time the intellectuals who made the witty pictures and the tough-minded producers who found the subject matter of films in newspaper headlines were not feeling at all unrelated to the world; quite the reverse. They were connected—with events, with the audiences for their pictures, with the spirit of the age. They expressed their exhilaration by the light satire that was, after all, an importation from the stage of the late 1920s, and they took advantage of the air of freedom around them to do what they had seldom dared to do before: they tackled actual problems with some sense of reality—strikes, the KKK, lynching—and, while these were in many ways echoes of the "proletarian theater" of the Hoover era, they were something new in the movies. Eventually one phase of the Depression was brought to the screen in a picture that was overdue by ten years, but was a landmark just the same, because it proved that the materials of poverty and rebellion could be used for successful movies; that picture was *The Grapes of Wrath* (and perhaps it is characteristic of Hollywood that its Oscar-winning picture for the same year—1940—was *Rebecca*).

The movies had begun to cope with ten-year-old actualities when the actualities of the present fell upon them: the Second World War broke out.

By that time the character of sound movies had been set, its principal types exploited, and a phenomenal number of images had risen by the side of the silent figures of the past. It is hard for an enthusiast of the early movies to concede the point, but fair's fair and a critic's duty is to follow his critical nose: except for a very few stars, most of whom rose over the horizon in the early maturity of silent pictures, the dominant people of the first decade of sound film are not only more interesting because they used more of their faculties on the screen, they are also more commanding, they press more deeply into our consciousness. I am speaking of the intensity of the creative process, which, with the coming of sound, required simply more intelligence, more ways of understanding what a movie "was about" and what part each character played. I am speaking, also, of the great exceptional people. The moment the demand for intelligence was relaxed, talking pictures could exploit physical attractions and an actor's bag of tricks as fully as the silents ever did. But, fifteen years after the first decade of sound ended, we are still living under the spell of a dozen apparitions created by sound-and-sight. Not only our memories, but our wide-screen movies and our television shows are peopled with the lineal descendants of Cagney and Dietrich and Gary Cooper and Joan Crawford and the Marx Brothers; of Bogart and Boyer, of Stanwyck and Colbert. These are the people who established in our minds the images in action of the gangster and the courtesan, the soft-spoken Western hero, the hoyden and the shopgirl, the bandit and the seducer, the mother, the mistress, and the murderess. Sergeant Friday in *Dragnet* is the child of Sam Spade, and the psychoanalysts of TV in 1956 are graduates from the same school as the movie-analysts of 1940. The Martins and Lewises are trying to create the same phantasmagoria of lunacy as the Marx Brothers—and none too well.

And this is remarkable because the one thing the enthusiasts for the silent picture were sure of was that with sound the movies could no longer set before us people larger and greater than life itself. We thought then, whether we said it or not, that instant communciation from the screen to the subconscious would be interrupted by sound and that common words, spoken as we speak them in our everyday errands, would be an obstacle between the half-unreal figure on the screen and the half-buried instinctive responses in ourselves. It didn't happen because in the end the essence of the moving picture—its movement—survived the coming of sound. Directors learned to use sight and sound, movement and dialogue, for mutual support or for powerful contrast, and the essential element asserted itself. Even in the pictures of Mae West and W. C. Fields, where dialogue was often a series of well-remembered phrases, the flow of pictures and the specific movements of the stars—the undulations of Miss West and the aggressive self-propulsion of Bill Fields—were immediately effective and unforgettable. As for those artists whom we had known first in the silent days, it was natural for us to remember best some moment of pure gesture: the droop of Garbo's hand over Robert Taylor's shoulder as the lovers embrace in *Camille*, a forewarning of death; Chaplin as M. Verdoux reaching across the table and taking the wineglass from the prostitute's hand, sparing her life. But even those whom we hardly knew before sound are memorable to us through the images they create—the texture of the movie was more varied and more interesting because of the dialogue, but the impression made on us still came chiefly from the created picture. Even Marlene Dietrich, who integrated voice and form and movement better than anyone else in the creation of her early characters, is recalled for moments of singing rather than of talk, and most of all we remember the flowing sensuality of her movements, which had an eloquence needing no words.

These are the great images of our time, and we think of them as being great actors and actresses also, but the two things do not necessarily go together. There were others, figures imposing themselves on the imagination for a decade or a generation, with less talent, and some of them were not even particularly good mimes even in the silent days. They had a bag of tricks, they made a few faces. They left to Chaplin and a few others the creation of a complete character with every movement of every limb, the harmonious relation between eyes and lips and shoulder and, perhaps, the angle of the heel or the accent provided by an elbow. My instinct is to take the Keystone comedies and the Westerns as the training ground for good players (they were both the best place for a director to start). I think of W. S. Hart: I am not sure whether he was a great mime, a great actor, because I cannot completely separate myself from what I was when I first saw him; I admired him then almost as much as the French critics did who called him "Rio Jim," the incarnation of our national epic (*"le ouild-ouest"*). I like to believe that Hart was really good; he was certainly better than anyone else in his line, and if he wasn't a great actor, he could combine a straight jaw and lackluster eyes into a counterpart of the impassive Indians of Frederic Remington and eventually into *The Virginian*—one of the most enduring images of our time.

I do not know whether this Virginian has any forebears in the actual history of the West. As the sad sheriff who will hang his best friend to uphold the law (with an almost Christlike compassion for the criminal), he has a prodigious family tree in our fiction. Bret Harte's gamblers are his cousins, and his atmosphere is charged with the Teddy Roosevelt legend—the dude with a lion's heart. It was Roosevelt's idolater Owen Wister who gave him his only name, which is not a family name, and Arthur I. Keller his lineaments. In a sense, Bill Hart was playing *The Virginian* all the time, and so, in fact, were dozens of others; the superimposition of Gary Cooper's features or Joel McCrea's doesn't change the image. It continues to our day, and one scene in the creation of the legend is so elemental that it has become the standard bit for parody: the two men stalking each other around the sides of the buildings—the saloon, the feed store, the low-railed porch around the hotel, the hitching-posts—they are always the same. Yet a hundred burlesques leave the effect undiminished. It is always on the stroke of six, the punctual sun is setting, and our hero (sadly) double-checks his gun and goes outdoors, while all the others fall silent, to shoot down the horse-thief whom he loves (and who is checking his gun at the far end of the street)—and as they move toward each other the old magic of the movies reasserts itself and we know that this is one of the things which will not ever vanish from the screen.

It may change. The sheriff may be transformed into the city detective who must track down the killer although the slum or society or the Oedipus complex is really guilty. We may meet the lonely hero again in a meaner West, as in *High Noon*, where the whole community abandons him and he wins his battle and (sadly, proudly) throws the badge of office into the dust. It was, indeed, *High Noon* that provided the clue to the real nature of the Western—it is not only a private myth of the American past and an answer to his demand for freedom ("don't fence me in")—it is also a morality play, it is *Everyman*. In an essay as yet unpublished, Joseph Newlin, a student at Columbia University, has traced the parallels between *High Noon* and *Everyman*; they are remarkably close, and they suggest the connection between other Western types and allegories in the historic memories of all the races from which our mythology flows down to us.

Bernard De Voto, who knew and understood the West, had a low opinion of the cowboy, good man or bad, the law or the thief, the Yippee-shooting-riding-pal or the lone-wolf-with-a-past. Our Westerns, he said, are make-believe on a national scale; the period to which they refer was brief (hardly more than twenty years) and unimportant. There were no Robin Hoods—only hired thugs, as repulsive as the hoods of our gangster wars. "The cowboy," he said, "seems an illogical choice as a master symbol of the West. If the symbol is to stand for wilderness skill, the Rocky Mountain trapper . . . would have served better, for his was the most complex skill ever exercised on this continent. If importance for the future makes a culture hero, then it should have been the homesteader. . . . The cowboy image is in great part phony, a counterfeit. . . . Past or present, there is a lot more to the West than a cow outfit."

The reference to homesteading is a clue. The cowboy became an outlaw when the settled people and the sheep-raisers began to enclose the range, and what makes him so attractive is that he has created—and, sadly, he enforces—a law higher than the laws of property. It is not because a horse costs money and is a personal possession that stealing it is such a crime; the horse-thief is the enemy of society because horse and man are a unit and it is slow murder to take away the horse. And murder is the only other crime for which the true Western sheriff will go after his man.

I have quoted De Voto because setting the Western in relation to actuality is the best way to discover not only its inner nature, but the essential nature of many other kinds of movies as well. The Remington who gave us the Indian as the last figure in the procession started by James Fenimore Cooper also gave us the West of the range and the scrub and the waterhole. He has a kind of grandeur, there is a moral size to him. The background of the Westerns is the setting that Remington found—one could almost say the setting he created—and in a way the stories he tells in his pictures are the true and romantic stories the movies tell. It is not a matter of being *true to life*. Anyone trained for a year in an art school can draw or paint a buffalo or an elk; Landseer's *Monarch of the Glen* is an almost photographic presentation of antlers, hocks, sides, and shoulders, but the picture is pure romanticism because the thunder and magnificence of the background are composed to throw an aureole of royalty and make a Scottish stag into a British king. Remington's fidelity to nature is closer, but his supreme quality is still his imagination, so that, next to the covered wagon and the starving men in the gold rush, his pictures create the most vivid image in the back of the American mind of our adventure, our greatness, and our romance. All the movies had to do was to animate his people and his animals against the backgrounds he had found for them.

No other type of movie could possibly be so important to us. No doubt Mr. De Voto was right about the real cowboy, but the "cowboy" image is shorthand with us for the whole movement of our history from the days of the "liberties" and the Western Reserve, through the brief period when the cowpuncher really was a central figure, down to our own time when, politically, socially, and through the movies themselves, the Westward movement, if not the West itself, dominates our lives. The movies took over a fragment of history, they dramatized the significance of the frontier in American life, and in the Western they showed us, if we had been smart enough to see it, what they were trying to do.

We did not see it. We (and in this I include myself without reservation or excuse) kept on asking the movies to do something different. We asked them for plays according to the canons of the well-made *pièce* of the French theater or at least in the style of current Broadway dramas; we belittled their players because they were not, by a totally different set of standards, actors and actresses; we asked for an elevation of thought and feeling never demanded from the allegory, the fable, the legend, and the myth.

The movies resemble the other theatrical forms just enough for us to be misled, and for a brief misguided time the movies capitalized on this resemblance and tried to be theatrical; actually this occurred twice—at the beginning of the silent days and again in the uneasy false starts of the dialogue film. Another difficulty is that the movies drained away from the theater the lowest of its elements—the melodrama without character, the drama using local color, the sentimentalities of the early 1900s

—so that as we try to distinguish one from the other, all the words we apply to the movies seem belittling; but at least this does not lead us into the confusion of judging them by alien standards. Parallels in the other arts, although inexact, may be helpful: the movies resemble the theater as the photograph and the poster resemble painting. The landscape artist who recomposes the elements of the visual world and gives them a form, bringing out an unseen beauty or a new significance, does not set the standard for the aerial photographer or the poster-designer or the magazine illustrator. All of these are craftsmen and the painter is an artist, according to the pyramid of excellence established in the classic tradition. I accept this and add only that the intent of each differs from the others and each one has his appropriate dignity and excellence.

I think we can approach the excellence of the movies by looking again at one of its magnificent vices: the star system, which it inherited from the theater and progressively debased for a long time. I have noted the worst features of this system (in several places in this book) and noted also that the movie fan made the movies; as the fan was a star-worshiper, we can take it for granted that the movie as a popular art could not have existed without the virtues of the star system and perhaps not without its vices. The special point here is that the star is not necessarily an actor; the resemblance to acting is part of the tricky resemblance of the movies to the theater, and the instinct of the producers may have been entirely correct when they stopped importing "famous players" from Broadway and began to place their fortunes in the hands of the Pickfords and Mae Marsh and the young Fairbanks, who was hardly a great actor when he went to Hollywood and became a movie star who didn't have to act at all. On the stage, as a juvenile lead, he occasionally had to be on his feet when it was plain, as only the movies could prove, that his element was the air, that he lived in movement, flying, touching the earth only to be refreshed for further flight. It was not a character he created, it was a symbolic image.

And this is what a hundred others did, the talented and the hapless alike, Garbo and Clara Bow, Gable and Keaton and Tom Mix. The slapstick comedians and the trick riders in the Westerns were instinctively right; they weren't actors any more than are clowns or the cowboys of the Miller Brothers' 101 Ranch (with whom Thomas H. Ince made the proto-western in the far beginning of movie time). One says that Emmett Kelly is a great clown, not that he is a great actor playing a clown, and I think that similarly one could say that the famous men and women on the screen were great sheriffs or vamps or shopgirls or gangsters.

A few people trained in show business managed to take their talents into the movies, and some of them did far better in Hollywood than their careers on the stage seemed to justify. Like Fairbanks, another "juvenile" (in an embarrassing comedy called *Cradle Snatchers*) left New York when young; unlike Fairbanks, Humphrey Bogart made a spectacular re-entry on Broadway after his first success in the movies; it was his creation on the stage of Duke Mantee in *The Petrified Forest* that crystallized his mask, the sad gangster, parallel to the sad sheriff and different from the delinquent aggressive type (Cagney), the good but sinister pal (Edward G. Robinson), the utterly impressive Paul Muni. (When he came to play Zola and Pasteur he was called "Mr. Muni" in the ads, and it is rather mean to remember that his best picture was *Scarface*.) Cagney, Robinson, and Muni all had experience in vaudeville or the legitimate theater or both; each has a flexible talent; they can present other types, outside their regular ones. Stage training, if combined with an instinct for projecting the movie mask, did not hinder talented people—Boyer was as successful as Gable and Barbara Stanwyck as Joan Crawford—but the untrained were usually found at the highest peaks of popularity. Nothing stood between them and direct communication with their audiences. Not even talent, the hostile critics said, looking for the wrong thing, for acting, and missing the projection of the image and the mask.

The cycles through which the movies went and the great individuals who created lasting images for us are matched in importance by the creation of a number of classics—pictures to which people go back again and again. Some of these are in the repertory of film societies and are "revived" as part of the history of the films; a greater number return to small art theaters or often to neighborhood houses a year or so after their first runs. *Hell's Angels*, with the startling Jean Harlow, and *Public Enemy* may be shown in a double bill from the far past; but quite common was the appearance in 1954 of *The Asphalt Jungle* (released in 1950) and *The Cruel Sea* (1953), as well as *The Maltese Falcon* (the 1941 version made by John Huston, with Humphrey Bogart and Sydney Greenstreet), the celebrated *Blue Angel* of Marlene Dietrich, and almost always something starring Alec Guinness. For years *The Informer* kept playing in small houses, and, as if to prove that merit isn't everything, a third-rate arty job called *The Scoundrel* lasted nearly as long. Also remembered were *Citizen Kane* and *Casablanca* and *Hold Back the Dawn*. Robert Montgomery could always put on a festival of his own pictures, including the superb and sinister *Earl of Chicago*, *Night Must Fall*, which is almost as good, and *Rage in Heaven*, with Ingrid Bergman. As often as the owners of the prints permitted, the comedies of Fields and the Marx Brothers had long runs in the big cities. Sometimes it was better to hold off for a time and then to make a splash, as *Gone with the Wind* did, threatening on its second time round to surpass the first-showing grosses of all pictures except itself. (As I have noted, the second release of one Chaplin picture paid for making his *Limelight*.) When pictures were withdrawn from re-release, the chances were that a remake was in the works.

Remakes were becoming an important part of the movie business just about the time when the new screen dimensions were developed. They ranged from a distasteful vulgarization of *Show Boat* to an overblown but effective *A Star Is Born*. The chances are that the whole repertory of films will be re-examined now to see which would gain most on wide screens, and this will not necessarily indicate a failure of original creative power in Hollywood; it will indicate at worst only a shift from one source of inspiration (new books and plays) to another.

The future of the movie, it is already plain, lies in the hands of men who know how to balance the known elements with the new. Without committing myself to any "great-man theory" of progress, I find encouragement in the careers of a few individuals, all of whom, in different ways, have fought the battle of Hollywood. When the Abbé Sieyès was asked what he had done during the French Revolution, he replied, "I survived it." These men did more. They persisted and flourished and added something good to the movie.

John Huston is a variable man who has let the world know it. He made *The Treasure of Sierra Madre*, a movie so dazzling that we thought for a moment we were witnessing the coming of a new art, and followed it with a half-arty, half-matured little job of his own, *We Were Strangers*, which might have ruined a less versatile director. The good picture had not made enough money to suit the Warners; the bad one was an independent production that should have bankrupted everyone concerned.

Huston went back to Hollywood to make a bad picture that would make money. With *The African Queen* he gave notice that Hollywood was not going to make a martyr out of him, at least not so long as he had first call on the services of one of the most desirable properties in the business, Humphrey Bogart. In *The African Queen* he had also Katharine Hepburn and a good story, and out of these elements he made a picture in which two or three sequences were interesting and a few hundred feet were good color; all the rest was without taste and even without cinematic skill. In *Moulin Rouge* color was *used*, it was arbitrarily changed to create effects, it was taken away from realism, and the effect was pure magic; within this magic a cold, ferocious dislike of humanity suffused the screen, reflecting the hatred Toulouse-Lautrec might have felt for the world, preventing us from having the faintest sympathy with him. It was a masterpiece of sculpture at the top of a glacier, and the great popular success it achieved is a tribute to Huston's uncanny skill as much as to José Ferrer's technical brilliance in the lead. The odor of sexuality which occasionally came from the screen was a secondary item; the shooting of every scene to expose the vanity or the ugliness or the absurdity of the people involved was carried to the exact point at which a spectator might derive some pleasure from thinking himself superior to the unfortunates on the screen. The picture lacked all the elements of greatness —and was a triumph.

Huston is an exceptional figure among Hollywood directors. He is an intellectual of the particular type that would rather be called a bum; he is genuinely romantic in his approach to his materials; and he is a first-class artist in handling the machinery of movie-making. The publicity he has received in the past few years—Lillian Ross's account of the making of *The Red Badge of Courage* and *White Hunter, Black Heart,* Peter Viertel's novel about the unmaking of a scenarist—has encouraged Huston's tendency to make drama out of the events surrounding the shooting of his pictures, but it has not corrupted his peerless sense of what a sequence of shots should look like and what one sequence after another should do to the audience. As Miss Ross's study indicated, Huston is rude and rebellious, he has a justifiably nice opinion of his capacities, he hates interference; but he needs some outside influence to check a tendency to prove himself right by overdoing whatever strikes him as novel and other people as doubtful. Warner Brothers did not interfere with *The Treasure,* but being aware of them in the background seems to have brought Huston to the exactly right balance of all his talents. He has enough individuality to come to terms with the front office, the hard money power of the studios, and to come out on top. He is parallel and opposite to Orson Welles, who has as much talent but cannot come to terms with American production methods and remains eccentric to the main course of movie development—to our great loss.

The influence of single individuals on the quality of the movies—even of the pictures they make—is hard to assess; it can be done only when a director or writer or producer (or a combination) has consistently created one kind of movie or made movies distinguished by a difference from the works of others. In Huston's case, the mark of distinction is the complete and well-nigh perfect use of the movie machinery; since he writes or collaborates in the writing of the screenplays, there is no conflict between dialogue and pictorial image (the image always comes first). The stories he chooses for himself have also a distinguishing characteristic: they are adventures that are also searchcs. The sense of the "larger than life" which the movies give so copiously exactly suits Huston's temperament, and at his best he can always draw the line between the action that has grandeur and the one that is merely grandiose.

The position of an independent in Hollywood has grown immeasurably stronger in the past decade, and studios are now setting aside large sums to invest in productions over which they will have no control. This means that a producer who has demonstrated his capacity can offer a studio a story he believes in, a sympathetic writer, and the kind of director who will attract popular stars. Pictures so made will still be far from having the powerful single impression that Welles created with *Citizen Kane* or Chaplin in any of his major productions, but they have greater unity than the average studio product that is subjected to daily supervision by the front office. The free hand for independents, once the project has been approved, parallels the successful system of Filippo del Giudice in England, which resulted in *Henry V* and *Odd Man Out* as well as *Tawny Pipit* and *In Which We Serve*.

The career of Stanley Kramer, highly satisfying in itself, is interesting as a sort of producer's progress. His first production to attract notice was *Home of the Brave*, the story of a Negro in an outfit dominated by whites, a harsh, true-sounding picture that lacked many of the smooth graces of the Hollywood war picture but had abundant strength. A veil is generally drawn, out of sheer kindness, over one later picture, *So This Is New York*, which ruined one of Ring Lardner's great works, *The Big Town*. (*Champion* dealt more faithfully with Lardner's masterpiece.) But *The Men*, an honest story of paraplegics which introduced Marlon Brando to his public, and the pictures that followed, confirmed the impression that Kramer was proposing something slightly different from the average producer's schedule for himself. In his own words, he intended to make successful pictures that would at the same time satisfy all his own requirements. To maintain his freedom, when he made a contract with Columbia Pictures, he reserved all authority to himself as long as the budget did not go over a million dollars; if the studio had to put up more money, some of Kramer's absolute authority was taken from him. It was his expressed intention, at that time, to make no picture costing over a million.

He did not stick to this, and the relative failure of a few pictures made his departure from the studio easy to arrange. He returned to his first principle: to make only such pictures as he cared for, to make none by deputy. Part of his permanent staff is the versatile writing-directing team of Edward and Edna Anhalt, who held faithfully to the delicate line of *The Member of the Wedding* and also did the script for the melodrama of "unmotivated" murder in *The Sniper*. For his most absorbing production in the past few years, *Not as a Stranger*, Kramer became his own director. His pictures have a habit of falling just short of sensational success; even *High Noon* and *The Caine Mutiny* fell short, even *The Wild One*, which made Marlon Brando's leather jacket the chosen emblem of the Tough Adolescent; they lacked the super-publicity values that a faint whiff of scandal might give them or the hint that the true story of some Hollywood star was being told. Kramer is, none the less, a key figure, for as he succeeds he demonstrates the capacity of Hollywood to use intelligence and taste. It is his good fortune that at the moment he needed most to recover his creative independence Hollywood found that it had room for the individual.

For the weakness of the Hollywood system had been that it needed talent and was willing to pay for talent only in money, not in creative freedom. In the thirty-five years that included the best days of the silent picture and the entire history of sound, the system used up the vitality of dozens of good men who were willing to settle for less than freedom and rejected others who found that they could not function without freedom. There were eccentrics among writers and actors who took their revenge on the studios outside of business hours: the trace of the madcap and the track of the neurotic were both visible. The two great independents who stayed through those years were both men who made enough money early in the game to finance themselves in their later productions: Chaplin and Goldwyn. Independence underlies everything in Chaplin's professional life; it is the soil in which his genius flourished. His genius is, however, the point of capital interest, and I have paid my tribute to it already. In Goldwyn's case, independence of action is the mark of distinction. He has made his own decisions—some of them disastrous. The publicity around him has been foolish. But he is the only producer functioning solely as a producer of whom one *can* say with assurance that he left his mark on all his pictures, the sign of a strong individuality.

4

THE LOVELY ART: MAGIC

To little children and to aesthetes, the motion picture has always been sheer magic, and one of the complaints the aesthetes have consistently made against Hollywood is that its direction has steadily been toward reducing the magical content of the movies, making them more and more *real*. They are certainly justified in one respect: even the part of the movies which is most magical, the animated cartoon, has been pushed toward photographic realism. It has, however, resisted. Driven out of its natural habitat—sheer fantasy and illusion—by one practitioner, it has slipped out of his hands and returned with a flourish, as naïve-seeming, as saucy, as mystifying as ever, in the hands of another. So here, before we approach the newest technique by which the movies think they can make us forget that they are something more than photographic records of the actual, we can stop to consider the one kind of movie which triumphantly asserts its non- or super-reality.

If we were not so accustomed to it, if it were not on view day by day, we should celebrate, in reverence or by shouting in public places, the incredible wonder of the animated cartoon. Many years ago the aged Henri Matisse came to this country and it was said that, while he wished to see many men, he intended to pay his respects to two: Disney and Thurber. (An irony to which I am not partial: when Thurber came to be done in animations, Disney was off on other concerns and *The Uni-*

corn in the Garden was beautifully made by the supremely talented group of people who have the most forgettable trade name: UPA.)

The animated cartoon, the *Silly Symphonies*, the Mickey Mouse series, *Bambi* and *Snow White* and the other full-length features in animation, and the dreadful mistaken concept that let real people be surrounded by cartoon characters—the whole Disney enterprise and whatever went before it and came after can be taken as the typical, focal, symbolic creation in the popular arts. Whoever entirely dislikes this manifestation of money, machinery, and genius sets himself apart from humanity—as a saint perhaps, or a fool; I pass no judgments. Whoever takes them all, without making distinctions, is a happier man, but not the happiest man. For I take my stand on the principle that no harm is done by knowing—and that satisfaction increases with understanding. Or, in the specific instance, I would say that the animated cartoon is one of the three supreme examples of the multiple or diversified nature of these arts, in many respects more typical, purer, and consequently more of a test case than the two others, jazz and the feature picture. For in the animated drawing the use and abuse of the mechanism is perfectly displayed, the pressure of economic necessity, down and up, exists at high intensity, and the entire enterprise cannot come into being without pure genius of the simplest, most universal order.

And I should add that the curve of goodness (that essence which every professional recognizes) is in itself a case history of these dear and exasperating arts to which I am so devoted; should add that the pang of disappointment and the resurgence of delight are also characteristic of these arts, for they seem condemned by their own nature to destroy their sweetest qualities—and to recover. In the special case of the animated cartoon, the recovery has been made by Disney's successors while he has created at least three new careers for himself.

There were animations before Disney, and some of them were good. Even before the Keystone comedies were becoming fantastic, the animators were staking out their claims. To be sure, I can now recall only those bits I recorded at the time: the imp coming out of the inkpot and going back into it, protesting; the cow walking up the side of a barn; and the great, lovely, immortal Krazy Kat, who announced his arrival on the screen with the simple, often quoted words, "Envy me, Mice, I'm going into pictures." The mechanism of the animated cartoon had been known for generations and was used for a mild type of "feelthy pictures"—fifty drawings, packed rather like a paper-match book, when flicked presented the hootchy-kootchy dancer. To transfer the process to film was simple. Presently a disastrous discovery was made: the more single frames drawn for a step or a jump or any other action, the more lifelike it becomes. No one at that moment asked, "Who wants an animated cartoon to be life-like?"

Because the genius and the enchantment of the Disneys were so various, so overwhelming, for a long, long time the master of the business could do anything. Or let us say that at the heart of everything an animator does there is an animating principle—which here seems like a pun, but is the essence of the art. It is not the single situation created when Pluto is climbing a mountain, it is the fact that a drawn dog can move at all which captivates us first. After that we want these drawings to entertain us, to make us laugh. No one suggested in the early days that animations might make us do anything but laugh. (In 1923 I asked Picasso whether he would be interested in making some masterdrawings, and we also talked about using the *Goyescas* for a series. Picasso had, however, not seen any good animations, and unfortunately we never took the project up again. In 1953 UPA did *The Telltale Heart*, the first uncomic animation I have seen, outside of industrials and educational films, in the United States.)

To pile up the circumstances of good fortune surrounding Walt Disney is not to imply any lack of genius. Everything was in his favor—but genius was in his favor to begin with. The animated cartoon had followed the normal course of production—it had become routine. Disney arrived, a cartoonist dissatisfied with his own work; he had barely finished a few cartoons on his own when Vitaphone struck. Sound had come—and Disney took it in his stride, as if he had just been waiting for sound before starting his real work. Within a year he was using sound in counterpoint to his drawings; there was a scene in a cave, with icicles: the reverberations of sound were precisely adapted to the movements of the drops of water forming into ice—and the sense of unreality was superb.

And then, as if to challenge Disney's capacities once more, color came to Hollywood. Again there was no hesitation, no perplexity. Color, which was lacking in *Steamboat Willie* and the dance of the Egyptian characters around a frieze, was exactly what the *Silly Symphonies* required. Let it be said at once that Disney made a few mistakes in the handling of color, slashing it about like a boy with a whitewash brush, but the major errors he never made; he never used color offensively. At worst, he used it without talent, and these occasions were few. He began by using a watercolor palette, a sort of wash in which his characters moved lightly; later he began to use the palette of an oil painter, which got thicker with every feature. I prefer the wash, because it seems to me to be within the tone of fantasy; oil is the medium of the real. But for a long time Disney had the instinctive feel for his work and seemed incapable of making a mistake. (I said this once a little more broadly; I wrote that he had never done a picture I did not like. That same week he released one about Midas, probably *The Golden Touch*, which was plodding and pretentious, and a year later he and I compared notes and I discovered that he disliked the picture almost as much as I did.) In those years he turned out masterpieces—not in comparison with the work of others, but absolutely, works that were perfect in detail as they were simple and, in a magnificent way, grand in their basic concepts. You can tick them off, this title and that, but you will run out of fingers because they came one after another, apparently without end, alternating the sheer magical loveliness of the *Silly Symphonies* and the intricate, ultra-logical fantasies of Mickey Mouse and the great character who was to outshine him, Donald Duck, and the dear beasts who peopled the world in which these two lived.

There came a time, a few years after the shine and gaiety had become familiar, when people discovered a streak of cruelty in Disney; and it would be foolish to deny that it was there, as it was in Grimm and Hans Christian Andersen. But we have now the perspective of the years, and we can look at the Disney product as an entity, a single complete thing, and deliver ourselves of a nice judgment. And I think the first element in our judgment is the one no court would allow: it is sheer love. These fifteen-minute games played out in front of our eyes were— and to this day are—like candy and ice cream in our childhood, things about which we say, openly and freely, that we *love* them. They are like holidays about which we say "I can't wait . . ." because in a true sense we could hardly bear the long wait, in the early days, between Disney pictures.

I know that it is my business to say why and how these things occurred, since I am a professional critic, and if pushed, I think I can say why and how. But I think it also a good part of observation, if not of criticism, to utter the innocent childish cry of surprise and admiration with which we greet Roman candles in the summer night, or a moment in the circus when dexterity turns to loveliness. For Disney always had this moment when he was running true to his own form. It might be only the muted croak of a frog after the full chorus, it might be the sudden resemblance he showed us between a mammal and a machine, it might be the flow of one color into another or one sound into another sound, but always there was the special, sweetly knowing touch that skillful men before him had lacked. They had all his elements at their command, they seemed to do what he was doing, but the final ingredient was missing. It was not taste, not imagination, for these things Disney shared with others; and, while he developed a vast complexity in production, with machines as menacing as those that stamp out whole car-bodies in one operation, the difference between him and the others was never purely mechanical. I think that actually it was a moral difference, composed of two attitudes: a mischievous impertinence toward the public and a loving kindness toward his own creations.

I am still speaking of the short pictures, in which violence existed but was somehow held under control, as the fury of the hurricane was magisterially subdued to the beat of the music in *The Band Concert* or the tantrums of Donald Duck were justified and tamed. Since the animated cartoon, even more than the regular movie, can satisfy our wish to be omnipotent, defying the laws of gravitation, defying time and space, endowing animals with human attributes and making men and women into machines (and then giving the machines an apparent will and life of their own)—since these things are so, animations must have their own logic; we must rejoice when the Mouse or the Duck walks over the edge of a precipice and keeps on walking on air; we must rejoice because we would like also to be able to walk on air. And we must not let questions come into our minds, we must be under the spell of the picture. Then when the walker sees what has happened and panics and scrambles back to the cliff or falls and bounces back, we must recognize that also—the kind of morality of the cartoons, the laws by which they live; for it is their law that until we are afraid of what happens to us, we can do anything on earth or in the air or under the seas.

There was an additional quality in these early pictures: they missed completely the dreary quaintness of animal stories. They were partly Aesop with a touch of La Fontaine, perhaps, but they were never children's-book animals. They were carefully created characters with sustained motives, placed in situations which seemed plausible to them and in which they acted according to their lights. They were not Aesopian in any sense of delivering moral lessons, nor were their approaches to the society of human beings as satirical as those of La Fontaine; they were animals with lives of their own to lead.

The strangest thing about the early Disneys is that they did not make money—for Disney. The intricacies of the system of releasing movies can be of interest only to those in the business; they were defeating to Walt Disney, who saw his *Three Little Pigs* become an attraction capable of pulling in more money at the box office than the feature picture, yet was paid a lump sum, so much per week or per day, regardless of the take. This was the customary arrangement; everything except the feature was a filler and excluded from the percentage arrangements. There was a rough justice in this, but in the case of Disney it became intolerable and it compelled him to take the road to corporate enterprise, a big studio, big pictures, and eventually the virtual disappearance of the work that had made him famous.

The making of long pictures is in itself a natural outcome of making short ones. Chaplin had hardly arrived in the Keystone comedies when he was put into the support of Marie Dressler in *Tillie's Punctured Romance*, which some people professed to find pretentious on the silly ground that no comedy could last for seven reels. Actually, Disney waited ten years after the beginning of Mickey Mouse before doing his first feature cartoon: *Snow White and the Seven Dwarfs*. By that time his releasing arrangements were better and his studio was constantly enlarging and endless experiments were being made with color, with sound, and particularly with two qualities that Disney began to value more and more: depth and smoothness of motion, two qualities giving the effect of realness, as if he were in competition with regular movies. Some five years later he went back to a technique with which he had had a small success long before Mickey Mouse, a combination of cartoons and live actors. Eventually he made the picture that, one would have said, he was destined to make, as if the rest of his professional life was a preparation for it: *Alice in Wonderland*. Nothing so marked his fall as the tasteless, elaborate defeat he inflicted on the imagination and logic of the original—and I speak as a non-idolater.

Was it entirely the "curse of bigness" which had overtaken Disney? I am not sure. I know that midway in his work with one of his long features he wanted to call it off, but allowed his staff to go on, withdrawing only his supervision (it was either *Dumbo* or *The Reluctant Dragon*, both up to the Disney standard and, in parts, highly inventive). He had also made teaching films for one or more branches of the armed services which were miracles of inventiveness not only in his own field but in the field of education; the abstractions and fundamental principles and definitions that are so tedious and necessary were simplified, projected, and connected with happy devices, so that a mind positively allergic to ohms and amperes would remember the angle at which an animated and anguished arrow moved into a mass of bubbles, and even eyes not peculiarly observant learned to tell the nose and wing of a friendly plane from those of the enemy. And Disney made a feature in which he came to believe profoundly and passionately: *Victory Through Air Power*. The refusal of the high command to accept the thesis of this picture infuriated Disney. It was virtually that victory could be won by air power *alone*, that all other commitments of men and money and material were wasteful, and in the background was the implication that unless the Seversky principle were accepted, we could never hope for victory at all. Long after the picture was made and even when victory was beginning to be possible Disney spoke of it with a peculiar fanaticism, not with the genial enthusiasm he had for his entertainments. He was in rebellion against the government, and presently a less important event aggravated his feelings. A strike broke out at his studio.

It is hardly worth while to recall the passions of that time, but the effect on Disney was particularly strong because of the general assumption that all strikers were favored by the Administration. Disney was confused by the strike and kept saying to his friends, "I don't understand it. . . . Every one of them calls me Walt. I call them by their first names. . . ." He was back in the early days, the small studio, everybody sitting around the drawing tables, making a crack or a suggestion; he forgot the acres of buildings, the five or ten story boards simultaneously in use, the armory of sound effects, the huge machinery that photographed through several layers of gels to give perspective, the commitments to releasing organizations, the contracts, the income—he did remember the taxes. I have no position on the strike, having nothing to go on beyond Disney's own statements, which were not illuminating; I know that from that time on a certain sweetness left the studio and men of prodigious talent and pleasant natures found it difficult to work there. The last feature that seemed to me to capture anything of the quality of Disney's art was *Saludos Amigos*, which was really a grouping of unconnected shorts. In *Bambi*, which was made the same year, the naturalistic backgrounds and a mixture of the heavy and the arch brought the whole picture down to the level of illustration. The earlier elaborate *Fantasia* gave itself airs, but again, because it was made up of separate sections, seemed to have more brilliant episodes than the full-length single-story films. In addition to putting Carmen Miranda among cartoons, Disney also illustrated and hammered up *Casey at the Bat* as if its simple story needed to be helped to fame, and, laying a rough hand on whatever needed to be treated respectfully—not with reverence but with understanding—he finally came, as noted, to *Alice*.

And it must have been around this time that Stephen Bosustow and a few associates, some of whom had undergone the Disney treatment, began to make cartoons totally different in character—the first challengers to Disney sensible enough to know that they could not compete with him on his ground, the first to go back to basic principles in animations, perhaps the first since Disney to believe in their work and to enjoy it. They made a short, and suddenly everyone became aware of them and for several years they were constantly identified as "the people that made *Gerald McBoing Boing*." The surprise and elation brought by the first Disneys were again in the air, a kind of delight all the more pleasurable because it was remembered as well as new.

The men at UPA had the advantage of Disney's twenty years; they could begin with human figures—squat and round and unreal—where Disney had begun only with animals; they had all the experiments with comic sound to fall back on. The one thing they did not have was Disney's plant. They could not duplicate his backgrounds and perspectives, nor could they afford as many separate drawings per movement or gesture as Disney could give. They had to make flat backgrounds and spasmodic movements acceptable, and their particular stroke of genius was that they turned these two things into positive attractions, making them the essentials of their work. As I said, they reverted to first principles, which wouldn't have helped them if the pictures had not been supremely attractive; it is, however, agreeable to find that on occasion good theory results in practical success.

The theoretical approach is this: a caricature is not a photograph; an animation is exactly what the name implies—it makes a non-alive thing seem alive. The cartoon is not a series of photographs of reality, it is a series of photographs of drawings. A drawing has no real depth, only an appearance, and some drawings (notably cartoons) intentionally avoid even the appearance. So you have flat surfaces upon which a totally un-real movement appears to take place.

As a matter of pure speculation, I would say that without color these UPA pictures would not have succeeded; for color supplied what we might miss and accentuated the good things that we saw. In a wall of neutral color a rectangle of brightest blue was a door; colors distorted in a mirror showed us what the short-sighted Mr. Magoo imagined he saw. Sometimes a house is merely diagramed in white or brown, or with lines of different colors; sometimes all the rainbow is called on for a rich contrast. Color in the first years of UPA had the freshness and the innocence of the early Disneys; it came from a child's colorbox used with discretion and delight. (One thing Disney did which was beyond the UPA resources: when a hurricane or a whirlwind of passion started Donald in pursuit of an enemy, when a cyclone threatened Mickey and Minnie Mouse, these characters would take off, as characters always do in comic strips, in their equivalent of "a cloud of dust." Miraculously the Disney artists made this real, for as the characters moved faster, all the color in them changed and amalgamated until it became like a rubbing of crayons, the whole outline of the figures gone and the quality of the color changing as they gathered speed. The first time I saw this effect I felt that at last I understood the theory of relativity —for here the speed at which an object moved had altered its qualities; since Disney had shown it to me and it seemed perfectly logical, I need no longer worry at the thought of a yardstick being more or less than thirty-six inches long under certain circumstances. As usual, the "omnipotence effect" of the animated cartoon had brought a high de-gree of satisfaction.)

The satisfactions created by UPA are of two kinds. One is parallel to that of any other cartoon organization—a series in which a familiar figure appears. In UPA's case, it is Mr. Magoo, the myopic gentleman out of whose misfortunes you would have thought no comedy should be drawn. The comedy really lies in Mr. Magoo's sublime confidence and, of course, in his eventual success; it lies in his irascible scolding of other people for not looking where they are going, in his conviction that he has done the right thing when he takes off in the fire truck instead of the examiner's car to demonstrate his right to a driving license. The situations are ingenious, the drawings and the combinations of line and color are enchantments to the eye, and the tone of almost violent high spirits is exhilarating.

The other UPA cartoons are single shots with a wide range. In addition to the famous Gerald, who did things like sound effects with his voice, there was the child who demanded a jet plane under threat of turning himself into a rooster if refused. Another was about a child whose mother was going to have (or perhaps did have) a baby. A remarkably sound psychological lesson was conveyed in this cartoon with astounding virtuosity in its dream sequence, an intelligent use of symbolic images, and a wonderful scene at a circus in which the whole audience was like a painted curtain of faces, moving in unison as faces do at tennis matches at Forest Hills. And, among others, there has been *The Unicorn in the Garden*, a beginning perhaps of a whole series of Thurber. It moved intellectually out of the field of the usual cartoon, having a point, but it stayed well within the mode of comedy. *The Telltale Heart*, macabre in handling to match the material, was not entirely successful, but entire success was not to be looked for, and the question remaining is still whether a medium so "unreal" is suited to material as real in its significance as Poe's story or, to take another example, Orwell's *Animal Farm*. This was done by the British team of Halas and Batchelor, who have at times shown a light palette similar to UPA's, but in this satirical work chose to be somber, to work in semi-darkness much of the time, and to follow too literally a not-too-inspired original story. It was as if Disney's menagerie had suddenly turned pedantic, and I felt all the time that you cannot have animals in cartoons without letting us have at least a little fun out of them.

Outside of the field of entertainment, UPA has done the most entertaining TV commercials and also films for industry; some of these have been so good that they have been shown in regular movie houses. A film on cancer and when to be afraid of it, a film on the oil industry which was a brief history of the United States, and others have been as impressive in their way as the films made for fun.

The coda to the story of the cartoon is that Disney has for several years been making films of the actual lives of animals. At the beginning he insisted on making his animals behave the way his menagerie used to behave; by skillful cutting he could time the movements of a bear scratching his back or a beaver flapping his tail to the beat of a familiar piece of music, or the croaking of frogs, with the pulsation of their throats, would become a male chorus. This trick has been somewhat abated and Disney has gone forward to make serious reports on animal life in America, pictures of restrained power with just enough showmanship to make them popular. These reports grew gradually longer until a full-length feature, *The Living Desert*, was produced, and this held its own in the smaller houses at least. It was nice to know that Disney had found something interesting and important to do. Continuing these features, Disney also turned to television and won a dazzling and deserved success. He used his old materials and developed new ones; he made his television program an advertisement for a playground he had built in California; some of his material was not first-rate. But he was bold and enterprising. Even before he was established, he refused to conform to routine. Into his time period he put different kinds of programs—animation or movie, comedy or fact—until his Davy Crockett series (a straight filmed program) captured the imagi-

NO FLOWERS

A three-line notice on the fifth page of the *Hollywood Reporter* announced the death of Robert Flaherty—the only recognition by the movie industry of the passing of one of its great men.

Flaherty disliked much that Hollywood would have asked him to do, but the movie-makers in Hollywood had no cause to dislike what he did. He made *Nanook* and *Moana* and *The Louisiana Story* and *Man of Aran,* transmuting fact not into fiction, but into poetry, creating the documentary as an interpretation of life.

Hollywood gave him no Oscars when he lived and sent no wreaths to his funeral when he died.

nation of the country. By that act he told a dreadful truth about the producers of those children's programs which were vile and violent and were presented "because children wouldn't look at anything else"— the truth being that their producers were not only liars but men of no talent whatever.

I said at the beginning of this brief history that the animated cartoon could be considered typical of the popular arts. It was typical of the best product in these arts because the trained and critical mind was totally in sympathy with the innocent spirit in admiring the cartoon and, in fact, the uninstructed turned away from the ill-conceived later features of the Disney studio, not as decisively as the critics did, but in a substantial way. All the stale equations in which good and bad and popular and highbrow figure were exploded by Disney first and by UPA later. At the same time the influence of technology on the arts was made visible in the various phases of Disney's work—from simple black-and-white through color to lavish and superfluous use of color. In the next phase the economics of the business affected the techniques of UPA by forcing them to use fewer masterframes and flat backgrounds, restoring some of the original freshness. The whole progression is a warning to us never to despair and equally a warning never to be satisfied with the second-rate, for the first-rate can be at least as popular.

5

THE LOVELY ART: SPACE

It is reported—but I do not know on what authority—that when Jean Cocteau was asked his opinion of wide-screeen movies, he replied, "My next poem I'll write on a big sheet of paper." This is the wisecrack of a poet and an ignoramus: a poet who thinks that the word is all-important (as if the silent screen had never existed) and an ignoramus who does not know that every new technique is a challenge to the artist to find and surpass its limitations.

Paradox has been defined as a half-truth so stated as to be especially irritating to those who believe the other half, and the definition holds for wisecracks as well. I can appreciate the temptation to which Cocteau succumbed (if the quotation is right), but the whole of his own work in the movies is against him. In his *Blood of a Poet* Cocteau often found visual forms corresponding to the remarkable personal imagery of his poems; and in *Beauty and the Beast* he used words less for themselves than for their overtones. To experimenters like Cocteau, the movie has always been a highly private form of communication; whatever they do not need, whatever they cannot use, seems to them sheer superfluity and probably wrong. French aesthetes in general act as if there had been a kind of cinematic Garden of Eden when everything was pure and innocent; I do not know where to date the fall and the expulsion, but most of them placed it at about the time

Chaplin made *The Kid,* in 1921, because they said it was literature, not "pure cinema."

The intelligent, not intellectual, man is more flexible because he has no preconceived theories. He is pragmatic and wants to know what effect the new cinematic devices will have on his pleasures. He is, moreover, indifferent to the technical means employed. Actually, the competition between various systems has tended to obscure the one significant fact: the true three-dimensional picture can be projected on the ordinary flat screen, and the curved screen is in a sense a substitution of width for depth.

These wide systems, while they vary in detail, are alike in presenting their pictures on a curved screen that is much wider and a little shallower than the one we have been accustomed to. The proportion of the old screen—the relation between width and height—was 4 to 3; this was established by Thomas A. Edison (making him in a sense one of the most influential men who ever lived because he taught us to see in those simple proportions). The new dimensions are between 7 and 8 to 3, and the screens are curved, some more deeply than others. This curvature is actually a matter of convenience: if the average movie house could accommodate a screen as wide as a city block and the average customer could sit far enough back, the screen could be flat because, in that size, the effect of being *in* the picture would occur. This effect is associated with our "peripheral vision," the things we see out of the corners of our eyes, unaware often that we are seeing them. Fred Waller, the inventor of Cinerama, had worked with wide-angle lenses projecting several images on a wide, flat screen in an effort to produce the illusion of depth. He was asked by Ralph Walker, the architect for the Petroleum Industry's building at the World's Fair in 1939, to solve some problems of projecting movies on the inside of a sphere—and from this conjunction Cinerama developed. In its early phases it used eleven cameras and eleven projectors; it is now using three of each. CinemaScope uses a screen not so deeply curved, and the attachment of a single lens to the ordinary projector is all that is required for showing the picture. In the Todd-AO system the film, which is twice as wide as the standard 35 mm., moves through a single projector at the rate of thirty frames a second, the frequency of frames in TV, instead of the standard twenty-four.

To the viewer, the significant difference is only in the effect of being surrounded. The Cinerama screen comes nearest to being a semicircle with its 146° arc; others run to as low as 60°.

Many of these systems use stereophonic, directional, or multiple sound systems. Cinerama has five loudspeakers behind the screen and others placed strategically in the auditorium; CinemaScope has used three—in each case the number of loudspeakers connected to the screen is the same as the number of microphones used for recording the sound. (The auditorium speakers are extras.) The purpose is to make us aware of the point on the screen from which the sound comes and, if an actor is moving as he talks, or turns and walks away from us, to give us perspective in audio as well as visually. This is another move toward realism, and it has resulted in some peculiarly unreal sounds—bellowings and mufflings and misdirections—but these are early errors. The magnification of sound in the auditorium is perhaps the only mistake in principle, and even that can be corrected by a good house-manager.

The revolution of the screen began actually with a search for depth, not width. As far back as 1900 experiments had been made using specially prepared film that produced a blur on the screen until the spectator put on a pair of glasses with one green and one red transparent filter. Later the polarizing filter invented by Dr. Edwin H. Land (and familiar in other Polaroid developments) was adapted to use in cardboard frames so cheaply that they could be issued to movie-goers, and Arch Oboler, once a specialist in radio thrillers, produced for the three-dimensional screen a picture called *Bwana Devil* in which it was not the perception of depth that gave the audience its great sensation, but rather what came out of the depth—the wild animals apparently leaping over the heads of the audience or into its laps. Only a few pictures were made by this method. Several of the wide-screen methods I have described were in various stages of development at the time, and the vast success of *Bwana Devil* and the next few films in its genre put pressure on the inventors. Within a short time the wide screen, imposing no demands on the audience, commanded the field, and the 3-D system vanished (although the Polaroid Company may still bring a variant to the screen).

The combination of wide screen or 3-D with interplanetary travel and prehistoric monsters, the avowed intent of the producers "to throw things at the audience until they begin to throw things back" were evil omens. But in a surprisingly short time the movies recovered their sanity (helped perhaps by the fact that the Oscar-winners and the box-office successes were nearly all good plain pictures) and became movies again. The second CinemaScope film was a light comedy, and by the end of 1954 Charles Brackett could produce a deft social satire, *A Woman's World*, whose story required virtually no scenic effects, and unfold it as simply and smoothly on the curved screen as he could have done fifteen years ago on the flat.

This quick recovery argues a flexibility and reserve of intelligence that few critics expect to find in the front offices of Hollywood. It should also be a warning to aesthetes not to assume that the imagination must shrivel to one dimension if the picture has three. The American directors saw what the aesthetes did not: that the new shape and size and effect of the screen would bring up the most interesting questions, that all the answers so confidently set down for the problems of the silent screen or the flat sound-screen would not serve for the new contours in which pictures would be seen. The hardheaded, practical men who made the first foolish pictures were aware of this. They knew that they had to make at least one fundamental decision: should the audience see the movie as if through a window or should each individual spectator forget the screen and feel that the action surrounded him? It is interesting to discover that the practical scientists were on the side of the aestheticians: the audience must see through a window, nothing must come out of the window into the auditorium. The practical producers came to the opposite conclusion: you cannot come too often into the laps of the audience. This is a complicated problem because the machinery of the eye and the machinery of the movie have to be related to a whole range of psychological effects: what do we see, what determines what we see, how do we identify what we see, what part is played by anticipation and habit and interest, and so on? Before any picture was made, the questions were at least being asked by the men in the business, and they kept on asking. In 1955 Darryl Zanuck was showing to professionals a film of pure experimentation, a sort of training school in the techniques of shooting for CinemaScope; a single scene is shot with the camera at different heights, angles, and distance from the objective; a sequence is shown with more and then with fewer cuts, with closeups of different sizes and durations. The purpose is to discover the optimum shot, the best for the desired effect.

Anyone who has thought about the art of the movie is tempted to give a categorical answer to the primary question I have mentioned: the action must take place behind the "window," the spectator must know that he is sitting in an auditorium and the event he sees is taking place elsewhere; if this sense of separation is lost, how can he get any aesthetic experience? What will be the difference between actually riding on the toboggan and feeling yourself ride on it as the screen enfolds you? How can you give to fiction that "willing suspension of disbelief" which is the essence of your enjoyment if there has been no disbelief, if the baseball bat swung around at you makes you duck your head? The satisfaction we get out of any work of art is a double one: the art work is and at the same time is not life, the photograph is life-*like*, the characters are *true to* life, the emotion is a quintessence of our own emotions, the shape of events has a meaning we did not see before the artist placed them in his special relation. This is the mere surface of simple aesthetic experience. It relates to the fascination that actuality may have for us if we see it in a certain way. In the early days of TV, people were spellbound by pictures of traffic moving and stopping in response to the lights along Park Avenue—because it was real and not-real; and this not-real that the moralists object to in art cannot be too much attenuated. We want to catch a glimpse somewhere of the creative force because even as we say that a parodist is perfect, we know that the perfection includes the difference from the original. That is the aesthetic argument reduced to its lowest terms. It has validity for me. But I am not at all sure that it is final.

One of the pioneer producers (of the Natural Vision system) is Milton L. Gunzburg, by profession a screen writer. He says, "To insist on a screen or window between the action and the audience is to keep pictures artificially behind a flat barrier. We in the initial stages of Natural Vision felt there was danger in coming out into the audiences' laps too often. But we have changed our minds. Depth, whether before or behind the screen, is the real dramatic tool in 3-D. It is to be used."

Depth behind the screen is as natural as the horizon; "depth before" the screen is an illusion and the words are inaccurate (although this does not, in any way, invalidate the argument). The prejudice of the spectator, his ingrained habits, tell him that if a man walks up to a window, the sill being level with his hips, and continues to move for-

ward into the space over the heads of the audience, everything below
his hips will remain behind. If a hand reaches out into the auditorium
and waves about, the audience accepts it until the movement of the
arm puts the hand beyond the right or left limit of the screen; then
the audience, no longer seeing the hand, instinctively feels that it must
have gone behind the screen while the arm is still outside it—and
this causes a mental conflict. I take these examples from a study by
Floyd A. Ramsdell, a longtime professional in Polaroid film-making. His
essay, as well as the one by Mr. Gunzburg, appears in *New Screen
Techniques*, edited by Martin Quigley, Jr. Another contributor is
Polaroid's Dr. Land, who says:

"To conceive of the motion picture as a painting in motion leads
to one kind of aesthetic policy; to conceive of it as a flexible, readily
changeable version of the living stage leads to an entirely different
one. The champions of the first point of view would believe that stereo
is too much, just as in the past they thought that color and sound were
too much. But the evidence is that after each of these advances in
realism is accomplished and technically perfected, we all prefer the
greater realism."

(I break the quotation to note that after each of these advances
had been perfected, the new techniques were put to the uses not of
realism *per se*, but of the imagination, and that this is already happening with the new methods of picture-making.)

"One important qualification, however, must be added: to intrude
too obviously on the real world of the *auditorium* can detract from
our ability to enjoy vicariously the world of the motion picture as
it unfolds on the *screen*. Those who voice a general objection to the
heightened realism of stereo may well be protesting against the violation of this proper boundary. Our great goal should be to make movies
as real as life around us, but this reality should be confined to the
'other side' of the proscenium. The greater the technological perfection
of this other world, the more wholly we can identify ourselves with
it—while safely outside."

Another inventor, Dr. Brian O'Brien, who represents the American
Optical Company in the development of the Todd-AO process, says
that his system "makes the viewer forget the screen and think he is
looking through a window." But the less scientific enthusiasts for this
process, as for most of the others, speak of the screen "engulfing its

audience," giving "a feeling of actual participation." Whether looking
through a window is compatible with being engulfed is a psychological
question. I leave it in the air with a prediction from Mr. Gunzburg:
"We feel that the day will come, and soon, when audiences will watch
a motion picture performance as though the screen were eliminated
entirely and life itself unfolded."

The first moving picture I ever saw was of railroad tracks on which
presently the theater balcony where I sat seemed to move, and when
a locomotive appeared on the tracks, coming toward us, I ran screaming to the exit—and reassuring daylight. This visceral effect can now
be had with a roller-coaster or a bobsled. We do not yet know
whether other emotions can be as profoundly stirred if we are engulfed in Elsinore and the ghost of Hamlet's father is walking over
our heads as well as under his feet. The inventors have presented a
nice set of problems to the psychologists and the aestheticians.

I think that Dr. Land has given us a clue to part of the answer.
"While safely outside . . ." he says, thinking perhaps of tigers jumping at us or scorpions dangling over our heads. But his phrase has an
overtone: the audience is *safe* from the passions of the characters on
the stage. Those passions are too great and they are also often too
trivial for us to be involved in them. We are moved, as we often say,
by them, by what we understand of them in the light of our own
experience—but we must not want to murder the adulterer, we must
only understand that our brother, our *semblable* on the stage, wants
to and will murder. There must be a limit to empathy as there is a
limit to identification-with. And this corresponds physically to Dr. Land's
"proper boundary." For a joke, you can make us think we are being
nibbled by mice, as Olsen and Johnson did in *Hellzapoppin*; for a
stunt, you can reverse the ventilators and send a whiff of peppermint
into the auditorium just before the candy house comes into view in
Hansel and Gretel (this was done in a Federal Theatre production by
Yasha Frank). But you must not literally deafen the audience by the
gunfire that deafens the hero, you must not stupefy them with gas
when you want to appeal to the subconscious—and somewhere in each
art the boundary must be found beyond which it is not safe to go
because the audience will be distracted or displeased and the intensity of experience will be dissipated. It is not a matter of arriving at

abstract principles for a new *Laocoön*, but of finding the practical framework within which the best effects are produced.

Not enough pictures have been made in different ways for us to know how the decision about the "window" affects the other techniques of making pictures. It is a fair guess that characters in polite comedy will not be jumping out of the screen as often as the Fourth U.S. Cavalry (pounding over our heads on the way to rescue the beleaguered widow of the scout who died while the Indians were whooping over our heads in a war dance). It is another fair guess that as long as the television screen is small and flat, the new movie techniques will be much used for spectacular effects—musical shows, open air, historicals, and the like. In this way the mechanisms will, to an extent, dictate the choice of materials. But, as I have already noted, relatively intimate comedy was done soon after the first big-scale pictures were made. Even animated cartoons have been adapted to the proportions of the new screens. We have therefore to consider how the fundamentals of the screen art are going to change—and the effect of the new movies on us.

The physical essentials of the motion picture from the beginning have been these:

- A series of photographs so taken and so projected as to give the illusion of motion;
- the ability to control the attention of the spectator by showing as much or as little of any given scene as suits the purpose;
- a variety of ways to go from one scene to another (the fade, the dissolve, the direct cut are the familiar ones);
- control of the time-sense by breaking any action into many parts, showing the audience some of it, skipping other portions;
- creation of various feelings of movement by riding the camera or panning;
- creation of a sense of beat or rhythm by the system of cutting.

None of these need be dropped for 3-D or wide-screen effects, but their relative importance will change. The camera will not need to pan around, hunting for this person or the other, because several individuals converging near the center of the screen will each be perfectly observed by the audience; the single picture becomes a panorama, and the best panoramic shots in the new medium are those taken from planes—a vast expanse of prairie or the whole skyline of New York. The first consequence of the big picture is that the camera cannot keep its secrets so well—it is hard to isolate a single element when the view is so wide. (It isn't, incidentally, so high—and if a woman's face betrays terror, the camera can pan down or up to find Eisenstein's mouse or lion—more convincingly than it can move to either side, where, by the logic of the screen, we should see everything.)

The closeup itself can now be used exclusively for dramatic purposes —to concentrate our attention on a single object and prevent us from thinking of anything else. In the past it has been used for identification: to bring us so close to an individual that we could see whether the smile on his face was genial or malicious; this remains essential to small-screen television, but after twenty-four-inch becomes standard and many sets are even larger, a well-composed picture of two heads will leave each one large enough to deliver the detailed knowledge we require, as the wide movie screen already can place three or even four people so that we miss no shade of expression. This is using the camera for the human eye; when the camera is used for the brain, to concentrate on the one person we want to see at this moment, the closeup must eliminate everyone and everything else. The wide screen is not happiest with one huge head-and-shoulders in the center and a blur of color on both sides. It is a little better when we see one person far to the right or left side facing the opposite end of the screen; the audience, which has accepted a hundred conventions in movie-making and thinks nothing of a man walking with no feet visible, will not balk at simple and sensible devices such as letting the screen be dark at one end with the color gradually coming in full at the point of closeup. The dramatic purpose will be served as long as the eye is not distracted. (Light and shadow, prime elements in giving "depth" to paintings, are still neglected in the new movies.)

The success of costume pictures and others in which large groups of people dominated much of the action was perfectly natural and seems to have established the idea that the wide screen requires long sequences of uninterrupted action, eliminating cuts for closeups and reducing even the number of changes of angle. Dr. Land spoke of the screen as "a flexible, readily changeable version of the living stage," and the experience of many directors of dramatic pictures shows a decided preference for scenes that last much longer, without cutting, than we have been accustomed to. For one thing, there is ample room for movement and actors walk toward and away from the camera, providing closeups naturally—arriving at the correct spot as they say the significant words, and then retreating. This has an effect totally different from that of the camera riding in to get a closer look at a character, for in the second case we, the audience, go in with the camera, we have a curiosity to be satisfied or some doubts to be resolved and we get the feeling of action when the camera carries us to where our interest lies. And the natural change of size, however smoothly handled, has the defect of its virtue—it cannot be so sudden or dramatic as the mechanical cut.

It is clear that when we have longish scenes—each one conceived "as an act in a play," according to Zanuck—our tricks with time will be strictly limited. We shall fade out as if we were dropping the curtain in the theater, but the true manipulation of time, as we see it in the last-minute rescue (analyzed on page 13) or in any biographical film, will not be within our powers. As long as we follow a scene without cuts, time on the screen is the same as our time—but if we insert another scene lasting ten seconds, we can pretend that five minutes have elapsed by the time we return to the first. A distinct tendency to cut for the sake of cutting, to give the spectator something different to look at every fifteen seconds, was becoming noticeable in Hollywood productions just before the new devices came in, and the slowing up of the tempo of cutting, for the wider screen, is a good corrective. But I doubt whether the movies will for long abandon the traditional cutting system. The manipulation of time and the creation of a flow and rhythm in the movies both are based on this system, and so is some of the pure excitement of the eye. For the most part, these things are absorbed without effort, reaching us below the threshold of our consciousness; while our minds follow the spoken word and our eyes the physical movement of people on the screen, the beat of the picture touches our pulse and we respond to it.

The story that is told may be utterly matter-of-fact; the illusion of movement is now so familiar that it is like any other accepted convention. But wherever the movie touches time, it is as mysterious and primordial as the beating of the heart. Absorbed in new techniques, directors may neglect essentials as they did a generation ago when they immobilized the camera to favor the microphone; but, as they recovered mobility then, so I am confident that they will recover the art of using and manipulating time in the substructure of their pictures.

I return for a moment to Dr. Land's concept of the movies as realistic. Of the three elements—movement, sound, and color—the middle one is the most intractable. You can speed up or slow down movement, you can alter colors at will, and you can do this so gradually that audiences will hardly know what you are doing; but alteration in a speaking voice, the use of speech in any artificial way, is dangerous. Directors stop the dialogue and go into music and sound effects when they want anything fantastic or mysterious to touch the imagination. Color is supposed to be true to life, but the total effect is not literal realism; for fifteen years grass was anything from lavender to yellow, hitting green on happy occasional long shots, and the human face was an angry magenta in closeups—and no one objected much because they were not expecting true colors. Nothing is more unreal than the background of almost any domestic interior in Technicolor from 1930 to 1950—because the entire psychology of attention is disregarded, the eye is made aware of separate colors, is made background-color-conscious, which is precisely the opposite of being aware of color in the background. In the past few years color has been better handled, and from the time of the Olivier *Henry V* the idea of color as a component of a movie, rather than something added to the movie, has gained ground. Color is to be used for its effect regardless of realism.

I do not think that depth and perspective are going to make the movies peculiarly realistic. People will move back and forth, but the spectator has seen them appear to do this for a generation. In stereoscopic pictures we will have a sense of space behind the characters on the screen, they will have air to breathe; but if this gives them reality, we have to ask ourselves whether anyone ever thought that Scarlett O'Hara was unreal because she lived in only two dimensions. When Hollywood goes into aesthetic theory, it is important only if theory actually has an effect on production.

Fortunately for us and for themselves, the producers of entertainment pay little attention to their own theories. Early radio technicians thought they had in the microphone an instrument for *secret* communication, but they developed broadcasting; and, though all Hollywood will no doubt continue to pride itself on the *realism* of the screen, all Hollywood will probably produce works of the imagination filled with illusion. The value of good principles in these matters is only that they eliminate errors; a producer who knows a great deal about the way people see things and the psychological effect on them of certain shapes and colors and tricks of perspective will not have to make a half-dozen false starts. But the false starts have their value too, exposing error at times and at others exposing the limitations of a theory too rigid for daily use.

The new devices in the movies will ultimately be put into the service of the imagination as well as of reality; in Kipling's words, the wildest dreams of Kew and the (newsreel) facts of Khatmandu will both appear. If a producer wants to think out his problems in advance, the histories of art can be of the greatest help to him.

There is a story as old as art, I suppose, about the Athenian Zeuxis, who painted grapes so faithfully that the birds came and pecked at them; silly birds and a silly painter, too, one suspects, because if he wanted to attract birds, he could have used real grapes. But there is a legitimate side to this and it gives great delight—it is called *trompel'œil*, a deception. In the whole history of art it has stood at the opposite pole to realism. There are many books on the subject, but a particularly painless way of acquiring the rudiments is by looking at the 1954 issue of the *Art News Annual*, in which one will find the tiger (cat) jumping out of the frame and horses and chariot racing right over the heads of the audience in paintings ranging from the Renaissance to our own time—you would think you could pick the newspaper right off Picasso's cane-bottomed chair! In addition, there are discussions pertinent to the new techniques of the movies, particularly as to how you play tricks with frames, painting a frame on your canvas. The analogy becomes closer still when one notes that in such a system as CinemaScope the picture is taken through a distorting lens and projected through another so that it appears normal—and this distorting lens is called "anamorphic," which is precisely the term for the controlled distortions in those illusionary paintings that become "real" only if we hold them at eye level or look at them standing on our heads.

The vocabulary is the same because the intention is the same,

and you can follow the word "reality" through the discussions of aesthetes and into the releases of press agents. Thus, Fabrizio Clerici (in
the *Annual*), speaking of still-life, says, "It is as if the painter, seeking
to rival reality, wanted to demonstrate that two and not three dimensions are enough to obtain stereoscopic effects. They set themselves
to observe reality with an almost scientific eye, introducing the complex rules of perspective and the theories of light and shadow into the
picture. They left nothing untried in their attempt to create the perfect illusion. Their aim was to astonish, to dazzle and hallucinate. Perhaps it was just these hallucinatory and astonishing effects that suggested the name of *trompe-l'œil* (literally 'fools the eye') for this kind
of painting *as if to mark a boundary between it and freer, naturalistic
still-lifes.*"

I have emphasized the final words because otherwise the contrast between reality at the beginning and naturalism at the end might not
be noted. In another place the distinction is clarified: "The 'Grand
Illusion' has a double meaning. All art, and painting in particular,
creates some degree of illusion—at its highest that 'loftier reality' of
which Goethe speaks. However, the first definition of the Grand Illusion . . . is really illusion*ism* in art. It signifies the *counterfeit* of reality . . . variously called *trompe-l'œil*, magic realism, perspective illu-
sionism and so forth." (The italics are in the original.)

And then, coming directly to ideas held about painting which are
close to those held about the movies, this writer says, "It is the popular
belief that art aspires or should aspire to the state of the Greek artist's
fruits which were painted so real that they deceived birds to peck at
them. The typical prosaic spectator . . . insists on this where a poetic
one does not. Out of such a misconception—or . . . fractional conception—of the whole nature of art there [has] grown the ever-increasing
quarrel over representation vs. imagination in painting." And *trompe-
l'œil*, the Grand Illusion, the counterfeit, the effect "done with mirrors," lies "at the extreme of . . . representation"—but it is not plain
realism, it is *magic* realism.

This is worth remembering because from the beginning, even in
the dead days of silent flat pictures, people have believed in the reality and the magic of the movies, and I think that we now can see
the whole question of realism in its right proportions. The newsreel
and the travelogue were on the screen to prove that the camera doesn't

lie—and the camera and the projector were creating the monumental and wonderful falsification making us think that the photographed man was walking across the photographed room. Occasionally strange attempts were made to be realistic, the oddest of all being the notion that photographing a play while it was being performed on the stage was somehow more real than expressing it in terms of the camera and projector. Parallel errors have crept into TV: because each person has only one head and cannot change the object of his vision abruptly, television with one camera, without cuts from this scene to that, has been considered "purer" than multiple-camera production. In television to an extent, and in the movies far too often, good marks are demanded because the picture is taken on the actual spot (*Romeo and Juliet* in Verona, dear God! *Romeo and Juliet* takes place behind magic casements in faery lands forlorn). If at the end of fifty years the scenic designers of Hollywood have proceeded no further than the state of theatrical design before Robert Edmond Jones reintroduced the imagination in 1915, they are a sorry lot, either trying for the wrong thing or failing to produce the right one. It is the fault of producers that they think of fiction happening in front of backdrops and therefore imagine they gain by having it happen in front of growing trees and real houses; fiction happens in the imagination. There are practical advantages, as when Eisenstein found the vast steps in Odessa and used them for the most memorable scene in *The Battleship Potemkin*, a sequence not in the original scenario; there are advantages in making pictures wherever a studio has funds in blocked currencies. But these are adventitious. It is not the business of the fiction film to be anything but fiction.

The Russians, wearied of stereotyped gestures and frightwigs and heavy makeup which were destroying character, began to use nonprofessionals in the first enthusiastic flowering of revolutionary movies, and this was supposed to have some political virtue, too, as if the happy peasant, emancipated from Czardom, automatically became a communicator of emotions and ideas. Some magnificent bits were recorded and the Russians found, as the Italians did thirty years later, that you could take a man or woman or child who "looked the part" and in many cases could teach them the rudimentary art that simple movies required. Considering how confidently young "discoveries" proceed from-extra-to-bit-to-star because they look and sound exactly right for a specific image, there is nothing surprising in the capacity of an old woman to look more like an old woman than a young one does, no matter how much wispy hair you drip over her face. But whenever the movie demands the full creation of a character, whenever it uses the individual for himself and not as part of a mass, whenever a specific unusual situation generates an emotion unlike any other—then the fact that the gas-station attendants really are gas-station attendants is of no more relevance than the fact that Lunt and Fontanne, playing husband and wife, are married to each other and live in Genesee Depot, Wisconsin.

The failure of the American film to cope with reality has often been noted. It is a failure to confront the actualities of human passions as they express themselves morally, physically, socially, and economically. It has nothing to do with the surface reality of the screen.

Nor in essence do the new dimensions of the screen serve reality. They serve the imagination, and that is why we have the exciting prospect of experiencing, for the third time in our lives, a new art of the movies. Looking forward gratefully, we can afford to forget the blunders and the bad taste and the stupidity that have attended the movies in the past. We can even say that these less engaging qualities had their share, as surely as talent and devotion had theirs, in making the movies what they have been and may again be, the great lovely art of our time.*

* "I think the cinema is the very greatest art, with the possibilities of becoming the greatest art form that has ever existed."—H. G. WELLS (1935)

6

THE USEFUL ART

The special form of love which the movies inspired never welled up for radio, which almost immediately after it appeared became such a necessity of life that romantic affection seemed superfluous. The entire relation of the public to the broadcasting arts, from the first radio signals to television today, develops from this beginning, and one of the astounding aspects of this relationship, never completely understood by either broadcasters or the public, is that it was implied by the first official observers of radio, the commission appointed by President Hoover to study what was happening in the life of America. Mr. Hoover had been Secretary of Commerce when radio was beginning. He entered the White House at about the time the *Amos 'n' Andy* program was becoming famous. By the time his term was over, his commission, reporting on Recent Social Trends, marked the true significance of radio.

I have used the *Amos 'n' Andy* program as the focal point in a revolution and noted how rivals for public attention had to defer to this variation of the end man and interlocutor. The significant thing is that, while work, late shopping, visits, or playing catch with the children after work were affected, inside the home all was well. Meals could be prepared and eaten without missing a moment of the adventures of the rogue and the simpleton who were presently joined by the Kingfish and Madam Queen and a whole community of people who seemed to have come from nowhere and, with a single giant stride, planted themselves firmly at the very center of American life.

They did not come from nowhere; they had forerunners; in the end they did not become a permanent part of the new American mythology. They were significant because at that moment in 1929 and for several years to come they were riding higher than anyone else on the great waves of a revolutionary change in the ideas and habits of the nation. Whatever else the revolution was bringing, its day-to-day effect was simple enough: although more people had more money to spend than ever before in that summer before the crash, millions of them were going home and staying home for entertainment. They wanted to hear *Amos 'n' Andy*. Perhaps it is closer to the truth to say they wanted to be with these two people, to pass fifteen minutes of their lives with two men whom they never saw and whom they knew in the same way that they knew their own friends, anticipating and relishing familiar turns of phrase, knowing that the exploits related were gross exaggerations, remaining loyal in friendship even if on occasions Amos and Andy were a little long-winded or dull. Because Andy said "I'se regusted," his friends (the listeners) took pleasure in saying it to one another; and they followed the affairs of the Fresh Air Taxi Company as they followed the stock market (a rival excitement at that time which did not, in the end, do so well by its enthusiasts). The market and sports and dance marathons and flagpole sitting were diversions around which, as in a vast continental stadium, the people of the United States sat observant, all but a few of them mere spectators. *Amos 'n' Andy* was different. The small doings of its characters were shared by millions of people into whose homes they came as daily, eagerly expected guests.

This sense of being with—or, as they said in the Midwest, "visiting with"—the disembodied characters of radio is a clue to the double revolution that was taking place in American life. Entertainment had become less expensive and more accessible when the movies spread over the land, but it was still something to be bought at intervals when you could afford to go downtown or to the nearest city; with the coming of radio, entertainment became a free and uninterrupted part of domestic life, and after a few years it had become a *right*, not quite so inalienable as life and liberty, but essential to the pursuit of happiness, with which it became more and more identified. And while this was happening a second revolution, in the nature of entertainment itself, occurred. Radio took over the forms of vaudeville, the theater, the night club or roadhouse, and the concert hall, but as it developed, these things all underwent many changes and radio, which seemed merely to be the continuation of other entertainments, was not even trying to do what the older forms had done. For better or worse, it had other ends in view.

The two comedians whom I have, for historical reasons, placed at the center of a profound disturbance in the way Americans lived were incomparably popular and just short of being first-rate. Even in the easy, sometimes shabby field of blackface comedy these two were far below their contemporaries in vaudeville, Moran and Mack, the *Two Black Crows*, whose recorded conversations are delighting a whole new audience after twenty-five years. The *Amos 'n' Andy* characters were fuzzy and shapeless, without the natural simplicity of the minstrel show's interlocutor and end man, on which they were modeled, and less exuberant than the grosser caricatures of the Florian Slappey stories by Octavus Roy Cohen, whom they also resembled. Their distortions of language were calculated, the words spoken having no specific relation to the originals; they were not like Durante's inspired headlong rush at a word —and let the consonants fall where they will. Their plots were puny and suffered from complications, showing signs of malnutrition as they were dragged through the long pull of five episodes a week. By their success they helped to perpetuate the insulting stereotypes of the shiftless or roguish Negro even while they were making these figures amiable.

Yet they were first-rate in one way: their instinct for the right use of the techniques of radio was faultless. Listening to them, you never felt that they wished people could see them or were afraid their comedy was not getting across because they were invisible. It was their great good fortune when they began that talking pictures had not yet reached the public ear, but long after the movies provided image and voice together, the *Amos 'n' Andy* program gave the impression that sound itself was enough. Something more than that, even. It took positive advantage of the freedom radio gave: by a change of voice or of accent, by attaching a word or a phrase to a person like a tag of identification, two men at a microphone populated the air with men, women, and children, until when they looked back and made a census they discovered that they had invented over a hundred different characters and made them real to millions of people by their voices alone. Out of these characters a sort of bubbling of activity rose, surrounding the principals, and these two, using the drawl and the slow take and the occasional pretentious language of the stage Negro, gave a pace and rhythm to their show which was almost the true beat of life. Life was not, to be sure, what they were trying for; like the makers of movie cartoons, they used animation instead, and in the new world of radio it was enough. There were programs to come which had not a fraction of their inventiveness and which used their techniques for dubious purposes; *Amos 'n' Andy* was without pretensions, a light trifle floating in the air.

The two men who created the program were Freeman F. Gosden and Charles J. Correll, and they came by their sure instinct for the techniques of radio in the most natural way. As far back as 1920 they had appeared on an experimental station in New Orleans, and it took them eight years to reach Chicago and the networks; during that time the nature of their work and the very names of the characters underwent many changes. After that, no changes were needed. Like clowns, like the figures in comic strips and the heroines of daytime serials, they neither aged nor changed; living fifteen minutes a day, they could not grow old with the years. It was, indeed, the essence of their relation to their audience that nothing should change. In this, as in their flexible handling of the sound system, the two men were among the pioneers of radio; they parceled out their events in little segments, finishing off a small incident in a single broadcast, but keeping a major story going for many months, as they did with the adventure into marriage and divorce which involved Madam Queen and was perhaps the longest dream sequence in history. Knowing that they would be loved only if they became familiar friends, they repeated their "check and double check" and other tags just often enough to introduce them into the common language and then said them a little less often so that each time they came up they were familiar, but not stale.

In the nature of things, they could not stay forever at the top of the heap, but nearly twenty years after their beginning the Columbia Broadcasting System bought *Amos 'n' Andy*—the characters, their past and their future, with an option on the services of their creators—for $2,500,000 (unofficial estimate). A series of television comedies was made on film under the supervision of the original creators, but without their appearance in the cast. The films were skillful, but not too well received. Complaint was made against the representation of the Negro, although Negroes played the principal parts and the tone was, as before, indulgently amiable. The farcical characters and exaggerated situations seemed to be offered as "true to life," and because the characters became visible, people could no longer visit with them in the imagination; Amos and Andy were no longer with their audiences, but separated from them. Five years later Gosden and Correll made their ten-thousandth broadcast and announced their retirement. They did not stick to it; but that did not matter either.

I have noted that Herbert Hoover was entering the White House when Amos and Andy were becoming regular visitors in the American home. As Secretary of Commerce, he had not backed a proposal for regulating radio commercials, being convinced that "the American people would not stand for advertising on the air." In a way, his Commission on Recent Social Trends made up for this error because in its report it used radio as a conspicuous example of the effects of invention on American life. In a summary I made at the time, I noted that over a hundred general effects (including perhaps a thousand detailed ones) were listed and that they ranged from a new entertainment for the blind to standardization of diction, from a new instrument for teaching languages to new occupations for vaudeville artists. The list included abstractions like "minimizing regional differences" and practical effects like prevention of crop losses and upsetting the lecture business, checking the spread of rumors, bringing rapid aid in case of fire or flood, and competing with newspapers as advertising media. Under the general heading of "interest in sports increased, it is generally admitted," there were fifteen separate items ranging from "more energetic recruitment of college players" to greater advertising of the climate of Florida or California when broadcasts of games originated in these states.

The report is a sort of outline of the formative years of radio since it first startled the public by flashing the news of the election of Warren G. Harding. From that moment it moved out of the hands of the "hams" and the ingenious assemblers of homemade crystal sets, and it kept people interested—first as a novelty that brought them voices from a submarine or the magnified heartbeats of a butterfly, then by music, games, news—while the characteristic program types of the medium were being worked out. We learn that more people were doing morning exercises, to the count of an invisible but sympathetic instructor; and people knew melodies from a new musical comedy before the sheet music or the records were on sale at the local stores. The triumph of getting a distant station lost its splendor; everybody could "get Pittsburgh" now, and the people who sang or gave advice on the *Farm and Home Hour* there began to be known by name. At the beginning, stations went on the air for a short time—in New York City three of them used the same transmitter one after another. Slowly broadcasters entered the business of selling commodities and spread their programs to the daylight hours, so that women had popular music and even some little sketches to keep them company as they washed the dishes and made the beds. These things the commission duly noted. Not noted was the fact that millions of people who had rarely had any entertainment whatever were now offered more of it in a day than the average man, from the time of the Circus Maximus to the opening of *The Great Train Robbery*, had had in a year. In words so moderate as to be almost shocking, radio itself is described in the report as "another agency for recreation and entertainment." It is to the credit of the men who wrote the report that they noted so many symptoms of revolutionary change. The revolution itself had not yet come to the surface.

A generation later we are only beginning to understand what has happened—and is happening. When a continuous flow of free entertainment came into the home, into virtually every home in the land, it became an integrated part of our lives, a necessity. From the beginning it affected the lives of those who did not hear it almost as much as it affected those who listened to it all day. It had two features virtually unknown to entertainment in the past: it was closely tied to commerce and thereby to the commodities we used and to the rate at which we bought them—and it was also a prime means of communication. News and ideas were considered as separate elements at the beginning. Presently we discovered that the manipulation of symbols and the use of entertainment itself to create the atmosphere in which our ideas are formed were among the vast potentialities of the new medium.

We began to encounter the public arts.

7

SOUNDS AND ECHOES

The special feeling that people have for their various diversions tells us a great deal about the quality of each of them—as it tells us also a great deal about the people. The sense of "visiting with" the characters on the *Amos 'n' Andy* show extended to many others—to *Fibber McGee and Molly*, who were early arrivals in the comedy of domestic life, and to *Vic and Sade*, in which radio came close to creating an authentic piece of humor in the American language, and to the tart characters created by Goodman Ace for himself and Jane. It was the dominant response to the daytime serial—strange as the adventures might be, the heroines were somehow neighbors, and when a child was born to one of them, thousands of cards and gifts were sent to the mother (the actress) in care of the various stations carrying the program. When, in less happy circumstances, the happiness of a wife was threatened, a listener began a letter by saying, "My dear, I want you to sit down before you read any more . . ." and went on to say, "I think your husband is being unfaithful to you. . . ." This complete familiarity with people like themselves was an obstacle to the kind of adulation received by the movie stars, who had glamour and were always so much bigger than life and lived so far away. Shopgirls aspired to be like Joan Crawford, but women felt they were talking to the harassed heroine of *Our Gal Sunday* and getting lessons in the business of living from the wise *Aunt Jenny*.

In one field, something like the movie passion did occur. The comedians and the MC's were popular, but mass mania did not set in for them or any of the other stars of radio until the crooner arrived and set the sidewalks on fire. The complete manifestation of the bobby-soxer in relation to the radio singer seems to have occurred first in the big cities when the singer came to the showplace movie theater and was dutifully mobbed at each performance. The press agent's part in these shenanigans has often been confessed, but it is not the decisive factor; the Vallees and the Crosbys and the Russ Columbos had to be adored before the publicist could go to work. The testimony we have, from those who survived their own adolescence without entirely forgetting it, indicates that the emotion was violent and almost always belligerent, the campfollowers of one crooner fighting in the streets with those of all the others. There were overt sexual phenomena and some hidden ones. The whole thing was reduced to Marxian terms and was then rescued from Moscow by pretending that it was nothing but youthful high spirits. The phenomenon—a sort of irreligious children's crusade—can stand a lot of analysis, which I do not propose to supply here. The original connection with music is a prime consideration, for between Vallee on the sentimental side and Benny Goodman on the hot, hysteria came with its special rhythms, and what happened afterward, when mobs were supplied like claques at the opera, is not important.

These outbursts differ from the manifestations of love for the movies because at their core there is always a personal object: Vallee or Crosby or Sinatra, not radio; whereas even the most rabid of the idolaters of William Powell or Joan Crawford arrived at their personal adoration from a central love of the movies themselves. The differences between these two approaches become even more marked—and more important —when television makes the contrast, and the nature of the actual response to broadcasting is therefore discussed after a look at the nature of television programs. One point from that later discussion should be noted here: the acceptance of the receiver in the home as a prime necessity, like a lamp or a telephone. This is a clue to our intense feeling that whatever comes out of the receiver has in some way the quality of everyday truth; it is not an accident that the most famous of all radio programs was the broadcast of a work of fiction which listeners took to be an on-the-spot report of an event.

As a commercial property, radio did not withstand the shock of television. The question never to be answered is whether it could have survived as entertainment for another ten years if television had been delayed. The reason for wondering is that radio had developed so many routines and so few creations of its own. In toplofty terms, radio was an entertainment with hardly any aesthetic interest. To speak of "the art of radio" always seemed grossly pretentious—unless it seemed merely funny. There were some interesting technical inventions, some entertaining tricks—but the beautiful structure of the movies, the interior life a good movie always had, where were they?

I cannot say that radio was not loved precisely because of this aesthetic lack; I note it as a coincidence, and proceed with the observation of things as they were, to see whether they illuminate the case of television and its future.

The first triumph of radio was that it learned to live with itself, within its limitations, and that the good men in the profession never lamented the absence of the visual. Their position was that of King Vidor and of Charlie Chaplin when sound came to the movies: they would use sound, but they had not missed it because they had learned to tell their stories with the materials the silent film afforded them. This getting the most out of the conditions imposed on you, getting a positive advantage where others see only a loss, has always been recognized as the true signature of a master craftsman. The good professionals in radio never said or implied, "If you could *see* this, you would understand. . . ." Without a picture to illustrate the genes and the chromosomes, they could strike a chord on the piano two or three times to establish one combination of genes and then, altering only the top note of the chord, illustrate how the slightest variation creates an entirely new entity. They learned to use evocative words, they worked the pictorial and inevitably fell into the merely picturesque—but one thing stood always to their credit: in the days of the motion picture and later in the days of the movie with sound, no one actually found radio lacking in power to stir the imagination, to deliver what it had to deliver fully and well.

The head of one network was heard to say, after watching a brilliant but fanatical director rehearsing a play, that radio would never grow up until someone took away its "playthings"—by which he meant the whole apparatus of "sound effects." Writers in particular were prepared reluctantly to wait while a director tried to get exactly the sound of a sandstorm (a sound he had never heard) and the precise timing of a bell in the hand of a walking nightwatchman as well as the other, less intricate, sound effects of a half-hour program; this would take about three hours, after which the remaining time, perhaps an hour altogether, would be devoted to getting the right meaning of the lines, the tempo of speech and response, and all the other values that the writer had considered paramount. A famous director, to impress his clients during a rehearsal, rejected the crackling of a dried branch because it was right for October whereas the script called for a dried branch to be stepped on and to crackle on Thanksgiving Day.

The enthusiasts for sound effects were being literal. They were using the microphone as some directors use the television camera, to act for the human sensory organs. They did not consider the way the mind acts —to eliminate the insignificant, to become absorbed in whatever is made to appear important. An angry man leaving a room slams a door, and the echo of that noise may beat on the heart of the woman he has left behind; but the mind does not hear a Western Union messenger leaving the room while a woman reads the telegram from the War Department, and the sound of a door closing at such a moment would break, not sustain, the mood of tragedy. Radio needed to develop a kind of expressionist technique and never quite did so, although attempts were made, especially in England, and by Corwin and MacLeish, the only men with any serious sense of the aesthetics of radio who tried to write for it in America.

The use of music, quite apart from the broadcasting of music, was a natural development; the silent movies had provided elaborate cue sheets for "moods" and transitions, and as long as the sound did not have to be accounted for, the movies were free to keep music running all the time. Radio simply took over the freedom of the movies; a fanfare of music ushered in a program; there was music under announcements; when a scene ended, music came up and made a bridge in time or in mood to the next scene; and when a writer or director felt that the actors could not get the necessary quantum of emotion out of the spoken text, music could be brought in from the starry heavens or from limbo—the old theatrical trick of playing "Hearts and Flowers" in the wings. The jargon of the trade indicated what music was used for: you could find directions like "MUSIC: STINGS" or "SNEAK MUSIC IN," or a military piece would "SEGUE TO HERE COMES THE BRIDE." The stings and stabs of music were often dissonant chords that underlined shock or horror; the music that went "UP AND UNDER" was to support the words. It was highly functional, and it supplied to those writers who needed it a substitute for the visual image. In the end, the audience became so used to music doing this job that a production which tried the austerity of having music only when it could be explained as coming from an instrument or a concert or a radio would have been considered thin and untrue to life.

The only other missed opportunity, in the field of legitimate devices, was the use of silence. Just as a station feared to go off the air even for a few moments, so directors of radio productions seemed to fear silence; when a script called for utter quiet after a climax had been reached, the director would usually put in a sound effect or let his music "sneak" in. He had, to be sure, a delicate problem: if he waited a split second too long, his audience might think the play was over and turn to another channel. No one can say whether he was right or not, but the later experience of some FM and educational stations would indicate that listeners might have accepted silence as a conventional element, just as they accepted music from nowhere. Station WGBH-FM, broadcasting the Boston Symphony concerts, did not attempt to fill the intermission with talk of any kind; the microphones were left open so that the listener at home felt himself in natural communion with those in Symphony Hall, and the suggestion, not in words but in this action itself, was that the natural thing to do between parts of a concert was to move about and talk and prepare to listen again. This innovation of unfilled air caused much comment, most of it entirely favorable.

The time and place for an art of radio to develop did not come together in the United States. The beginnings were made when CBS, bucking the twofold power of the networks that are now NBC and ABC, found itself with unsold hours and particularly those hours during which its adversary had exceptionally popular programs. Into these spots programs had to be set which were not too expensive, and here, too, was an opportunity to make significant tests of the public taste. The *Workshop* and later the programs created by Norman Corwin were the most notable of the CBS experiments, the former more interesting for using material excluded from commercial programs, the latter for the techniques Corwin exploited, particularly in his massing and dividing of choral voices. A considerable number of radio's best experiments were made during the days of the WPA, and many Federal agencies participated in programs—the Office of Education, for instance, authorized the series *Immigrants All—Americans All*. In such programs it was desirable to employ a large number of players, and the realistic or poetic handling of crowds was carefully studied by directors. A writer of a historical program might put down: "Voice shouts, 'John Peter Zenger is in jail for libel' " and add: "MIXED VOICES REPEAT THE WORDS"; under Corwin's dramatic guidance, the words would swell from a mere whisper into a cumulative roar with a climax of sudden silence.

Like several others, Corwin made his particular mark in the radio documentary. The name—taken over from British films, where it loosely covered many types of informational or factual movies—came to mean one of two things in the United States: an inspirational program during wartime, or a study of a disagreeable subject. (It has been observed that "documentary" connotes to the average audience a study of syphilis, Communism, or juvenile delinquency.) During the war and again when he went around the world (on the award established in honor of Wendell Willkie) Corwin's was the most eloquent voice using radio in behalf of the liberal aspirations of Americans. Between the changing temper of the times and the coming of television, his type of documentary lost ground, and it was, in fact, a program executive of CBS who announced that the poetic documentary was dead. The fact that it has persisted in the movies, notably in British and Canadian productions, and has been used, with a difference, by Walt Disney, has apparently escaped the producers of the form in television.

In radio the defect of the rhetorical documentary was a tendency, marked in Corwin, to soar away from fact, to start with the number 88 for radium and then make, not radium, but 88 the figure in the carpet. It worked when the subject was a great idea, and it failed when the subject was a great fact. The rhetoric stemmed from Walt Whitman by way of Pare Lorentz's catalogue in his great poetic-documentary film *The River*; at best the cadences and the rhythm cast a spell—and used radio for one of its natural purposes. But it remained a rather special taste, and documentary of another order supplanted it.

Actually, long before Corwin began to create his world of words, a new sound came into radio: *The March of Time*. In spite of its preposterous tone of portent and doom, this program was right in most of its innovations. By the time it began, radio had already worked itself into half a dozen comfortable ruts. *The March of Time,* put together all the known techniques, invented a few new ones, tricked the whole thing out with a kind of glamour of intelligence, and produced the program with aggressive power. The shock technique of the magazine, the misleading caption, the sly adjective were less prominent in the radio version; instead, we got a kind of frankness of approach to the material, unabashed by the importance of people or events, and the selection of the most exciting three or four events of the week, even at the expense of the significant. Politically and socially, radio came to life with this program, which escaped the singular defect of its movie counterpart— in radio everyone knew that this was a re-enactment of the actual event; in the movie, especially at the beginning, the re-enactments passed as reality. (The exception in radio was that Bill Adams too perfectly imitated the voice of President Roosevelt; at the request of the White House, these impersonations were dropped.)

We are close here to radio as transmitter of the actual and proportionately far from radio as creator of entertainment on its own. This is typical of almost all discussion of radio—it tends to depart from those fields in which radio made its money and concentrate on the programs of service to the community. The reason is the weakness of the creative impulse in radio. It was a new way of transmitting music, but one does not recall much beyond snips and bits that were composed for it. It was a new way of creating drama, but most of its impressive work was derived from novels and plays; original work was largely confined to melodramas and tales of the supernatural with the singular merit of being forgotten the moment they were heard. These things are not said to condemn the broadcasters, who would have welcomed the chance to serve the nation better if the composers and dramatists had sensed their opportunity, especially in the early days when the station managers had no idea how to fill their air time. That the poets also were aloof is the greatest pity because radio was made for them. Readings from anthologies were familiar in the 1920s and are still heard; but, apart from MacLeish's two dramas, no work from the established poets was created for radio while it dominated the commercial field. In the minor area covered by FM, poetry has been heard, often through excellent recordings made by the poets—but again this is transmission and not creation.

For all that, radio contrived a few program styles so acceptable that they made their way easily into television: the daytime serial, the hodge-podge hour centering on a comedian, the half-hour tale of violence, the personality program. It is not much of a showing; even if one adds the magnified parlor-question game, one has the feeling that these things were put together, more than created. Perhaps an exception should be made for the form so proudly called "situation comedy," which came to mean almost any comedy routine not based on a gag or an insult, as if the comedians had fallen upon something unknown and wonderful (except that it had been the staple of comedy since Aristophanes). One star, at least, was magnificent in this field because she was an actress and could create character by a look of the eye, so she had no trouble doing it with a change of voice, a whisper, a howl: Fanny Brice. The savage brat she placed before us, who could also be an endearing (but not altogether trustworthy) waif, was as delicate a creation as low comedy could carry. As the years went on, Baby Snooks could have no surprises for us except the constant surprise at how freshly she was presented; the routines were old, but Fanny Brice was still "making up" the character, not merely repeating herself. We had in her one of the great comic artists of our time, with an instinctive sense of what was funny, who seemed entirely uninhibited, letting herself appear awkward or ungainly or foolish so long as she was creating her characters, of whom only Baby Snooks had permanent life in radio. I have a recording of Baby Snooks reciting "Three Little Kittens" which is a masterpiece of grace and humor, and all of us who saw her and many who only heard her cherish equal memories. In a way, one is relieved to think that she never had to downgrade her work to the level of the weekly TV show.

This process is so constant and so marked that one begins to think there is something inherent in television, in the mechanism or the circumstances of reception, that compels TV to lower even the lowest of radio's standards. There is not. The factors that drag artists down are entirely human: they are preconceptions about the public taste, they are to a degree the taste of producers and sponsors. The medium itself can carry the best as well as the worst.

There is, however, a pull that has to be resisted, and we may get a clue to its nature if we examine some fairly superior people who have never made themselves entirely at home in television—or perhaps I should say have never been allowed to make themselves at home there.

The great failure has been with Fred Allen, for whom everything was done and overdone, always on the presumption that to let him do what came naturally would not work. For a generation he had been popular, once actually sitting on top of the world of popularity ratings, combining his oblique sense of comedy with his sardonic wit. But the masters of the business knew better than to let him go his way, and the TV image that is left of this shrewd, intelligent, somewhat displeased man is the sight of him holding a pig in his arms, unable to let it go because the cue had not arrived and the program was going off the air—an embarrassment from which everyone concerned except Allen himself should have died, professionally speaking. He has put in time as MC of an exceptionally silly guessing game and as a panelist in another, and he remains a symbol of conspicuous waste. (Fred Allen died while this book was being set in type.)

It is possible that the characters of *Allen's Alley*—Mrs. Nussbaum and Titus Moody and the Senator Claghorn who reminded us that it was safe to laugh at pomposity even in office—these people perhaps could not easily be presented in television (although more complicated and less rewarding groups have appeared). The pity is that nothing was tried, and that the closest radio came to creating solid grotesques—like figures out of comic strips with a broad streak of satire added—vanished with nothing to take their place. A smear of folksiness brushed across the television screen like the oil slick that marked a sinking at sea—what was sunk this time was a good part of the individuality and character of radio comedy. With the "failure" of Allen it became progressively harder for lesser satirists to make their way. Henry Morgan, whom Allen "sponsored," and Bob and Ray were intermittently seen and heard. Morgan, with an almost suicidal compulsion to rid himself of sponsors, became aggressive and almost unpleasant in his attack; he did not save his savagery for powerful adversaries, and his wit coarsened; he was making a personal vendetta out of his dislike for stupidity, as if he were all alone in the battle for intelligence. He had been refreshing, as a touch of lemon is in a drink, but he turned sour as his fortunes sagged. By a piece of good luck he held on to a place on a panel show and presently took over Garry Moore's job for six weeks, developing a softer personality, so that he could continue on the air and perhaps return to his original stance, which was personal in the highest degree, but not with his hand against every man.

Like Allen and Morgan, the team of Bob Elliott and Ray Goulding began in radio and were most happily situated there. Bob and Ray were, in fact, an avatar of Stoopnagle and Budd, whose business it was to make fun and only incidentally to make fun of some specific thing. Bob and Ray picked up part of the claim staked out by Henry Morgan, making fun of radio and its commercials even when the actual commercials on their programs were a trace more idiotic than the parodies that preceded them; but they also were funny without objectives, and through their "home expert," Mary Magoon, and a few other characters, all played by themselves, they began to create a small gallery of comic figures more broadly caricatured than those of *Allen's Alley*, but in the same general mold.

In radio and in television for a time they demonstrated a wild wit and a controlled satire, sometimes putting them together. The objects they sold "at laughably low prices" from their "overstocked surplus warehouse" included burglar kits with "aliases you can use over and over again, for example Benjamin Franklin and Mary, Queen of Scots" and goggles for Channel swimmers with the white cliffs of Dover already painted on the top half. Their characters had a habit of identifying themselves: on the telephone one would say, "This is Dr. Gregory Norton, your husband," and I believe it was another member of the same family who often identified himself as the doctor's "ne'er-do-well, no-good, blacksheep brother." Friendly philosophers and long-lost sweethearts and certain other familiar characters took on a certain attractive staleness under the withering look of the boys, and their occasional sorties into anger were refreshing. One of their personages was allowed, frequently, to talk to his customers: "This is Ferris Gallagher speaking in behalf of Ferris Gallagher and the Ferris Gallagher chain store. . . . Now I'm sick and tired of you folks running your carts right into the pile of Chinook salmon. . . . If you can't behave better than that . . . And tomorrow's special is . . ."

They had their troubles and planted themselves after a time on a morning radio program, locally, in New York. They had not quite proved that radio and television could use bright wit and broad farce if these things carried also a barb of satire—but they had made a very good try. They carried with them the seeds of their own destruction because they were men of an independent and satiric cast—and they could not find exactly when and how to conform.

8

PERSONALITY BUSINESS

At a time when the whole drive and direction of American life was toward smoothing out all differences and making every unit exactly like every other unit, the public arts kept up a stubborn fight for the different, the exceptional, the individual. It had to be a fight because both the mechanics and the economics of these arts were favorable to the system of identical and interchangeable parts in entertainment—as their sponsors had to be in the production of razor blades and motorcars and cigarettes. In one way or another, the men and women who could make a mark and assert their freedom instinctively fought back against the machining of entertainment. They demanded the right to approve of scripts in the movies. They refused to appear more than once a month in television. They broke out of the mold in which producers cast them. They insisted on something different, running the risk of disaster with audiences that had been patiently trained to expect nothing from them but more of the same.

They had their disasters, too, at times, but they survived and returned. And, in all the complexities of a business full of the uncertain and the unexpected, a kind word must be said for the whipping-boy of the mass media—the financier, the sponsor, the banker. For, reluctantly or not, these people did take chances, they did permit experiments to be made, they paid for those movies and broadcasts which demonstrated that routine and repetition were not always and altogether the essence of mass entertainment. In the long history of the war between art and commerce, art usually comes off best, because the historians are artists and because for generations, if not for centuries, it has been intellectually the right thing to belittle the commercial interest—and also because a large part of the commercial interest has been hasty for profit, short-sighted, and ignorant. But almost everything we admire in the popular arts (at least since the coming of sound to the movies) has been commercially produced—from the bootleggers who financed a Durante musical to the bankers whose money went into Paramount's *Lost Weekend*. There was the usual sponsor's money behind Orson Welles's *Lear* in television and behind grand opera on the air and behind Edward R. Murrow's bold social action on *See It Now*; and I have noted that the brilliant satirists of the style of commercials, Bob and Ray, were sponsored by a soap company whose own messages they were burlesquing. The prevalence of self-satire in sponsored programs is in itself an almost permanent phenomenon in broadcasting, from the time of Ray Knight and his *Cuckoo Hour* to Henry Morgan (and in both cases getting and losing sponsors seems to have been highly regular procedure).

The fight to remain one's self was not always successful. Some good men went down, and there were moments when it seemed as if in all the wild mixture of good and bad, of intelligence and cunning, in Hollywood, there was no place for a man like Orson Welles who had nothing but an instinctive genius for making movies—just as, for a few years, all the millions that went into television programs seemed to have as their object only a demonstration that Milton Berle was a great comic artist and that Fred Allen and Bobby Clark and Bert Lahr and Bea Lillie were not. Truth is mighty and may prevail—but not soon enough. The wastage of talent that might have been used is tragic. On the other hand . . .

Suppose we put sheer, beautiful genius aside and look at the career of a partner of genius, Garry Moore, as fine a straight man to Durante as McCullough was to Clark or George Burns to his Gracie. In the memory of radio audiences, the Durante-Moore shows have a special fragrance—particularly because before radio the great comic genius of our time never flourished when he was transplanted into alien soil. Neither the movies nor musical shows had given him that special circuit over which his high charge of electrical energy could reach the audience as it did by direct contact in a night club. Radio seemed a forlorn hope, because what Jimmy said and sang existed—or we thought it existed— only when you saw him creating, when he shouted and spluttered and strutted, responding without any inhibitions to any impulse that entered his head, throwing away the book or the plot or the routine sheet and existing, creating, ad lib. To confine this spirit within the rigid time span and the planned unspontaneity of the radio program seemed a gross stupidity.

And here enters Garry Moore.

Let me not jeopardize his future by suggesting that Garry Moore is an intellectual; let us say that when playing opposite Jimmy Durante he appeared to be an intellectual, it being part of that great man's charm to make people seem so. The part played by Moore—which was a Moore-ish character for whom Moore wrote the dialogue—was artful. It left Durante free to soar into his world of inverted logic without ever seeming to strain for his effects. Moore was patient with him, corrected him, went along with him, humored or chid him, but never exposed him to mockery. It was as if the Moore character stood off and relished the contrast between himself and Durante, enjoying both personalities. You could feel Moore's delight in the sudden and unpredictable spurts of Durante's lunacy as you felt, also, that he himself had a taste for verbal arabesques as complicated in their precision as Durante's were in their instinctive and magnificent misfires.

The combination broke up, and in radio Durante was never so good again. Garry Moore probably did not disappear, but I did not hear much of him again until he came on as the MC of an afternoon TV show, compelled to ingratiate himself with hundreds of women in the studio in order to be acceptable to millions of women at home. Television then was death in the afternoon, and it seemed a shame that this unpretty boy with his crew cut and his curt and ironic delivery, his keen mind, should be sacrificed to it.

From the start you could feel that Moore was not going to be entirely submerged; he could not belittle his sponsors and deride his audience (as Henry Morgan might on a local station at 11:30 P.M.), but something candid and free was going to persist. Moore began by taking his microphone to the studio audience—usually a signal for insipidities and gigglings. With a brief brushing-in of the routine introductions, he would ask people what they did not like about his program, and would explain why he had to do certain things and could not do others—a frank and shrewdly critical approach to his own material and to the conditions under which he labored. He was successful enough in this first attempt to acquire sponsors, and although his program has had ups and downs, represented by changes of time periods, extensions to ninety minutes or contractions to thirty, he has gained freedom (as all people in television do, if they would only know it) by the mere fact of longevity; and he has known it and capitalized on it.

His program is one of half a dozen that seem to have no form. It breaks itself up at times, it varies in quality as the conversation of any group of people might vary with changes in their frame of mind or even in their rate of metabolism, but it is never stupid. You feel yourself in the presence of a man who has clearly set out to please you—but not at the expense of his own integrity (or yours). He makes little jokes and he does foolish things—all comic television is still under the spell of Milton Berle's foray into transvestitism, and a new way to appear ludicrous is considered funny to the highest degree. On the other hand, Moore can dissect the follies of television, often with only casual reference, sometimes full-scale. When he acts out the usual commercial (for a cold-remedy) and then shows "what really happens" (the victim downs a huge slug of whisky instead of the advertised pills), you know that he is doing a man's job in an area populated, for the most part, by agile adolescents.

Garry Moore and his program are examples of a kind of creative adaptation in which commercial broadcasting has been notably successful—and, along with half a dozen other individuals and programs, they stand as a warning to critics not to judge the popular arts by standards drawn from older entertainments—even from older popular entertainments. No one who remembers the last flare-up of vaudeville (between 1929 and 1932) will doubt that he saw far better entertainment than these afternoon grab-bags of fun, but the intentions of the two entertainments are fundamentally different. Vaudeville tried to entertain a small, self-selected, paying audience gathered once a week, at most, in a particular place and prepared to give all its attention to a variety of acts produced with bright lights and loud music and "broken in" by previous tryouts in smaller houses or perfected over a long period of

years. The objectives of the afternoon catch-all program in television
are so different that you could safely go to the opposite of each of the
conditions I have mentioned and you would have a reasonable definition—not only of intentions, but of the actual operation. And when
you had all this—the daily stint, the universal audience, the distraction
of attention because the audience is surrounded by the sounds and
sights of home, the tone that can vary between the intimate and the
almost boisterous but can never be the "high" theatrical tone—when
you have all this, you must still add the overriding condition and the
overriding purpose: the entertainment must please in such a way that
the audience will buy soap.

It is possible to make a moral judgment and to say that this was a
better country when we had vaudeville; you can say that vaudeville
challenged the mind and uplifted the spirits, whereas afternoon TV
shows do not; but to judge these shows by the standards of vaudeville
is as unfair as to judge them by the standards of grand opera. And this is
brought into focus by one element that these afternoon programs have
in common with those final days of vaudeville which are so fondly remembered: the master of ceremonies.

The pre-history of this character probably can be traced back to the
conferencier in the early French theater; for me, it begins with the second half of a bill at the Palace when Joe Cook began to wander
through the acts preceding his own. I particularly recall the Alexanders,
who did notable stunts with tennis balls and on whom the curtain was
summarily lowered in mid-act; whereon Joe appeared and went into
his complicated lunacies including why he would *not* imitate four Ha-
waiians, and presently the back curtain rose again and there were the
Alexanders just catching the ten tennis balls which had been in mid-
air when we had last seen them. I heard later that Cook owned part of
the act, which may be; I know that he liked the faint disturbance and
the strong boost he gave to other acts by sauntering into them. From
this it was not a long step to making introductions, but if Joe Cook
ever took over a whole Palace bill, I never caught it. The famous names
in this connection are Frank Fay and—in my mind, one of the supremely
fine comic monologists of our time—Lou Holtz. It was Holtz, leaning
sideways on a cane that seemed to wilt under his weight, only half
interested in what he was doing (he usually was thinking of the fourth

at Belmont during the matinee), not disliking the audience, but having no intention of sucking up to them, aware that vaudevillians were craftsmen, not dedicated artists—it was Holtz who set for me the image of the vaudeville MC, and the essential thing, of course, is that he himself was in those days an incomparable teller of stories, all of which were long, involved, with a profusion of comic details along the way and usually without a snap ending. He told the classic about the man who was asked by a stranger in the club car to tell him the time and responded "Drop dead" (or, in his pronunciation, which escapes exact spelling, "Drahp d'ad"). Asked to explain this rudeness, he did so: if he had told the stranger the time, they would have got into conversation and then one thing would have led to another—but the essence of Holtz's style was that he told you every single thing and what every single thing would lead to, until the stranger would ask for the daughter's hand in marriage and "then I'd say to you 'Drahp d'ad' . . . and so . . ." Holtz knew that a story which takes five minutes or more to tell cannot depend on a surprise ending, but must live as it goes along. One of his classics about two people who "cried each other" with side bets as to who could cry most was unbearably funny but always defeated Holtz, who confessed that he had never found any ending for it at all. What he had found was his own dilatory, casual, disinterested style, as if he were not making his living by doing his work anyhow. There was in Holtz's manner a kind of almost sadistic cynicism which is rare in any popular entertainment and which may account for the fact that he never became one of the four or five best-known comedians of his time (another reason is that he was incurably lazy and never worked unless he had to).

I have given so much space to Lou Holtz not only because it gives me pleasure to pay tribute to him, but because he illustrates so specifically the different position of the MC in television. The acts that Holtz introduced in vaudeville were separate and complete organisms, chosen for excellence and brought together on a particular bill because, ideally, they provided the various pleasures that vaudeville's other name, variety, implied. The MC could and often did stay on week after week while the rest of the bill underwent changes, or he might be called back to introduce a totally new bill within three months. He was there because he was fluent and made himself liked and because he was a prodigious talent in his own right. The total success of the week's bill depended a great deal on him, but the value of any separate act was usually independent of his services.

But in television, if the contents of the grab-bag are not properly shaken out and displayed by the MC, the show is all low in tone. The MC who has no specific act of his own (as Ed Sullivan has none in his hugely successful nighttime hour) tends to become more and more part of all the other acts: he will be the straight man or he will sing (preferably off key, as this is *very* funny) or he will do a dance step or hand the juggler his props. He will by this be omnipresently before the camera and will become in due time recognized as "a TV personality" and appear as guest on other programs, like dozens of women and a few men who have parlayed lack of talent into a successful career.

This description, "TV personality," has become standard, although it has never been clearly defined. It is a recognized profession, like pianist or snake-charmer, but it implies neither training nor special skill, and is applied to people who seem to have no other qualifications, although it could not be said in most cases that they have no visible means of support. That is the special point, for these people have a kind of high visibility. The women among them either have a regular beauty, the maxfactory product associated with the covers of fan magazines, or they have a remarkable capacity to project breasts (and even on occasion buttocks) for the purposes of provocation; as real sexual provocation is rare in television, its few practitioners are doubly welcome.

They are, however, often silly people, and there is something silly about the exploitation they get. Even worse, the constant tendency to assimilate people of real character into the personality mold is irritating. The genuine talents of Faye Emerson, for instance, are not of the first order on the stage, but of a high order as a conversationalist on the air because of her great capacity to understand other people and be interested in them. These talents have been neglected, first to allow for the exploitation of her equally genuine good looks and then of the clothes she wears, so that a fictitious character has been created and the fundamentally simple, fundamentally intelligent person can now be caught only occasionally on a TV show, whereas it is copiously present every day on her radio program.

Yet even at its worst the TV personality points to something essential and not discreditable which television can do: it can "deliver" a kind of essence of each human being set before the camera—deliver this essence, without too much distortion, to the screen in the living room, so that, no matter how false the program format may be, something genuine will usually come through. This does not mean that a fraud cannot impose himself over the air waves, the TV camera not being provided with an X ray; but TV will transmit candor and will even distinguish between moments of candor and moments of faking. The business of exploiting personality, which seems to be exactly the reverse of the business of developing character, has gone on a long time in America—not always gracefully, not always to the advantage of the people who have allowed themselves to be exploited—and we have suffered this for so long that any carefully built-up front may get by in television. But the face of reality and the accent of truth do come through well enough to give us hope.

9

THE THRESHOLD OF ENTERTAINMENT

The kind of entertainment people prefer and the amount of it they can use depend on a variety of circumstances: Are they rich or poor? Does their work interest or bore them? Are they introverted or extroverted? Are they highly intellectual, highly emotional, or a mixture of the two? There is, in addition, the factor of availability: How much entertainment of what kinds can they conveniently get?

In the tenth year of television as a going concern, the families who gathered around some thirty million TV receivers were sure of getting a large number of programs whose genealogy could be described as "out of the parlor game by sheer necessity." They were the panel and quiz programs, and their quality, ranging from the witty to the inane, represented the triumph, over all other characteristics, of amiability. It is not a bad quality in social intercourse, and it is a natural quality for television because the people in front of the cameras and the people in front of the home receiver are engaged in a sort of conversation—a being together. The successful programs, in this spontaneous kind, are the ones that are most unselfconsciously aware of this—the ones that do not so much talk *to* people as talk *with* them. On the other hand, amiability without certain other qualities is lukewarm tea with too much milk.

The mistresses of the kings of France played at being dairymaids, and the intellectuals of New York brought back the crossword puzzle and

Guggenheim. (The French Revolution followed on the first, the great market crash of 1929 on the second.) The first program to capitalize on the smartness of playing games was *Information, Please!* (It is interesting to note that the program was rejected by the first network to which it was offered because there was already one quiz show on its stations and the sales department was afraid it could not sell another!) Although the inventor of *Information, Please!* had originally planned to have telephone and railway people and encyclopedists and lexicographers among the members of his panel, these were not the experts whom the public was eventually invited to stump. Instead, well-informed and witty laymen took the regular places, and guest stars appeared who were either eminent in their work or became eminent in new fields as a result of their appearance. (Wendell Willkie's march to the Presidential nomination was enormously accelerated by his brilliant performance on the program.) Actually, *Information, Please!* inverted the quiz formula, and its true character was for a considerable time hidden: it was a device for getting some merry conversation from people without the danger of getting too much of it, since the master of ceremonies changed the subject every three or four minutes. In the person of Clifton Fadiman, the MC became particularly pleasant because he seemed never to cut off any of the panelists, but gave the impression that he was joining in their play and then, to let them proceed to the next question, shut himself up—an act of grace instead of an interruption.

One great virtue of this program was that it altered the image of the intellectual perpetuated by so many other radio programs: the solemn, incompetent figure of fun. Useless to say that the members of the panel were not great intellectuals and that most of them would have vigorously rejected the description; to the public they were intellectuals, and yet they were colloquial, cheerful—and sponsored. It was a cultural work parallel to that of Theodore Roosevelt when he changed the image of the "Harvard dude." Messrs. Kieran, Adams, Levant, and Fadiman, with the help of the guests, were building a bridge over the gap between the educated and the ignorant, the intellectual and the public. The average listener, it appeared, thought the program "educational" and was surprised to find education so pleasant; the appetite for unrelated facts, always an innocent, almost childlike, feature of the American mind, was satisfied. It was as if the odium of the New Deal's "Brain Trust" had been lifted.

The program was sponsored for years and even when its ratings dropped it held on, but the delay in bringing it to television was fatal. On film, the series had paid off, but it lacked the ease and gaiety of the radio version and was over-visualized; the thought of letting some attractive people talk without diagrams and pictures and props and girls dressed like drum majorettes doing charades—this was too revolutionary. When the program arrived as a summer replacement in television, it utterly lacked conviction, as if everyone felt it ought to be given a chance, but no one thought it had a chance. (Someone vitally concerned with the production had made the dogmatic statement that it ought to be on film—the art of the spontaneous subordinated to the art of the editor.) Mr. Fadiman's hand had meanwhile become subdued to the inferior materials of *This Is Show Business,* as successful a program as was ever built on the assumption that human beings are contemptible idiots.

The failure of *Information, Please!* is relatively unimportant; the disaster is that the lesson it had so proudly taught in radio was not learned. No commercial panel show in TV aspires to one tenth of the general air of civilized men and women, in pleasant converse, that *Information, Please!* had at its best. Precisely such a program, tucked away at midnight on WNBC-TV (later WRCA-TV), stayed alive in 1954 for a few weeks. It had no element of the parlor game; it was called and was meant to be *Conversation.* After its brief run it retired to radio with Mr. Fadiman as its guiding genius, and, after a brief period of trying to be smart, it settled down to being completely intelligent, and exciting.

Remembering that Mr. Fadiman wrote one of the most intelligent and damning judgments on our mass media, "The Decline of Attention" (in the *Saturday Review*), we are justified in comparing his two sponsored programs, warning ourselves that the evidence is too limited for us to draw conclusions for radio and television in general. The two programs had, basically, separate intentions. *Information, Please!* was an effort to extract wit and erudition from intelligent people and, in effect, said so, whereas *This Is Show Business* was a fake from beginning to end and was a shoddy framework for the exploitation of theatrical talents. The wild supposition was that the stars of entertainment would come and ask civilized, serious questions as to their careers, and what happened was that they came and simpered, and if Miss Grable was not on the program asking how to make her legs shapely, it was pure oversight. Embarrassed by a sort of intellectual hypocrisy in his approach to the stars, Mr. Fadiman took refuge in the tones and gestures of the commercial announcer, down to saying "but first . . ." (which is the stigmata of stylistic death on the air) as he invited the star to perform while the panel was supposed to ponder the phony question put by the guests. After three years a breath of common sense overtook everybody concerned, and the pretense of deep personal or professional problems was relegated to the background or dropped entirely. Shortly after its worst element disappeared, the program left the air.

We are here on treacherous ground and had better explore it a moment, departing for this purpose from the panel-quiz format to concentrate on the problem that touches all shows which are or pretend to be totally unprepared, caught on the wing. The professional knows that some preparation must be made: How is a contestant to signify that he thinks he knows the answer? Where are the cameras going to be?— and so on. The essential thing is whether the show is fundamentally honest.

There was, during World War II, a radio program called *Blind Date*. It was not the kind of program one would hurry home to hear, but if one was at home, one listened to it, and at times one was rewarded by the rarest of sounds on the air, the accents of the simple truth. (It is rare in the ordinary intercourse of human beings, too.) The structure of the program was simple. Two men, each from a different branch of the service, telephoned to a professional model; each gave (or "fed") her his line, trying by his wit, his candor, his blandishments, to persuade her to choose him over his opponent. There were three or four sets of these conversations, and each young woman chose from the pair of suitors the one who seemed more attractive to her. The winner in each case took the young lady to El Morocco—all expenses paid until midnight; after that, if our armed forces knew anything about it, free enterprise would suffice.

That this program was totally unprepared would not be true. The men were not chosen at random; they had to represent separate services and often came from different regions of the country; they were told how long to talk, and (I say this without certainty and also without censure) they may have been guided as to the "line" they took so that no pair, pursuing the same girl, were even remotely alike. Nor do I recall a single program at the end of which all four of the successful suitors came from the same branch of the service, although I am told that this might have happened.

The charm of the program was that often, in the excitement of the moment, whatever had been coached into the contestants was forgotten. A Marine might start in good Ivy League English and, properly awed by the turn of fortune which had translated him from a friendless warrior on final leave into a possible companion of a New York glamour girl, would end up in pure Ozark or Down East, would go silent or rush into an endless stream of confusion—would, in short, behave unpredictably, humanly, amusingly.

The program went into television and should have been fine. It had nothing to lose, everything to gain, by showing us what we had only heard.

The war was over and the contestants were not, as I recall it, necessarily in the service. As far as the quality of the program went, they might have been four teachers of Romance languages against four garbage collectors, because what they were had ceased to matter. They came on, completely supplied with dialogue and gags, coached to wait for their laughs, even to milk the studio audience for laughs. The girl prospects were, for the sake of appearances, blindfolded while their suitors made their advances, but each advance was known beforehand and the riposte was also memorized. Not one trace of the unexpected, of the actual, of the natural human being remained. The program might as well have hired professional actors to impersonate the contestants; even Arlene Francis, among the most skillful of spontaneous people on the air, was cabin'd, cribb'd, confin'd.

The program failed, and those who had seen in television a magnificent transmitter of the truth about people and a remorseless exposer of the fraudulent sighed with relief; the program returned and was sponsored. In the end, someone else took over the place of Miss Francis and the whole fraud drifted away—if not into oblivion, into the lower brackets of popularity.

I have made a study of audience reaction to this program—as complete as discussing it with some five hundred GI students can be. Most of them were aware that the whole thing was faked; some did not care; some thought it was rather fun to know it was fake while their friends and neighbors thought it was honest; and some brought up the parallel problem of the wrestling matches which are so familiar a part of the all too prevalent phoniness of commercial sport and commercial entertainment.

The answer here is that wrestling matches are produced as sheer entertainment and neither the customers at the ringside nor the television viewers believe for a moment that the matches are on the level. And the proof of it is that no television audience would for a moment tolerate the production of a prize fight or a boxing match, even at a small arena, if there were the slightest suspicion of faking. There are areas in which honesty is required, others in which it is not. Entertainment is in an ambiguous position, but not at all ambiguous is the rule of sense: a program presented as unrehearsed must be unrehearsed. The importance of being honest about these matters is a double one: if the audience is being deceived, it may resent the imposture; and if the imposture continues, the use of television for downright falsification will become that much more common. One is a practical, the other a social, effect, and they are interconnected.

For television, which uses the vacuum tube, does not exist in a social vacuum. It reflects our morals and manners and, in turn, it helps to change them. It is part of the nation's news service, part of its industry and commerce, and part of the educational system of our society, so that it becomes one of the prime institutions capable of creating ideas and altering the pattern of our thoughts.

It happens that we have been for some years in an era of small fakes. The time of the big lie is not over, but the reaction against it is powerful. The little phony, the unimportant, insidious fake, the slurred adjective, the true-and-meaningless statement that seems to say something superlatively important—all these are part of our daily existence. The dangling, unrelated "better than" and "more than" of advertising slogans are incantations, not specifics; the event re-enacted for the cameras is offered as the event that took place; the studio audiences do what they are told and have become so knowing that they are as phony as professionals. Rebellion against authority (the cameraman) is rare. Several years ago the New York *Herald Tribune* carried the story of the hapless young man who flung a bottle containing his name into the Pacific and years later flew to Ireland to meet the young lady who had

SOME BRAVE MEN

The newsreel men had set up their apparatus and were ready to interview Congressman Velde after an attack on him by Congressman Roosevelt. They instructed Velde to register surprise. "I can't," said Mr. Velde. "Nothing Mr. Roosevelt does would surprise me."

When President Eisenhower and his son were reunited, the newsreel men told him to put his arm around his son's shoulders. "You're not directing here," the President said. And refused.

There was a man on a participation program who looked at the MC when he talked to the MC. The MC kept pushing the man around so that he faced the camera; the man obstinately insisted on looking at the man to whom he was talking. He won.

There was a man who looked like Jackie Gleason. The resemblance having been noted and acknowledged, rather wearily, the MC said, "I suppose you imitate Gleason, too." The answer was no. The MC insisted. The minute or two that followed were as unpleasant as any I have witnessed, an agony of embarrassment met by a hard, demanding power. The MC won.

It was a setback for the independent American individual, the rock upon which our democracy stands. But at least the man had tried. A few more good tries and we may live to see the day when two Americans will shake hands, each looking into the eyes of the other, neither "cheating" for the camera. On the other hand, I do not expect ever to see anyone hand a trophy of any kind to the winner of a sporting event without both of them trying to get in front of the cup.

found it. It was a good story that did not pan out; when the youth re-turned, he told the news- and cameramen who had assembled to meet him at Gander that he and the Irish girl had not hit it off. The camera-men, however, made him rehearse, until they were satisfied with it, the phrase "Like MacArthur, I shall return," and this was the story as mil-lions of people got it.

The television machinery is an incomparable transmitter of the truth; it is also a magnificent vehicle for the imagination. Does it need the third element that lies between fact and fiction and is a corruption of both: the fake?

This is not entirely a moral problem. It has to do with the quality of programs and with the kind of enjoyment we get from them. And it is peculiarly the problem of those shows which must be arranged and rehearsed to move smoothly, yet can challenge the wit and intelligence of participants only if they have no inkling of what they will be called on to do.

There is evidence—not too much—that some of the "totally unpre-pared" programs are not quite candid with the public. As a guest on a program (long since gone from the air) I was told not the exact ques-tion, but the area in which a question would lie, so that I might think up a bright remark even if I did not get the exact answer. I was told that the regular members of the panel did not get this degree of help, but at least one MC on the same program quit because, to his certain knowl-edge, the most popular member of the panel was privy to the questions in advance. That MCs have signals to prevent the questions of the panel-ists from becoming too rough in their innocent *double entendres* is natural and necessary; there is some evidence that a hint given in ad-vance makes sure that the chance for a sly suggestiveness will not be entirely missed. A small amount of rigging goes on in respect to audience voting, and implausibilities have been observed in some giveaway pro-grams.

On the other hand, some of the programs most suspected of faking are entirely guiltless and the most scrupulous care is taken to keep panelists and their questions from one another until they are shared with the public. This is done out of professional pride, out of a sense that the program gains by the actual challenge to the contestants, as much as out of fear of exposure if any faking is done. There have been persistent reports that the panel shows will be "exposed" on a large scale, and this also may help to keep the less ethical producers in line. The one thing lacking is any public response to the question of faking, either way. The general feeling seems to be "If it's a good show, who cares?" and indeed the morals of a quiz show are not, in the days of atomic energy, the citizen's primary concern. But if the citizen is not concerned, the statesmen might be. Without proposing laws and penalties, the statesman might begin by asking whether it is a good thing for the citizens of a country to have their senses blunted so that they cannot tell fact from falsehood. He might go further and ask whether this is not exactly what a demagogue would desire. And he might speculate on the possibility that those who fake small things may eventually fake large ones— all in the name of showmanship.

It is a prime characteristic of the popular arts that they lead us to the gravest of questions. Challenged once for a new definition of my own name for them, "the lively arts," I said that they are the ones that get into the Supreme Court. They are, in fact, the public arts, which are also media of communication, and bring up social questions so important that at times it is hard to remember their primary function as entertainment.

As entertainment the panel show is relatively pure. It does not exploit the poverty and unhappiness of individuals. On the contrary, its assumption is that everyone is intelligent, of good disposition, and well dressed. Programs coming from the West Coast add a kind of factitious bonhomie, the panelists never being surprised into appreciation of one another's wit, but laughing twice as loud as the Easterners do, as if on cue from the MC. (On the Coast they play charades, which were exhausted by 1940 in New York production centers; the contestants guess rhymed couplets of twenty and more words in a minute or so. Very impressive.) The most famous of the panel shows, the one that, when bought by the BBC, became the most popular program in England also, is *What's My Line?* John Daly, who seems at times as incisive and independent a news analyst as any in the business, can also be part of a well-oiled, but not oily, program machine. The program is pleasant and is pleasant in exactly the same way every week; Daly says his words without difference and almost without interest, and the panel sings a four-part motet; and every week, for two years at least, after the guest movie star or football player had been identified, Daly asked the next contestant if he or she knew how the game was played and the contestant said "yes" and Daly explained it all over again. It is, I have been told, a matter of policy to keep the routine identical from week to week, and this has become standard for virtually all shows of this kind. The sense of game is lost, but the program moves at its required pace and is never hurried; it accomplishes the producer's ideal—it comes off "on the nose." This program has pretty much established the style not only for panel shows, but for panelists: two men, two women; one man anecdotal, one satiric; one woman glamour, the other career. When color comes, the division between complexions will, no doubt, be equally firm. It is not the funniest of these guessing-game shows; *The Name's the Same*, turning up a man named A. Baby, can be counted on for accidental innuendoes a little more often, and *I'll Buy That* is far more of a romp, the panelists having established a kind of hearty, backslapping relationship with one another. Out of Chicago came a variation, the game children used to call "Hangman," now called *Down You Go*, in which the letters of a phrase are represented by blanks and the contestants have to fill in the blanks. In *Down You Go* the atmosphere is relaxed—rather refreshing after the strict observances of the New York panels—but each panelist can make only one error: if there is no E, down you go. A punning clue to the phrase is given, and after it has been guessed or all the panelists are down, the moderator, Professor Bergen Evans, talks with his four friends (divided roughly as above) about the origin or meaning of the phrase. The New York programs had got so deeply into the habit of borrowing one another's panelists that this Chicago show seemed fresher than it actually was. New faces and a sense of the amateur, and the occasional frank exasperation of the panelists when they went down, did not, however, keep the program from becoming, after a half-year or so, pretty much in the mold of all the others. Within a year the producers made the cardinal error of allowing one of the women on it to do the commercial. The contrast between Mrs. Toni Gilman, the handsomest panelist on record anywhere, being almost entirely natural, and the same Mrs. Gilman on film being arch and coy and insistent and using as many expressions and gestures as a Wigman dancer, was too depressing. The vast superiority of live television over film precisely in the area where film is most used—in the commercial—was demonstrated here, as a comparison with the most publicized of all the commercial announcers would show. Miss Betty

Furness has been caught at times totally ignorant of how her product works (which means only that she has forgotten the words and actions of a new commercial), but she has been persuasive and, in her young-married-station-wagon style, absolutely right. No woman on film has been so convincing—not even Miss June Havoc, who, I fondly believe, could in her own person make a mathematician concede that the square of three is ten, but who, on film, failed to make many women believe she was actually using a certain shampoo.

The contrast with the filmed commercial points up the great, the egregious, merit of the panel shows: they deliver to us, to a high degree, the actuality of a human being. Even the high formulization, the slickness, the known necessity of getting five challenges before the panel per half-hour, cannot prevent real people from coming through the camera to the receiver at home. I quote the acute judgment of the English critic William Salter—that "the TV star is the [movie] star reduced to the level of the domestic pet." One thing certain about our domestic pets is that they are real, and we know them and want them around the house. We love them, too, but with an indulgent, not an adoring, love.

10

THE ANATOMY OF MISERY

Even more conspicuously than the panel shows, the giveaways of television bring a kind of actuality into the home. It is all too often the misery and sometimes the painful agony of people who appear on programs in a last desperate hope of finding the pot of gold at the rainbow's end. Like so many other programs, these have also found their way into the Supreme Court, which, declaring them legal, destroyed one of the most formidable instruments of control left in the hands of the people.

The legal play was in many ways more entertaining than the programs involved. The F.C.C., wishing to stamp the giveaway show as a lottery, was bound to prove that "a valuable consideration" changed hands— that the public, in some sense, paid to see the shows on which a part of the public had a chance to win money or other valuable commodities. The F.C.C. chose for its test case *Stop the Music,* a lineal descendant of the *Pot o' Gold* program of many years ago. In that (radio) show, one had but to answer the telephone at the right moment and gold flowed; under threats of legal action and considerable opposition to "buying an audience" within the broadcasting business itself, the program was withdrawn and its right to the air was never established. *Stop the Music* was far more elaborate and had to be because of the huge prizes cumulatively piling up while week after week passed and no one guessed the mystery melody, although in many cases the correct answer had been published by various gossip columnists.

The average non-legal mind cannot see how you can say that a game with prizes is a lottery unless someone has sold tickets. What has been sold when you sit at home and someone phones and asks you to identify a tune? What has the audience paid? The lawyers of the F.C.C. came up with a pretty answer and a revolutionary one: the audience has given its time, its attention. That is the "valuable consideration" it has paid to the advertiser. Therefore, when the prize is won by somebody who has listened to the melody and identified it, he or she has held, in a sense, the winning ticket; but everyone has bought a ticket through listening and looking.

The moral significance of this position is clear: if we are all giving something of value to the sponsor, we are morally entitled to tell him what we want. The supposition has always been that radio and television programs are "free" to the public; the actual truth in the days when radio was dominant was that the public paid out for sets far more than all the sponsors together paid out for time and talent. It nevertheless was felt, by the public, that the sponsors were spending a great deal of money to bring a superior gift into the home, and that, in gratitude, the least one could do was to buy the product sold on the favored pro-

---

PH.D.'S TAKE NOTICE

TV Guide noted that the comedian Orson Bean began a broadcast with this offer:

"Just write in, folks, and we'll send you $5,000 worth of secondhand sneakers, six miles of dental floss, an all-expense vacation in Youngstown, Ohio, and a screen door equipped with 200 flies."

TV Guide also reported that people wrote in quite seriously for each of the gifts.

gram. (Skeptics of the efficacy of commercials and particularly of the "gratitude pitch" are warned that both worked in practice.)

And this sense of gratitude for a free gift dovetailed beautifully into the other beam upon which the broadcasters rested their moral structure: if you did not like a program, you had little cause for resentment; others did like the program, and you did not have to listen to it. You did not pay for it, no one asked you to attend to it. If the F.C.C.'s position was correct, the situation altered. You had tuned in to a program, paying for it by that simple act, and you had listened to it, hoping it would be good, until it was too late to turn to another station; in short, you were dissatisfied with your purchase and, although you could not get your money back, you were entitled to complain.

There was, as I have suggested, a moral problem. Perhaps it was only an abstraction, but on such abstractions as "the pursuit of happiness" laws have been erected and national habits developed. I doubt very much whether the broadcasting business would have been much affected instantly if the Supreme Court had upheld the F.C.C. position. In the event, the case was decided in favor of the broadcasters. The court, with perhaps a low opinion of the American mind, refused to accept the principle of time and attention as "valuable considerations," and one justice, concurring with the verdict, said he believed that people watched certain TV programs out of "vacuity of mind." This is not an unusual attitude for intellectuals, and, of course, it may be justifiable. But it is not helpful.

There is precious little stimulation for the well-stocked mind in the average giveaway, and in those that are frankly guessing-games for prizes, the materials out of which entertainment is built are very slender. Indeed, one of the most successful seems built on the premise that sheer skill in production will attract an audience, especially if you play the entire program as if you were always one minute late. This is *The Big Payoff* as observed in 1954. In half an hour it presented a fashion show, a vaudeville show, a quiz show, and gave away mink coats and trips to far, romantic places. This is a program on which the contestants do not so much need the money as wish they had it; the tone is genial even when brides or fiancées watch their men fail to identify the Postmaster General in Lincoln's second Cabinet.

The neatness with which the various elements are fitted to one another reminded old-timers of the precision, machine-made, of a Ziegfeld show. Television, timed to the half-minute, has generally no tolerance for individual emotions, and the contestant on one of the misery shows, breaking into sobs, unable to tell her story, has to be surrounded by a flexible framework, whereas the program that gives things away to those who do not need them so much gets in return co-operation in timing which keeps safe the program's prime quality, a quick and easy movement. On *The Big Payoff* a contestant entered and was identified, and his partner was escorted to a seat; before her, two models displayed clothes and prizes, while singing a song or enacting thirty seconds of a sketch, and a recent Miss America described the clothes they wore; then the quiz proper began, and with each right answer, a new dress show, a new song or sketch, and all the other elements were brought on. Nothing whatever was of a high order except the skill of production—and it sufficed. The number of different elements in *Stop the Music* was about the same, but the program had more room to turn round in—and needed it because at the end of a few weeks of bad guesses the program could have spent all of half an hour showing the accumulated prizes, which were the solid attraction of the show. Otherwise, it had an orchestra that played indifferently, a studio audience that participated in a minor way whenever a contestant on the telephone failed to identify the preliminary tunes, a soloist or two, and an indefatigable and tiring MC, Bert Parks, who would flip out his shirt front and dance around and would cry into the telephone, "Did you say *Aïda?*" and then with mounting excitement, "Did you say *Aïda?*" and then, "Oh, I'm sorry . . . it isn't *Aïda*." Anything for a laugh.

The identification of the audience with the contestant and eventually with the winner is spectacular. It comes out best in the misery shows, where members of the audience can be seen biting their lips, wringing their hands, and weeping, out of sympathy for the contestant. It comes out also in audience reaction to a winner on *Stop the Music*—but not so purely. On one occasion when a Bostonian of seventy won and counted among his prizes the services of a baby-sitter for a year, the studio audience in New York danced in the aisles, one man at least broke his ankle leaping on a chair, and the excitement and hilarity were amusingly agreeable. The studio audience, however, was not entirely disinterested: to the man or woman making the most noise and in general being the life of the party, the sponsor awarded a $25 bond—so that the visible audience as well as the one scattered throughout the nation was, in the industry's own word, "bought."

Of all the giveaway programs, the ones most criticized are those capitalizing on the poverty and helplessness of the contestants. They are also the programs that, more than any other, use television for one of its fundamental values—the transmission of the literal truth, the actualities of existence. It may be appalling to watch someone sobbing over the merciless blows of fate, but it is appalling only because what one sees is true, not false, and in a world where the false is virtually standard currency, the sudden breaking out of a true emotion purges us, for a moment, of second-rate ones. This is not the catharsis of Aristotle; it is, in a sense, television's medicine for its own illnesses: the low concept, the weakened will to create, the intellect betrayed; and it comes to us in the course of the most flagrant exploitation of misery for profit. But in its dreadful way it reaffirms one of the greatnesses of television, its capacity to transmit the truth. It reaffirms also the too-often-doubted human capacity for facing the truth and finding exhilaration in it.

It should be left to a social scientist to discover why, in a period of vast prosperity, when even the enemies of the American system admitted that we had come nearer than any other to solving the problem of poverty, why at this moment so many people were interested in the desperation of others—desperation brought on by sickness, accident, occasionally by desertion, but in all cases needing only money to turn into security and confidence. And, beyond this, the social psychologist might note that the whole idea of the giveaways ran counter to the basic American philosophy, the celebrated "way of life" which was all against handouts, against the helping hand, and was all for individual effort, preferably in the face of odds. The Republican party, enemy of "creeping socialism," had been in power three years when the philosophy of getting rich by magic, by gift, by the intervention of a stronger power, reached its climax—exactly a thousand times more dramatic than it had been under the New and Fair Deals. With a bow to the program that had put "the 64-dollar question" into our vocabulary, this one offered Cadillacs as consolation prizes, and the grand prize was $64,000. It was "American" in its passion for bigness—but the glorification of the giveaway was like a vote of "no confidence" in the America of the pioneers, the robber barons, and Horatio Alger, Jr.

The phenomenal success of this program makes it a useful specimen for dissection. It illustrates a dozen qualities and brings up a hundred questions. Since the program itself is universally known I shall only summarize a few of its more significant points of interest:

- It is a descendant of radio, the prize multiplied, but the dramatic moment of decision, between the security of the lesser prize and the risk of losing all, is retained.
- It corresponds to home entertainment.
- It is an event, not a fiction.
- Its mechanisms are smooth and ingenious.

These could be called primary features and it should be noted that they interact. Without the other basic ingredients, the mere size of the giveaway would not be effective.

- It is a vast exploitation of "personality."

The program hunts out incongruities: the minister who knows jazz, the "little old lady" type who knows baseball, the Marine specialist in high cuisine. A well-chosen, unaggressive MC, Hal March, allows their personalities to unfold without pressure. The atmospheric pressure is high and is symbolized by the isolation booth into which contestants enter when the stakes grow big enough. If there is something close to brutality in dangling all that money before people who desperately want it, the tension itself contributes to the impact they have on the audience.

- The reverberations of the program are endless.

Newspapers give front-page headlines to big winners and magazines run feature stories. Successful contestants are reexploited: the cobbler who knew opera was received by our Ambassador in Rome and had an audience with the Pope before returning to America and a new job with a rubber-heel company. The minister was not permitted to speak at a

Southern university because he had said he might give some of his prize money to the National Association for the Advancement of Colored People, and the Marine resolutely rejected all offers from manufacturers of cake mix, but most of the other winners kept recurring in the news.

• The program has an effect on television in general.

This may be temporary. Other big-money giveaways have entered the field and the older quiz programs have stepped up their pace (with more guests, more gimmicks). The winners themselves formed the basis of a quiz show in which they functioned as experts.

For all of these aspects of *The $64,000 Question* we have facts and figures. It is of interest to the critic and should be of interest to the citizen (and statesman) in other ways as well.

The program brings into high relief the essential dual nature of radio-television, a nature at war with itself, being partly entertainment as we knew it in the past (drama, variety, etc.) and partly a lower-keyed effort to engage (not necessarily to absorb) the attention of masses of people by having something going on—chatter, exhibition of personalities, games, and the like. This program gave a high electrical charge to the low-pressure amiable quiz, to be sure, but it skilfully integrated all the essentials of the other type.

For millions of people television has the same quality as a conversation with friends, almost the same quality as the mere presence of members of the family who needn't do anything exciting or unusual, so long as they are in the house, but who would be sorely missed if they departed. A kind of sub-attention is all we give them and getting this response is the objective of many programs. Critics, being professionals, consider these programs "empty" and in this they are not far wrong, because the programs are full of excitement about nearly nothing. But judgment cannot be rendered against them by the precedents of the past. A new thing has come into the world and for lack of a new word we still call it "entertainment." That is merely a convenience. The new thing, of which this program is a remarkable example, must be judged by itself.

By its standards it ranks high. Like many others, it does no demonstrable harm. The question for statesmen (and the answer is worth more than $64,000) is whether the best use of the air would be made if the mass of programs offered to us merely satisfied the negative quality of being innocuous, when so few are bold enough to be disturbing, to challenge the mind and uplift the heart of the audience.

This brings us to the heart of the giveaway program: what the audience feels. The other aspects, ethical or social, are relatively unimportant, since they concern only a handful of people, chiefly those who get on the program to improve their lot, those who try to and are worse off because they are stranded in New York or Hollywood and have to be sent home by the local police, and the sponsors of the program, who see nothing sordid in what they are doing.

I have noted that the studio audience for these programs is face to face with the unfortunates who have to tell their miserable stories, unpacking their hearts of fear and resentment and despair, and then have to answer a series of quiz questions. This studio audience is, one assumes, a microcosm or cross-section of the audience for the same program at home. Nothing is more impressive than the lively sympathy of those who watch, their empathic clenching of hands, the flood of relief when the last question is correctly answered; or when disaster has overtaken someone, the eager turn to the MC in the hope, so often justified, that a second miracle will take the place of the one that missed. On *Strike It Rich* there is always "the heart-line"— a telephone call from the sponsor, to make sure that no one goes away entirely empty-handed —and often this is not needed, for, whether the big prize be won or lost, it is a rare appellant for help who does not receive half a dozen offers—of jobs, of worldly goods, of money, coming from people who know nothing except that there, before the cameras, but for the grace of God, they themselves might stand.

With this comes the feeling of comparative security given by the distress of others. We do not have to accept the maxim of the Duc de La Rochefoucauld that there is something not altogether displeasing to us in the misfortunes of our friends, for his egregious psychological skill is not needed here. These people are not our friends, and in the misfortunes of strangers we can take only a secondary pleasure—the pleasure of knowing that our own withers are unwrung. Nor is the final explanation in the old saying that "misery loves company"; it is rather that company loves misery, that we feel stronger and more certain of ourselves when we can make comparisons with others.

The reduction of the audience attitude to these simplicities still leaves us with a few questions: Is the audience of women in some six million homes so insecure that it needs the constant reassurance of the deeper misery of others? One study made of the daytime-serial audience indicated that this might well be so, and the relation between these two program types is very close. A second question is whether our standards of entertainment apply to the misery-giveaway programs at all.

At this point a clean break must be made, I think, with all preconceived notions of entertainment in the sense in which the word is usually understood. Let us bluntly say that the audience wants and the audience gets not merely different kinds of pleasure from different kinds of entertainment; it also gets satisfactions from programs that are not entertainment at all. No one attempts to equate newscasts and tapdancing, and no one should attempt to equate giveaways and comedy shows. The trappings of the giveaway suggest "production" and "showmanship," to be sure, but the woman who watches the program is aware of its difference from *Portia Faces Life*, even if she does not figure out the difference in her own feelings. Because critics and intellectuals generally apply rigid principles to the mass entertainments, they do not make themselves understood by those to whom these media are directed. We have to recognize the fact that new things have come to pass, that inside and outside the areas we used to call entertainment, new combinations have been effected, with new ways of capturing the audience and new intentions on the interests of the audience. We must be sure that the standards of judgment we set up are appropriate to the subject.

Even in the loose group of programs I have been considering here, ranging from parlor games to the misery-giveaways, we can see significant differences. The parlor games are diversions, intended to amuse; and we may say that if people need a great deal of that kind of diversion, and need it regularly, and consider it of the first order, they are lacking in experience, maturity, and also opportunity. We can apply to them such judgments as we apply to certain spectator sports, perhaps, or the simpler card games, or high-school graduation exercises. But for the misery shows we have no comparable activities in our immediate lives. Indeed, the only parallels I can think of lie in the distant past: when the polite world went visiting in the prisons, and not on errands of mercy, and the gallants of the town took their ladies to see poor Tom in Bedlam.

11

DOMESTIC MANNERS IN THE 49TH STATE

Life in the 49th state differs from life in all the others in one phenomenal way: the 49th state is inhabited by one group of citizens during the
day, another at night, and these two seem to have no relation to each
other. Moreover, their separate characters and their different actions go
against the established principles of American life, for it is the daytime
group that sins and suffers, whereas when the shadows of night fall on
the twenty-one-by fifteen-inch area of the state, all the scenes of domestic life are gay, sunny, and sexless. Crime exists in this nighttime area
and the remorseless tracking down of crime, but not sin. And the 49th
state declares itself also against the principles of all amateur analysts,
for the night people, repressing their sexual impulses, are the sane ones,
while the libertines of the day are full of frustrations and bitterness.
The men and women who live at night are married, but do not live
with their spouses; the day people have been married, are divorced or
divorcing on the grounds of adultery, or are living in sin, and in all this
sexual turmoil their lives are suffused with hate. When Garry Moore
ends his pleasant daily appearances with "Be good to one another, won't
you?" he seems to be addressing us, but the people he should be talking to are those who have immediately preceded him, the hating
people of the TV daytime serial.

I do not propose to enter into the wearisome details of life in the daytime serial. So much was written about its counterpart in radio that its general quality is known. During one six-month period when I watched it steadily, I found the incidence of crime very high and the suffusion of hatred almost unbearable; perhaps because the writers and actors lacked skill, the presentation of love or affection, rarely tried, was never convincing, and I felt something sinister as well as hateful coming off the screen. A serial intended to portray the sunnier side of American life, as lived by moderately prosperous, charming newlyweds, was involved in arson by its ninetieth episode and overestimated its staying power exactly fifty times: it was called *The First Hundred Years* and lasted two. Murder, blackmail, and syndicated gangsterism can sometimes be found in half a dozen serials at the same time, and all involve women as victims or accessories, with children well to the fore. A peculiarity of the TV serial is the presence of totally unmotivated evil, which is, I suppose, a natural development of the "badness" of secondary characters in the radio serial. On the other hand, the weakling husband or lover, who was used in radio to exalt the Strong Woman, seemed to me to be less important. The Strong Woman can now apparently pit herself against the incarnation of evil in Man. She is usually very handsome and sexually attractive, but she is so busy hating and fighting that her "love life" becomes inconceivable, although a sexual life is always implicit.

Things are sunnier at night, where men and women do not go to bed with one another at all; they bicker. You do not beget children that way, but the impression comes over that it's nearly as much fun. This may account for the fact that there are no children in the nighttime families (with the exception of the real children of the real Ozzie and Harriet Nelson). In the earlier and larger projection of the 49th state, on the moving-picture screen, children abounded and took part in the bickering of their parents; somewhere, sometime, men and women had lain together and conception had taken place; but, though the television people are as remorselessly and irrevocably married as the movie people, children are not for them. There may be a practical reason, too: these children live at the rate of half an hour a week, whereas the child actors live and grow older and their voices change and their figures also, so that the characters have to be fluid to keep up with appearances—and this goes against the grain of the nighttime comedy of manners, since the adults do not change, nor, for that matter, do they grow. They are immortal. They are perfect and we would not want them ever to be different.

Perfection is hard to come by, and the reader may too hastily assume that I am being ironical; but as Burns and Allen as well as Ethel and Albert are among the people involved, it is clear that I am only being immoderate. There are also *I Love Lucy* and *Life with Father* and *The Honeymooners,* and, while the status of *Our Miss Brooks* is doubtful, *Mr. Peepers* got married at the end of the 1954 season. As an exception to the statement made above, there was *Jamie,* a domestic comedy centering on a child, the remarkably adroit and beguiling Brandon de Wilde. And, as if to disprove my original statement that these people are immortal, there now rest in oblivion, earned with prodigious effort, a dozen comedies of domestic life which were too imitative or too heavy-handed to make the grade.

Among those that were instantly popular or had endurance enough to acquire an audience, two came out of radio: the two I have put at the head of my list. This has a special point of interest because, in general, radio said little about the domestic life of Americans.

In early days, and particularly in programs coming out of Chicago, people actually told what had happened to themselves, and the audience was interested. Presently the writers took over, and the serial was formed out of this simple reality. From that time, radio cared little about home life; hospitals and courtrooms became more familiar than the living room, and the bedroom appeared only as the sickroom. But out of fragmentary conversations between Fred Allen and Portland Hoffa, between Benny and Mary and Rochester, and out of George Burns's dogged efforts to comprehend Gracie Allen—which would be like holding a fistful of water—the comedy of manners (air style) was created and came to a high point in television. And also to a low.

The low is, of course, *I Love Lucy,* which sacrificed two-thirds of the talents of an incomparable comedienne, combined the tempo of the silent slapstick movies with the sound effects and loud voices of early radio—and became the most popular entertainment ever devised by the mind of man. (As it had between twenty-five and fifty million followers over a period of several years, the total number of times it was observed must have run into several billion.) It was acted as if for projection in a movie house, and, although nothing could entirely destroy Lucille Ball's physical charms (as nothing could entirely destroy her comic instincts), the third year was not so good as the first two and the creators of the series—which had lost its prime position in the ratings—were talking about a change of formula. That they might have a program without formula was unthinkable—in the sense that no one has thought out a way to present the same group of characters, week after week, without the help of a basic situation. This is not so damning as it sounds, because it corresponds to something in common experience: the people we know have a tendency to be, as we say, "in character." Married couples, particularly, seem to have a pattern of behavior in company, when they are with friends, so that you can "count on" the Smiths having a fight or the Joneses wanting to go home early. The difference, and the saving grace, is that before the formula operates, the Smiths and the Joneses are interesting in many ways and go through a variety of experiences; and although their essential natures do not change, they appear to us in different guises because on one occasion they emphasize one element in their conjugal life—perhaps their worry over their children—whereas on another they may be concerned with politics or the durability of ranch houses.

In television the formula takes precedence over the characters, so that one week they are going hunting and the next week they are going fishing—but what happens to them is always the same. In the case of *I Love Lucy* the formula was boldly shattered when the decision was made that the pregnancy of Lucille Ball should neither be concealed nor sentimentalized (a decision redounding to the popularity of the program, so that in the end the birth of the baby was close to being a publicity stunt—without, however, the vulgarity that might have been expected). The programs centering around the actual domestic life of the stars of the program had to have some variety because the process of birth and the changes during infancy cannot be squeezed into a rigid form. This group of programs, riddled with clichés appropriate to the event, but pleasant and funny, seemed to have exhausted the fertility of everyone concerned. When the baby was safely tucked away, we were offered nothing but the crudest slapstick, done without essential belief in it, done without the naïveté of the old Keystone comedies or the sophistication of Chaplin or Fields or Bobby Clark, and done with players who are totally unfit for the style—except for Lucille Ball herself. She understands everything about all the varieties of comedy, and should be allowed to communicate all she knows to her admirers—of whom, after three doleful years, I remain the most abject and devoted. She is rowdy and lovely, a genuine slapstick co-medenne with an incredibly delicate handling of her person. I recall a moment in *Best Foot Forward*, in which Miss Ball, playing the part of a movie star on the way down, was trapped by a press agent into making a personal appearance which she believed was to be at an Ivy League college, but which turns out to be at a prep-school dance. The hapless youth escorting her into the gymnasium, where a hundred dates, all seventeen and all in white tulle, were dancing, tried to make conversa-tion and stumbled over a phrase something like "of course at your age. . . ." I swear that, although Lucille Ball's back was toward us, you could see her heart miss a beat as she was about to—and then didn't—trip on the stairs. On the more intimate screen of television, she never tried anything so delicate. All the effects have been broad, all funny, none great.

Dozens of programs were revamped to make them seem like some part of Lucy; women in comedy had to be zanies, like Lucy. Eventually Lucille Ball was imitating herself as reflected by her imitators.

Among those who were not so influenced are the two teams of *Burns and Allen* and *Ethel and Albert*—Ethel is played by Peg Lynch, who also writes the program, and Albert is Alan Bunce. There is a vast difference between the two programs. The first is a calculated work of art in which everything is timed and fitted to perfection. The second is still in an unfinished state; its components do not always fit well together, things don't always come off exactly right—because that is the way life is. Ethel and Albert seem to be making up the words they say at times, at others to be fumbling for the best way out of the fix they have got themselves into; this may be the very pinnacle of the art that conceals art, but I doubt it. The program, which began as a sketch on the original Kate Smith show and became an independent quarter-hour on radio, reappeared with Kate Smith in television and again established itself in its own right. It had in its radio version a quality well nigh unique. A great many people have had the same experience; they turned the dial to get a certain program and were arrested by hearing a real human voice, not an actor's pro-jection, on the air. The two characters were talking to each other, not to the audience—and this was a rare thing after radio had developed its techniques and its artifices. What they were saying was what most couples on the air were saying; they were saying that women have to put up with a lot from their men and that men are pretty stupid anyhow—but somehow they were also saying "no matter what men and women are, we two, Ethel and Albert, are ourselves—we're not types and we're not a bundle of old jokes tied together in a package—we're not even 'folks'—we're people." And more than any other team on the air they said then, as they say now, "We're married —we've been married for some time." Something of the staleness that can overtake a marriage comes out in the way they talk to each other; they have an ear for the cadence of married speech, for the short takes of conversation between people who have lived long together and have built up their own idiom, and for the unfinished statement or question—the way one stops halfway, saying something, and finds that it is not worth going on. They use the right words, the right common words, but more important is the way the words are put together, the shape of the combinations of words. The grammarians call these combinations "sentences," but Ethel and Albert do not speak in sentences, nor does the total of what they say constitute "dialogue"—it is the special kind of conversation which is properly called "talk." It is such good talk as to give the impression of impromptu, and it is possible that in preparing the scripts, for which she gets "writer's credit," Miss Lynch leaves room for the unrehearsed remark, confidently assuming it will be appropriate.

The situations in which this talk occurs are not always so fresh as the talk itself. The old, broken-down jokes of the 1900 comic strip plus the stock situations of TV comedy are bound to occur: the visit from an old suitor, the misunderstanding about an appointment, the trip to the woods which tests his prowess as a hunter or hers as a cook, the backseat driver, the keeping-up-with-the-Joneses effect. But no half-hour passes without at least one scene, lasting perhaps only a minute or two, in which you become aware of the substantial element: that Ethel and Albert have made a life together. (I should say that at the moment of writing I have no idea whether the two actors are or ever have been married, to each other or to anyone else.) By the current rules of TV comedy, man and wife must be irritable. They must represent a sort of backlog of quarrels, and Ethel and Albert frequently follow the rule. But the sense that they could not be happy without their little quarrels is always there. It is part of our feeling that they have had a past and did not come suddenly to life at 7:30 to disappear at 8:00. When Albert is grouchy and does not respond to a pun, Ethel taps him with a ladle she happens to have in her hand and says, "That's a joke"—and, after a moment, "I always laugh at your jokes"—without rancor, just stating a fact. And the fact, so flat in itself, creates a third dimension, a hundred episodes in the past of Ethel and Albert which we have never seen, which were never written, but which exist in the background for the writer and the actors, and so for us.

What does not exist for the characters in any of these pleasant charades—and cannot exist for us—is any sense of the passion between the sexes. The small screen has proved unsatisfactory for the presentation of voluptuous women, and the requirement that all themes be acceptable to the family circle was added to the sponsor's demand for stories not disturbing to the mind or the spirit. Television is consequently "purer" than the movies under the Code.

Yet a touch of sex does occasionally appear, and a few years ago a man known as The Continental began to enjoy a sort of foolish eminence in the field. His style is a parody of the "Latin lover" played straight—and straight into the camera. *The glass of champagne poured is extended to you, dear lady, don't be afraid, it is only champagne, the wine of love, and this is only a man's apartment.* His target is the woman who has listened to daytime serials and then gone to her husband's employer's house for a dull evening, and now hears her husband snoring in the bedroom . . . he only snores when he has drunk too much . . . lately she has heard him snore more often. . . . The Continental is what she read about at high school.

In the Midwest, on radio only, there is a woman who does the same for men. For traveling salesmen alone in hotel rooms, for anybody awake and alone—a seduction without warmth, but with heat. A striptease for the imagination.

You see and hear these things and you say these are aphrodisiacs, which is true, but there is something else about them: they sound like certain advertisements. In a voice that strokes the nerve ends you hear of a shampoo that "makes you feel every inch a desirable woman." The insinuated suggestion of sexuality is not so deft in most places.

WOMEN IN LOVE

Whenever any protest is made against the stereotype of the spinster teacher in radio and television, the name of Eve Arden is brought up in rebuttal. Miss Arden is a handsome woman with a gift for saying things so that they sound bright and brittle—a sort of distaff *Man Who Came to Dinner*. In *Our Miss Brooks* she plays a schoolmistress.

The following is quoted from *This Week* magazine, April 3, 1955:

"For eight years now the . . . show has thrived on the fact that Connie Brooks (Eve Arden), a high-school English teacher, can't get her man. Her dreamboat is an ultra-shy biology instructor. . . . The romance has been deadlocked for years. . . . But Connie did kiss him once in a dream sequence.

"However, figuring that a real kiss would spice up the program, they [the producers] decided to allow Miss Brooks to plant an affectionate smack on Mr. Boynton's lips. It was risky business. Viewers might misinterpret it as the harbinger of mutual love.

"The solution . . . was to find a workaday, unromantic pretext. . . . He lends her five dollars . . . in gratitude she busses him. But before blooming on the air, this kiss was debated, auditioned, and timed by ad-agency account executives, liaison men, network producers and publicity vigilantes.

"It came out perfect: prissy, noncommittal and antiseptic. . . ."

This is the program that is so favorable to the women teachers of the country that they actually write letters of gratitude to the producers. It does not make the teacher hideous—only prissy . . . noncommittal . . . antiseptic. . . .

Note that this shampoo does not make women desirable, it makes them *feel* desirable. A fine distinction. Nothing is said about being responsive to desire—or about desiring.

Like the ad for Tabu perfume, complete with the shadowy bearded violinist of the 1890s, these approaches to physical love seem vulgar without being very funny. But this can be said for them: the un-official censorship of our mass media has been reducing sex to "a little winter love in a dark corner," and of the two escapes—through wit or through vulgarity—the second is as legitimate as the first and will be understood by more people. If we have been fortunate, we may feel sorry for those who need these stimulations, but before we begin to be censorious, we must remember that the same sort of thing exists in other forms, at higher levels of organization and so-phistication, and has existed as far back as we know the story of our own kind. There is even something to be said for the ingenuity of the producers and sponsors of these soft proposals—they restore the smell of humanity to the dried-up wastes of our mass media. This needs to be done every so often to remind us that our appetites range beyond crunchy cereals and effervescent pops, and that the sat-isfaction of these desires, discreetly accomplished, is not against the law. The reminder was given to us years ago when Paramount, in desperate straits, openly defied the censors who had intimated that Mae West was untouchable, put her into a series of films, lifted the hearts of the depressed American, and made several million dollars. Miss West did her bit for radio also, causing one of the few spon-taneous protests in its history because the combination of her insinu-ating voice and Charley McCarthy's impudence seemed out of place in a sketch laid in the Garden of Eden; the protest was against an implied sacrilege, however—not against the use of the same material in another setting.

In broadcasting, generally, the "continuity acceptance" division of station or network will pencil out whatever can be thought to be vulgar, and the cleaning up of dirty stories is not usually accepted if the new version inevitably brings the older to mind. (In Britain co-medians are forbidden to use cleaned-up dirt.) The position has no logic, since it assumes that the dirty story is known, and this goes with the parallel and opposite assumption that dirty stories should not be told lest people hear them. But logic is not required in this matter, and we know perfectly well that protests would follow whenever rowdiness was allowed to move into the rough country of smoking-room conversation, tedious as that is.

We get, then, an occasional leer from Arthur Godfrey and a bit of double meaning in the panel shows, where it appears so conspicuously innocent that the worst innuendo must be accepted as an accident. For the rest, TV has barely taken over the skills developed from the days of Lubitsch in the movies. David Riesman has held that the existence of the Code in Hollywood, presenting a challenge to writers, has provided the movies with a satisfactory way to treat sex—a judgment in which I cannot concur. For, while it is true that games at love have been the staple commodity of the movies for many years, they have been more games than love, more ingenious than impassioned. The spectator who caught the wink and the smile was intellectually gratified at the skill shown by writer and director in getting around the Code, but I cannot believe that this was morally equal to witnessing something true and important in the relation between men and women. That this could be done within the frame of comedy is obvious. I have alluded to one instance when it was done, without even a wink: at the end of *The Thin Man* when Nick and his wife were preparing to go to bed in the Pullman sleeper and the dog Asta was on the lower berth with Myrna Loy; in the person of William Powell, all marital rights were confirmed as he swept the dog out of his way. I say that this is important because the assertion there was not merely that men and women sleep together and anticipate and get lively pleasure therefrom; it was also that among these men and women could be husbands and their own wives—a suggestion largely lacking from the movies for a generation. That it happened on the screen, demonstrated by a man and a woman who were "ideals" of smart conduct for millions, was an added value. It was as if a ray of light had struck through the murk of movie morality and let us see the laughing face of the Great God Pan.

12

"WHAT A WORK IS MAN!"

Turning people into punks is one of the easiest jobs in television, and the only surprise in the business is the enthusiasm of the victims.

Perhaps it began with the "guest shot," perhaps with blackmail. A skillful manipulator can find four or five different ways of persuading a reluctant celebrity to appear on a program, all of them legal in the strict sense. Getting movie stars to take part in radio programs was difficult at the beginning; they did not see why they should be bothered. Later everyone saw that radio and the movies helped each other and that appearing on certain programs led to several kinds of favorable publicity. The next step was the interchange of radio stars, a kind of candid mutual-admiration job which had several stages. If a sponsor had a comedy program and a dramatic one, a way was found for each to advertise the other. Imaginary feuds were played out on the air with the opponents meeting once a year or so. Presently guests became almost essential to almost every type of program, the one element that differed (in name) from week to week, and for several years stars working for one network might be heard on the others, until this kind of palship was forbidden by a vice-president who probably figured out that his company had given two-tenths of a point more than it had received. All of this was legitimate, and —while it got tedious, because without all the personal jokes the personal appearance was not considered genuine—it presented professionals more or less in their professional capacities. But even here the sweet process of punkifaction had begun to work. For it became traditional to fake up the appearance of the guest. His participation had been announced in the newspapers and on the air several days in advance and his name got next-to-top billing from the announcer as the program began, but the actual entrance was as carefully plotted as the entrance of a musical comedy star who is not too sure of herself. Instead of a formation of two converging lines of chorus boys all looking up to the top of the stairs, radio provided a flourish in the orchestra or occasionally the hush reserved for momentous announcements. Then the resident star would cry out the name of the guest in a paroxysm of astonishment, and then the studio audience would applaud—and the guest might explain how he happened to drop by. After this the routine insults would be exchanged until the host said, "But seriously . . ." and told the audience what a great performer the guest really was. Fred Allen used to burlesque this every week when as surely as Portland Hoffa called "Mr. Al-len!" he reacted with "Why, Portland!"—but even he fell into the trap once in a while with his actual guests. The only refreshing moment in the whole business came after a few years when someone said that he was on a program because he was being paid—and this presently became standard procedure. In television the parallel moment came when Ray Milland was guest on George Gobel's program and Gobel refused to let Milland play an instrument or otherwise perform, insisting that a guest should *be* a guest.

Before television multiplied a hundredfold the opportunities for faking, radio had branched out to include nonprofessional guests. Press agents for good causes, for plays and books, for prize fights and foreign countries, were always ready to supply famous names, and, while the names were often submerged under a flood of chatter on women's programs, they not only made their points but often became as well known for their radio appearances as for their major work. On *Information, Please!* nothing was required of a guest except his presence and his presence of mind; on some others everything from a spurious friendship for the MC to an equally spurious enthusiasm for the advertised product was demanded, and innumerable people were ready to say whatever was written down for them provided they could get in a good word for themselves, their cause, or the commodity they wanted to sell.

The advantage of radio was that you could not see the distaste of a guest for his job, if he felt it, any more than you could catch the cynical look in an announcer's eyes. One man only, to my knowledge, attempted to leave in the middle of a broadcast: Frank Lloyd Wright, who actually declared that he could stand no more of the stupidity and aggressive sales talk that surrounded him, but was almost forcibly detained in the studio. On television he would have caused a desirable scandal.

The scandal now current is only that no one is scandalized by the steady degradation of the human personality. I have never seen anyone I know completely delivering himself or herself in one of these guest-personality appearances. The only place left for individuality is on an unrehearsed controversial program, such as the interviews on *Meet the Press* and similar shows, on *Author Meets the Critic* when the attacking critic is genuinely hostile to the writer—and perhaps on some local programs unknown to me. The smell of the palpable fake hangs over the others, and its marks are the glazed eyes not quite looking at the audience because they are reading the teleprompter, and the three-note laugh, ha-ha-ha, at nothing.

These programs live at various stages of vulgarity, and the lowest is the *Stork Club* show, which has now been seen on three different networks, each of which pretended while the program was being shown that it was operating in the public interest—an intellectual achievement of a high gymnastic order indeed. The fawning adulation of the "famous personalities" when the "fabulous innkeeper" Sherman Billingsley accosts them, their ecstatic surprise when he shows them photographs of themselves, their praise for whatever product sponsors the event, are prime in their field, and Mr. Billingsley's "What's the latest in muscular dystrophy?" can also be considered classic. Several other programs seem to have arranged themselves on the model of this one, but none has the genuine instinctive snobbishness and coarseness of perception of the original.

At the other extreme is *Person to Person*, which seems to have been based originally on the idea that people are interesting even if they are intelligent and accomplished. The handling is the simple interview, with one new feature: Edward Murrow sits in his home or office or in a studio and the guest is at home—across the city or across the continent. I cannot testify to the qualities of Mickey Spillane, Roy Campanella, and Coach Blaik, none of whom I have had the pleasure of knowing, but professionally and personally, and in varying degrees, I have known perhaps twenty of the men and women interviewed in two seasons, and in every instance I have felt that they were being prevented from coming over, from being what they are. Of the fifty people I have watched, two were remarkably effective: James Petrillo, who launched into a familiar attack on the Administration, and Krishna Menon, who looked like an Eastern Christ as he brilliantly answered the critics of his country's international policy. At one point he sharply asserted his official position in the United Nations by saying, "That is an improper question for you to ask me, Mr. Murrow," bringing from Mr. Murrow an instant candid "Perhaps it is an improper question for you to answer"—the entire discourse being on a high plane, between men of integrity, making the little screen overflow into a kind of rare greatness. This was what had been foreseen first in the earliest days of British television when simple interviews at Alexandra Palace demonstrated not only the capacity of the medium to report faithfully, but also the imperative duty to use it at times in its essential purity. What was not foreseen was how seldom the duty would be performed.

Mr. Murrow figures more importantly in his other function, as the essential individual in *See It Now; Person to Person* is a sort of diversion for him. He does no part of it shabbily—he is a workman with respect for his tools—but it is clear that the seriousness of our world in a twilight zone between war and peace absorbs him, and on his lighter program he can meet less disturbing people and let his other interests play. No one should grudge him this pleasure. Yet his program becomes part of the process of making people less than they are, and it does this mostly by taking over some of the technique and some of the habits of those programs which deliberately set out to exploit, rather than explore, the human personality.

For one thing, the program presents itself to us as spontaneous. No fraud is perpetrated on the audience, to be sure, but both Mr. Murrow and his hosts give the effect of suddenly hitting on a notion—Mr. Murrow may ask whether something he has caught sight of is a trophy or a work of art, and the hosts often say, in effect, "Look, why don't we go upstairs and I'll show you . . ." In all these cases the whole apparatus of cameras and microphones has been set up in advance to cover the movement or the object because the equipment is still cumbersome and freedom to bring in the unexpected is strictly limited. This trifling deception does something to the people involved. Murrow, who has talked and can talk with the masters of nations, with scientists and saints, is ill at ease asking his pleasant people where they won this cup or which child takes after the mother. The subject matter grows more and more trivial, the handling of the machinery more and more important. Benny Goodman and a daughter get into coats and go out to their pool in California and the daughter throws a prearranged stone into the pool so that we will know it is real; everyone goes upstairs or down; everyone shows trophies. The texts of the interviews are not rehearsed, and when Mr. Murrow asks, "Is that your dining room?" the answer is "Yes, this is where we have dinner." An obsession with prizes and signed photographs becomes the standard mark of the successful American; if ideas develop, they are quickly smothered and the camera picks up another souvenir. It is as if everyone was determined to prove that, no matter what eminence a person has achieved, the great ones of this world are not only folks, they are rather dull folks. When Murrow had an interview of genuine significance, with J. Robert Oppenheimer, he did it on *See It Now*, sensing perhaps the impropriety of subjecting a great man to the spurious chuckles and the jocose banalities of *Person to Person*.

There is a parallel to his program, one which is made for posterity: the *Elder Statesman* series on NBC. By its choice of subjects, by the emphasis so markedly placed on the age of Bertrand Russell, Robert Frost, Frank Lloyd Wright, Carl Sandburg, and (within discretion) Wanda Landowska, and by the attempt to let the subject direct the current of the conversation, the program lets us think that what we hear and see is a kind of summing-up for posterity. The speakers themselves seem to be aware of this and, while none of the interviews I have seen appeared to be too much *sub specie aeternitatis*, they were all thought-out, earnest, and honest. This is not a weekly series, and I do not suggest that *Person to Person* should have the specific gravity of recordings for the future. I mention the series because it proves that people can be brought to the camera and asked to speak as candidly as they wish—and they will deliver themselves to the audience. The program has won prestige for all concerned in its preparation, and in the long run each of the interviews will be seen by an audience as vast numerically as the audience for *Person to Person.*

The nagging question about Murrow's program is whether it could exist, sponsored and with a reasonably large audience, if it were less superficial, less trifling. Obviously it is a program combining solid elements—the interest of people in others, the curiosity of people about others—just as it exploits two emotions lying a little deeper under the surface—the desire to be in the company of famous people, the desire to have them brought down *almost* to our own level. We shall never know whether this is the highest practical level; we do know that if Murrow, with all his prestige, did not try for anything better, he has made it harder for anyone else to try.

On the other hand, the persistence of people, their obstinate insistence on coming through to us, has been demonstrated again and again, even by individuals who are not dramatic or over-colorful—and conspicuously, as it happens, by the most easygoing and genial of all our entertainers: the incomparable Bing.

13

THE INCOMPARABLE BING

It is a pleasure to think about Bing Crosby.

I had known Crosby as a pleasurable voice for a long time and I had also seen a few of his forgotten two-reel movies when I became aware of him in a new phase. He was wandering aimlessly about in his radio program and suddenly he said something about Marcel Proust. I discovered later that this sort of glancing reference to the intellectual life was one of the inventions of Carroll Carroll, Crosby's chief writer at the time. What I liked was the offhandedness. It was like a throwaway gag line, and it was not even meant to cause more than the faintest ripple. It was not what Jimmy Durante would do today with Kafka (and I would be happy to see him do it if he wanted to). There was a sort of gentlemanly ease in Crosby's approach, an indifference to effect.

And this makes it all the more remarkable that Crosby is the man who, all by himself, almost wrecked the whole network broadcasting system in the United States and did, in effect, profoundly alter many of that system's most cherished practices. Remarkable but entirely in keeping with the Crosby character, because Crosby wanted to be easy about a lot of things and the networks would not let him. They had an idea that a program on the air at nine P.M., Pacific Standard Time, required the presence of the star in the studio at nine P.M., not to mention rehearsals the same day—all of which interfered with Crosby's inalienable right to pursue golf balls or to fish whenever and wherever he pleased. An invention showed him how to circumvent the opposition: the machine that records sound, on a disc, on a wire, on a tape—it hardly mattered. The moment a record was made, it began to be possible for the East Coast to hear Crosby at nine in the evening and for Idaho to hear him also at nine—their time, not the time of the radio bosses in New York. It became possible for Crosby's program to be spotted on one station on a Wednesday and on twenty others on Friday, if this was more advantageous to the sponsor—if, for instance, in certain regions Crosby's regular time conflicted with the broadcasts of local sporting events.

Now, the managers of network broadcasting have an almost supernatural regard for the idea of a network, and they are justified in this because, as I have noted elsewhere, in a sense networks do not exist, but are mythological entities. The network is a great creative force in broadcasting because programs are created in the studios of its principal stations and these are taken by the affiliates; it is also the financial web holding stations together. And while the F.C.C. may not recognize them, networks are among the most profitable corporations in the entire economy. The thought, therefore, that Crosby's mavericking would cause networks to crumble was highly displeasing.

Network-worship was based on a supreme defiance of geography—a defiance so successful that a woman driving home from a bridge game in Salem, Oregon, her thoughts turned to whipping up a nice meal for husband and children, could hear on her car radio the same production of *Hamlet* that was being heard in Salem, Massachusetts, by families who had finished their after-dinner coffee hours ago, had already heard a news broadcast, a lighter drama perhaps, and now, with the very young put to bed, listened to *Hamlet* as they might if they had gone to the theater. The network-idolaters were determined that the woman in Oregon and the woman in Massachusetts should hear the same program at the same time, saying darkly that the whole idea of a network would disappear if they did not. The fact that it was not the same time in the two Salems did not matter to them. They were dealing in mystic powers, not in realities. (They were also great non-listeners to radio.)

Mr. Crosby persisted. Presently it was discovered that people did not know whether the program was pre-recorded or not, although the F.C.C. rules required this identification on the air. It was also discovered that the networks continued to exist. Actually, Crosby had done them a good turn: he had made them flexible when they threatened to get hardening of the arteries—a dreadful disease in the communications business. When television arrived, it came piecemeal, and the quality of the TV recording—the kinescope—was markedly inferior to the original. It was, moreover, poor in comparison to the shabbiest movie photography. But the East wanted to see Ed Wynn and Groucho Marx while the West wanted to see Ed Sullivan—and the networks obliged without compunctions about simultaneous viewing.

Flexibility as to time is important because television *interferes* with other occupations more than radio does and the kind of television available at any moment of the day must be appropriate to the hour. The woman in Salem, Oregon, has no TV set in her car; when she gets home she will turn on her set or let the children look at their late-afternoon programs while she gets dinner. She will not mind missing bits and pieces of unimportant programs, but if *Hamlet* were on and she could not give her attention to it, she would be vastly irritated. The kinescope gives her a chance to get the program at the right time.

It is useful to stop a moment and see what the next step will be. At present, audiences can see three types of programs: live, kinescope (a movie of a live program), and film (programs never on the air, but made in a film studio). The first two are, in a sense, the same; unless a really awkward mistake occurs, the kinescope will not be altered, it will transmit the naturalness of the original production. Technically, the results are still unsatisfactory—the picture is not so bright and clear as it should be. Within a few years we shall have another system of recording: sound and image will both be put on magnetic tape. To the uninstructed mind this is one miracle piled on another, for the electronic impulses that create the original television picture will be translated into an invisible equivalent of the zigzag lines of a sound track and will be re-translated back into the picture in all its original colors. The effects of this are manifold. The television industry becomes independent of film for recording and may become independent of the Hollywood studios in the making of programs. And the pre-eminent virtues of the live program are recognized because this recording system favors the creation of a program as television, not as movie.

And, still thinking with pleasure of Bing Crosby, we can try to estimate what harm he has done, out of his admirable laziness, to the almost artless business of radio and (by extension) to the possible art of television. For it was Crosby who made an issue of the recorded program—the program never heard live over the network at all. The networks might have settled for programs done live on the Coast, recorded from the actual air performance, and broadcast from kinescopes at a later time in the East.

The difference was hardly technical; the listener was, as I have said, unaware of the process. But there was a psychological difference. A program recorded in advance was subject to improvement. A quiz show that used six contestants could get seven or eight before the microphone and camera and then choose the six most entertaining ones for the actual broadcast. A crooner like Crosby might fluff a song and re-record it. The straight challenge to the performer—"this is it"—the sense of the present audience even if the audience is scattered in ten million homes across the continent, cannot be duplicated if you have an editor, a film cutter, and the like. The essential difference in the making of movies and television revolves around this factor. Physically, the movies are made in short takes that are pieced together, and television is made all in one piece; psychologically, the movie piecework is not shown until it has been perfected, and the television piece is created under the eye of the audience. The kinescope of today and the magnetic tape of tomorrow are both ways of approximating the single piece, before-the-audience techniques of television without necessarily doing the show on the air at all. You can do it on the air and make a kinescope; or you can do it in a TV studio, *as if you were on the air*, and make your recording then. The "as if" is most important. Only in cases of serious errors will a program be redone, and the feeling, after a certain amount of rehearsing, that *this is it*, that this is being seen by the producer and the potential sponsor and is going to be seen by an audience—these combine to give almost the effect of being on the air.

But note that the indolent Mr. Crosby opened wide the door for the program that was never on the air, and eventually for the comedy program done in a small studio with laughter dubbed in. Opened the door for a bit of faking which was not too offensive in radio, but which went against the grain, entirely, of the candid TV production.

Look for a moment at the parlor-game programs of television. They are, by any standard of intelligence, unimportant, and their chief virtue is that they are innocuous, superior in this respect to some others. With this lack of prejudice, we take a second look and discover that these programs please us because they are real; we see an expert losing to an amateur, or a woman who never got a chance at an education getting the right answer by sheer luck or lively intelligence—whatever the case, it is the reality, the presence that counts. I have already noted (on page 89) that live television can be faked and that obviously recorded television can be so skillfully produced that it will look more real than the reality—to the careless eyes. The moralist may feel that something is wrong, and you do not cure the ill by muttering a few words at the end about this program being recorded or taped; you pretend that you are not pretending, but at bottom you bank on the ignorance and indifference of the audience, and your program seems to be spontaneous although you have cut and edited and remade. Yet the really important objection is that a prime quality—the quality of the real—has been compromised and destroyed. That may be a moral view also, but it is not one that declares one thing right and another wrong; it holds to the principle that many kinds of excellence are desirable and that to destroy any kind is a pity.

It is pleasant to think of Bing Crosby in still another way: as the savior of the small radio station. There was a time, not so long ago, when it was truthfully said that no hour of the day or night, year after year, passed without the voice of Bing Crosby being heard somewhere on this earth; and in the album with which a grateful Decca commemorated his activities appears the statement (which Decca should have printed in solid gold instead of mere gold ink): "The voice of Bing Crosby has been heard by more people than the voice of any other human being who ever lived." We do not always arrive at the standards of excellence by the sheer weight of numbers, but it is a satisfaction to discover an excellence so artless and so unaggressive being recognized in this statistically supreme way. There are those who are certain that Russ Columbo, had he lived, would have outstripped Crosby; there are benighted ones who think that someone else (and they make the oddest choices) actually sang better in the style than Crosby. They are, I am sure, misled, misguided and (in the theological sense) invincibly ignorant. Crosby sings best. And, as we have seen, he also sings most.

He is himself authority for the legend that a node on his vocal cords was to be removed, but the family lacked money (and it is a fair bet that the young Bing was not anxious to do anything about it). He (or a pleasant press agent) carries on the legend of a series of accidental meetings, half-formed decisions, driftings which brought him in 1926 to Paul Whiteman and his first recording, "Muddy Water." He has made over two thousand separate recordings since—not bad for an easygoing man whose artistic symbol is the half-out, many-colored sport shirt.

The radio business was just beginning to get its growth in 1926; ten years later the small stations were dotted over the land, the 250-watters, the ones they called "coffeepots," which played recordings all day long and some of them all night as well, and often played nothing but Crosby records for hours at a time. Around the Crosby records—and, for all I know, interrupting the records—the little stations brought in their endless local commercials. It was not great creative broadcasting, but presently the techniques were refined and the disc jockey became an established man, if not an artist, in broadcasting. He, in turn, led to the development of strong local personality programs in both radio and television—so again the influence of Crosby pops up. To be sure, you can say that the stations would have used other records if there had been no Crosby—but if we go in for ifs, how do we know that the broadcasting of records would have paid off as well if there had not been this constant stream of Crosby?

I am told by those who should know that Martin Block and his *Make Believe Ballroom* are as much of a highlight in the disc-jockey business as they seem to be in New York. Certainly he went straight to one of radio's essentials, its power to create the visual image precisely because it offered nothing to inhibit the imagination. I do not know who began the trick of talking to the artist— ". . . you don't mind singing 'Always' for us, do you, Bing? . . . Pretty nearly always, ha, ha, eh, Bing? . . ." It always struck me as sad because it seemed so utterly improbable that anyone should think Crosby was really there, and because precisely this sort of thing destroyed the latent image. Nor do I know who first began to bring people in to help him over the bad dull spots—perhaps Stan Shaw with his *Milk-man's Matinee*, which ran along from around midnight to dawn. The big flagship stations of the networks would pay their respects to the F.C.C. and sign off around midnight, and then the local stations seemed to take on more confidence, more authority, as if their voices grew louder—and they would start the recordings rolling, and then the jockey would chat with the engineer, and presently people would telephone and ask for a special record. It began to be a buildup, a known thing, that you could phone and ask for a song to be "dedicated" to a friend (who was having a birthday party) at exactly twelve minutes after one. The exploitation continued and went on a little too long, perhaps, but there was always the feel of the late hours and the white night, or of the cabbies at a hot-dog stand, or the drunkard arguing at a speakeasy. Some programs prospered so that they could have a team, and this proved particularly acceptable at the other end of the day's work, when a station went on the air at six in the morning with news and with songs and something, for Heaven's sake, to cheer the waking hours. These duos had to have stamina. The successful ones could hope to get up a few hours later —picking up the morning chore, as Bob and Ray did in Boston at around nine A.M., and proceeding into the midday and evening salary brackets.

In New York and Chicago and, I am told, elsewhere also, the night-time record show branched into the nighttime celebrity show—records were only fillers because the whole show originated in a night club or restaurant and the patrons became the "guests" of the jockey. Fred Allen was partial to Jack Eigen and, by constant reference to him and by appearing on the program, elevated him to a high position. Another night-program man, Barry Gray, began to make himself felt as an outspoken liberal commentator on politics and on other things as well, and fell foul of Walter Winchell, which gave him additional eminence; he became a newspaper columnist, a commentator on both radio and television, and for a time was the moderator of *Author Meets the Critic*—a position not so suitable as a commentator's program for one accustomed to do virtually all the talking.

Television was coming in when some of these later phases of the disc-jockey business occurred, and the managers of the business must have decided that they could not (with a straight face) declare that they operated in the public interest by reserving the late night hours for decrepit Western and British pictures that never made the grade in theaters. There is an audience for these, but even that audience does not need to be bludgeoned on the head with the same picture twice in one night. There had long been a tradition in radio of a late-evening roundup of news, eleven o'clock being the standard hour, and, missing a golden opportunity to repeat some of the programs that had been produced at other times, radio stations began at 11:15 or so to pick up name bands from hotels and near-by roadhouses; at two or so, and earlier if the station could not afford to bring the bands in, records were played. Something like this general program plan needed to be worked out for television, omitting—for the present, at least—the final hours from two to dawn.

The situation was attractive in many ways. The programs originating in New York from eleven on are local; the network folds in on itself and goes to sleep. This means that a new set of sponsors can take over—those who cannot use or cannot afford network time; this may mean a local brewery or a local bank, and can also include a manufacturer of a new product who wants to try out his TV campaign cheaply. The time charges, which can amount to seventy per cent of the total cost of a network program, are minimal because no tribute is paid to AT&T for its wires and relays, and because the local station makes a reasonable estimate of the number of people watching at each quarter-hour and adjusts its rates accordingly. As for the production, its cost can be what the sponsor chooses, but the program itself cannot be too elaborate and it will do well if it is merely affable, varied, and does not bring up any disturbing problems. (In most of these programs, if news is brought in at all, it is carefully separated from the comedy and chat and fun of the rest of the hour.)

In New York, Steve Allen has been the chief beneficiary of the late-night schedule. Allen is one of the most versatile men in television and also one of the few who seem to be educated and not afraid of using their brains. When he moved from one station to another, expensive advertising made him appear an unpredictable zany—and it is true that the least interesting of his qualities is the one he shares with others—with Ernie Kovacs, for instance, and with all those who do not understand the nature of television and the nature of comedy, who consequently work terribly hard to appear crazy and give the effect of working terribly hard. What the team of Martin and Lewis could not accomplish, these laborious acts obviously can never hope to do. And, on the whole, ought to be glad of it.

The merit of Steve Allen, as of Henry Morgan, is that he has an interesting temperament and a cast of mind unusual in his business. Both these men are, in fact, debunkers in the style of the 1920s; but the debunkers of the 1920s had only pedantic historians and "homely philosophers" and Main Street and foolish movies to debunk, while the boys of the 1950s have the whole colossal beautiful area of processed bunk in the large economy size, the bunk of the advertising that, particularly late at night, surrounds them. Morgan chose to attack his sponsor, Allen mocked at the mode in which advertising and publicity were cast; each wanted to know who was being taken in by what foolishness. Each, in the end, yielded somewhat. Morgan was alone for a quarter-hour's chat, occasionally reading and commenting on his own radio scripts of ten years before; Allen had an acceptable lot of youngsters singing, perhaps dancing, with him. He used to emphasize the zany note by bringing in Jim Moran, the bearded philosopher who had sold iceboxes to Eskimos and found out how long it took to find a needle in a haystack—that was part of the zany effect. Much better were quick darts of satire—a word to a member of the audience or an "offbeat" introduction to a song. In everything the value of his own character was present. It is interesting to note that just before NBC took him over, some complaint was heard that Allen had lost his rapport with the studio audience and consequently with the audience at home. Perhaps it was not so—perhaps it did not matter when Allen became a nighttime network star.

It must now be clear that I have been using Bing Crosby for surprise effect. Everyone knows Bing—who could have known that his casual movements across the face of the entertainment world would have so many repercussions? Least of all, I should bet, himself.

And, oddly, in one field he was, as far as I can see, without influence: in the movies. There was something too relaxed about him in the playful shorts he made, something transparently and obstinately refusing to be an actor, which seemed to show up the movies and at the same time showed how pleasing they could be when they tried the right thing. The right thing eventually came to the mind of the half-dozen men, writers and producers, who share the great honor of creating the series of *Road* pictures as if in one tremendous blow of inspiration. They seemed to have invented a form, found all the elements for it, and perfected all the processes simultaneously; and, on top of that, they were able to return to the form and find it so flexible that they could use it over and over again without the effect of repetition or routine. I am not suggesting that Crosby was in any way the creative spark of these enterprises; they are much more the outcome of a dozen inventive personalities exchanging ideas. Actually, the *Road* pictures, like many of the adventures in them, happened to Crosby, as if he were the innocent bystander. (And in one of the most attractive moments on the screen, he is just that. In a picture called *My Favorite Blonde*, Bob Hope and Madeleine Carroll are pursued by dastardly villains across the country. They try to hide by joining a queue for a club picnic, and Hope sees a man standing near by, looks sharply at him, decides that it cannot be, and shrugs off the resemblance—and it *is* Crosby, doing nothing at all, seeming to have sauntered into the crowd there, into this picture where he has no business, as he saunters into the pictures where he is one of the stars.)

These *Road* pictures were impudent to the point of sauciness. They poked fun at themselves and at the movies, at Dorothy Lamour, who was the third star with Crosby and Hope, and at Paramount. They were the second great series of comedics with a group of stars made after sound came in; the first was the Marx Brothers' series; and the great comedies made by a single star were those of W. C. Fields.

These belong elsewhere, and I mention them here to round out the professional career of Bing Crosby. I have not attempted to pay tribute to his talents. The fact that the use of his talents affected so many elements in the whole field of entertainment can be taken as tribute enough.

But the special endearing quality he has makes everyone want to appropriate him, and how can one take possession better than by seeing the essential more clearly or catching the miraculous trifle that others have missed? I am sure that I see in Bing Crosby nothing that everyone else does not see; he is transparent, he has no obscurities. But once, a long time ago, when I first heard his recording of "Adeste Fideles," I imagined that I caught in the last bar of the song a tiny, delicate syncopation. It seemed to me right and reverential, making me think of another popular artist who did what he could, as well as he could, to honor the Queen of Heaven, and entered into literature and into legend as the Juggler of Notre Dame.

14

THE PREVALENCE OF COMEDY

Comedy is the axis on which broadcasting revolves. We take this for granted—it seems the natural thing, since people have always loved clowns and "anything for a laugh" could be one of our minor national mottoes. But the truth is that the central position of comedy on the air is a totally new phenomenon in the history of entertainment. The clown is on the periphery of the circus ring; the comedian hardly exists in contemporary musical comedies; Ziegfeld flourished although he hated the "comics" forced into the *Follies* by his associates; the immortal trilogy of "songs, dances, and funny sayings" might have been a definition of vaudeville, giving comedy third billing—and even so this left out the elements of wonder and surprise which were prime ingredients of variety shows and had nothing on earth to do with laughter. As for the movies, they seem to live without comedy altogether: eight of the ten most successful pictures of 1954 were totally without comedy, and in *Variety*'s list of the "all-time top grossers" the presence of comedy would be identified by a scrupulous cook as between "a trace" and "a pinch."

Since 1949 the status of comedians and their programs on the air has changed, both show and star now being pieces of chattel property and also weapons in the long battle for supremacy in the empire of entertainment. In that year CBS began a series of raids on NBC's stable of comedians and most conspicuously made off with Jack Benny, his wife, his writers, and his enterprises, past, present, and future, in a deal involving what was then a large sum of money (pitiful as it seems by later standards) and attracting added publicity because of the disputed bearing on such a property of the capital-gains tax. For a time it seemed that NBC was permanently maimed by the blow, but it was only stunned—only a year later a masterly counterstroke was evolved. By some complicated maneuvers, the network freed itself from a long commitment to a religious program at six P.M. on Sundays, the time at which comedy begins to take over, and so was able to start a new and brilliantly presented program before Benny appeared on CBS. Moreover, the new program ran ninety minutes, overlapping Benny's time, and NBC could confidently expect to keep a large segment of its audience from turning to the opposition. The program mixed old and new styles in radio, with Miss Tallulah Bankhead in a new role as mistress of ceremonies and mistress also of insult—which bounced off the whole galaxy of NBC's comedians, including Jimmy Durante, on his way to becoming a great television star; Bob Burns, brought back from near-oblivion; old vaudevillians like Smith and Dale; movie stars with special personality traits that made them just right to receive or to throw back Miss Bankhead's acrid remarks; and, moving into new fields, Miss Margaret Truman, who was a sensational success.

This expensive program was produced to protect the radio interest.

BRIEF INQUIRY INTO THE ESSENTIAL NATURE OF COMEDY

Red Skelton is a very funny man at times, a good low comedian, but until judgment utterly forsakes me I shall not accept the idea that calling a character Mr. Kadiddlehopper is uproariously comic. Not the five-hundredth time, at any rate. Not the fiftieth. Not at all.

On the TV front the initiative lay in the hands of NBC, which had taken over the comedy field in two impressive styles: the rude hit-'em-with-everything-you've-got approach of Milton Berle, and the relatively understated and ingratiating manner of Sid Caesar and Imogene Coca. The former's staked claim to Tuesday night was unchallengeable, but NBC saw a threat to its place on Saturday night and contrived a sort of parlay, a *Saturday Night Revue*, all of it for laughs, running from eight to half past ten E.S.T., adding an hour of a boisterous comedian to the ninety minutes of the established Caesar-Coca program. The facilities for network broadcasting were limited, and by preempting the coaxial cable for the central hours of Saturday, NBC might be able to make a package, so that any station that wanted one segment of the evening's comedy would have to take all. The placing of the program was as important as its content.

This maneuvering for position could be successful only if the networks, which controlled the time, also controlled the programs. In radio the great comedy programs had been created by talent—or advertising —agencies and the networks did everything possible to attract the sponsors, who had the final word. With the coming of television, both NBC and CBS went back into the business they had forsaken some ten years earlier, the business of creating entertainment. By direct ownership, the networks create a seller's market, putting sponsors in the absurd position of begging CBS and NBC to accept their money.

Not that the sponsors were at all hesitant about accepting the network-produced programs, and the comedy shows in particular. Radio had supplied a singular demonstration—against all logic and against all predictions—of the staying power of the laugh-makers. In 1949, when television was for the first time turning into the straightaway, the leading radio comedians were those who had been leading in 1939; and, for the most part, they were using the same, or simple variations of the same, routines. By that time also, Milton Berle had demonstrated that the stale and tasteless routines of small-time vaudeville and the techniques of the smoker could bring the title of Mr. Television to a performer of sufficient energy (the demonstration that these qualities would not keep him out front was still several years off). Berle was fortunate because, not being a valuable radio property, he could plunge in while Hope and Benny and Crosby and Durante were trying to find the framework just right for their talents. Any framework was sufficient for the borrowed talents and the brash personality of Berle. In a sense, he lit the fuse that turned the arrival of television into an explosion. Before the old-established radio comedians had solved their problems, a dozen others had flashed across the horizon: Chico Marx from the movies, Borge and Coca from intimate night clubs, Bobby Clark from the theater, and from the austere Metropolitan Opera House, in the person of Helen Traubel, a comedienne who made good with the early Durante. The variety of backgrounds gave TV comedy more change of pace than could have been anticipated, and when the panel show developed as a tangent to comedy, talent was discovered in writers, newspapermen, and people totally outside the entertainment arts.

And, by an incomparable stroke of luck, right at the beginning a program turned up which was pure television, setting standards of technical excellence and of good taste which could not have been expected in so young an enterprise. It was *Kukla, Fran, and Ollie*. Kukla and his gang (or, in my estimation, Ollie and *his* retinue) had sunny fortune from the start. They accomplished that most desirable miracle of reconciling the fastidious to the average taste, of being admired by one and all. The alls were simply pleased; the ones were startled as well: here was television, the latest of the upstarts, from which no good was to be expected because it was so mechanical and commercial, coming up with, of all things, a program that was new and out of the whole range of formula, a program that did not hit you on the head every two minutes to make its point—there was no end to the virtues of *K, F, & O*. It was great for children, and one eminent dramatist* found that it came at just the right time for him to watch it while he shaved of an evening. Aesthetes could point out that it was pure television, and the enthusiasts for the Chicago school of TV originals could note that it was also spontaneous. Before television had lived three postwar years, it had created a masterpiece. At the same age the movies were barely more than a peepshow and radio was still transmitting the heartbeats of a butterfly caught in a submarine.

It was a masterpiece. If there is any undertone of mockery in the report above, it is for those who could not believe that it had

* The late, admirable Robert E. Sherwood.

happened. The man who remained behind the scenes for years, Burr Tillstrom, had a sure instinct for television. He knew, for instance, that you could perfectly combine the live Fran Allison with the puppets, whereas you could not combine the human-movie-figure of anyone, even Carmen Miranda, with the Disney characters. He knew—or he and Fran Allison together worked out—the right relation between her and Ollie and the Kuklapolitans: she is a favorite aunt who occasionally is vexed by their antics, but she is never a mother, too proud or too severe.

It is impossible to list all the points on which the program was right—from the single-toothed dragon to the structure of the booth in which they all appeared. The program had only one relatively unimportant defect. When that was corrected, the ceiling seemed to fall in. Suddenly, one day, NBC announced that the program would be reduced from half an hour to a quarter. I doubt whether the company's motives were purely aesthetic, but the fact is that by this move the program was vastly improved. It had been too long, and among the fillers that extended but did not improve it were daily songs by Fran Allison—good enough, in all conscience, but not peculiarly appropriate or needed.

The moment the news broke, the aesthetes and the intellectuals seemed to rise in a body and cry shame. They cried commercialism. They accused NBC of the darkest ingratitude. All the sins of commercial broadcasting had come to a head. The situation was unbearable.

The joker in the matter, quite apart from the better balance and tempo of *Kukla, Fran, and Ollie*, was that the fifteen minutes taken from them was handed over to Bob and Ray, who were equally the darlings of the intellectuals. And for about three months Bob and Ray did very well by us. Eventually the strain (or something) was too much for them. Eventually *Kukla, Fran, and Ollie* took over other time periods. They have never ceased to be quite superior, and the circumstance that they have lost much of their popularity (as measured by ratings and sponsorships) is not discreditable to them. For they have remained first-rate; only people have not.

The history of this program brings little comfort to those critics who have dogmatic opinions about broadcasting, particularly those who hold that nothing good is *ever* put on the air and those who believe that, given a chance, the public will *always* support what is good. It is probable that *Kukla, Fran, and Ollie* was such a great success because at the start the competition was feeble. My own opinion is that their quiet and delicate humors could not withstand the coming, in huge quantities, of rough and raucous comedians. Not all of these lasted as long as the Kuklapolitans. Some, heavily touted for a season, vanished into the obscurity of local-and-late shows. They were not only bad guesses; often they were conspicuous instances of the arrogance and invincible ignorance of those who produce and those who pay for comedy shows. By its third year of commercial life, television had established routines, and, while the critics were ready to applaud excellence, or even attempts at excellence, in any style, a large number of executives were convinced that the public wanted more and more imitations of a few successful programs. The public never got a chance to render a verdict on Fred Allen in a program suited to his talents, but it did get a bellyful of comedians in the manner of Berle. It got Allen in slapstick, and it got and for a time was even persuaded to love Martin and Lewis. Chico Marx was put into the straitjacket of a situation comedy (the Italianate proprietor of a college-town soda fountain), and all the huge engines of television turned over to prove that Beatrice Lillie was not a great comedienne. She was, though.

Compared to their successes, the networks' failures in comedy were minor, and perhaps the only point worth remembering about those early years is that while these experiments were being made, the critics also were feeling their way, asking for a little more enterprise, a test case to discover whether something more delicate than the transvestite bellowings of Milton Berle would be acceptable. Their effrontery was denounced, they were accused of hating the common man, and, worst of all, they were called theorists, in contrast to the practical men who were meeting the weekly payroll and who alone *knew* what kind of comedy the public would accept. In those years about a hundred and fifty programs failed each season, and a goodly proportion of them were comedies—not one of which was written or produced by a critic.

The Caesar-Coca team was an immediate success with the public and was instantly hailed as an artistic masterpiece by the critics. The remarkable thing is that, while the critics were pleased that so good a production, combining so much skill and intelligence and taste and talent, could form a high-rating show, the hard businessmen persisted in treating it as if it were a freak, as if the public did not really care for it; they knew best, and they kept on satisfying the real taste of the public, for second-rate Berles. In the four years of the Caesar-Coca combination, not a single program of its quality, or anything near it, was attempted. In the meantime, the search for a low-grade Berle had been successful and Jackie Gleason moved from the small Dumont network, where neither he nor anyone else had been much aware of his talent, into the big time of CBS and the biggest money up to that time in entertainment.

Between the arrival of Berle and Gleason's capture of Berle's sponsor, one other event occurred: *I Love Lucy*. Apart from its own qualities, *Lucy* is important in the history of the comedy because of its effect on others. There were practical broadcasters who knew what the public wanted and turned down *Lucy*; they were among those who, after *Lucy* was launched, believed that the public would not pay attention to any program that did not resemble it. A number of programs with considerable individuality were assimilated to the Lucian style; some went on about as before in their ratings, some did not.

With *I Love Lucy* we have arrived at a summary of all the major types of comedy, unless a separate (and pretty) framework should be set around the polite domestic comedy of George Burns and Gracie Allen and the slightly less polite but fundamentally first-rate work of Peg Lynch and Alan Bunce in *Ethel and Albert*. *I Love Lucy* is domestic comedy with the high voltage of an old Keystone production and high-voltage runs through Berle and Gleason in their most characteristic phases. With less pressure, the original team of Caesar and Coca and, to an extent, each of them separately, and the soft-shoe approach of George Gobel, are the counterweight. The material used is much the same, the difference lying in the pressure under which it is presented. And standing outside these various ways of making comedy, using the same materials and methods and creating something totally different by their own essential qualities, are Jack Benny and Jimmy Durante, in mode so opposed to each other, in sum the ideal of what comedy can be.

These programs and people, marked with talent of the highest order or with genius in some of its simplest and most endearing manifestations, tell us almost everything we need to know about actual comedy on the air. There are a dozen other kinds of programs essentially, which testify to the importance of comedy as a force in creating audiences and in selling goods. Virtually all the panel shows outside of the area of news and discussion are played for laughs, and when the questions are wildly malapropos or almost suggestive (guessing the occupation of a mattress-tester can bring up some dandy innuendoes) the programs are funny enough and the element of the contest gets submerged in the laughs, as it got submerged in witty conversation on *Information, Please!* Programs based on charades, on the richer giveaways, on the talents of amateurs, and the afternoon grab-bags that often exploit little children for doubtful comic value pay further tribute to the over-whelming need we have, or think we have, for copious, constantly available fun. But these programs, which teach us a lot about ourselves, tell us little about the nature of comedy; whereas the kinds I have mentioned above tell us a great deal—and they are worth looking at more closely still.

It is natural to begin with Milton Berle.

15

THE GOOD-BAD BERLE

The careers of this man are various—not always distinguished, but invariably instructive. Thoroughly unlikable in his beginnings and intolerable in his triumph, he "got wise to himself" when things went wrong for him, and showed something approaching grace after returning to popular favor—and then he was tripped up by the man who exploited all his least attractive manners. Nothing, in short, has been more becoming to Milton Berle than adversity.

Considering what Berle was in his early vaudeville and night-club days, the mind shrinks away from the thought of him as a child actor. The Palace Theatre was within a few years of its end when Berle came to manhood and, as a young, brash, impudent snapper-up of other people's trifles, exploited his own lack of originality, telling his rivals' jokes louder than they did, willing to do anything for a laugh, and apparently committed to the technique of contagion because he always laughed first—and loudest—himself. Perhaps his show of delight in his own talents was compensation for knowing that they were of a low order, but there is no doubt that his push and self-assurance were positive factors in his early success. It was a time when few people had much confidence in anything, least of all in the aggressive drive of the American system that had ended in an economic depression and an emotional wallow of self-pity and despair. Berle was always in there pitching.

He worked in night clubs, and he appeared at those peculiar social gatherings given by charitable institutions at fifty dollars per person (deductible) for the most noble of purposes and for men only. Few performers could resist the pressure to play these stag parties, and fewer, I should guess, enjoyed them more than Berle. For years his style had all the stigmata of these occasions: the loud voice that had to make itself heard above the talk and laughter of men who had eaten rich food and drunk copiously and were free of their inhibiting women; the big leer that could be seen through the smoke of hundreds of cigars; the broad gestures that had to carry to the ends of a room intended for dining, ill-shaped for concentrating attention. And these physical qualities run parallel to certain psychological ones, one of the most urgent of which is to demonstrate that the entertainer is aware of what the audience wants and is going to provide it—plus just a little more smut than they expect. He does not have to ingratiate himself because his audience is captive; and a single standard prevails: how much dirt? The aesthetes in the company may want to know how dirty the dirt is; the general view is that quantity alone will do the trick. Obviously this has an effect on the style of the entertainer, and this is all I am now trying to isolate from the complex and fascinating subject of the smutty story (the dirty joke, the filthy comic picture, pornographic literature, and the like). I know of no treatise on this important topic, and I wish that one would be written, preferably as a thesis for a master's degree. One can see its sections: psychological; national differences; historical and anthropological relations. My only contribution to this would be confined to my own field, which is public entertainment. The off-color story, as privately told, is quite a different thing, and it gets its final piquancy from the knowledge that the teller has probably told it and the listener will probably tell it to a person of the opposite sex. The natural gift of telling these stories well has nothing to do with the arts of the entertainer. I know a first-rate professional comedian who bogs down deplorably in the middle of a moderately "blue" remark, although he can talk freely and rationally about sex otherwise; and several hundred (perhaps a thousand) people know as well as I do that among the amateur practitioners of the art of telling dirty jokes, a celebrated medievalist and a great man in one of the major arts are the nonpareils of the Eastern seaboard. Neither taste nor manners seem to be involved; education and general culture may have something to do with the frequency of recourse to smut, but they have little effect on the vocabulary or the style. The only exception I know is also the only entirely offensive kind of smutty story I know: the pedantic kind that manages to brush an added slick of morbidity over whatever is normal and healthy in "good clean dirt."

The basic material of the stag entertainer, whether he dresses in women's clothes, pretends to be homosexual, or develops some other specialty, is still the off-color story, and his basic style is always the public one of maximum projection. Lower the volume the least bit, reduce the projection slightly, and we have the style of the night-club entertainer who may surprise his audience by a sly innuendo, but is not in competition with the audience and does not have to assert himself or demonstrate his manliness. The geniality of the night club contrasts with the rowdiness of the stag dinner—and the graduate from night clubs who best represents the type in television is the genial Durante. Compelled to clean up his routines, Berle held on to the aggressive manner and ended (in his first phase) as a figure familiar to us all: the village cut-up or the life of the party. Instead of putting on the women's hats after dinner, he put on lace panties in public, and his whole career seemed a huge practical joke. The long patience of the electronic scientists and the enterprise of the broadcasters had come together, and out of the entire world of entertainment, the world that held Chaplin and Bea Lillie and Fred Allen and Bobby Clark, there came Berle—the triumph of the hotfoot.

He had little competition at first—the honor of making television talked about belongs to him and to the low-grade boxing matches that attracted the saloon audiences—but he would probably have been popular in any case. His personality is strong, he comes across without reservation, nothing about him is shaded. After watching him for a year, I wrote: "His voice is loud, his grimaces wide, he points and labors his jokes without making them either pointed or worked-out; he is constantly reaching out for millions of people, not for two or three individuals sitting at home; he gets the millions and constantly interferes with their enjoyment of other talents on his program—and he is obviously well-liked." The last phrase is an error—it recalls the fine distinction Willy Loman made between salesmen who were liked and those who were well liked, and it points to a special quality in Berle's following. Many people had a sort of contemptuous liking for him, as if he were a mildly obnoxious character whom they admired because "he got away with murder," which again recalls the ambivalent feelings one has for the party cut-up, so useful when things are bogging down, so expendable when people are enjoying themselves.

The audience liked Berle's cocky assurance and the sardonic way he called himself "Uncle Miltie"—a mockery intended to recall not Uncle Don, but the legendary blooper when that reader of comics for children thought himself off the air and said, "That'll hold the little bastards for a while." Although television was young, it had taken over all the professional sweetness of radio; the stars insulted one another with synthetic cracks, but insisted upon an equally synthetic reconciliation, reassuring the audience that it was all in fun, "but seriously" they were the best fellows in the world, the best of pals, and just plain folks. With this Berle had no truck. It was obvious that he relished the cracks he delivered and that he could not play "he who gets slapped"; he hated his guests to get the better of him. In this, I think, the audience sensed a kind of rude honesty, and they felt it, too, in the projection of his vulgarity, deep-grained and cheerfully exploited, in contrast to those comedians whose vulgarity was an imitation, a veneer, covering their uninteresting personalities. While they were, in their own phrase, "knocking themselves out" to be common, Berle's vulgarity flowed like the Mississippi, muddy but powerful, and he spent his strength in knocking out the audience.

This is the only satisfactory explanation I can see for the way Berle succeeded by playing against the grain and nature of television— namely, that he only seemed to be against it and was really in the groove. He did not play for the two or three people at home, but for the studio audience; he played for the audience of millions as if they were all in a single place. He did not let the camera and the circuits through the control room to the seventeen-inch receiver at home attend to the magnification of personality—he inflated himself. He was not so much conscious of the camera as determined that no one else should ever get a closeup. These antics seem to knock askew all the sound principles of TV production because the audience did not mind at all, it loved Berle—and that is the clue. For the audience was testifying to the great truth underlying all the good techniques of television: it transmits the reality of people. It took me a long time to apply this principle to Berle because it means that the exaggerations, the mugging into the camera, the extra widening of the mouth and the display of teeth, the facial contortions and the whirlwind of action are all Berle's *natural* way of being funny. The audience saw a genuine man.

The producers of other shows saw only a bundle of tricks and, like Hollywood in search of a new cycle, found imitators who worked terribly hard to be as bad as Berle doing what came naturally. They were consequently rejected by the public because they were not so good as Berle was. Not until Jackie Gleason moved into a major spot on a big network did television acquire a genuinely unfriendly personality aggressively joined to a huge talent that had been schooled, moreover, in the type of night club closest to the stag dinner. By that time something singular had happened to Berle. The shrewd publicity that had turned him into "Uncle Miltie" had also staked out for him a claim to the obnoxious title of Mr. Television; he had a thirty-one-year contract running into millions of dollars; and suddenly he was nobody. In one season he tumbled from first place in the ratings of popularity to seventeenth.

It could not have happened to a more offensive "Personality," and it could not have happened to a man of more intelligence and guts, for as he was going down the bumps Berle began to shed his bad manners and his overworked techniques. He accepted a new framework for his show, being in no position to refuse—but he also transformed himself into such a remarkably good comedian that he half persuaded you he had always been one.

The intelligent producers of the Berle program knew what they had to get rid of. The parallel merit of Goodman Ace, the chief writer of the new show, was that he knew he had to supply a program of superior quality using familiar elements, without a trace of intellectual comedy. It had to be rowdy but not bawdy, it had to be unlike what Berle had been doing, and at the same time it had to use Berle and capitalize on his vices as well as his virtues. I know of no more difficult assignment in comedy-writing, and I know of none so triumphantly accomplished. After the first two or three programs, which were more a demonstration of intentions than good in themselves, the new writers and producers neatly and confidently brought a clear comedy concept into existence week after week with a growing sureness of touch in which their star also shared.

The show remained a catch-all of comic devices, but at the center there was a new element that held the other parts together. Instead of being the monster who swallowed all the other entertainers, Berle was now the point from which all the others radiated. To utilize his former self-concentration, while burlesquing it, a new character was created, half bobby-soxer, half sex-maniac, who threw herself at Berle's head with a singleness of purpose unmatched in our time except for the pursuit of Li'l Abner by Daisy Mae. It was a skillful invention because it elevated the running gag into farce, and the adolescent, superbly played by Ruth Gilbert, was not only an attractive nitwit, but was also Berle's audience of the previous years. Whether this was design or accident, I do not know. In the contagion of high spirits, Berle gained all along the line. He no longer had to fight for stage center all the time. He was not out to violate the entire audience, and the dreadful, half-apologetic laugh of a criminal caught in the act gave way to more civilized and more pleasant expressions of pleasure. All these marks of a talent of the third order were modulated into their parallels higher in the scale —and the program was immediately accepted by the public. Within weeks it had recovered a high place in the ratings.

This is where the story ought to end, because it is a good story of the blight of success, the fall from the heights, the hero facing the flaw in his character, reforming, and making good again. But while his work continued admirable and his ratings good, one of the great battles of the networks took place, and at its end Berle found himself, for a period of months, without a sponsor announced for his next season, his star dimmed and his great contract overshadowed by Gleason.

It is, nonetheless, a heartening story, especially for those enemies of the popular arts who are convinced that the public will never tire of an entertainment if it is bad enough, preferring it to whatever is better. The public did tire of the Berle program. The second good omen is the promptness and the success of the change. There was, to be sure, an enormous stake in Berle's return to popularity: all the millions still to be paid out under his contract with NBC, and all the damage to NBC's program structure if his hour should fail. Still, the Berle story— up to the advent of Gleason, at least—is all to the good, and the best of it is the part played by the public—dazzled for a while but not permanently hoodwinked, usually discriminating, and always generous.

16

AVE, VALE, AND WAIT

It took a year to remake the reputation of Berle and something less than six months to undermine the standing of Sid Caesar and Imogene Coca, whose second career also reversed the first, but in the opposite direction. There came a moment which each of them may well consider the low point of fortune; the program which was so popular that, in the lingo of the trade, it priced itself out of the market, broke into several parts and no segment appeared to advantage in whatever new combinations were made. It could be said that Caesar and Coca needed each other and that both needed their presiding genius, Max Liebman (and it certainly could be said that he needed them). It could also be said that "priced themselves out of the market" merely means that someone thought more money could be earned by the two stars separately; it is possible that the magnetism of the stars was beginning to weaken and they could only make money separately. In such cases we have no solid ground to question the decision; we can only wonder whether the stars in a combination were really as good as people said they were.

It seems to me that Caesar and Coca, in their years together, were *as* good, but not necessarily good in the way their more analytical admirers said they were. Naturally while Berle was making an arena out of the seventeen-inch screen the critics and the customers were refreshed by the spectacle of two people who were notably, irresistibly funny and yet seemed to observe a few of the decencies of human intercourse. They did not yell at the audience, they did not insult anyone. They were available for a physical effect as basic and broad as a pratfall when needed, but never gave the impression that this was by all odds the funniest effect in the world. They were, as it happened, both muggers, but their mugging was in a sense counter-clockwise; where Berle's challenge was perpetually "try and get out of the way of this one," these two comedians were playing a game of tag with us and dodging, weaving, with a constant taunt—that we would not catch them at it. Each of them did a few things with great decorum—usually their solos. Miss Coca singing "Wrap Up Your Troubles in Dreams" recalled Chaplin not only because she was dressed as a tramp, but because she, like Chaplin, can communicate three or four simple emotions at the same time without letting any one of them get out of control—that is to say, without exaggeration and sentimentality. Caesar's typical man—the unrealized individual, the male who cannot cope with females, modern gadgets, or his own floating and undefined desires—is usually rendered in broad strokes. If he is nervous about the set of his coat, he shrugs himself into it not three times but seven. Only when this same character suddenly becomes aware of himself as a fraud, when he brags and instantly confesses to himself that he is afraid—only then, for a penetrating moment or two, is Caesar's technique, invisible to the naked eye, effective. Then he can stand being named in the general neighborhood of the masters of the art, for it is when Caesar forgets all his miraculous observation of *how* a person behaves and begins to let us see *why* he behaves so that he comes closest to Chaplin, who, at his greatest, always fuses the outward and inward, leaving us unaware of the moment or the place where the two are joined.

Television comedians cannot live by exceptional moments; they must have many broader techniques at their disposal. Caesar and Coca did—and what made them in their happy time together so good and so different from the dominant sub-Berle type was that both of them used all their skills to put over—to put across—not themselves, but the series of characters they were creating. This is the simplest of all distinctions, and it applies to acting in all its aspects. To Bernard Shaw it is the difference between devoting yourself to the drama and devoting the drama to yourself. It underlies the complaint of critics that stars choose vehicles best suited to their own personalities; and, in reverse, it is one of the essential factors in the creation of the fan club, for the fan always devotes himself to the personality rather than the talent, to the player regardless of the character played. This becomes supremely important in television because in this medium the personality projects itself with tremendous force. At the same time, all the machinery of promotion is used to make the stars, with all their real quirks and with a hundred invented attributes, familiar to the public. In the vast ballyhoo about stars, their salaries, their quarrels, their private lives and public services, the mere intention to create characters, as Judith Anderson created Jeffers's *Medea* or Durante created *The Well-Dressed Man*, is exceptional and rash. Caesar and Coca kept on creating one character after another and did it at the expense of becoming "personality" headliners in the newspapers. When they parted company, the event was an important item on the television page; when Godfrey parted company with a third-rate and almost unknown singer, it was front-page news in big black type and sometimes in red. Godfrey, like Berle and Gleason, had become eight feet tall; his voice had authority in the fields of aviation and politics; like theirs, his contract involved millions; like each of them, he had put across a priceless commodity, himself. Caesar and Coca had brought into the American living room a variety of people. Some were so close to the familiar average person that the only response was a smiling recognition. Some were extravagantly conceived or presented with frank exaggeration. They were not even all new, but merely variations on the absent-minded professor, or the fussy woman shopper, or the husband too tired to go out, or the schoolteacher abroad. But Caesar and Coca spent all their energy and skill rendering these people, so that we knew the characters and forgot the actors who created them.

Their style corresponds to the one-line caption of *The New Yorker*, whereas so much other comedy is still in the He-She stage. In a sense, but not to be taken as final, their material also reflected the intellectual and satirical approach of the highbrow wit, *The New Yorker*'s approach exaggerated so that it could be apprehended by the less intellectual, could be taken in while one watched an ever-changing show without the chance of going back to page fifteen to discover the small element in the picture that is the clue to its humor. Ten funny pictures a year in *The New Yorker* depend on your noticing the clerical collar, and the artists do not go out of their way to call your attention to that detail. When Caesar or Coca repeats a small gesture, it is the equivalent of giving us a second or third look at the drawing. The broader school of comedy substitutes a blow for the small gesture, a guffaw for the timid smile—and repeats these effects until the cretins in the audience get the point.

The places Miss Coca had worked in before television were on the small side—intimate revues and night clubs with more quality than crowds—but she never tried for subtle effects, any more than did Fanny Brice, whom she resembled; in those days she also used the broad and funny strokes of Beatrice Lillie, getting a lot—perhaps just a little too much—comedy out of a long, mangy furpiece and other grotesque props. She could not have been unaware of those great people, and consequently it can be said that she used to imitate them, or formed her style on theirs; but she continued on, developing and combining the right elements until she discovered exactly what was best for her. The swoops of her voice, as if she had no control over it, and the expressiveness of her small face, which can go blank as a baby's or expressive as the snout of a nice small animal, are her best endowments. In her solo work she is happiest with music and funniest doing parodies of singers or dancers.

Caesar began show business while in the service. He was with a band in a Coast Guard production and, after a moderate success in a night club, did very well in the revue *Make Mine Manhattan*. Joined with Miss Coca, he had several kinds of comedy to do, although the central character was pretty much the same in all. He appeared with her and other characters in "situations," being always the one who did not fit in—the one frightened passenger on a routine flight who expects just a routine crash, the one man in the theater who came to see the movie and not to neck with a companion. These scenes range from conventional embarrassing moments to recurrent and familiar nightmares, and in nearly all of them Caesar projects some variation of that image of the non-coping man who is parallel and opposite to the aggressive successful man of Berle and a host of others. It is a sympathetic character, the man too simple to master complex machinery, too polite to insist on his rights or too unaggressive to exercise them when they are recognized —not quite Casper Milquetoast, the "Timid Soul" of Webster, being more intelligent, but kin to him. It is also the butt, the fall guy, and it is an image of defeat—with honor, with dignity, as if in this world it is below the dignity of man to come off winner.

Another of Caesar's routines is his solo performance, either in panto-mime or soliloquy, and of these the second is the better. A favorite device is to start a man arguing with himself and to carry him to an un-expected conclusion; it has been used by others, and I suspect that the gag-writers have been studying the ancient Italian comedy, in which it was already a set piece. Somewhere in the works of Carlo Gozzi there is a sequence about a man starting off to borrow a pot from a neighbor and congratulating himself on having a neighbor so willing to lend; then asking himself why, after all, his neighbor should not be willing; and so, by gradual degrees, working himself up into such a rage that when the neighbor comes to the door, he knocks him down without even asking for the pot. Caesar will start with a man congratulating him-self on being turned down by his fiancée and in five minutes will go through a dozen phases of emotion, through all of which, by minute variations of voice and gesture—by the way he buttons his cuff or fumbles with his tie—the degrees of self-delusion are communicated.

In solo pantomime, his range is wide and his imagination agreeably wild. A recent article in *Newsweek* listed some of the characters he has created or imitated: "a woman arising in the morning, an expectant father, a 6-month-old baby, a white sidewall tire. . . ." The charm of the last item is so great that I am making no effort to discover what it consisted of. Caesar and Coca appeared together at least once in each show. Sometimes they did burlesques of movies. Sometimes they were man and wife in a domestic interlude, usually a wrangle, and some-times fellow wanderers in the world—in a bank, in Mexico, at a restau-rant. They were like "Mr. and Mrs." in the old Briggs cartoons. The dialogue was often a satiric utterance of clichés that they punctured with a sudden jab of observed truth. They met in a foreign city and seemed to be racing for the privilege of being the first to say "It's a small world." They cooed over their surroundings—"so quaint"—"so exotic"—"so picturesque"—a pause—"so expensive." They despised the Americans who take tours and are guided; Miss Coca went off by her-self, saw the native life as no tourist ever can, did everything she wanted —"I had a miserable time." Caesar got off the beaten track of inter-national restaurants and ate the native dishes—"phooey!" It was a for-mula job, but still fresh, the parody line clear, the delivery just barely over the edge of exact mimicry.

The separation of Caesar and Coca diminished their separate virtues and called attention to the exceptional skill of the man who had brought and held them together: their producer, Max Liebman. With experience in camp shows (both summer and military), Liebman came to television with a great deal of assurance and not much respect for the techniques or the quality then current. This gave him a fresh attack—he handled Caesar and Coca as if television of the Berle kind did not exist. At one time he was so independent that he produced shows as if the audience did not exist either, putting on large choruses and placing everything so far away from the camera that on the home screen a comedy routine had something of the effect of the wide open spaces of Western movies. He got over this fondness for large effects, and, although he became a producer of the big "spectaculars" for NBC after the combination broke up, he no longer assumed that it was good for the audience to have to strain in order to see what was going on. Dogmas about production methods are exceptional in the field of comedy (they occur steadily in the big dramatic productions) and most of them merely rationalize or make publicity out of a director's bag of tricks. The essential value of Liebman's work lay in his perception of exactly the right way to bring out exactly the right television elements in Caesar and Coca, and in particular the need to surround them with an atmosphere of good humor rather than the spurious high spirits of most other comedy programs.

Whether that atmosphere can be recaptured by either of these comic spirits, whether they can come together again, we have yet to see. It seems a pity that the bright combination had to break up—but it is always possible that the break-up saved them from the creeping staleness which is the malady of all routine shows.

17

MR. BENNY

One of the most amusing ideas of the always interesting CBS publicity department is the charcoal drawing published to announce each appearance of Jack Benny in television: noble, distinguished, slightly pained, faintly reminiscent in style of a self-portrait by a very self-satisfied artist, and looking with disdain on mere popular comedians and mere men of distinction.

Very funny because Jack Benny has with infinite pains created for himself the character of the ineffectual, the truly undistinguished human being. He is the comedian who does not say funny things and who gets laughs only as they ricochet off him. It is Rochester or Don Wilson or Mary Livingstone who delivers the laugh line, and in Benny's apparently awkward technique, with the timing so seemingly wrong, after the laugh has subsided you hear him murmur, "Don't say things like that" or even an unfinished "Aw . . ." or "Oh, well. . . ." And he proceeds to the next moment, moving with exquisite precision of timing and intonation, preparing every inch of the ground for his collaborators, until again they spring the trap on him. He is the most skillful comedian I have ever seen work before the public. He was a pleasant comedian to watch in the days of vaudeville, and with almost scientific accuracy he made fine adjustments in his methods when he came to radio, where he had his long and admirable career, becoming such a fixture, so much "the" comedian, that everything about him was taken for granted. If the revolting phrase had been common at the time, he would have been called "Mr. Radio Comedian." His name was the first that came to mind, for praise or blame, when people talked about radio comedy—and, for a long time, whenever people talked about radio at all. He was certainly the least flashy top star in any kind of entertainment, but when CBS took a long, hard look at the future, it seemed good to them to buy the Benny enterprises, which meant Benny, for two and a half million dollars. No one seemed surprised. Everyone took it for granted that Benny was worth that much.

He was worth it as a pivotal element in the struggle for power, and yet, in the event, Benny had almost nothing to do with the progress of television. He came into it after a long, long period of observation, watching with his calculating eye the tribulations of others. He saw good men die in front of the camera, and strong and versatile men wilt on their third appearance, and comedians with whom he would have refused to appear in Sauk Center being hailed as geniuses. He bided his time, and when he made his entrance he came on quietly. To this day he is gingerly in his approach, and until late in 1955 he continued to do good, solid radio programs.

It was my good fortune to appear once as a guest on a Benny show and to observe at first hand the operations that made his half-hours appear so effortless. What went on in the way of conferences and planning before Saturday afternoon, I do not know; I was asked to appear at Benny's house in Palm Springs at two P.M. for a reading of the script and, knowing how radio rehearsals are conducted, I considered myself prompt at 2:15. By that time the script had been read to the halfway mark and to my cue. We went on from there and finished in about fifteen minutes; the cast dispersed and I was asked to come to the theater from which the broadcast would originate about an hour before air time on Sunday. There, in a small room, Jack and the cast were making final cuts while on the stage the musical numbers were being rehearsed; the commercials were to be piped in from somewhere else. There was no dress rehearsal, no complete run-through, no accurate timing—and this program had another nonprofessional besides myself, as well as Dennis Day returning from service to greet his fans prior to joining the program officially. The sheer professionalism of everyone concerned in the production was magnificent—and, without a signal that I could see, without haste or worry, the program marched to its exact conclusion twenty-nine and a half minutes after it began.

In all this Benny was the old pro, to be sure; he had done hundreds of these and why should he worry? He was also the complete professional in another way. His writers were there; they had supplied the script. But Benny was there also. Out of all the possible ways of handling the theme, he had chosen the one he felt was best; and whenever he came to a line that he was doubtful about, particularly if it was for him to speak, he would discuss it. He once even asked me whether I thought a line was funny *the way he said it*. Again and again he would drop a line or two because, as he said, it was right for someone else, not for him. I have seen Durante do much the same thing at rehearsal—it is the creative part of the comedian's work when he is not, as Fred Allen had been, his own writer. For each comedian it is composed of a shrewd assessment of his own talents plus an instinct about audiences; in the assessment, the good comedians are not apt to overrate themselves.

The writers of the program on which I appeared were Sam Perrin, George Balzer, Jack Tackaberry, and Milton Josefsberg, and I mention them because they accomplished the miracle of making me seem very funny indeed; and this, in turn, I mention because the occasion was typical of a sort of inventiveness which Benny encouraged in spite of the dreadful routining of comedy shows. I had written a paragraph in *Esquire* protesting against the reduction of virtually all air comedy to jokes about Jolson's age, Benny's miserliness, and a few other insults. I had said that there were other sources of fun, and had even mentioned the pervasive sweetness of the Durante shows. Benny's response was to do the first half of his program as usual and then do it all over again with a cloying gentility in place of the cracks. My part, I understood, was to take a bow as the author of the protest. Actually, I had been written in through most of the second half, and, although I had never before spoken a word "in character" nor a word I had not written for myself, the dialogue assigned me was bright and at one or two moments insanely funny. The attack on the Benny style was given a hearing, the parody was as extravagant as the original, and my exit line was an insult to Benny which left him apparently defeated. When we talked about the program, Benny said that he liked to break from his routine but recognized the fatality that the breaks can become routine also—as when he devoted most of a season to a contest for the best ending to the sentence beginning "I hate Jack Benny because. . . ." The risk of suggesting a critical approach was not too great, but the atmosphere of non-idolatry was implied, and this, for an air star, is dangerous enough.

In one of the celebrated and spurious feuds on the air, Benny replied to a sharp remark from Fred Allen with his own best: "You wouldn't dare say that if I had my writers with me." The odd thing is that it does not matter whether at that moment he did or did not have his writers— because the line is inside Benny's dramatic character. He is himself a rather thoughtful person, easy to talk to, making no effort whatever at wit; but his own judgment of what is funny for him and even for other people is infallible. He does not always insist upon his judgment as regards the structure of an entire show, and, as happens often enough, when an idea has been developed to a certain point, it cannot be summarily dropped. There may not be time to prepare another, and all one can do is patch and improve. Some of Benny's TV appearances have been of this kind, particularly those in which he has featured himself as an actor. He has been casting about for a style for himself, and the best he has done is to be something like the radio character, which is a composite of the eternal victim ("he who gets slapped"), the supermiser, and the insensitive fellow who is convinced that he is universally admired. In various guises these characters have appeared again and again, and sometimes the variations have been exceedingly delicate. During the holiday season at the end of 1953, Benny played a beautiful role —the man so sure of himself that he has not made a date for New Year's Eve and then watches one group after another drift away from him, finds himself rejected by those he knows, shouldered out of the way by strangers he tries to join, and then, utterly forlorn, goes home, but tries for a moment to brazen it out before Rochester (who is infinitely more resplendent, in white tie and tails, than his employer, and is moreover about to start out jubilantly for what promises to be the best party in the world). Rochester sees through the deception, and one of the most touching comedy scenes ever done in television follows: the two men sit down together and drink champagne and talk to each other. There were "social values" outside the range of comedy there, too, but they could not have existed if the characters had not been so soundly and solidly created before us. A professional critic seldom feels grateful to a performer for being good; he takes it for granted. This was an exceptional occasion. The professional satisfaction I had in seeing a job well done turned into profound gratitude that Benny had wanted to do this particular kind of program. It was the work of a good citizen and a sensitive and intelligent man.

18

THE GLEASON CASE

Comedy is a dangerous field for fighting over taste, public or individual. The area has been strewn with mines—prejudice and pride
and semantic follies are all over the place. I am aware of this in approaching the case of Jackie Gleason, in many ways the most prodigious,
although not the greatest, figure in the comic field. He is a test case for
the critic and for the average man as well—because Gleason's comedy is
composed of so many different elements, of such a range of qualities,
that his admirers make almost as many reservations and have almost as
many preferences as the critics. The Caesar-Coca team was as various in
materials, but nearer to one level of quality; Berle has nothing like
Gleason's range, and you like him altogether or not at all. With Gleason all the attitudes toward comedy are brought into play, the strange
mixture of self-defense and aggression with which people react to criticism of what has made them laugh.

For it is the commonest of experiences to go on the defensive if we
have praised a comedian and someone says, "He isn't funny." It is also
common enough to find ourselves saying, "You think *that's* funny?"
precisely to assert a kind of superiority—in taste, in judgment, in experience. We are offended when our preference is belittled in literature
or interior decoration or music, but when our response to comedy is
questioned we become hypersensitive and most particularly so when we

laugh and are told, in effect, that we are braying. We may try to believe
that the person who does not laugh is merely pretending to be superior,
but there is always the uneasy feeling that perhaps he *is* superior. I do
not know whether anyone has discovered why we are a little ashamed
of some of the antics we find amusing. Certainly we begin to have mis-
givings about comedians and comic acts we have really enjoyed when
we come up against intellectuals who follow the classic Victorian line
and are not amused.

These are psychological problems, and all I can do is connect them
with my own interests: the shapes that comedy takes in popular entertainment, the techniques for getting various kinds of laughter, and the
response of the audience, which is almost always a mixture of elements
ranging from love of the comedian to self-satisfaction in catching his
comedy. In that complexity, it seems natural for us to laugh and at times
wonder why we laugh and perhaps be a little ashamed, in an unimportant way, for having laughed. The same thing happens in many other
responses we make—we are ashamed at times of our anger and bewil-
dered by our love. So that a faint regret at having laughed too easily is
not a symptom of a bad intellectual conscience. But when we are uncertain of ourselves and become aggressive, we are likely to fall back on
"*You* don't think it's funny—" when our taste is impugned and find
ourselves presently involved in the stupidities about "a sense of humor."

Manifestations of this celebrated sense and reflections of what people
think about it are frequent in television comedy, and it might be as
well to keep the atmosphere clear. We can escape the idea prevalent in
Hollywood that top executives who play practical jokes on their under-
lings do have a sense of humor and their victims do not. When Joe
Frisco stuttered his sardonic compliments to big shots or Dorothy
Parker let wicked lightning play through her reports on people regardless of size, they risked the next meal or the next job. But executive
pranksters were secure and could even impose their judgment on the
community—that the victim of the hotfoot has no sense of humor if he
suspects that a bit of malice or envy or sadism has been injected into
the good clean fun. One of our common phrases about the more civilized forms of "kidding" expresses our skepticism: "He can dish it out,
but can he take it, too?" The man who can do both is a folk hero. We
admire also the man or woman who says "the joke's on me." But these

are not the responses to calculated humiliation inflicted by people who are themselves secure. Even in the more pleasant area of good-humored kidding, all we are asking is for people to see how funny they look when they slip on a banana peel, to enjoy being "had" and to admire the artfulness of the booby-trap into which they have been led. If this is a sense of humor and if a sense of humor is nothing else, it is neither rare nor supremely valuable.

And it certainly has little enough to do with thinking that a joke or a scene or an act is or is not funny. Let us call this the sense of comedy, the perception of what is funny and what is not, on the printed page, on the sawdust, on the screen. This perception differs among individuals and among groups. The response to irony, for instance, is a highly complex one, and the fact that a considerable amount of the ordinary conversation of the English, in all classes of society, is in the mode of under-statement makes them more alert to the ironic approach than we are; whereas the mode of exaggeration is so natural to us that we cannot be-lieve the British do not respond to it—we think they are suppressing their inclination to laugh or that "the British have no sense of humor."

We recognize these differences in perception, which are almost identi-cal with differences in taste, and we try to establish a pure democracy in the empire of fun—absolute equality between one performance and an-other. It will not work, and "I say it is funny" does not satisfy even the man who says it because there are easily recognized levels of taste. The most generous upholder of the theory of de gustibus or chacun à has to come down to plain English and admit that, while there is something essentially funny about the man on the banana peel, it can amuse children much longer than it can amuse adults. At each phase (five years or so) of a child's growth, its sense of what is funny changes—and so we come to the tastes of normal adults, and from this it is not too hard to go on to the difference between those who have developed fully in the range and depth of their emotions and those who have remained half-grown. Omitting both intellectual standards and moral judgments, it is possible to say that the comedy of Bringing Up Father is of a lower order, because it calls into play less of the faculties and feelings, than the comedy of Life with Father. (And for an admirer of Clarence Day's work to pretend that this is not so, or to keep silent when the question is put, is sheer intellectual cowardice.) The moral judgment is that it is "bad" to like Bringing Up Father; the intellectual error is not to be aware of orders of excellence; and the sin is to be aware of them and to yield to the pressure of popularity.

It is interesting to apply these principles to the case of Jackie Gleason. He is, as I have said, the great test case for the critic and the amateur. For to like him in the way one likes Durante is to exercise freedom of taste, but it is also to show lack of discrimination; and, on the other side, to dislike him, which comes easily enough, and for that reason to deny his copious talents, is to show lack of detached critical judgment. (As frequently happens, when a critic describes the ideal critic, he is describing himself—I find Gleason distasteful and prodigiously skillful, and the combination is irritating.)

Gleason gives me the feeling that success has rendered him insecure, that he was happier, less aware of his inferiority, easier on the nerves of the audience, when he was on the small Dumont network. Translated to the big time, he began to press in all directions, a process known generally as throwing his weight around, which is an exact description of Gleason's most characteristic movements before the camera. He is a heavy man with the traditional belief of heavy men in their own lightness and grace, and he sashays and pirouettes with a faint and entirely inoffensive suggestion of effeminacy—he is so definitely one of the mob. He has been so since the raucous days of the Club 18, where he was part of a bomb that exploded ten times a night—a bomb made up of commonness and noise and insult and a sort of roaring impropriety which was altogether exhilarating. Gleason advancing toward the camera, saying to the audience at home, "Oh, boy, you're a good group tonight," is only the reversal of the merciless attack on the character of anyone who happened to come into Club 18—and his comedy still has, at times, the directness of the questions to which patrons of the Club were often subjected when they tried to go to the lavatories. This is all on the good side; it has vitality and combines some of the feel of the rowdier night clubs with a little of the tone of the stag party, hitting the audience over the head but not too often for comfort.

With this goes Gleason's inordinate concentration on himself, so intense that it often blanks out his genuine talent. He has composed, produced, and conducted (in white tie and tails) a most unbearably flossy ballet of Harlem, long and tedious in spite of its reminders of Gershwin's *125th Street* and Rodgers' *Slaughter on Tenth Avenue*.

He has not only formed a corporation to take care of his own interests (which is standard practice for comedians); he produces his own summer replacements, and when his new contract called for no more than half an hour a week, he undertook to produce the preceding half-hour on the air and conceived the grandiose scheme of filling virtually all of Saturday night on CBS by taking over an hour or more of the time directly following his own show for one of the costliest and most elaborate revues ever offered for sponsorship.

There is, to be sure, nothing wrong with these activities, and I mention them only because they reflect one facet of Gleason's work as a comedian. He began to be known because he made a point of presenting himself in various characters: a bartender, a rich ne'er-do-well, and a number of others. This was unusual. Most comedians played themselves or, like Benny, did not act but pretended to be the stereotyped figure of the cheapskate and social climber; their sketches were charades. Gleason's were dramatic, and there was genuine characterization behind all the exaggerated costume and gestures of Reggie on Park Avenue and all the harshness, often too realistic to be funny, of Ralph Kramden, the bus-driver. The last of these is the only one that proved to have staying-power, and part of its success, a large part, is a tribute to the excellence of Audrey Meadows and Art Carney, and to Gleason himself for giving these two remarkable players their due place in the foreground.

As the Gleason show mounted in public favor, this series of sketches, under the inappropriate name of *The Honeymooners*, pushed all the other elements of the hour into the background; moreover, it showed those extraordinary symptoms of life which artificial and even mechanical inventions often display. An element of the preposterous dwindled almost to the vanishing point and even farcical rigged-up situations were attached to something genuine—as when the whole Kramden living room, generally described as "crummy," is transformed with furniture borrowed from neighbors and appliances sent in on approval because the Kramdens want to adopt an orphan and must impress an investigator. The mixups and embarrassments about the furnishings can be expected; also traditional is Ralph's fury when the child turns out to be a girl. But the central emotion is genuine, and the two characters of Ralph and Alice are sustained with an inner light. A few years earlier the sketches were played for laughs at all costs and the occasional pathos was applied from the outside. I recall a longish episode in which Ralph was simultaneously rehearsing his address as principal speaker at the annual convention of the Friends of the Muskrat (or another improbable animal) and worrying because his trousers had not been returned by the tailor. It was all mishaps and banging doors and recriminations until at the end Ralph discovered that he was not to be the speaker after all. In his moment of black despair Alice said, "Never mind, Ralph, to me you'll always be the most important friend of the Muskrat," and the scene managed the rare combination of the ridiculous and the touching, although there had been nothing genuine to prepare us.

The similarity to *Ethel and Albert* is apparent; the difference, as Gleason's material is developed, is that Ethel and Albert are fond of each other after a long siege of married life; Ralph and Alice dramatize the bickering of the loveless, and the emotion delivered with the authentic ring of truth is actual dislike. This does not occur too often as a major theme, but it sounds loud and clear once or twice in each sketch, giving bite and an acceptable unloveliness to the program. Inflated to a half-hour sketch, the harshness is too much because the farcical situations and the tepid endings are wrong in key. When Alice and Trixie (who is the wife of Ed, the sewer-digger) complain that their husbands always go out bowling and to smokers and as a rule leave their wives at home seven nights a week, we are seeing the groundwork of a comedy laid, for presently husbands and wives will go out together with disastrous results; but in the groundwork we get a scene of high-pitched recrimination between Ralph and Alice which reminds us of voices overheard across areaways and on back porches just before doors slam or crockery is smashed. The difficulty of getting comedy out of this material is clear. The studio audience is supposed to be more suggestible than the audience at home, but it sat through the scene I have just described without any response beyond the closest attention. Then the laugh lines began to come up, and the reaction was illuminating. Stung by Alice's complaints, but determined to get his bowling in just the same, Ralph shouted and complained about her cooking and then, as a sort of parting shot, cried out, "Just for that, when I come home, I won't tell you who won." (Silence.) Alice said, "From this blow I'll never recover." (Silence.) Ralph made a fist and shook it violently in her face and said, "From *this* blow you'll never recover." (Very loud laughter and applause.) Actually, his threat in the previous line, taken with the expression of long-suffering contempt on the face of Audrey Meadows, was the essential comic line, but the audience apparently was waiting for the payoff in the angry and unpleasant battle between husband and wife and got it in the frustrated gesture of violence.

The prime virtue of this series, which employs half a dozen writers, is that it is almost totally unsentimental. Its defect is that the plots are as contrived as the characters are simple. And in the playing of the sketches, the two basic styles of television acting are in conflict, for Audrey Meadows and Art Carney are by this time submerged in their characters, while Gleason still manages at times to triumph over Ralph Kramden, letting us see Gleason acting a part. Although I am a professional critic, I cannot be sure that I would be conscious of this if I had never seen Gleason in the other portions of his shows, as the teller of jokes, the manipulator of the audience, the MC, and so on. In all these other manifestations he presents a personality, in the press agent's sense of the word—a concentration of a number of unlikable attributes, the most striking of which seems to be an incapacity to show fondness or admiration for others. This has nothing to do with the character of the citizen who has the same name off the screen—I am speaking of the character projected to us. Getting this sense of the character, I resist Gleason as an artist, I think he is below first-rate. But the power of television being what it is, with its unparalleled capacity to arouse highly personal emotions about people seen on its screen, I must in all candor say that if I dislike Gleason and still find him only short of first-rate, he must be a prodigiously talented individual. A good director might do for him what good writers and good directors have done for Berle; but Gleason will make millions of dollars as he is, and this may relieve him from worry about my judgment and the judgment of the future—which may not, after all, be identical.

19

"ME AND THE CAMERA

AND THE FOLKS . . ."

In a way, it is unfair to put Jimmy Durante anywhere in the neighborhood of Berle and Gleason—unfair to them and unfair to him, because the moment you begin to talk about Durante the tone of affection creeps into the critical voice, and this is true of millions of people who know him only as a professional. This intrusion of emotion often gives the impression that Durante is considered great because he is "lovable" whereas the others are the real talents. This is, moreover, somewhat reinforced because he is like a force of nature; you do not analyze the whirlwind and you do not analyze Durante. I find that when I want to say exactly what he is, I call him the great comic spirit of our time, not the great comedian, not even the great comic artist, which he very well may be. It is not by accident that the name of Bill Fields, whom I knew very slightly, is set beside that of Jimmy Durante, whom I know fairly well; for, in spite of all difference in their endowments, Durante is and Fields was possessed by the wild daemon of laughter. Everyone else we call comic, except one, is less endowed. The one, Chaplin, is greater because his range of interests, in thought and in emotion, is greater, and he moves entirely out of the strict category of comedy to communicate all he has to say. As between Fields and Durante, both can be called unlettered, but Fields was pretty much of an intellectual in his attitude toward some fundamental aspects of life, and Durante is not.

At the height of his career, Chaplin could not see himself outside of the special kind of comic situation he had created. He despised the belt system of production and was annoyed at the coming of sound to the movies, an event that made Chaplin look back on the silent days of the movies as a sort of rustic Paradise without motorcars, power-driven cameras, and the whole apparatus of picture-making. He was angry and apprehensive, but his way of tackling the subject was by comedy: *Modern Times*. When the subject came even closer, he still tried comedy in *Monsieur Verdoux*, which may turn out to be the greatest of his pictures but is certainly not the best comedy. It was created while Chaplin was under merciless and hypocritical attack for the commonest of moral lapses. He dramatized a series of relations with women, which might be taken as a portion of autobiography, and, contrary to the custom of personal literature, he made his hero-self morally worse than he himself had ever been accused of being—he made him a murderer. That he was still able to create a comedy around Verdoux is a final tribute to his genius.

The essential difference between Chaplin and Durante is exactly this power that Chaplin has of seeing a subject in its comic aspect, because Durante does not, fundamentally, see the subject at all; he sees only the comedy. You might say that he has no general ideas, no abstractions, as Chaplin certainly has. The quality they have in common is one they share with all the great clowns: the power to make us laugh and feel happy because we are laughing. Chaplin can also make us laugh without making us happy. Durante can, on rare occasions, be touching, but this is totally outside the range of his comedy; he is not touching when he is being funny, and Chaplin often is. I am one of those who will not separate Chaplin from the knockabout music-hall turns and the Keystone comedies where he absorbed the essentials of his art, and I am also among those who think that his incomparable greatness, rooted in these things, has flowered into a complete harmonious fusion of many other arts. Those who weep and beg Chaplin to go back to his baggy pants are, if they are sincere about it, asking for the return of their youth more than his; they want him to have died young and deplore his maturity perhaps because he compels them to face their own age. If I call Durante, rather than Chaplin, the great comic spirit of our age, it is because the particular roaring laughter, the uncontrollable, almost unbearable laughter Durante can bring out, may be an inheritance from

Chaplin, but it is now his, and the tone of that laughter, which is the tone of pure joy, no one else can evoke.

We come here to a paradox surprising to no one who has thought two minutes about the business of entertainment: it lives, or thinks it must live, on comedy, and its measure of comedy is statistical. Laughs are clocked: how many and how many seconds. Laughs are measured on the decibel scale; but the comedians describe laughs viscerally, with the belly laugh at one end of the scale and the titter at the other, and this is the only way in which the profession recognizes the fact that laughs differ *in quality* as well as in volume and duration. The clockers, who are not the creators of laughs, have reached the point where they do not need them: they have recorded all kinds of laughs on film, and they put in just as much of this canned laughter as seems advisable, shrewdly estimating what an audience reaction might be to one joke as compared with another, making sure that the half-hour of comedy has the correct total of laughs to make the home audience feel that it has witnessed something extremely funny. The canned laughter of filmed comedy carries a step further the deception that began years ago in the induced laughter of the studio audiences in radio, the obedient cackles and clappings when the sign was held up in the days before it was discov-

THE GREAT LAUGH

Bob Hope made a kinescope for one of his programs in London. As presented here later it included gales of laughter (coming from the British audience, apparently), including an outburst of glee over a mention of the pitching staff of the Cleveland Indians.

There are moments when one wonders whether canned laughs or genuine ones are the most depressing feature of TV comedy.

ered that a studio audience needs no prompting but only a little guidance as to noise level and duration.

There should be two names, one for the debased and degrading manufactured article and one for the sound of happiness. I have tried, as far as possible, to call one "laughs" and the other "laughter." I remember the way the great Fratellini troupe was billed at the Cirque Medrano in Paris: "the true and inimitable Kings of Laughter." That is what Jimmy Durante is for us in our time, the true King of Laughter, and, like the Fratellinis, he reminds us that laughter reverberates from the past. Even if his name were not Italian, even if his great nose did not instantly remind us of a picture in an old storybook, we would feel that Durante was doing what people must always have done when they wanted others to rock with laughter—which is what we mean when we say that he is in the great tradition. The misleading name of that tradition is *commedia dell'arte*, and any reference to it is nowadays considered pedantry. But I have seen Clayton, Jackson, and Durante do exactly what the characters of the old Italian comedy used to do—start off with a prepared or remembered bit and then go on, like great virtuosos in a jam session, watching one another in surprise and admiration, joining in to help, to rival, and, above all, to create. The first time they did their "Wood" number before an audience, they barely knew the lines of the lyric, but before they were through they had drawn on every wooden object in the night club to demonstrate their glorification of wood. An inventive fury took hold of them. Neither the moldings on the mirrors nor the ruder objects in the lavatories were safe, and as they shouted, and shook with delight in one another's unpremeditated dashes into new territory, they were not only the inheritors of the art of laughter, they were making it over again.

I have outlined the professional career of Jimmy Durante in connection with Garry Moore, who was so useful to him at the turning-point, and I have also noted that the producers of his various shows have worked just as hard to destroy or conceal his unique quality as they have to exploit it. This is quite natural. His sponsors and their deputies know that there is no one quite like him in the world of entertainment, but producing a program over a period of ten months may involve a million dollars in costs and may establish or jeopardize the prestige of a motor oil or a motorcar. A program merely unsuccessful can bring an agency close to ruin; a genuinely maladroit program might start a man-

ufacturer down a toboggan. The psychological consequence is to rein-
sure one's self, to add an ingredient, a "plus": the elegant male and
female stars who introduce dramatic films, the guests on programs that
do not need them—that sort of thing. In Durante's case, the foundation is himself—in relation to a number of stock elements: pretty girls,
guest stars, a small band. The added ingredient is whatever everyone
else is doing at the time: situation comedy, or fantasy, or bigness. At
the close of one season Durante wanted to do a show recalling the
favorite numbers of his night-club career. He was overruled, and television tried to cope with a capsule edition of his old extravaganza
Jumbo, circus and drama and glaring open moments, which went against
all of his instincts. It is not out of egotism that Durante keeps asking for
scenes that are, as he puts it, "me and the camera and the folks out
there." It is out of a precise knowledge of what he wants to do and
what prevents him from doing it.

He wants to do something that no one else among our major comic
stars seems to care much about doing. He wants to make fun so that
people will have a good time, and he wants to do this for their sake, not
for his, cheerfully knocking himself out to give pleasure, being super-
charged with galvanic energy when he is in the company of people
who love him, hurling himself into boundless activity—and doing this
with such self-effacement that you do not think of him, only of what he
is doing. It is the perfect night-club technique, of course—the bonhomie, and the pace, and the invisible join where one thing ends and
another begins so that the patron has not a second to wonder whether
he is having as good a time as he thinks he is. But even in the night club,
Jimmy Durante and the team of which he was the center were quite
unusual. They worked as hard and broke as many props and yelled as
loud as anyone—but they were not the Ritz Brothers, they were not like
any of the hard, bright headliners. They came closer than anyone else to
making a night club pleasant as well as exciting. To keep up the
vast fundamental pretense of the night-club atmosphere—that the management and the patrons and the account executives and the out-of-
town buyers are all equally carefree and gay—is hard enough, and even
the highly charged Jimmy could not swing it when the team opened a
club on the day in 1929 when the bottom definitely dropped out of
the market. The atmosphere of the early clubs in which he worked was
cozier than in the big places that are now the only ones able to afford

him, and there was always a rumor that gangsters were in the background, which was agreeable and almost common form in those days. (The story that Jimmy Durante was told to star in a revue "or else," with the additional element that the revue was financed by a prince of bootleggers for his girl friend, is an exaggeration, but it is not a fabricated piece of publicity.) All these elements, the business side and the expense-account side (which was beginning to be important when Durante began) and the background of beer halls in Coney Island, the sense that if he had been a singing waiter he would have been a pleasant one, are part of the variety of experience making it possible for him to like everyone who is not mean and to radiate his liking so that everyone falls under his spell.

He is not an actor and consequently has never been able to use the basic material of that kind of comedy which is rather grandly called "the comedy of insult." At a time when a subspecies of this Coward-Woollcott-Kaufman genre had become the staple of radio comedy, with the trenchant debunking of *The Man Who Came to Dinner* (low-level though it was) debased to jeers about Jolson's age or Benny's avarice or Crosby's wealth or the repulsiveness of minor players, the character Durante projected was as transparently and limpidly sweet as he is himself. The character was and has remained a version of Durante, larger than life, but not inflated, not exaggerated to impress us—only made bolder and clearer so that we can take him in, so that he can reach us across the barrier of the air. For Durante's communication has always been entirely from heart to heart. His great success came in the night club, and when he failed in a musical show or in the movies, it was because the flow from him to the audience was interrupted. As I have suggested, the unexpected triumph in radio was enormously helped by Garry Moore, who represented the audience and so became the transmission belt from Durante to the people at home.

Durante's limitations are his greatest asset—next to his genius. What he does not apprehend as comedy, he cannot put over; he has not enough technical resources to make things seem funnier than they are to him. In his business even the greatest stars are always doing what a dozen people, from sponsors to hangers-on, urge or advise or compel them to do. Durante does not entirely escape, but, for all the sweetness of his character, he has a saving obstinacy; he will not do what he cannot do naturally, and he constantly reverts to himself. The difference between "being a clown" and acting the part of a clown, which I noted in connection with the movies, is perfectly clear in that part of television lying between the instant fact and the imagined drama, and Durante is a great instance of the right way to work in this field. He is, to be sure, always himself or playing a version of himself, but he is not advertising his private personality. He offers himself where others exploit themselves. You see him, and if you think what a sweet guy he is, the chances are that you are still thinking of the entertainer rather than the man. As an entertainer, he has the fault of "breaking up," going out of the framework of a sketch, when he does not understand the action or forgets his lines, and here the candor and general niceness of his personality are of great help. But, for all the galvanic energy he generates on the screen, his program is not egocentric. His characteristic action is like his characteristic speech: it is an attack on the complexities of life, which mystify him and seem unnecessary, so he does his best, shattering a polysyllable or a keyboard, and all the time being, as he once called it, "exhubilant." He is uninhibited, untutored, with an instinct for the comic that is unerring in selecting what is right and what is not right for himself.

And an instinct for pathos. His pathos has to be totally separated from his comedy, to be sure, or it does not come off. The devotion he and Eddie Jackson have for the memory of their third partner, Lou Clayton, is touching, and at the Copacabana it is possible, in the late hours perhaps, to revive some of their simpler numbers, with a spotlight moving on the floor for Clayton, but the clash between the emotion and the noise and fun that went before is destructive. On the air, Durante's sign-off, beginning with the half mystifying and half mischievous "Good night, Mrs. Calabash, wherever you are" and proceeding to a remarkably effective exit "into the night," turning for another look where spots of light lie like flagstones, diminishing into the background, is good. It is the departure of a man of feeling, the traditional other ego of the clown, but with no overflow of sentiment. And when Durante first walked into a deserted night-club set, on one of his programs, sat down at a table, and sang "September Song," he created one of the half-dozen most memorable episodes in television. There was for a moment the fear that he had been persuaded to do a parody, and then an apprehension that his long triumph with comic materials would make it impossible for him to carry off the real feeling of the song—the sadness, the hope, the reproach to the fleeting years. But it was all perfect, and—on that first occasion at least, unspoiled by production or camera tricks—it was Durante, a man singing a song, melancholy and not slopped over. And it was perfect.

It was "me and the camera and the folks out there," it was Durante doing the right job, letting the camera take him into the homes and without hesitation into the hearts of his audience. This time he did it with material new for him, but right for him because he understood it. It was not a stunt. When the number was repeated some weeks later, either Durante or his producers had become self-conscious, and it impressed some people as being arty. This could be. But we ought not to complain if he failed to communicate entirely the sadness of love as long as he communicates so unfailingly the laughter that rises out of love.

20

"WHAT'LL WE DO FOR

LAUGHS, CELESTE?"

Endless questions can be asked about the consequences of our addiction to comedy—by the statesman, the social worker, the moralist, the artist. Of them all, one is most important: Does the prevalence of comedy prevent us from having as much of other entertainment as we might be getting? Phrased in this way, the question answers itself, for obviously any half-hour taken by a comic program is a half-hour not given to another type. But this is the only way to ask the question without implying a moral judgment that at this moment I do not wish to make. I therefore approach the matter from another side, with a cue from the attractive and talented Celeste Holm.

Miss Holm has recounted in some detail the discussions that preceded her appearance in a TV series of her own. With enough versatility and ambition, Miss Holm wanted to place herself in dramatic situations of considerable range; in particular, she wanted to do a series that would show "the impact upon the lives of people throughout the world, of decisions made by the United Nations." To every suggestion the reply was the same: "What'll we do for laughs, Celeste?" It was not only the last word on the proposed series, but on the program that was produced—they got their laughs where everyone else got them, out of farcical situations just like all the others, in a series affording little pleasure to the audience, less to the sponsors, none to the star, and ironically called *Honestly, Celeste!*

I have noted elsewhere the pressure of the commercial style by which certain program material becomes unacceptable because sponsors want only the shows in which the star will do the commercial. As always, the advantage of the free-enterprise system shows itself—there are other sponsors. Yet the fact is that the area of enterprise grows smaller whenever such limitations are imposed. When a sponsor says he wants comedy and nothing but comedy, he is saying in effect that he can get a bigger audience, of the kind he wants, with a laugh program. When he says the star must do the commercial, he shows awareness of one of the imperfections of the broadcasting system—you may have an audience, a big audience, but not an audience persuaded to buy your commodity. (This has happened in the case of newscasters, conspicuously.) To make sure of the sale, the sponsor wants the star as pitchman. If Judith Anderson and Katharine Cornell should refuse to praise creams and girdles, the classic drama starring them would be displaced by a program with Hollywood stars who are more flexible, stars who can be discovered in their dressing rooms, a moment after playing Ibsen or O'Neill, ready to thank the director, praise the sponsor, and, if necessary, demonstrate the product. It is not in the tradition of Charles Frohman and David Belasco, who prevented their greatest stars from being seen in public dining rooms, but the change in manners is not so important as the shrinking circumference outside of which programs are less and less likely to be produced.

With this runs the insistent pressure to get a little comedy into the act, whatever the act may be, and whenever this is mentioned a scholarly reference to the drunken Porter in *Macbeth* may be expected. This is reasonable, but not too appropriate. In television the Porter would be Macbeth in disguise—for laughs. Shakespeare's clowns and grave-diggers and porters are comic relief and they do not alter the essential nature of the plays in which they appear, whereas our script editors start with excited emotions, not deep ones, and end by destroying the intensity of all other responses in order to be sure of their laughs. TV daytime serials and some factual police melodramas have resisted the demand for laughs. For the rest, programs must be constructed with plenty of openings for the hotfoot of comedy: the discussion of contemporary affairs, the battle of wits, the revival of a classic, the serious play, each and all must have an answer to the recurrent question, "What'll we do for laughs, Celeste?"

I propose to list here the more intelligent explanations of the prevalence of comedy. This is, to be sure, an evasion of critical duty, but it has the advantage of scope and variety. The range is from one extreme to the other: the demand for comedy is so intense because the American people are (a) the happiest or (b) the most frustrated people in the world; and a third explanation combines or synthesizes the others: we need so much comedy because we are (a) and/or (b). In this magic formula all doubts can be resolved. We are happy because we are victims of illusions (of wealth, of youth, of personal success), and at moments, as we pierce through illusion to reality, we are dissatisfied with life and console ourselves "having fun."

There is the sexual variation of this basic theme. Next to the English, who are Anglo-Saxons and therefore, by definition, full of suppressions, the Americans, who are not Anglo-Saxons, tell the longest, dullest, and dirtiest of smutty stories. (This has to be assumed.) Prevented by custom from hearing such stories on the air, the public demands a substitute—and the act of laughing becomes a sort of sexual release.

The old, wise European, the Oriental sage, do not require so much diversion. On the other hand, their civilizations have for centuries been grounded in want, in insufficient food, in a class struggle that has stratified society—and ours is the first civilization in which at least two-thirds of a nation are well housed, well clothed, and well fed. That is why we can laugh. (I confess that this pro-capitalist economic interpretation seems sensible to me.)

I have myself been more interested in a group of ideas connecting the psychology of the audience with the apparatus for making the audience laugh. Obviously there is more laughter than there ever was before —or, at worst, there are more laughs. If laughter had size and weight, we should all be crushed under its bulk by now, and this is because the machinery can duplicate the stimulus of laughter without end—from the printed page through the pressed music disc to the film.

On the assumption that the belt system of production dulled the perceptions and the appetites of the workers and made them want the easiest laughs in quantity, we can say that the system provided its own antidote: only mechanically produced laughter could satisfy the demand that mechanized labor created. The comic strip arrived before the belt came to Detroit, to be sure, but we were already moving out of the farm-and-small-town era; we were becoming urbanized, and subways and trolley cars were as impressive in their time as streamliners and motorcars a generation later. The entertainment of the last decade before the Maxwell and the Essex and the Ford arrived in huge quantities had been the minstrel show tapering off into oblivion, the melodrama, the problem play, the musical show, the circus, and vaudeville —all of which reached the middle-sized town—with the burlesque wheel where it was accepted. This was also the time of the romantic historical novel and of the imaginary kingdom; there was a special form of fiction for the hammock trade. Also, dozens of humorous features began to be syndicated, some of them in dialect.

The one thing that era did not have was a single dominant mechanical form of entertainment, although the phonograph came close to it. The phonograph, in fact, provides a clue to another mystification, for when it began it used a lot of comic recitations ("Cohen on the Telephone" is now a collector's item). These have almost completely disappeared (although they exist, in bits and pieces, in television). At the same time, the comic strip designed to stimulate laughter has departed, and the incidence of comedy in the movies, which was never marked, has reached the vanishing-point: the Keystone comedy and the more polite situations of Sidney Drew were enlarged into features; Harold Lloyd and Buster Keaton and Chaplin, plus all the second-string men, had a long run, some of them moving across the sound barrier; the Marx Brothers ticked off one masterpiece after another, and Bill Fields did the same. But the grand staple of the movies was in the serial and the Western, the pure melodrama and the topical melodrama, the historical romance and the exploitations of sex and beauty and personality. All of these can be called forms of romance—to which, it is known, comedy can be fatal.

We are not called on to say that one kind of entertainment is always better than another, or that the past was better than the present. We can regret that certain types of entertainment have vanished on the general ground that we can always use variety—and this is really the only moral judgment for which I see any justification. A vast amount of entertainment is supplied to us, but almost all of it lies within a narrow zone of interest, appealing for two or three simple responses to a group of people so vast as to be called loosely "the public." But this bulk of entertainment leaves untouched other responses within its own public and does not attempt in the slightest way to serve another audience, smaller than the majority but far too big to be denied some representation on the air that belongs to all the people.

Yet a good part of the comedy now on the air can satisfy the average intelligent man or woman. Much of it comes from experts trained in the earlier schools of vaudeville and radio; some of it comes from new arrivals, like George Gobel, with careers as local entertainers. While a lot of comedy still seems to be trying to see how low you can get in the scale of taste and wit, a contrary direction can be marked also —in a smaller degree, but definite enough to encourage the hopeful. As far as comedy raises problems, it is in the tradition of all the forms of mass entertainment—taking *mass* in the physical sense of the word, signifying the total amount of comic material broadcast (which is parallel to the idea of *mass* as the number of people entertained). British critics wonder whether "having fun" has become the major objective of American life, and when American social critics hear the long bray of nationwide enthusiasm for imitative comic acts, they wonder whether we are on the way to some kind of aesthetic or intellectual perdition. If we are, it is only because the quantity of comic stuff proliferating on the air may choke off the other normal species of entertainment.

And, looking at these other forms—the movies and the comic strip particularly—noting that comedy has become less essential to them, we come to the conclusion that comedy is so popular in broadcasting because the sponsors insist on it. And they insist on it not only because comedy attracts audiences, but also because it leaves audiences in a most favorable state for persuasion—the non-critical, gratified mood of consent, the mood most hospitable to the commercial message. As long as the sponsors believe this, comedy will continue to dominate the commercial networks, and the public appetite for non-comic programs may become so feeble that even pay-TV will not want to satisfy it. I do not think this is likely. For one thing, the producers of pay-TV can get their licenses only by promising to supply programs different, in part, from the commercial programs, and this means that, unlike our familiar networks, they can be held to strict account: the F.C.C. will be empowered to demand other kinds of entertainment. Even if the F.C.C.

THE SELL

No one has made a study of the radio-television commercial in relation to what it is trying to do, connecting the emphasis of the "sell" with the quality of the product, the competition in the field, and all the other essentials. We have taken the sponsor's word that all he is trying to do is sell goods.

The truth is that he is doing this, but the most conspicuous of the advertisers on the air are, for the most part, trying to get their competitor's customers away from them. Nine-tenths of all cigarette advertising urges the listener to drop whatever he is smoking and try this one. Many other commercials use this approach less blatantly. That is why the promises have to be so extravagant, the copy so loaded with tripled adjectives.

Of all the buyers of any brand of cigarette at any given moment, it is probable that ninety per cent are habitual or frequent users, yet broadcast copy is hardly ever addressed to them. They are supposed to be kept loyal to the brand by the spillover of the sales pitch addressed to the non-user—and at the same time they are left vulnerable to the competitor's appeal to switch.

A soup or a soap essentially like other soups and soaps has to offer something beyond soup- or soap-quality. Usually the promise is social advancement or eternal youth or success in love and in life. The voice has to be pitched high. The deep note of confidence might persuade your satisfied customer to continue—it cannot seduce the satisfied customers of your rivals.

The relevance of this to the essentials of entertainment is clear: if the commercial did not have to do the job of making people give up the brands they like, the pitch could be lower, the discourse more reasonable, and it would not be imperative to put the audience into the semi-comatose state that is necessary now—the state in which anything is believed if it is said often and loud enough. If the audience need not be left in a state of mental and emotional torpor, a wider variety of entertainments, appealing to sharper mental faculties and the deeper emotions, could also be offered.

uses this power, the non-comedy program will for a long time be fighting an uphill battle. The important thing is that if pay and free television fight for substantially the same audience, the quality of comedy will not, normally, rise. Only when the two kinds of broadcasting compete for audiences now left on the fringe of the sponsor's calculations can we expect any significant change. Is it important for us to have such a change?

I am haunted by the figure of a blind man whom I saw once a week over a period of several months, singing in the subway trains in New York City. He was a youngish man, robust, handsome, and with an agreeable clear voice. He made his way skillfully from one car to another during stops, sounded a chord on his metal guitar for attention, and began to sing as the train started again. The passengers dropped coins into the cups he carried. For nearly a month, every Saturday morning, I heard him sing "Tweed-lee, tweed-lee, tweed-lee dee," the second line of which is "I'm as happy as can be."

In general, I do not like to endow unimportant events or individuals with symbolic significance, but the semi-imbecilic syllables, the desperate assertion of happiness by the blind beggar, affected me so that I began to wonder whether the voices of doom for our culture, if not for our economy, might not be right for once. After a time the balladeer began to sing other popular songs, some of a revolting sentimentality, and when I made my last trip for the season he was offering the synthetic "Davy Crockett." None of these could exorcise the figure I had first encountered. It still seems to me worth speculating on the reasons why we are so determined to have our laughs prepared for us and separated from our private lives. And if our appetite for laughs is so demanding, to consider how to make sure that it is not exploited, but is decently and reasonably satisfied.

21

THE 52-MINUTE HOUR

The programs I have been considering are the staple commodities of television. They are not the ones broadcasters mention with hurt pride when they are accused of short-changing the public artistically, nor are they the ones likely to be mentioned in the case for the prosecution. Without exception, they were developed in radio and transformed into television, and both these processes represent the creative talent of these entertainments at all but the highest level—far more so than the "spectacular" productions of *Best Foot Forward* with the routines but without the talent of the original stage version, or the duplication in a studio of the mechanical effects of *Peter Pan*. The transmission of sports events has probably attracted to television larger audiences than all of its created programs, and it is quite possible that the greatest profit, in proportion to investment, in the broadcasting business was made by small radio stations playing recorded music all day and night. It is known that the first TV station ever to operate in the black from the day it went on the air began to transmit before the coaxial cable reached it and the owners, making a tidy fortune out of old movies, looked with distaste to the day when public demand for created programs would force them to join a network. Flagship stations of the networks also turn in a tidy profit by using movies at off hours, and this is totally unobjectionable (provided the commercials interspersed in them are not too frequent and too false, as they have been at times). It is, of course, morally desirable to have a high degree of creativeness and to have it widespread so that our entertainment remains varied and humanly interesting. But we can no more object to a TV station transmitting a film than we can complain because a magazine reproduces a painting.

When the non-creative takes the place of the creative, we are justified in wondering whether the managers of the entertainment business are being as farsighted in their own behalf and as considerate of the public needs as they ought to be. The stamped-out product of Hollywood has twice in forty years come close to ruining the movies. The faster pace of television has already brought disaster to individuals caught in their own routines. Yet, for psychological and economic reasons, routine is useful to broadcasting, and the seesaw between repetition and originality will probably be a permanent characteristic of

---

FIGURES ON THE SCREEN

By May 1956 more than 1,500 old feature films had been bought for television.

In a typical week, the New York flagship of the CBS network transmitted twenty-five different films. An independent station showed film twenty-nine times (running the same film several hours in succession). Another station showed the same film twice a day, five times a week. Elsewhere transmission of film has occupied as much as one-third the total time of a station on the air.

General Sarnoff, who, through RCA, dominates the National Broadcasting Company, warned the industry that it must create its own materials, that it could not afford to become a transmitter of entertainment devised for other purposes. In the week noted above, WRCA, the flagship station of NBC, transmitted exactly one film.

It is always agreeable to see precept followed in practice.

television. In one field the two forces have begun to conflict seriously, and as it is the field of the drama, the consequences may be significant.

The presentation of plays got off to a surprisingly good start in television with the production of hour-long dramatizations of novels or adaptations of contemporary drama in *Studio One* on CBS and in a few years the astounding feat of creating a genuine television style, with original materials, was accomplished in the *Television Playhouse* —which was as if the movies had produced *It Happened One Night* in 1927 (when the best they could do was *The Jazz Singer*). Both of these programs continued to be distinguished, with the customary ups and downs, for several years, and the roster of individuals to whom various degrees of credit must be given is too long for inclusion here; assuming that the original producer sets a tone and standard for a program, the high marks for TV drama must go to Worthington Miner for *Studio One* and to Fred Coe for the *Playhouse*. (Miner left CBS to do less interesting work at NBC, and control of the *Playhouse* was taken away from Coe.) Both of these series were good in all respects, with more tricks of the camera in the first, more creative writing talent in the second. For the future of television, the emphasis on the writer is incomparably the more important and seems to have been part of a deliberate plan of Coe's, who surrounded himself with a group of dramatists still too young to have had conspicuous success or failure on Broadway or in the movies and more than ready to adapt themselves to the facts of life in the TV studio. They exploited the latent possibilities of a new way of telling a dramatic story, and they chose those stories that television could tell best. Three of these writers reworked their plays for the stage or the movies—Horton Foote, N. Richard Nash, and Paddy Chayefsky—and the minor success they achieved in the second medium was proof, in a way, that they had done their work well in the first: they had written television, not theater, not movies. (*Marty* ranked 59th at the box office in 1955.)

Essentially their work is marked by a high concentration on character more than on action, and they reveal character in a series of small episodes rather than in a long-continued action. The techniques of television are admirably suited to this approach because the intensity of the close shot creates an interest in people, and the capacity to cut from one scene to another (with lapses of time implied) frees the dramatist from the necessity of bringing all his people together in one place and compressing their interactions into a single sequence. In this, television differs from the stage, and the limitations of size of picture and of total duration (imposed by the manufacturers of receivers and the sponsors of plays) exclude the temptations of the movies: the dramatist cannot let himself go to wide spaces or undue lengths.

These liberties and obstacles together shaped the form of the typical *Playhouse* drama of which *Marty*, which was later expanded into a movie, is the best-known example. It was a study of a small, genuine emotion, and the principal characters were a butcher of thirty, his mother, who was nagging him to get married, and an ungainly girl whom he almost lost because all his companions thought she was a "dog." The happy ending came when he broke with his pals and called the girl, but both the writing and the casting of the play were against the Cinderella tradition—the girl was not to take off her spectacles and become beautiful. Other plays in the same series went even further and arrived at a sad, if not tragic, ending, and the predilection of these writers for this "downbeat" effect was one reason for taking the program out of Coe's hands. Within a year or so the *Kraft Theatre*, usually given to domestic sentiment, produced a play called *Patterns*, by Rod Serling, which was substantially in the same style and told the story of a vicious, driving, business tyrant who, in effect, kills an upright old member of his firm in order to be rid of his bad conscience. Three years after *Marty* had been hailed as a milestone in television, a good critic was complaining that all TV drama was about little people in small situations coming to no conclusions and without happiness in action or nobility in frustration. It was not statistically a true bill, being true only of a number of conspicuous playwrights who had adopted a kind of genteel Southern futility as their equivalent for Chekhovian sadness.

The danger was not that TV drama would become small and delicate and melancholy; the danger was that it might cease to exist. For while the tradition of intelligent hour-long drama persisted in New York, dozens of producers in Hollywood were working on series of their own. Almost all of these were half-hours, and many were so arranged that commercial messages could be inserted by local stations if a national advertiser was not found; for national advertisers they usually had a handsome movie player as master of ceremonies—in effect to join the star and talk cozily about the sponsor's product. The remaining time, about twenty-two minutes, was considered ample for transmitting A *Doll's House* and was more than enough time for most of the "original" plays produced. When the series consisted of dramatizations of short stories, they were often as artful as the originals, but the oil slick of Hollywood converted even the tricky story of *The Necklace* into a drama of domestic devotion with a happy ending. To be fair, this particular misdemeanor was common enough in the live productions of the New York studios, and the real difference was that the major TV theaters had room for some seriousness and presented their drama with some sense of its significance. It seemed "for real," or it was the equally genuine and legitimate "make-believe," whereas the millions of feet of film rolling out of Hollywood had the peculiar quality that only Hollywood could project, which is neither truth nor fiction, but is fake. With negligible exceptions, the films were made as if they were to be shown in theaters; the acting was projected on a huge scale, and the feel was always that of a theater movie, not a home movie. The whole output lacked resonance and overtones.

These were half-hour series, and, in a way not clear to the layman, they could be made at a profit whereas the hour drama could not. One factor in this situation has a general bearing: a half-hour film is made so that anyone's commercial can be attached to it and is available for endless showings, but a film lasting an hour, while physically available, simply does not attract so many sponsors because local and regional advertisers do not use that much time. It should also be noted as part of the economic substructure of television that a live program, reproduced on film as a kinescope, can be used once within thirty days of the original performance and thereafter must be retired or destroyed unless special arrangements are made with all the unions concerned. Films made directly for television are not so restricted, and for a time they were a bonanza to the producers, who had nothing additional to pay to actors or musicians or technical staff, no matter how often the pictures were shown. Somewhat belatedly the unions stepped in, not to prevent the repeated showings, but to see that their members got a percentage of the receipts. Even so, the economics of the situation are favorable to the spread of the filmed play, and the only hope for a reasonably intelligent TV drama lies in the hour-long play done live —and (so far) chiefly in New York.

Toward the end of 1955 a project almost frightening in size began on NBC: the production of an hour-long play every afternoon, five days a week. The producer who undertook this prodigious assignment was Albert McCleery, who had for several years produced plays for the *Cameo Theatre* in a thoroughly non-realistic style, using draperies rather than scenery and concentrating on medium-close and closeup pictures—a system admirably adapted to intense psychological melodrama, not quite so useful for *Macbeth*. Even misapplied, McCleery's theories gave his work a specific character and had another prime value: they eliminated one of the great expenses of dramatic production, the sets. More economical still was a series of *Monodramas* in which a single actor appeared, doing *Hamlet* as a serial lasting perhaps a week. (I quote from memory: "What would you do if you came home and found your mother married to your father's murderer and everyone trying to keep you from marrying your best girl . . . ?") In many ways, intelligent or merely inventive, directors and producers have been discovering the nature of television, finding out how to use it in the ways right for the camera at one end and for the receiver in the home at the other.

It is in the production of dramatic works that the techniques and the art of television have been most fully developed, and this is the place to look briefly at what has been accomplished. The essential conditions for making television something more than a transmitter of previously manufactured motion pictures are known: an event (a play, in this case) takes place before the cameras and is seen, precisely as it occurs, on a small screen by a small number of people sitting at home. In all dramatic productions, the conditions of reception—where the audience is, how isolated from distraction, how far away from the players, and the less definable elements of mood—are considered, and in each form of presentation some conventions suitable to these conditions are accepted. Even in our realistic theater, players do not stand far upstage with their backs to the audience when they have something important to say, although the situation—a wife too proud to let her husband see that she is crying—might make such a position natural. In grand opera it is accepted that a quartet will stand in a line and sing, although each member is addressing the message to one or more of the others. When the gallery disappeared from the theaters, the level of projection, for voice and gestures, could be lowered. In the silent movies the full-screen closeup was used (chiefly by incompetents who wanted to com-

pensate for the lack of dialogue) and was found excessive, and in television the full-screen closeup began to diminish as soon as the screen
got up to sixteen inches. Finding the right conventions and using them
for the right psychological effects are the base of technical excellence.

As in the movies, the television director creates a flow of images.
Unfortunately, the movies had a fifty-year start, and the TV director
was under the necessity of satisfying some of the demands that the
movies had created. Over the years the tempo of cutting from one picture to another had been accelerated; movie producers felt (there is
little proof that they were right) that they had to give the audience a
slight visual jolt—the change from one angle to another, from long
shot to medium to closeup at a rapid rate—so that just before the
wide screen appeared, the eye was seldom at rest for as long as thirty
seconds. Whether the home group watching television, relaxed in comfortable chairs, eating, drinking, smoking, would require the same tempo
of cutting was never discovered because too many directors tried at
the beginning to make their plays look like movies. To this they sacrificed the sense of "being with," the intimacy of the medium. A few
resisted, particularly those with some experience in the theater, where
there are no cuts, the change in angle being effected by the movement
of the actors, which the eyes of the audience follow. These directors
were also the ones who recognized another essential: in the modern
theater the characters on the stage interact and the audience overhears
what they say to one another. The "tirade" of the classic French drama,
in which the hero addressed himself to the audience for ten minutes
while the rest of the cast stood motionless in a circle around him,
disappeared with the apron stage, and the soliloquy and the aside soon
followed.

Yet the interposition of cameras between actors and audience, the
repeated assertion that the camera represents the audience, has led to
some bad habits. I would say that half the bad acting in television
rises from the desire of the actor to play into the camera rather than to
the other characters of the drama. The other half comes from directors
who tell actors which camera to play to.

Once a director tried to put an end to this. He removed the telltale
lights that inform the actor which camera is on the air at the moment.
Immediately the actors, schooled in other studios, began to act for both
cameras. This was early days; if there had been four cameras, the actors

would have developed multiple schizophrenia. As it was, they acted so constantly for both cameras, and so badly, that the lights had to be restored.

An old-new race of actors is needed—actors who play to one another. And a race of directors who resolutely say, "You're an actor—act. Act within the space allotted, standing here, facing there, as we have rehearsed. But act in character. Hamlet isn't aware of cameras, he is aware of Ophelia. In his soliloquies, he is aware of himself. We will find you, we will pick you up, we will transmit you—that is our business. Yours is the more significant one. You create. Do not let our machinery stand in the way of your creation; it exists only to bring it to your audience."

Since writing the above, I have read in *Harper's Magazine* an essay by Lynn White, Jr., the president of Mills College, which provides a remarkable parallel to the point I have made. Some time in the thirteenth century, he says, "a conservative Spanish bishop, Luke of Tuy . . . denounced pictures of 'one-eyed virgins,' by which he meant representations of St. Mary in profile. . . .

"Christian art up to that time had been largely frontal, as that of the Eastern Church still is. Such images establish a direct and almost hypnotic relationship with the worshipper whom they fix with their eyes. . . . But as soon as the eyes of the image shift from the worshipper, religious art becomes drama rather than sacrament, and the worshipper tends to become merely a spectator. . . ."

The ways in which the Last Supper has been treated pictorially is a prime example. The earliest representations show the disciples facing us, and the stress is on the sacrament, not the prediction of treachery. In Leonardo the dramatic interaction of all the disciples is conveyed by the direction in which they are looking—at one another or at Jesus, not at us. The lesson is clear: when we want to hypnotize the audience (to sell them something), the direct gaze into the camera is correct; for drama, people face one another, not us.

In another aspect the techniques of television have undergone several changes of fashion and are still in a fluid state. The simplest way to approach this is by way of the totally non-dramatic program, the program that, in principle, delivers a person or a simple event to the home screen.

There the problem is seen in its barest terms—but it has a bearing on the dramatic art as well and casts some light on a unique quality of television. It is the matter of translating the material of a program into visual terms. The parallel problem in radio—translation into sound without sight—had been solved to the satisfaction of the audience, which took natural sound (a door closing when we knew that someone was going out of a room) and "wild" sound—music coming from no identified source—with equal satisfaction. It would seem easier to express anything and everything when both sight and sound are available. For a variety of reasons, this was not the case.

To the *theory* of "visualization" I contributed, I believe, as much nonsense as any other single individual. It was my fortune, good and evil, to work in television in its earliest years and also in some years when we had learned some things and, owing to lack of equipment and then to shutdowns because of the war, were unable to put our ideas to work. So we sat and spun webs of theory, some of which, I am happy to say, became firm principles of TV practice. Among the more theoretical discussions (our own version of the number of angels dancing on our particular pinhead) was the mathematical formulation of the relation between radio and television on one hand and the attention of the audience on the other. If television demanded so-and-so much more attention, should it not give thus-and-thus much more satisfaction? Or, why should anyone sit and look at a newscaster when the total interest is in what he is saying? We were not formula men, we were making guesses; and we were, in a sense, practical. We knew, for instance, that in the daytime we could not ask women to drop everything in order to follow a daytime serial, and we tried to guess how often we could count on their being attentive, how often we should let entirely neutral things—recapitulations, memories, flashbacks, repetitions—take place so that the devoted listener would not feel that she had lost anything.

We made a rough guess: if eighty per cent of the essence of a program was purely in words or other sounds, we had no right to ask the audience for the hundred-per-cent attention that (we thought) television requires. We were thrown back on some simple facts of life: a newscaster reading late bulletins was between ninety and ninety-nine per cent pure audio. We had by that time done a great deal of newscasting—all of it during the war, when maps and pictures were available and necessary;

we had had the ingenious Charles Holden (later a vice-president of ABC) to animate our maps and make special effects for us; but we had not had to visualize the opposing philosophies of the cold war. We were on solid ground theoretically, and everyone else in the business was arriving at the same conclusion. Years ago Samuel Goldwyn had objected to a publicity photograph of some of his stars because, he said, "it's just two faces looking," and a face or faces looking (and especially reading from a script) was what we most wanted to avoid. We wanted to have people move about, to catch the eye, and if what they did had point and meaning, so much the better.

This was theory. We were all obsessed by the Chinese maxim about a picture being worth a thousand words—a silly notion except for a language written in pictographs. If it were true, the human race would have become a pictorial, not a verbal one. There are combinations of words—five or five thousand at a time—worth millions of pictures. We discovered this. In practice we were compelled by circumstances to pretend that four people sitting around a table, discussing a matter in which they had a passionate interest, had visual interest all its own. We had to do this because we had no money to pay for elaborate programs, nor the equipment to rehearse most of our shows, so that four faces looking, usually at one another or at an MC, were precisely what we put on the air. Much of this was before Pearl Harbor, and we had one topic that never failed to rouse the passions of our panelists—neutrality or intervention. In nearly a year of such programs we only once had a truly visual topic—modern art—and the most exciting portion of that came when one speaker announced that Picasso had turned Nazi and that the stigmata of his fascist nature were visible in all his degenerate work—which was, of course, promptly denied. The presence of a painting by Picasso was by that time the merest illustration; it even distracted from the vehemence of the argument.

For several years after commercial television began, theory seemed to win over practice; the effort to keep everybody moving about (motion without motive) and to provide something to look at for every word spoken made the screen more hectic than exciting, and all the time the panel-quiz shows were immobilizing people without boring audiences. The average person still felt that he was missing something when a newscaster sat and read a bulletin to him—the truth was that the spectator was gaining, over radio, the sight of the newsman's person. But the basic sense that "we ought to see something more, if we're going to look—we ought to see more than we merely hear"—this turned out to be rather fundamental. A Gerald Johnson and an Elmer Davis, with the massive gravitational pull of their personality, could try to read a fifteen-minute commentary on the news; the average newscaster resorted as soon and as often as possible to movie clips and, visualizing like mad, often reduced the news to the level of newsreel, featuring those items on which actual clips or relevant recent shots were available, passing over important items with only a bulletin if no pictures arrived in time for the broadcast.

All the more the producers of straight entertainment programs felt obliged to keep the eye constantly attracted to the screen by having some object in motion all the time. An observer of the adaptation of a novel by Henry James, in which videoactivity was high and the inner play of character was nothing, might have remembered James's own dictum: "If a woman stands and looks at a man in a certain way, that is drama." As production shifted to the West Coast and the jerky cutting of the movies was imposed on television, the effect of jumping-jacks pretending to be men and women was increased and only a few soundly conceived dramatic programs kept up the demonstration of good production principles. They were so successful that the chances for the survival of the good style, the style natural to television, are bright.

The danger is that Hollywood will learn how to cut down its overhead and move aggressively into the field of the full-length dramatic production without learning the difference between television and the movies. The economic fact is that a thoroughly good movie is one of the most successful of all the programs television can transmit, and even the second-best attract large audiences. Constantly before us is the possibility that television can pay enormous profits to the station- and network-owners who rejoice in the licenses given to them by the F.C.C. without developing the broadcasting art one step further than it has gone today, letting all its great potentialities wither on the vine. We face also the simple fact that nothing, except the almost abstract circumstance that the profit-makers use portions of the public air, can prevent this. By 1956 ABC had bought three million dollars' worth of film from the J. Arthur Rank Organization alone, and all of the new programs it announced for the following season were to be made on film. The

Mutual New York station had become a huge film-projector because its owners had bought all the properties of the RKO studios. Between old films and television shows made in Hollywood, the exploitation of television as a separate creative enterprise was slowly coming to a halt.

This is all the more regrettable because the live productions in New York and two or three superior series produced on film were beginning to suggest that television was finding its way to an entirely new kind of entertainment. I put this in the most tentative way because the indications are still vague. One of them is the inconclusive history of Walt Disney's series on Davy Crockett. As part of his brilliantly successful first year in television, Disney presented a romanticized biography of this legendary hero, ending with the Alamo. A skillfully promoted craze swept space helmets into the trash cans of the country, their places being taken by synthetic coonskin caps, and the backwoods pioneer became a valuable piece of property—so valuable (it seemed) that more programs were put into production. For this second series Disney departed from the romanticized story of Crockett's life and went into pure fiction. This was candidly announced, there was no imposture, nothing for the moralist to worry about.

The significant point is that the imagination of millions of children had been captivated by a kind of truth, and to satisfy the appetite so created, a kind of fiction was offered. The truth had been half fiction; the fiction was to recall the truth. In a dozen other programs, including the successful *Dragnet* and *Medic* series, a core of actuality gave a kind of magnetic power to the dramatized stories. Sergeant Friday, in *Dragnet*, was for at least a year the best-known police officer in the country. His manner of speech was completely artificial, his inexpressive countenance was a stylized mask, yet he lived in an atmosphere of reality which had nothing in the world to do with the created reality of Sherlock Holmes. Not only police files and hospital records are used as sources for programs; case histories in law and psychiatry appear also, and events of recent history which the audience can check for authenticity out of its own experience. These things tie themselves to the actual, satisfying the same desire that children have when they insist on a story that is true, when tales of wonder become a little unacceptable. It is still a story they want, but it must be a story they can believe.

I have a feeling that more and more of the stories told on television will have this double quality, and that this may be one of the forms that television will create for itself. The sense of the actual is greater in television than in any other dramatic form, greater than that of the stage because it can escape the theatrical limitations of time and space, and more immediate than the movies because nothing intervenes between the action before the camera and the reconstructed action on the home screen. When television comes to create its own style, its own special way of telling a story, it will naturally draw on its essential nature. Unless it finds this way, television will remain half-grown—and only half alive. If the movies had never gone beyond photographing plays on the stage, if they had not created their own rhythm of presentation through cutting and camera movements, they would have remained a small and shabby thing. Television, with its infinite possibilities, can be stopped short of using its creative powers. The new devices I have mentioned may capture on tape most of the quality of a live production, but the capacity of television to transmit without any intervening step will still remain unique, its identifying feature, the essence of its character. When the essential character of a man is left undeveloped, he has not fulfilled his destiny. And that is true also of an art.

At the moment the creative strength of television centers in the hour-long dramatic program. It has been commercially successful, although it seldom touches the highest levels of popularity. At least half a dozen series, some with alternating sponsorship, continue year after year, holding their own against varied competition. All are live productions, all do a few superior programs, many excellent ones, and only a few really contemptible ones each season. It is a high average for the theater anywhere and in any age.

I have gone to the theater since I was seven and have worked in it, and it seems natural to place dramatic programs at the top of the pyramid of values in television. I have to warn myself against overrating their importance. It is quite possible that the drama, as every generation until the present has known it, is not the form best suited to television, the kind of thing television does best. Up to now most serious TV drama has been essentially stage drama broken into smaller scenes and photographed. But every form of entertainment eventually discovers its own true materials and usually discovers its own special way of telling a story and succeeds—even though some other entertainment tells the story better. The important thing is to find the right combination of elements, the new ones and the ones derived from older arts, and to put them together so that the layman and the critic both feel that something new has occurred, that the magnetic pole has been discovered. To this we respond instantly and without reservation, the critic knowing that the new thing, imperfect though it may be, has the future in it because it could not have been accomplished in any other medium, the layman saying (to himself perhaps), "Man, that's television!" The new created thing has to come into being; if not, we have a fad, like a new card game, enjoyable and profitable and occupying time and space until the next one comes along.

That sense of the unique created thing has come to us most impressively from the hour-long play, and the word of caution which must be added comes out of admiration, not dislike. Again and again our good critics have praised the theme, the basic interest of the writer in doing his play, and have added that a fine effect was lost because the play petered out or failed to hold true to the course set at the start. This was something more than a false "happy ending." It was correctly identified by Ring Lardner, Jr., in an essay in the *Nation* as "the *Caine Mutiny* effect." Essentially it consists of bringing into play a vast amount of sympathy for liberal or unconventional ideas and people, and then slapping the audience in the face for being sentimental idiots. In *The Caine Mutiny*, after the naval advocate has vindicated the young officer who took control of his ship to save it from the catastrophe into which his senior was heading, the triumph of the victors is interrupted by this same advocate, who denounces the celebrants and asserts that the men who give blind obedience are the ones who save our country. In *Patterns*, after a businessman had driven a loyal old employee virtually to death, the young man who is to take his place, who has upheld human values against corporate greed, succumbs to a speech asserting the superior rights of the company, the excitement of driving people to the last extreme of psychical exhaustion. Wherever the individual rebels, succeeds, and seems to triumph, the last word goes to the established order—or all words are drowned in soft music and everybody in tears. By the name Mr. Lardner put on this shift, he indicated that it is not exclusively a television device. It corresponds to something in the atmosphere—to the same element that took all the fight out of *See It Now* and steadily reduces documentary to documentation of non-controversial public interests. It may be a temporary phenomenon, but it must be noticed—and watched.

22

THE CONSEQUENCES OF TIME

A familiar "liberal" gambit in criticism is to say, "No one sets out intentionally to write a bad novel," and a good case might be made out for the idea. It is, however, a semantic trap with two springs—"intentionally" and "bad"—and the way to escape it is to be realistic. In the businesses we are discussing, no vice-president in charge of debasing public taste exists, no fiat goes out ordering half a dozen offensive pictures or programs. On the other hand, every Hollywood writer has heard the head of the studio say, "*I* like it . . . and *you* like it . . . but will *they* like it?" and the equivalent phrases in broadcasting are equally familiar. If no one says, "We've got to hoke this up," it is because everyone is a little self-conscious, but other words will do: "It gets a little heavy in through here, don't you think?" or "Why don't you have your man forget he hasn't got his pants on?" The process *is* deliberate. When the writers of the *Amos 'n' Andy* script were tentatively invited to do the television version of *Life with Father*, the intent was not to see how much of the wit and human richness of the original could be preserved; the intent was to make exactly what was eventually made by other writers: a rival for half a dozen other programs that had already debased the situations and the characters under other names. No edict was necessary. It never is. The professional knows what is expected of him, and the professional in certain segments of the writing

"MAN IS THE MEASURE OF ALL THINGS"

The most irritating problem in broadcasting, although far from the most important, is that of ratings—the measurement of the size of the audience attracted by a program. Challenged on the simple ground of inaccuracy, the various rating systems are modest, but the use made of the figures they supply goes to the opposite extreme. With a flick of the wrist, a deft semantic sleight-of-hand, the size of the audience is equated to popularity.

At best, the various systems tell us that at any given hour so many sets are tuned into Station A, so many to B, and so down the list. It may be assumed that if at a given moment B has three times as many listeners as A, the audience is expressing a preference. It cannot be assumed that tuning in to either program is a genuine expression of liking. All that can be said is that the audience does not actively dislike the program on view. That people do enormously like many programs goes without saying—but it is not proved by the statistics of listening. In fact, "listening" and "looking" are both unrealistic terms. The various rating systems can only testify that a set is turned on and that the person who answers the telephone call knows what program is current.

No other way has been found to give sponsors even an approximate estimate of the size of their audiences. On the other hand, no measurement of size can be a measure of the affection in which a program is held or even of its *relative* hold on the audience as a whole. Two simultaneous programs of great popular appeal will divide an audience almost equally, whereas a program of relatively low attraction may attract three quarters of the total audience because all the other programs available at the same time are inferior. To say that the rating in the second circumstance indicates a popularity greater than that of the first is sheer nonsense.

business is all too apt to call his work the second-oldest profession in the world if he does not in self-pity or mockery insist that it is the first. To pretend that this lowering process is never intentional is as silly as to believe that it is universal and inescapable; it is, in fact, to eliminate the human factor from the business of producing entertainment, to eliminate greed on one side and aspiration on the other, to forget the thousands of battles men have always put up for their integrity and the thousands of compromises into which they have been driven.

In the broadcasting business any single exclusive theory is particularly misleading because programs develop out of the interaction of a dozen factors. They may begin with a sponsor's notion that he wants his name associated with culture, and end with the availability of four stations in the Midwest at 6:30 on Tuesdays. The advertiser and the time-buyer and the head of the network sales department and a dozen others must make executive decisions before a program can go on the air, and all of them may be reversed if another program on another network shifts its time period or becomes suddenly popular. In simplest terms, the sponsored programs must sell the product (unless the purpose is to create general good will for a corporation that does not sell to the public, like U. S. Steel); in order to do this, the program must attract an audience and induce a mood of acceptance for the commercial. Beyond these fundamentals the complexities begin, and many of them have direct effect on the kind and quality of program we get and also on the obstacles that prevent us from getting the programs we want.

An audience is "attracted" to a program; how powerful need the attraction be? In logic, the answer should be: "That depends on the power of the counterattraction when the program goes on the air." Actually, a great deal depends on what the audience has been doing just before. In one case, three-quarters of the total audience of a dramatic program were inherited from the preceding melodrama on the same stations—the viewers did not switch over to the melodrama that followed on another network. This does not mean that the second program could afford to slack off; it means that between ten and fifteen million families gave this program a chance to interest them. They had been listening to a melodrama, and another melodrama followed, but they did not take the trouble to switch to the rival station (between seven and ten million people did switch). Unless a program of exceptional popularity or a highly publicized one is coming on another station, six out of ten listeners stay with the channel to which they are tuned. When programs of the same kind follow one another, the audience stays put—as high as eight out of ten remaining with the station. When programs totally different in appeal follow one another, the audience may scatter—but if the first program is extremely popular, the audience it delivers to its successor will still be of impressive size. However, the networks do not like to take chances. When *The $64,000 Question* became the top-rating program in the summer of 1955, CBS did not continue Murrow's *See It Now* in the following period, although Murrow's audience would have been greater than it had ever been before. A program was needed to keep the bulk of the previous audience. After a time the ideal one was found: another giveaway-quiz program.

The make-up of an audience for an average successful program is something like this: Of all the people listening to the previous program, about three-quarters automatically stay tuned and become the bulk of the new program's audience; a very small number of people turn on their sets for this program (that is to say, the vast majority have been watching some program already). About one-fourth of the total audience arrives *during* the program, most of them deserting other programs to do so—and fifteen out of every hundred members of the audience depart, some to try their luck elsewhere, some giving up entirely. Near the end, a sizable group of people tunes in, presumably getting ready for the following show, and out of every hundred people who saw our program, sixty will see the next one as well.

The knowledge we have of the flow of audience is not matched by any understanding of motives. The broadcasters are pragmatic and are on safe ground. They do not say that the audience is too lethargic to press a button; they say that over long periods of time the greater part of the audience does not press a button. Since this is even more marked when programs of similar types are contiguous, they used to put ten daytime serials in succession on the air, as they now pile one TV mystery on another. Then, when a break in continuity must come, they like to have a program similar in tone to one that is just going off the air on another station so that the new program will bring over some part of the audience from somewhere else to make up for those who will not stay with the station. The fact that people do tune out after a program begins, looking for entertainment elsewhere, is not forgotten—but this is considered a reaction to the merits of the individual program, whereas the audience captured at the beginning is motivated by willingness to watch a kind of program, especially if no effort of searching for it on their sets is required. All that flow of audience guarantees is actually the priceless opening moment, the chance to say to the audience, "Don't go away—this is going to be great."

Back-to-back programing of similar shows on a single station is not the only phenomenon based on audience flow. Another is the competitive scheduling of programs of similar appeal so that the lover of comedy or of drama cannot see all the best programs but must choose among them. This positional warfare of the networks is pursued at times with the most contemptuous disregard of the public and, although the F.C.C. has not noticed it, in direct violation of the law which says that stations must operate in accordance with the public *convenience* (as well as the public necessity and interest). I cannot see how the public convenience is served by making it impossible to see certain programs; on the other hand, I see no way in which the F.C.C. can put an end to this practice without an intolerable and unprecedented use of its power.

The solution of this difficulty is known to everyone in the business: it is simply the repetition, at different times, of the rival programs. This recognizes two of the facts of broadcasting: that the number of peak listening hours is limited (some thirty-five a week), and that a vast number of people who would like to see certain programs do not see them—for many different reasons—and would like a second chance. Some clashes would still be inevitable, and nothing whatever can be done to prevent the placing of good programs of different sorts opposite one another—which would come down to asking X to underplay his hand against Y's good cards and, in effect, asking X or Y not to produce as excellent a program as he can. But a repeat performance would allay the justifiable irritation of the public, which does not see the complexity of the commercial broadcasters' problems.

I use the term "commercial broadcaster" to include all those engaged in the business—the network executive, the sponsor, his agency, the owner of the affiliated station carrying the program—and at this point it is important to note that, while they must collaborate, their interests are not always identical. In this single matter of conflicting programs, a sponsor may resent the necessity imposed on him of losing half his potential audience—but the network may have sold the time to him before the competition developed. The network's interest may be the preservation of half the audience so that it can make an advantageous contract for the succeeding time period. If the agency has created the program, it has an overwhelming interest in keeping it going so that it can be sold to another sponsor if the present one drops out. The station owner may wish that the program would vanish, leaving him free to sell the time to a local merchant at a much higher profit. These and a hundred other complications are all consequences of commercial rivalry, and all we can legitimately ask (unless we are ready to scrap the social system under which we, as well as the broadcasters, are living) is that the excesses of cutthroat competition be mitigated in favor of the public right. There is a way to make sure that this mitigation will occur, turning commercial rivalry to the benefit of the public, and in Chapter 33 I have outlined the way—with the strong, unexpected, and possibly unwilling support of a network president.

The hour at which a program is presented is only one of the ways in which time dominates the broadcasting business. The parceling of hours into halves and quarters, rigidly enforced because an overrun of even ten seconds may interfere with a commercial, has had an equivocal effect on the quality of dramatic programs, giving them pace and spirit, limiting the freedom of writers. And the other parcel of time, the multiples of thirteen weeks through which contracts run, has had the profoundest effect of all. For in practice a new program does not have thirteen weeks to prove itself; notice of cancellation must be given at the end of eight or nine weeks, and if a sponsor intends to substitute another program, his agency may have begun shopping for one or creating it within a month after the doubtful program has gone on the air. He cannot, by that time, have had conclusive evidence about the selling-power of his program, because there are too many variables involved. In general, if a program has had reasonably good notices and a fair rating, a sponsor is likely to give it another thirteen weeks before making sale-of-product the decisive factor. The risks are too great for him to do more.

The vice-president in charge of radio and television may be spending over $50,000,000, but he is allowed little margin for error. He is not like a book editor, who may reject a manuscript that turns out a best-seller and accept an undistinguished failure—provided he does not do this too often. The stakes in broadcasting are too high. And even more stringent is the life of the advertising agency, for if it makes a mistake on a large scale, if it commits a sponsor to a disastrous program and loses his business, the consequences are catastrophic: an agency employing 750 people may shrink to 100 overnight; the big account has not used all of the staff, but the profit from a single sponsor has paid the salaries of research workers and planners and has paid also for the huge apparatus for creating and presenting programs and campaigns to other, non-competing clients. The calamitous effect of a change of agency by any one of the ten leading advertisers haunts the hucksters' dreams.

In these conditions, everyone concerned looks for insurance against failure, and this means, in effect, that they want guarantees of instantaneous success. The elements considered "sure-fire" must be old and at best can be made to seem new; they are often extraneous to the essential character of the program and may even be hostile to it. Sometimes a personable man or woman from the movies is engaged to introduce a dramatic series—and three minutes more are lopped off Ibsen or Tennessee Williams. Sometimes the comedy has to be altered to fit a guest star who is also insurance. Two things can always be counted on: a touch of comedy and a happy ending. The sardonic immorality of Somerset Maugham provided dozens of good plots, but insurance had to be taken out against his difference from the routine writer; so one after another his stories were altered, whole new acts were added, and (to the pleasure of a few people) even then the series was not impressive. The Maugham affair is, incidentally, a first-class exhibit in the matter of "deliberately" doing a bad piece of work. If the producers were not absolute cretins, they knew they were putting out inferior stuff, and their only defense could be that Maugham had committed the unforgivable sin and permitted them to do what they pleased.

Finally, time operates as a deterrent to change after a program has been established. Within the half or full hour the essential ingredients must be presented or the audience will feel dissatisfied. This is not a consequence of the commercial use of broadcasting; in the non-commercial British system, programs occur on schedule and are substantially the same, time after time. The value of routine has been underestimated because intellectuals and artists often genuinely like, and always say they like, the unexpected, but there is an effort involved in every encounter with newness, even in laughing at a new joke compared to the easy satisfaction of laughing at a new version of an old one. We are irritated when we are not sure whether something is "supposed to be funny," as Bernard Shaw knew when he made one of the critics in *Fanny's First Play* ask "How can I know if it's a good play if I don't know who wrote it?" The followers of the Gestalt school may smile, but they will not laugh at this, since they know and have taught us how profoundly the framework alters our perception of detail. We expect to be amused when Jack Benny appears, amused in a specific and limited number of ways. When this happens, we experience a great sense of satisfaction, not only because Benny has been amusing, but because a whole psychological system of desire-and-fulfillment has been in action. Before Benny can do anything totally different, we have to be reconditioned, but we do not object if he pretends to be doing something new and it turns out to be the good old reliable Benny after all.

We have to salute those enterprising men who jeopardize their position by changing their formula, as Ed Sullivan did whenever he abandoned his variety show for two successive weeks to present the life and works of a movie producer or a musical-comedy team—the material was bound to be popular, but a new format always is troublesome. Jackie Gleason varied the acts inside a rigid framework until he found the right ingredients. Kate Smith has never received enough credit for the initiative she and her producer, Ted Collins, showed in both radio and television, introducing new acts and keeping them on week after week until they established themselves. The best of these was *Ethel and Albert,* but the merit of the Smith program was not that it picked winners; the great thing about it was the chances it took. It did not demand that the marks of sure success be sticking out all over an act before investing air time in it. The deep devotion of her audience allowed Kate Smith to do many things, and most of them were good. Better than the good was the consistent variation and change in her own program, a rare demonstration of enterprise that continues free-wheeling after it has made its millions.

The problem of balancing routine and experiment involves all the major elements of the broadcasting business and the broadcasting art.

In radio, experiment was relatively inexpensive, and the sustaining program was always available for a tryout. The sustainer is, in fact, the greatest invention of commercial radio. It came into being because stations had to put something on the air between their sponsored hours. A newcomer in the field after NBC had established two networks, CBS had these wide open spaces, and one of the permanent high standards of broadcasting was established then. Intelligence, flexibility, and a profound conviction that broadcasting could be as good as people wanted it to be—all of these, combined with small budgets and youth and the support of the company's executives, created something close to a miracle. The economics of television preclude a repetition: sustaining programs are, in general, commercial programs waiting to be sold and a few cultural offerings on Sunday afternoons.

Fortunately, experimentation goes on at the opposite extreme—in the most costly of programs. The extravagant temperament of Sylvester Weaver as president of NBC is a piece of good fortune for the whole television business. He has a flair for publicity, and, apparently, a dislike for established time periods. After his ninety-minute "spectaculars" to launch color productions, he started a forty-hour continuous program on radio and announced that regularly sponsored time in television would be pre-empted by the network to present long programs on subjects important to the public, with historical backgrounds. A casual observer may see no special merit in calling forty hours of broadcasting one program, but the intention to break through the artificial limits of broadcasting is in evidence, and it is not necessary for all the experiments to succeed—it is only necessary to have imagination and enterprise enough to make a lot of them.*

This is most important at present because the pace set by one network must be met by the others. Aware of losing leadership in creative programing (although not in popularity), CBS has done well in matters of public policy, and the third network, ABC, acquiring money for programs after several lean years, had a phenomenal stroke of luck: the Disney programs were sensationally popular and provided a groundwork for future action. (In the meantime, Dumont virtually abandoned all network operations.) The rivalry among the networks is our strongest safeguard against the dead hand of routine and will be so until new solutions to some of the basic problems of broadcasting are developed.

* Mr. Weaver has since been named Chairman of the Board of NBC.

These problems are best observed in connection with those portions of the schedule which are not primarily entertainment—the great area of news and discussion, of events and the interpretation of events—in which the public service of the broadcasters is most evident. When we have surveyed this area, we shall be able to formulate the problems involved and see how they react upon entertainment also.

23

BLESSED NECESSITY

Thirty years after broadcasting began, ten years after television added its fascinations to radio, the managers of the business made an alarming discovery: the American people were not passionately and devotedly in love with what they got on the air. Under the blow, they reeled right out of the "American way of life" and into state socialism, imploring the Federal government to prevent any other broadcasters from giving the public what they themselves had failed to provide.

The discovery came about during the early stages of the battle over pay-TV, but is independent of the rights and wrongs of that controversy. When the F.C.C. invited the public to make itself heard on the subject, a large number of letters reached Washington, and the early (unofficial) reports indicated something like a six-to-four ratio in favor of some pay system. A vigorous campaign of publicity followed and various polls were taken; before the hearings had advanced very far, the networks could say that seven out of ten people found the present system satisfactory and six out of ten could not conceive of any circumstances in which they would be willing to pay for alternative programs. This was, on the face of it, a remarkable tribute to the satisfactions of commercial television and a manifestation, no less remarkable, of its capacity to deaden all appetites except those it could easily and profitably satisfy. Certainly these figures, if they held up, were more important than the unscientific testimony of polls conducted by newspapers and magazines. In them, the professional touch was lacking; it was supplied when Elmo Roper and his associates made a study for CBS.

The actual (not the apparent) results of this study are so astonishing that I felt obliged to check my analysis of the figures with experts, who assure me that the Roper study actually says what I think it says.

It begins with a basic question and comes up with the basic answer: out of ten people who had television sets, seven were well satisfied with the programs they received. The sample audience consisted of nearly four hundred and fifty citizens in Columbus, Ohio. When the idea of a pay-TV system was presented to them, in the most attractive terms, with no suggestion whatever of any difficulties or drawbacks, only three out of ten said they would be interested. Six out of ten said they would not. It is at this point that the advantage of a scientific poll becomes apparent.

For this thumping vote of confidence in the present broadcasting system turns out to be nothing of the kind, turns out to be an almost scientific demonstration of the thesis developed in this book and elsewhere that only a fragment of the total audience cares *much* for what the broadcasters transmit. It is true that the audience would rather have what it now gets than have no programs at all; it is probably true that most of the audience cannot think up programs preferable to the current ones; it is also true that sponsors are satisfied with audiences indifferent to the programs (and I shall presently note a fragment of evidence that lethargic audiences may suit the sponsor even better than interested ones). But all of these put together do not constitute proof that our programs satisfy public demand, and the refinement of the Roper figures supplied in the Columbus study indicates that actual satisfaction is limited to a tiny fraction of the audience.

For the Roper office was not satisfied with the mere statement (made by six out of every ten set-owners) that they would not be interested in pay-TV, no matter how attractive it was. The next question was *why*. And to that question *only two out of every ten people* instinctively said: "Because we are satisfied with the present system and the present programs." Another two said they did not watch or did not like television enough to consider paying; nearly one-fourth of those who were indifferent to the idea of a pay system said they could not afford to pay or thought paying for the set was enough; a few said they would rather go out to see the kind of special attractions pay-TV might offer; and among the scattering reasons was the rather realistic thought that an additional system would cause disagreement in the home. These various reasons for refusing to endorse a new system do not alter the damning mathematics of the situation: when asked if they would like to have programs different from the ones now on the air, even if they had to pay for them, three out of ten people spontaneously said that they would, and of the rest such a large majority either could not afford to pay or did not care for television anyhow that those who spontaneously declared themselves satisfied shrink to an almost negligible minority.

Even in my ignorance of statistical method I have not made the mistake of thinking that all the others are actively *dis*satisfied with commercial television. I say only that a considerable number of set-owners are far from being entirely satisfied (those who are willing to pay and those who hardly use their sets). Even if all the rest are "satisfied," we have still to watch out for the moment of hocus-pocus when "satisfied" is translated into "wouldn't care for anything else" and becomes virtually equivalent to "enthusiastic."

The quality of public response to any entertainment is important; it is especially so in broadcasting because of the stipulated relation between the broadcasters and the public, the obligation to consult the public interest, which is also the public taste. In this case, the broadcasters were infatuated with figures, with quantities. Years ago they refused to inquire whether people really listened to radio or merely had it turned on while they did something else, radio being for them a background noise or, as Alistair Cooke once called it, wallpaper. They made the mistake because in their business the way people listened did not matter; they were selling to the sponsor "so many sets tuned in to this station at this time, buy it, the listeners will hear your message"—and there the semantic sleight-of-hand occurred, because the link between "sets tuned in" and "listeners" could not be guaranteed. When television came, sponsors and broadcasters both could find a positive value in public indifference, for a discovery was made: when a program was especially good, when a drama brought up a psychological problem of intense interest to the audience, people at home began to talk about the show the moment the commercial began, to discuss the message of the play while the sponsor's message went unheard. *It was better to give them programs they were not so excited about!* An industry that had taken indifference to imply satisfaction could now go into the business of creating apathy and would no doubt call it "giving the public what it wants."

It is my judgment that most of the errors of the broadcasters, in quality of programs or in public service, can be traced to this basic confusion between indifference and acceptance, between acceptance and satisfaction. In their confusion they failed to acknowledge the monumental fact that, far from being a diversion or an entertainment, they had become a prime necessity of common existence. They kept talking about themselves as if they were in competition with the movies. They were really in competition with life itself, and the Midwestern housewives who said they "visited" with *Aunt Jenny* and *John's Other Wife* were only extreme instances of the relationship that Franklin D. Roosevelt established with the entire nation when he began his Fireside Chats, the same that came into play when Murrow said, "This . . . is London" or Durante said, "Good night, Mrs. Calabash—wherever you are." In a phenomenal and irrational way, substituting television for gossip with friends, going on a theater party, or reading *David Copperfield* was entirely satisfactory in spite of the deficiencies of radio, the illusion-destroying dimensions of the TV box, the recall to reality every fifteen minutes by commercials. The sign that used to announce a new Chaplin picture in his earliest phase—"I Am Here Today"—could have been reduplicated a hundred million times, for the people of radio and television were everywhere, in each of our living rooms and kitchens and nurseries and bedrooms. They were *present*, "in person," as no star on a personal-appearance tour had ever managed to be. They became the super-realities.

Broadcasting had all this, but it could not escape the natural consequence: it was a daily necessity, like meat and bread, but people do not go into ecstasies about staple foods. The history of the motorcar proved this. For at least twenty years, millions of people had felt a personal regard for *their* cars, giving them pet names, treating them with jovial affection, lavishing on them tender care. Then the car became a utility and the love affair came to an end. A full generation later, the manufacturers tried to recapture the emotions of an earlier day with fancy station wagons and later with sports cars. Radio's career as an object of personal love lasted a year or so and television was denied it altogether. The TV set, like the radio receiver, made the passage from gadget to universal household appliance faster than the washing machine or the pop-up toaster. Their essential nature was recognized by everyone except the broadcasters.

For if they had seen that they were providing an indispensable service, they would also have seen that "giving the public what it wants" is pernicious nonsense, since the public cannot know how much better it might be served. The public in the 1890s certainly "wanted" electric lights, and a poll taken would have assured the producers that seventy per cent of all the users of power were "satisfied" with direct current. It was the producer's job to improve his service and to make the users want alternating current because it was better or cheaper or more adaptable. As purveyors of a necessity of life, the producers of power could not be content with serving a segment of the public; they had to serve virtually all the people. If the broadcasters had seen their own position in these terms, they would not have misplayed their strongest hand: their immediate and universal contact with all the people. They did misplay it, and when the threat of pay-TV came, they panicked as badly as Hollywood did when television began to decimate the lines in front of the box offices. Reality had caught up with them as it always catches up with the sentimentalists, and they were stupefied.

They are not out of danger. That same "satisfied" public may hear some disturbing news from a Congressional committee; a new invention may make transmission in the now neglected frequencies necessary and the giants of the industry will find themselves ill-prepared to meet

---

NO INFORMATION, PLEASE

Testimony before a Congressional committee brought out the interesting fact that no part of network research goes into finding out what effect programs actually have on people— outside of the effect on sales.

competition from five or six new networks; their fight against giving pay-TV even a chance to prove itself may alienate a considerable part of the audience. And if pay-TV is tried and succeeds, the broadcasters will for the first time in their lives have to fight for the audience; up to now they have had the audience, and each one has fought only for a larger slice of it. In a sense, radio and television have not been in competition with any other form of entertainment except for brief periods, as when sound and new dimensions came to the movies. They have fought for audiences against the attractions of fine weather in the summer, and sometimes great events have displaced sponsored entertainment in the center of public interest. But pay-TV threatens to bring all the nationwide and all the local competition—the championship fight, the new movie, the Broadway opening—into the home, and the commercial broadcaster may at last find out what it means to face real competition. It will not help him to start with a totally wrong conception of what people really think of him. So it is for grim practical reasons, not for the sake of any theory, that the broadcasters need to revalue the value placed on their services by the public.

The preceding section of this book has provided a critical valuation of those programs on which the popularity of broadcasting presumably rests. The next section is concerned with another group of programs, those in which broadcasting serves as communicator of news, ideas, opinion, as educator, as a medium of controversy and persuasion. In the first, most of the problems are matters of taste, some are moral problems; in the second, we have public problems, essentially political and social. The two are not totally separate: the kind of comedy we get and the number of murders perpetrated on the screen each night are important to society as a whole, and decisions about such questions cannot be based purely on individual taste; but in this area we are unlikely to appeal to law, whereas the right of a newscaster to distort the news and the right of a victim to answer his attacker on the air are natural subjects for regulation.

In discussing these latter problems I do not pretend to be impartial. I am prejudiced in favor of the present system of broadcasting and am happy to put up with its shortcomings as long as it preserves its capacity to change. I am prejudiced also in favor of the interest of all the people of this country—above the interest of the "public" (as the broadcaster speaks of the public, meaning his audience). I am for the enduring interest of the people as against the interest of the public in what is on the air at 9:30 on Tuesday nights. (This repeats a distinction I made several years ago, but the complexion of Tuesday nights has changed. The success of *The $64,000 Question* has made all the time adjacent to it very valuable—and as a consequence or coincidence, the most important program in television, *See It Now*, is no longer to be seen on that night, and perhaps for other reasons will begin to lead the

THREE—COUNT 'EM—THREE

Between its mania for visualizing everything and its concept of the audience (which is low), television has brought a new series of gestures into the American living room and, I am afraid, into American life. Particularly I note the "headwaiter effect," which consists of raising the fingers of the right hand to indicate any number above one. "This is your third appearance on this program, isn't it, Miss Glunt?" says the MC, and Miss Glunt registers surprise and says, "Why, yes, this makes three—" and she raises three fingers—"times."

The announcer who has to say that someone's bread is eight times better (he does not, of course, say better than what) has a choice—four fingers on each hand or five and three. It is not true, as reported, that one announcer, unable to choose between these, went quietly insane. What will happen with fractions is, at this moment, a beautiful mystery.

From the movies, television has taken over the "brat effect" with the telephone. This consists of making a face at the receiver when the unseen party at the other end has hung up on you or has been otherwise unsatisfactory. No one ever did this before the movies invented it. It is now fairly common, and so is the finger count.

Yet some people doubt the cultural influence of the mass media.

vagrant and inconsecutive life of a prestige documentary called, presumably, *See It Now—and Then*. I shall return to this in discussing Mr. Murrow's career.)

In spite of the ill-temper of the parenthetical remarks above, I am proposing and will try to practice a new relationship between critic and broadcaster. The present situation is unsatisfactory because the heads of the industry are aggrieved by the "heavyweight critics," whom they accuse of blindness to the virtues, and morbid sensitivity to the defects, of broadcasting; the critics, on the other hand, know that, unless a gross breach of propriety occurs, they cannot arouse public indignation and are virtually impotent to affect the decisions of broadcasters and sponsors.

I suggest that, as a matter of good manners, critics do not use the broadcasters as whipping-boys for *all* the faults they find with the capitalist system, and that the changes they suggest should all be workable within that system. This would be intellectually more honest and would also save a lot of time. In return, I suggest that the broadcasters recognize the doctrine of *public right*—the right of the public to require certain services from the broadcaster—and also that they promise never to use any variation of the phrase about "giving the public what it wants" until a satisfactory study has been made of the way the public gets to want, or is persuaded to want, whatever it presumably wants.

In this spirit of mutual forbearance, critics and broadcasters can be useful to one another and to the public. Grandiose as it may sound, a new concept of broadcasting as a public art is needed, and the following pages are a preliminary survey of the elements involved. At the end of this section there is a report on a significant move made by a broadcaster indicating that the need for a new relationship to the public is felt on his side, too. The opportunity is a great one, the challenge equally great.

24

THE SITUATIONS OF EDWARD R. MURROW

In the course of his controversy with Edward R. Murrow, Senator Mc-Carthy informed the American people that Mr. Murrow had once belonged to an organization which, he implied, was nefarious to the point of subversion, if not of actual treason. In this way one fact about the private life of an exceptionally well-known person came to light. In a business essentially devoted to communication, using and abusing the arts of publicity, creating "personalities" overnight, Edward R. Murrow as a private citizen is almost unknown, although the way he works his tie loose and the somber gaze he turns on the tip of his cigarette are familiar to millions of people. One of the good minds and strong characters in broadcasting, to whom the prizes, the awards, and the solid returns of the business have come in full measure, Murrow enjoys the admiration of these millions and the respect of all but a fanatical minority of his opponents. He is a good workman with great gifts for his work and an acute sense of the broadcaster's responsibility to the public. The function that Norman Corwin could not completely fulfill because he was primarily an imaginative and creative force, Murrow takes over completely—he is the conscience of the broadcasting industry.

He comes from the Far West, and his early work was of the practical-idealist kind that barely falls short of uplift—he could almost have been called a do-gooder. The dangerous activity unearthed by Senator Mc-

Carthy was an entirely open effort to encourage the interchange of students between America and other countries, including, in the early 1930s, the Soviet Union. His interest in international affairs led him eventually to London and to broadcasting as the head of the CBS bureau there. Overseas broadcasting was largely a creation of the networks and was supported by them; until the threat to European peace became acute, the audience for reports from abroad was small. In all that time NBC and CBS kept developing their staffs, and Paul White at CBS supported Murrow, making him head of the European bureau, encouraging him to get good men and place them at strategic points (Shirer in Berlin was the most notable).

Because he was in London at the time, Murrow was not directly involved in the storm that broke over CBS when, by a single misstep, Paul White almost wrecked the brilliant international staff he had created. Quarreling with Cecil Brown, who had returned from working with Murrow in England and was taking a fresh look at America in wartime, White refused to let Brown continue to broadcast criticism that, he felt, was undermining citizen morale. Brown protested and left CBS. Rumors and reports in the press began to be embarrassing, and CBS, until then famous for its adroit approaches to the public, committed itself to a full page ad in the *New York Times* which attempted to state the network's position in favor of detachment and impartiality, but included an unhappy sentence implying that news analysts should have no "opinions" of their own. The analysts on the staff (who were not ever to be called "commentators") were affronted, and something like a total strike threatened. When the semantics of the matter had been cleared, Paul Kesten, the executive vice-president, made a speech on the responsibility of radio, and the internal maelstrom quieted down. Murrow's contribution to the public discussion was a rather indecisive statement in favor of truth and accuracy.

The event brought to light various concepts of the rights and duties of the broadcaster in relation to the news. These concepts still exist and are central to any understanding of the public position of broadcasters. After the war, and notably after the return of a Republican Congress (in 1946), a number of news commentators whose views were not hostile to the New Deal disappeared from the air. At the same time, commentators who favored the Republican party and held that the whole New Deal had been a move toward socialism were becoming more openly partisan in their reports, making no distinction between the news and their feeling about the news. Murrow, returning home from England in 1946, became a vice-president of CBS, in charge of news and public affairs, and while he held this position, he had to give the official explanation for the dismissal of William L. Shirer from the CBS staff of analysts. Shirer had been appointed to the Berlin spot by Murrow and had combined good reporting with an almost morose detestation of Hitlerism. After the war his general outlook remained in the liberal tradition, and when he lost his place at CBS, where he had been doing a sponsored analysis of the week's news on Sundays, it was suspected that his uncompromising attitude was at least a contributing cause. The CBS explanation was different: Mr. Shirer was accused of unwillingness to go after stories, preferring to reflect and analyze. (In *Stranger Come Home*, a novel about a broadcaster who is fired for his views, Mr. Shirer presents some highly synthetic characters who may bear some resemblance to himself and to Murrow; the latter figure is represented as hypocritical and spineless. The book came out just when Murrow risked his entire professional career in an all-out attack on McCarthy.)

When Murrow resigned as vice-president of CBS and became a newsanalyst, sponsored, his broadcasts were at first divided into the news and "one reporter's reaction" to the news, but after a time this partition wall was not so openly shoved into place. It still existed. Murrow separated his reports from his analysis and, it seemed to most critical listeners, tended more and more to be less and less bold in his utterance. Among the daily commentators, Fulton Lewis, Jr. was willing to say anything injurious to the Democratic party, and Elmer Davis was fighting with a magnificent armory of weapons for the free mind in our society. Murrow was never heard to make a mean or reactionary remark, but he was not fighting. One felt that possibly he did not think his review of the news was the place for the fight to be carried on. It is interesting to note that in private conversation Murrow has always expressed an unbounded admiration for Davis, and that he chose Raymond Swing, another aggressive liberal, when the pressure of TV programs forced him to get assistance in the preparation of his radio broadcasts.

It could be said, then, that as he approached his work in television, Murrow accepted the basic principles of news-broadcasting: fairness and accuracy in presentation of the news and no use of the broadcaster's position to further his private ends. He probably accepted Elmer Davis's thesis that, even if the reporter got all the facts, the dimension of meaning needed to be added and this meaning often required the presentation of other related facts. As Davis had pointed out, neither the commentator nor his sponsor should be allowed to deviate from the truth, but the commentator should be allowed to give his full judgment on meanings and motives. But Murrow was troubled by something. He was still a member of the CBS board of directors and powerful in its decisions on public policy, and he circulated to the CBS executives a memorandum that made his misgiving—his downright fear—explicit. He had perhaps noted that the singing star of a radio giveaway show had been displaced by another when the program went to television—the radio star had the better voice, but by far the ampler figure. He wondered whether an attractive dolt, beginning as a speaker of words written for him by a network news department, might not gain an audience, insist on becoming a "personality," and, step by step, use his position and the news to become a demagogue. Even if the final step did not occur, the debasing of the news was offensive to Murrow, who worked in the tradition of the great networks which holds that no sponsor, no individual, can turn the news to his own advantage. The memo was a warning. It had one amusing facet—the highly telegenic Murrow had less reason than most of his colleagues to worry about being supplanted.

For all that, his entrance into television was long delayed and carefully planned. He knew that the problems of the newscaster might be solved —not well, but at least passably—by using news clips, and that brisk operations might bring such films to the studio a few hours after an event took place. But the real and the factitious problems of the news-analyst were thornier. Illogical it certainly was for people to object to seeing Murrow read his reports, since they were so ready to hear him; but there was a psychological base for their feeling. Since they were paying attention with more of their faculties, they felt that they should be getting something more for their extra payment.

A man facing the camera and talking might pass, but a man reading a prepared text was not acceptable. This feeling was reinforced by the almost galvanic activity of some speakers who confused activity with visualization and gave the impression that a newscast was primarily a match between the reporter and the camera, to see which one would first reach the map or the photographic enlargement or the scale model.

(The most familiar question in this part of the business was "what to do with Walter Winchell," which was solved for a time by his refusal to go on television at all and then solved for good by doing nothing with him, but letting him do his show himself.)

Murrow's solution was different. He had given a sort of twenty-one-gun salute to radio by preparing an album of historical recordings called *I Can Hear It Now*. Reminding us of this title, he produced, with Fred W. Friendly, his series *See It Now*. Its only weakness at the beginning was that it depended so much on film. Its abiding strength is that it uses film with such brilliance of technique as to create virtually a new form. With this is coupled an editorial intelligence that makes *See It Now* the most important commercially sponsored program on the air—in certain ways the most important program, unconditionally and without reservation, of any kind. It is important for the solutions it has found for some problems and equally for the problems it has tackled without finding the right answers.

The techniques and the editorial intention work together, and the distinction of the program begins with the making of film expressly for the requirements of television, instead of picking up whatever footage has been shot for newsreel-theater purposes. Murrow has sometimes become infatuated with a phrase not necessarily appropriate to the matter in hand (as in his repeated assertion that television can "take you" places), but in this case his cliché fits into the nature of television. *See It Now* likes to give "the small picture" and does it by concentrating on individuals, or the expressions and gestures of individuals, rather than on larger effects. Both physically and psychologically, this is eminently what television most needs and can best handle. The emphasis on the small picture, the preference for showing not events, but the effect of events on people, served to separate *See It Now* from news broadcasts. Its relation to TV news is like that of a weekly news-review to the daily paper, and this remains true even on those occasions when the material is up-to-the-minute. The news cameramen of this program are exceptionally clear-minded as to what is wanted, and they usually manage to deliver; this is always true when Murrow himself goes into the field, as he did for his Christmas broadcasts from Korea. The sense of immediacy is great, and the slight effort to pretend that the program is not filmed is unnecessary and also misleading. (When Murrow says: "Come in, Berlin" in front of a TV screen bearing the word "Berlin," a faint deception is being practiced.)

Next to choosing the right shots, the outstanding technical device of *See It Now* is its intercutting for editorial effects. A typical example was the report on an event in Indianapolis, where, after being refused the use of many halls, a group of people met in the basement of a Catholic church to work out plans for creating a branch of the American Civil Liberties Union and, at the same time, a few blocks away, the local American Legion post met to denounce the other meeting. The issues involved were not trivial, and the passions were intense; by selecting those speakers who seemed to answer one another, the program had all the effect of an angry face-to-face debate. It had also the effect of almost mathematical impartiality. This aspect of the program was made even more conspicuous by a broadcast, within a short time of this one, in which Murrow gave all his time to one side: the case of Lieutenant Radulovich, who was to have been dropped by the Air Force without a stain on his character or a doubt as to his loyalty, on the specific ground that his sister and his father had been accused of holding certain opinions or of having received certain publications. Murrow gave only the young officer's side because the official side was not forthcoming in spite of his efforts. Failing to present both sides on the same program, Murrow offered time to the Air Force whenever it wished. (The offer was not accepted because the dismissal of Lieutenant Radulovich was revoked—with full credit given to Murrow for making the Air Force aware of the public opinion which, in turn, Murrow had so deeply stirred.)

This can be taken as the background for the most noteworthy of Murrow's programs: the series on Senator McCarthy. The essential element is a sense of responsibility, composed of several parts. It begins with Murrow's feeling about the world situation that makes news so important and the distortion of news so criminal. It goes on to his deep feeling that public emotion can be manipulated; his fear that the public may be so tricked that it will cease to want to be informed or will not too much mind being half-, ill-, or mis-informed; his concept of the duty of a broadcaster to his profession, which involves also his ideal of the sponsor-program relation (an ideal almost completely achieved with *See It Now* under the sponsorship of Alcoa). With this, Murrow has a concept of the way to handle controversy on the air which combines an editorial idea and a number of techniques of presentation. The parallel background for CBS includes the firm principle that news and programs connected with the news are not to be available to sponsors for handling —the CBS news department prepares its news programs and, for the most part, CBS analysts and reporters do the actual broadcasting. The right of stations and networks to go on the air and crusade for their corporate ideas has been established but hardly ever used, and, as a rule of thumb, controversies are excluded from sponsored programs on the solid ground that if they are not, the richest sponsor may completely silence his adversaries by purchase of preponderant time and by hiring the most skillful talents to present his views. Except for actual campaign time in local or Federal elections, time for controversy is allotted free by the networks. When, by exception, sponsored programs bring notable public figures to the studios to explain their work or defend their ideas, severe critics of the guests as well as supporters are usually present to ask questions and make incisive comment. In the Murrow-McCarthy case there was one other element: the tremendous prestige of the program itself. It had been running for two years, and each week it accumulated more respect, not only for its interest and skill, but precisely for its balance, its impartiality.

And one element was missing: the spirit of the crusader. A delicate sense of justice Murrow always had, and a capacity for resentment when justice was denied; he has also a feeling for the American tradition of independence. These were as much a part of him as his voice, giving tone and color to every comment he made. But he did not hunt out adversaries. He was not spoiling for a fight, for a chance to assert the truths that he held self-evident. And presently he undertook and carried through the most dangerous of all possible assignments at the time: he carried the war aggressively into McCarthy's territory, and for more than half a year thereafter McCarthy's fortunes went steadily down (there were other contributing factors, but it was plain that the McCarthy who appeared at the Army hearings had already suffered a tactical defeat and was aware of it).

What made Murrow decide to attack? Two factors, at least. One was the feeling that a juggernaut was rolling and that tomorrow or next day might be too late to stop it. The question had always been when the attack should be made and by whom, and Murrow had noticed that

Drew Pearson's sponsor had dropped him after McCarthy had virtually called for a boycott of the sponsor's product; also that a threat had been made against *Time* magazine; and that newspapers and book publishers were more and more under threat or under fire. And if the sands were running out and the danger was great, the machinery for the attack had to be the most powerful of all—which, for immediate effectiveness, was television and nothing else. Here, it seems to me, Murrow's second motive operated: his pride in the medium, his pride in its power properly used. With it, stemming from this pride, was the feeling that the power *ought* to be used, that not to use it was to commit the sin of *laches*; and here the exceptional circumstances of Murrow's relations with his sponsor worked beautifully in his behalf. For the Aluminum Company of America had accepted the old and almost forgotten role of sponsor-as-advertiser and had not asked for the common role of sponsor-as-programer. This meant non-interference with the material presented, and it also meant in practice that Alcoa did not necessarily know what any single program was going to be about. Alcoa, in fact, did not know that Murrow was going to exercise the privilege of dropping the commercial on six separate occasions in one year, and did not know that Murrow would repay his sponsor with a ten-minute feature about one of its operations as a reward to them for their indulgence. With this unusual backing, Murrow was able to commit a sponsored program to an attack on a controversial figure without committing the sponsor.

In discussing the ethics of the attack, Murrow referred to the network policy of offering equal time, yet it was not a network-produced program that started the matter, and the question of propriety remained unanswered. Could, for instance, U.S. Steel put on a play that was essentially propaganda for a political party? Could Reynolds Aluminum put on a documentary in favor of mccarthyism if not actually in favor of McCarthy? Is there a difference between these two suggestions because one involves fiction, the other fact?

In the political turmoil that followed the Murrow broadcast, one point became progressively more difficult to isolate: the propriety of his method. A weekly, generally liberal, refused to publish an analysis of the method lest it seem to be giving aid to McCarthy and all he stood for. Admiration for Murrow's courage and the feeling that television had at last, perhaps almost too late, come of age was widely expressed, and, with two exceptions, the only critics of Murrow's use of the medium were open adherents of McCarthy. The exceptions were John Cogley, who dissected the broadcast brilliantly in *The Commonweal*, of which he was then editor, and myself. I arrived long after Mr. Cogley, with the advantage of having also seen McCarthy's reply to Murrow, which proved what Mr. Cogley and I both suspected: that "equal time to answer" is—in television, at least—an empty formula. This is one of the central problems of broadcasting. Getting the right solution to all its component sub-problems is a matter of importance because if we take the wrong way out of our difficulties, the whole structure of free expression may be endangered, and with it, remote as it may seem, the structure of broadcast entertainment. The wrong answer will begin by giving too much power to those who hold the medium of television in their hands and will end by interference from the government in matters not only of controversy, but of programs. To prevent these things from happening, we have to examine the actualities as the Murrow-McCarthy dispute revealed them.

In describing the various elements that Murrow could bring into play, I briefly mentioned one: the prestige of the program. At this point it becomes the pivot on which the entire subject revolves. It is not for us to say that Senator McCarthy had his own prestige, because we have to separate the individual case from the general rule. We have to see not merely what happened to one individual but what might have happened to another. Partisans may test themselves by asking how they would have felt if news program "X" had devoted a program to the danger of creeping socialism, using Adlai Stevenson as its principal exponent; but we have to deny ourselves even that illuminating parallel. We have to inquire rigorously into the underlying principle—and the underlying psychological fact.

For here, as so often in any approach to television, we come to "the box"—the receiver in the home. To its screen, week after week, has come a program, and in the normal course of listening, out of every ten persons who hear it this week, six have heard it so often before that it has become an established part of their lives—familiar and, above all, *trustworthy*. I emphasize this because it appears to be a universal element, not limited to programs of news, discussion, or ideas. The listener has confidence in Jack Benny and in *Valiant Lady* and in something called *Rootytootooty*—confidence that it will be what he or she expects it to be. In the case of such a program as Murrow's, the confidence is that it will have a specific gravity, that it will be important, and, above all, that it will be what it claims to be.

In the case in point, Mr. Murrow said that this was a "report."

As a starting-point for virtually all consideration of the relation between commercial broadcasting and public affairs, it was the most important single broadcast ever made. After many months of discussion— with Mr. Murrow, with a group of professional analysts of the communications problems, and with laymen—the conclusions I reached within the month after the broadcast are somewhat modified. But my impression that it needed study in detail has become a conviction all the deeper because, as far as I know, the study has not been made. The questions Mr. Murrow brought up will rise to plague us again because the answers given are not, as lawyers say, "responsive"—they are not the permanent right answers, although they will do for the day.

To avoid even the appearance of quibbling, let it be assumed that in some senses the program *was* a report; in the overriding sense of the word *as it had been used for two years on that program*, it was not. A report on *See It Now* was and is as complete a report as Murrow and his associates can provide, filled out by relevant details, illuminated by the clash of opinion or by contrasts in approach. It is not necessarily a report by a neutral, but it is not, on the other side, a report by a partisan. It approaches the summing-up of a judge who marshals the evidence but does not prejudice the jury. It is not now and, except in this single instance, never was the summing-up of a hanging judge. In the Radulovich case the evidence or the argument of the opposition had been sought and refused; in the McCarthy case the evidence and the argument were copiously available, but were not used. Instead, the Senator was invited to present his own case.

Again we must approach the program as the audience receives it. The audience had come to ascribe a special meaning to the word "report" on the Alcoa program, to expect a particular kind of reporting. In addition, it had created in its mind certain associations, most of them pleasant, with the program itself. In a world too full of uncertainties, this program had the confidence of its listeners. Every time Murrow appears, he counts on this buildup—this stockpile—of faith and good will; whenever anyone else appears on this program, the continuity is broken— and, instead of confidence, a factor of doubt emerges. This has nothing to do with the public desire to hear the defense. It is a general challenge to the idea behind the formula of "equal time": the idea that a stranger appearing on a program to answer an attack delivered by the master of that program inherits the program's audience, prestige, and hold on the affections of the audience. Quite the reverse is true: he is psychologically an interruption that may be resented. He is attacking someone who has enjoyed the favor of the audience, and he is depriving them of what they are accustomed to have.

The formula blows up again because the accused may not possess the facilities for reply. In the McCarthy case the ratio of cost was something in the order of one to five—the average cost of a *See It Now* program is generally taken to lie between $25,000 and $30,000 and the cost of the reply was $6,000. A rather undignified squabble as to who should pay the bill brought this to light. The fact that an attacker might refuse to pay the costs of a reply completely nullifies the offer of free time—and demolishes the formula again—because it is conceivable that the offended person may have no resources. The ethics of the matter are simple. In the case of an unsponsored attack, the station or network should place at the disposal of the defense the same facilities, the same budget, and the same time on the air. A commercial program should put the same obligation upon the sponsor, who, it may be pointed out, loses nothing since the reply program takes the place of one he would otherwise have to finance. It would be Utopian to suggest that the attacker place also at the disposal of the defense the enthusiasm that is part of a good fight; it is not Utopian to suggest that among the facilities so offered there must be experts in writing, procurement of material, and production. Equal time, for all its essential value, must be filled.

The defense of the Murrow program is based on two things. The offer of time for a reply is one. The suggestion that no such offer needed to be made is implied in the second: the program was almost entirely composed of film clips of McCarthy in action, so that even in his introduction Murrow could suggest that McCarthy would be answering himself, not Murrow. This was good controversy, and it had a more solid base than, at the time, seemed possible, for the program as presented gave the impression of having selected *all* the clips unfavorable to McCarthy and virtually none in which he appeared to advantage. This was not the case. Murrow's most effective reply to my demurrers about his program was an offer to show me the unused clips—thousands of feet of film at least equally damaging to their subject.

The fundamental point still stands: by editing the films, by certain juxtapositions, by its commentary, the program created an integrated, one-sided picture of McCarthy. When it showed him being praised, the praise came from fools; when he was powerful, he met integrity and intellectual power stronger than his own; when he was pleasant, he seemed to be almost psychopathic. Arguable it may be that this is the true McCarthy—but it is not the only one.

And, in the nature of things, the other McCarthys could not be presented in such a way as to overcome the impression made by this one. That is the crux of the situation, and it leads to the dilemma of the honest broadcaster: how to use his striking-power freely and at the same time provide a defense which matches that power.

The McCarthy reply was a complete demonstration of the uselessness of the equal-time formula. It could not be prepared for several weeks, so it lacked quick reactive force. It was underbudgeted (because the formula did not supply funds), and the expensive job of collecting and editing and presenting the best materials could not be undertaken. And, for all his skill in argument, his persuasiveness or demagoguery, McCarthy apparently knows nothing about the technique of presenting anything but himself. His advisers must have been equally ignorant of the first principles of television production. The decision to use at least part of the time for an attack on Murrow's integrity does not come under the heading of unfair circumstances; it was entirely in keeping with McCarthy's technique of controversy. But the bad handling of cameras and the general air of sloppiness which made this error of judgment all the more disastrous can again be traced to the lack of time and money and to the unavailability, for one reason or another, of skillful, creative people who could compete with the superb crew that launched the attack.

Between the attack and the reply, Murrow devoted another program to McCarthy. It showed him and part of his committee examining Mrs. Annie Lee Moss. It was a performance in which, quite obviously, neither McCarthy nor his followers took any pleasure, for the Senator hurriedly abandoned the hearings to his counsel when the faint possibility that the witness was innocent began to appear, and counsel, giving the appearance of a man betrayed into a distasteful action, attempted to make good in McCarthy's absence. Murrow himself considers this a more effective broadcast than his frontal attack. It was not without comment of a sort—the camera picked up and seemed to hover over the empty chair —but McCarthy made news by vacating the chair, and the camera comment was justified. For the rest, this *was* a report, picked up by cameras on the spot—condensed and edited, no doubt, but retaining the essentials of the original event. The only objection a loyal McCarthyite could have is that Murrow never has shown McCarthy as a patriotic investigator scrupulously respecting the rights of others and acting within those rules of conduct which the Senate has approved, exposing a real enemy of our country who would otherwise have escaped. This is a legitimate point—it indicates precisely what McCarthy should have provided in his reply to Murrow; but it is not Murrow's fault that he has not been able to offer such a broadcast.

The *See It Now* series, of which the McCarthy broadcasts were a part, has naturally caught the attention of legislators and of organizations (such as the American Civil Liberties Union) interested in the possibility of establishing a new formula, if not a code, of fair play in broadcast controversy. Before any comprehensive solutions were offered, a much graver problem arose: was it desirable to have this program, with its hard-hitting character, on the air at all? The only ones who could actually do anything about it answered No. The program, as a weekly report touching on disputed issues, was dropped. The Aluminum Company of America continued its sponsorship, with avowed reluctance, for a year after the McCarthy affair. Then it bowed out. The motives leading CBS and Mr. Murrow not to go on are not public. The facts are: *See It Now* became an occasional program, of an hour or more, and among the topics announced were reports on New York and other cities; the first two put on the air were solid studies of the vice-presidency and of our school problem. Shortly after *See It Now* left the air, CBS found itself with a program of unexampled popularity, *The $64,000 Question*, which Murrow, if he had been kept in his original time slot, would have followed. Given the habits of the American people, their willingness to listen for a while at least to whatever follows on the channel they have been watching, this would have meant an audience perhaps five times as great as Murrow had ever reached. He never had a chance to attract that audience.

This is all the more significant because within the next six months several other provocative programs were either altered or dropped and even a brilliant anti-Communist single-shot documentary, *Nightmare in Red,* lost its expected sponsor and had difficulty finding another. Although most observers reported that the high passions agitating the American people during the McCarthy ascendancy had subsided, the broadcasters were palpably moving steadily toward safer positions.

This noted, I return to the lessons of the Murrow broadcast, for it is

---

BRAVE VP'S

The refusal of a network and sponsors to punish Lucille Ball for having registered as a Communist (to please her grandfather) shows that, no matter how obscure a person may be, no matter how few millions are invested in him or her, America gives fair play to all. And, as Anatole France pointed out, the law in its sublime majesty forbids the rich as well as the poor to sleep under bridges.

The networks have often been attacked for their timidity. Ten or fifteen letters send an executive into a tizzy out of which he issues with the new idea that the innocent are damned equally with the guilty because during the process of being proved innocent they have become "controversial figures."

It is all the more creditable, therefore, to the Columbia Broadcasting System that it did not yield to the hue and cry raised against Lucille Ball and also against Arthur Godfrey's politicking on his radio program. Godfrey has been controversial in half a dozen different ways—he airs his political views, his opinion on the rules laid down by the Weimeraner breeders, and his relations with drinking and non-drinking members of his company. But CBS has not been intimidated. Mr. Paul Draper must be happy to contemplate this exhibition of courage.

not only in times of violent argument, but in the day-to-day workings of attack and response that television has to observe good principles. The first Murrow program on McCarthy was, as I have said, the most important single broadcast in television, and if it was based on shaky foundations, we have to face the fact and proceed from there. Unless something better than the formula of equal time is discovered, I believe that the tremendous engines of communication must not be used for attacking an individual—except when they are being openly used in political campaigns or other situations accepted by the community. I do not believe that *at present* a sponsored program should be committed to such an attack, and I am not sure that commercial programs should have the privilege of attacking political or social or economic principles. I put it this way because at the same time I think that controversial ideas in all fields should be constantly aired and I fear that sustaining time will neither be amply offered nor, if offered, filled in such a way as to attract large audiences. I have a suspicion that attack and reply should occur at the same time—the only guarantee that the same audience will be reached and that the audience will not resent the presence of an adversary. If McCarthy had been given Murrow's facilities for fifteen minutes of the original broadcast, if producing the reply had been an obligation of the technicians who produced the attack, none of the questions here raised would have been significant.

The problem can be formulated in another way: standards of controversy in television must be established with due regard to the actualities of production and of reception, particularly the latter. Production will take into account both time and money, in the sense that unless the victim of attack knows in advance exactly what the attack will be, he cannot get his answer ready, in a well-made production, for several weeks, and he needs and is entitled to as much money as the attacker has spent. Reception will include those psychological factors I have mentioned—the stockpile of good will upon which the program rests, the dislike of breaks in routine, the natural tendency to believe one's friends (the constant visitors of radio and television are considered friends, even the fictional ones among them). Also taken into consideration will be the effect of an accusation that, giving all the appearances of being impartial, sinks deeper into the mind for weeks before any reply is heard.

I am impressed by a proposed solution to the basic problems involved which was offered by Professor Charles M. Siepmann (author of *Radio, Television, and Society*). It is that the broadcasters should not permit attacks upon *individuals* at all, and, on the other hand, should not be compelled to give time for reply when *ideas* are discussed. The basis of this is that ideas, even if they crystallize around the name of an individual, are in the public domain. I agree that nothing should be allowed to interfere with the free commerce of ideas, but I am troubled by the swampy ground lying between a solid attack on an individual and an equally solid attack on his ideas. The distinction is clear between a senator's finances or sexual morality and his vote on tariffs, but once these firm certainties are left behind, we come to a dangerous situation. It is that the broadcasters will be so intimidated by the threat of "free time for reply" that they will prevent the attack from being made. We shall have polite anonymous disagreement about abstractions—which is not quite the same thing as free speech on the air.

In the political campaign of 1954 the Democratic chairman asked for free time to reply to a televised meeting of the President's Cabinet on the ground that the timing of this event—the first of its kind—was political in purpose. (The handling of cameras and general "staging" of the questions and answers added to the "propaganda" effect, as if we were seeing, not an event taking place, but a "program.") Traditionally, a President is permitted to decide for himself whether he is being political or presidential. In this case, one network rejected the President's implied definition of his action and granted reply time to the Democrats, finding itself then in the awkward position of having to give a further period to the Republicans for rebuttal. The others stood on the issue of the presidential prerogative (but the specter of a vicious circle of replies and counter-replies had been glimpsed by all).

Without clear standards and rules, broadcasters will tend to play it safe, and the safest thing will be to avoid giving anyone any excuse for asking for free time. As for making rules, the difficulty is enormous, for rules are not so much made as evolved, and even when they are known and accepted, confusion can still arise. I note a parallel situation in the press with a tradition ten times as long as that of broadcasting. In the 1954 campaign the New York *Herald Tribune* ran a series of reports on the first two years of the Eisenhower administration, written by members of the Cabinet and other responsible Republicans. The *Herald Tribune* is a Republican paper, supporting the nominees of that party and often giving the appearance of wishing that the Democrats would not nominate such interesting candidates. After its series of articles had begun, Stephen Mitchell, then Chairman of the Democratic National Committee, protested that this was unfair and *demanded* equal space for Democratic leaders. The *Herald Tribune* gave the space, pleasantly enough. But no one, not even the paper itself, pointed out the huge impropriety of the demand. No newspaper is required by law to operate in the public interest; the press must obey certain laws, and if it does, it enjoys certain privileges; but the kind of pressure legitimate in broadcasting is totally out of place in the press, which is not the beneficiary of government action, which does not exist under Federal license and cannot be compelled to be impartial by any pressure except that of its readers. The moment a newspaper accepts compulsion (outside of the general laws of libel and a few others) it ceases to be part of a free press; whereas the conditions accepted by radio and TV stations spell out the obligations of the broadcaster and the conditional freedom he enjoys.

25

A PRIMER OF PROBLEMS

The Murrow-McCarthy case is in an important respect like many others involving the ethics of broadcasting: judgment on it was often based on the parallel between broadcasting and the press. A few years earlier, when the industry demanded the right to editorialize, the promise was made that the opposition would be invited to reply, as newspapers invite "letters to the editor." In a dispute over television coverage of a Senatorial committee following the Army-McCarthy hearings, the networks asked for the right to be present wherever the press was present. Regardless of the merits of the specific cases, this attempted assimilation of the camera-microphone combination to the printing-press suggests that neither the broadcasters nor their critics are completely aware of the social revolution through which we are passing. Broadcasters know that they are in competition with newspapers as disseminators of news and carriers of advertising, and magazine- and book-publishers know they compete with television for the leisure time of various segments of the public. The half-observed phenomenon is the arrival of a new form of communication on which a new culture can be based to combine with or supersede the culture based on the textbook, the novel, the biographical or philosophical study, the work of scholarship, the editorial, and—to be inclusive—the pulp magazine, the thriller, the tabloid, and the sexy best-seller.

In the following chapters I propose to discuss the major problems of broadcasting as they affect the public. My basic assumption is that these problems are aspects of a vast social change, not mere variants of the familiar problems of the press or any other form of communication. This is a heretical approach and leads even to such further heresies as questioning whether our new public arts actually are entitled to such privileges as freedom of the press. Knowing myself to be somewhat fanatical on the subject, I am presenting here a more impartial and more scholarly background than I myself can supply.

It comes from the work of a brilliant Canadian economist, the late Harold A. Innis, who wrote *The Bias of Communication* and *Empire and Communications* as by-products, in a way, of his studies of Canadian industries. Having dealt with the fur trade and cod fisheries, he came to another major source of Canada's wealth, wood pulp and paper. Here was an industry that prospered because men wanted to communicate with one another—for several hundred years paper and the human voice were the two basic means of communication. Innis went into the history of paper as far back as the papyrus and from that into a study of all forms of communication. The conclusion he reached was that *whenever you have a far-reaching change in the means of communication, a social change of equal consequence must occur.*

This is a simplification so gross that its revolutionary significance becomes almost a platitude. We had all known that the Reformation followed the introduction of printing. But Innis traced so many parallels in history that he was able to formulate the general law I have rephrased. By giving us this generalization, he provided an instrument for observing the present and, subject to correction, predicting the future.

The first application I make of Innis's principle is this:

Our intellectual heritage, the part of our lives which is crystallized around ideas, is essentially a "print" culture, and it overlaps the beginning of a culture of which the central instrument is the photo-electric cell—the "electronic" culture of the future. The development of high-speed color presses and the triumphs of pictorial journalism have shored up the foundations of the print culture, and we still think of ourselves as "readers." But our large-circulation magazines become more and more illustrations with accompanying text, and more and more they lean on the electronic arts—broadcasting and the movies—for subject matter. It causes no surprise to discover that the weekly with the third-largest newsstand sale in the United States is a calendar of broadcasting events to which a few pages of news and gossip have been added. There are other examples of the uneasy, in-between stage through which we are passing. Among these are the uncertain handling of television as an instrument of education, and the half-acceptance and half-rejection of the modes of broadcasting by political managers and by the churches. Even in small details we can see the signs of a transitional state: the statements printed on the label of a patent medicine are subject to stricter laws than the statements made about the same medicine by a television pitchman.

And it is not only transition we are undergoing, it is also upheaval, for another consequence of the Innis generalization is that each new form of communication is accompanied by a shift in power. Print shifted power from the preacher to the writer. The development of engraving took some of the power of the writer and gave it to the draughtsman, a shift made conspicuous by the appearance of the political cartoon on the editorial page of the newspaper. In the United States today, power has shifted to the manipulators of sight and sound, and these are largely associated with large-scale commerce in broadcasting and large-scale finance in the movies.

Whenever a shift in power occurs, those who are being deprived feel the earth trembling beneath them and hold fast to something firm— the institutions in which they have a vested interest and the principles on which these institutions are founded. They are often called reactionaries, but, by slowing up the process of change, they safeguard whatever in the old system can be useful in the new. The reason print did not destroy the Catholic Church, although it broke the Church's monopoly, is that in good time print was adapted to the uses of the Church. The parallel situation for us is the utilization of the electronic communications system in behalf of our print culture. It will not be completely successful; our print culture will have to adapt itself to the electronic system also. But, once we are aware of what is happening, we can control the speed of change and, to a large degree, the direction of change.

The urgency in the matter rises from the power of our new communications systems—the power to prevent people from understanding what is being communicated. I do not say it is their nature; certainly they have also the opposite power—to clarify ideas and compel attention. But the situation is the more dangerous because the whole entertainment side of broadcasting which surrounds its communication of ideas tends to create a mood of consent and acceptance; it cannot afford to stir and agitate the mind. We have the complex situation in which entertainment creates the audience for communication and then—to an extent—destroys our capacity to think about the facts and ideas communicated. The configuration in which the problems of the cold war and the ethics of using the hydrogen bomb have been discussed has been entertainment + high-pressure salesmanship + relaxation; and to this configuration we owe a new phenomenon: the average man and even the uneducated man have become aware of the major problems of their existence. It is profoundly important, it is as if popular education had suddenly been given the chance, which never existed before, of reaching everybody. And with it we have the warning that so far the configuration of entertainment and selling has not been favorable to the true purpose of education, which is to teach people to think independently, to discriminate, to use their faculties of judgment.

This is the background of the assumptions I have made in approaching the public problems of the mass media, most strikingly observed in television. They are problems of rights and obligations and lead inevitably to the question of whether the broadcasting industry must *necessarily* enjoy the same freedoms as the press has had or should be compelled to serve the public in totally new ways. The first three problems deal with aspects of freedom: the right to broadcast, the right to editorialize, and immunity from censorship. The others are concerned with duties and involve the introduction of color television, the complexities of using the ultra-high-frequency channels, the challenge to monopoly offered by pay-TV, and the possibilities of using either the commercial channels or a specially organized broadcasting service for education.

26

RIGHTS AND DUTIES I:

FREEDOM OF THE AIR

The most eloquent expression of the ideals of a free press is, I suppose, John Milton's *Areopagitica*, which was probably hand-set and printed in an edition of a few hundred copies, and, although truth is always truth, it seems rather unrealistic to impose seventeenth-century ideas on an instrument that sends sounds and images with the speed of light across an entire continent to a hundred million people who know Milton, to be sure—they call him Uncle Miltie—but have little in common with the handful of educated aristocrats to whom he addressed himself. It is a salutary thing to remember that freedom of the press was fought for because men wanted the right to criticize a king or a royal governor; it was written into our Bill of Rights by practical men (some of whom later attempted to suppress newspapers hostile to their policies). Taken as an absolute, freedom of the press has been used to defend the publication of sadistic and pornographic books for children and also to deny newsboys the benefits of the Social Security laws.

I use this most sensitive of all instances because I believe that all our general principles must be re-examined in view of the actual situation, which, as always, begins for me with the conditions of reception: Who is listening and looking? What equipment have they for discriminating between fact and falsehood, between the accurate and the distorted presentation of news and ideas? Where are they at the moment, and what else are they doing, and have they any habit of checking what they hear and see by consulting other sources? Do such other sources exist? Have people become conditioned to accept whatever they hear? Does the surrounding entertainment create a mood of consent? These are sample questions, and they should precede the other group, which can be more easily answered: Who is sending out the news? What training have the editors had? For what purpose is the news being used?

One of the questions above—do other, parallel sources exist?—is critical. The principles of free expression not only rose out of specific situations, they were accepted because of definite assumptions. Those lofty passages of Milton which cluster around the metaphor of a race between truth and falsehood assume that the truth will win when "the immortal garland is to be run for not without dust and heat," and every defender of the absolute right to publish takes it for granted that somehow, for every corrupt newspaper, another equally powerful will come into existence to give the reader the truth. We know now that this is an idle dream. We are familiar with a press totally free to publish what its owners want the readers to believe—where no opposition paper exists. We condemn it in the Soviet Union and tolerate it in a thousand cities and towns in the United States where only one daily survives. I do not put these two situations on a par because in the United States weekly magazines and radio and television all keep steadily before the citizen the warning that his local paper may be one-sided, while in the Soviet Union these other media exist only to reinforce what the State press has said. But in one essential aspect the two situations are alike: whether the opposition vanishes under the benign workings of the competitive system or because of a tyrannical decree, the result is still a one-idea'd community. According to our absolutists, the citizens of this community have no right to demand representation of other points of view—they have only the right to establish an opposition newspaper or broadcasting station. The right is theoretical—it must be implemented to be of any use.

The existence of an opposition, which underlies all nineteenth-century theorizing about freedom of expression, can no longer be assumed. Quite the contrary, we have seen mergers of newspapers and, even more impressive, the arrival of a kind of community of accepted ideas to which all the media of communication conform. It is roughly the body of accepted ideas of the vast majority of American citizens;

but as these accepted ideas make less and less room for the independent and the eccentric, the leeway for the slightest difference of opinion will become more and more constricted until in the end we will have a kind of one-level, if not exactly one-party, press, reinforced by one-level neutralized broadcasting, and our inhospitality to bold off-center thinking will be too close for comfort to the situation we abhor in the monolithic (which is also the monotheoretical) State.

As television can be a rival or countervailing force against a one-sided press, equal access to news sources would seem highly desirable. The only question is: How would television handle the news? Here the experience of the past few years is illuminating. When the broadcasters were barred from a Senate committee meeting, they protested earnestly and forced a modification of the rules. Conspicuously absent from the argument was any suggestion that the broadcasters had a duty to perform to the public. It would indeed have been embarrassing for the most powerful figures in the industry to speak of responsibilities because they had only a short time earlier ducked from under in the most frivolous and irresponsible manner.

The Army-McCarthy hearings were carried by the Dumont network over all its stations from the first day to the last. The American Broadcasting Company carried the hearings from beginning to end, but only as far as Denver. This operation cost the network ten thousand dollars daily; the additional cost to reach the entire West Coast would have been nearly a hundred thousand dollars a week. Neither Dumont nor ABC had to cancel as many commercial programs as their two more powerful rivals; on the other hand, neither of them had been making much money as compared with the big networks. NBC carried the hearings all the way to the Coast for a few days and then, announcing that *there was not enough public interest* to justify the expense, contented itself with copious excerpts from the hearings shown late in the evening. CBS did not carry the hearings at all, but put on the news clips late at night; the reason given was that it was not in the best interests of the public for all the networks to carry the same thing, since this deprived the audience of its right to select what it wished to see.

The action of CBS was an impudent smack across the face of the audience. (A few months earlier CBS had carried the Ford fiftieth-anniversary program and a few months *later* CBS carried the Anniversary of Light program, both of which were on all the networks—and both of which were commercially sponsored.) The simple fact is that canceling programs is an expensive business and carrying-charges for transcontinental transmissions are high; moreover, CBS has at midday a number of daytime serials which depend on unbroken continuity for their success. This financial circumstance could have been explained to the audience, had the simplest arrangements been made in advance— arrangements by which each network would carry a portion of the hearings, the division being made in such a way that the income lost by each would be kept to a minimum.

This would also have saved NBC from weakening its approach to the public. By starting off with the transmissions, NBC gathered some prestige, which it promptly sacrificed. At the same time, it was clear that NBC was thinking of the public as "audience," and to a broadcaster an audience has no rights except the right to turn off a program it does not like. The public does have rights, however; it has expectations; and if all the measuring devices say that the number of people watching the Army-McCarthy hearings is not big enough to interest a sponsor, it still does not mean that the portion of the public which is watching may with impunity be deprived of the opportunity. Actually, the intrusion of a *rating* into this discussion betrayed the network doubly. First, NBC had committed the unpardonable intellectual sin of thinking of the public, the people of America, as "audience." Second, interest in the proceedings remained high and reached new levels many days after NBC had dropped them. NBC had only succeeded in bringing up questions that may return to plague it: How much interest is enough interest —or how commercial-minded can you get?

This is the unsatisfactory background of the network demand to be allowed to transmit hearings. The managers assert rights as if they were entirely private enterprises—but they are, as Constitutional lawyers say, "affected with the public interest," and they function because the public allows them to. They are not actually so free as a newspaper may be to drop an event or even to smother it. The newspapers of the country covered the hearings in a variety of ways, and what the *New York Times* did may be taken superficially as a parallel to the action of NBC. The *Times* began by printing the testimony verbatim; after a week or so, it skipped repetitions and the texts of documents already known, and, in general, gave full but not total coverage. Other papers gave highlights and little more; no newspaper, as far as I know, omitted the hearings entirely. Nor did any TV station—because all of them mentioned the affair in their news summaries. But the record of primary coverage makes it clear that the broadcasters do not feel obliged in any way to serve the public if they can make more money by not serving it.

The right to broadcast can be discussed only in connection with the duty to broadcast. Neither the broadcasters nor the public is ready to define the right and duty, but this is clear: If a network will act on no principle, if it will carry a hearing when convenient and drop it when the cost is excessive, then the networks will have a profound influence on American political life—for the hearings they do transmit will acquire a special value, and those they ignore will be relatively unknown to the public. This has always been true of newspaper reporting, but the press does not use frequencies belonging to the public; nor is the press quite so capable as television of taking events out of the public mind, since out-of-town newspapers as well as magazines can correct the partiality or partisanship of the press. But if no network covers a hearing, vast numbers of people will either know nothing of it or consider it negligible—and the power so to manipulate our political responses should not be in the hands of commercial broadcasting.

27

RIGHTS AND DUTIES II:

THE RIGHT TO PERSUADE

By long tradition, the press in the United States has the right to publish
the truth and also to publish half-truths and lies at the risk of being
sued by an injured party. Television has only the first of these rights.
A broadcaster who consistently colors the news may be denied renewal of his license. By so much his freedom is limited. Until a few
years ago the broadcaster was also denied the privilege of persuading
his listeners. Although he now has this right, certain ambiguities still
exist, and this question is rather like a new continent whose outlines
are changed as fresh expeditions explore the coast. The right of a station
or a network to speak "in its own person" came into being because the
networks kept fighting the previous ruling, which was made in 1941
when the F.C.C. declared that a New England station had exceeded
its rights when its news editor, speaking for the station, urged voters
to favor one side in an election—this was known as the Mayflower case.
In 1949 the right to take sides was acknowledged by the F.C.C., but
only if the broadcasters provided an opponent to their own views—a
condition that has led to some embarrassment when a station came out
for a law that no one wanted to oppose in public.

The confusion about the meaning of the law rises actually from
the unwillingness of the broadcasters to use their freedom. In 1954

when Frank Stanton went on the air to put forth the views of CBS in the matter of access to public hearings, the event was marked as unique —it was the first time a *network* had so spoken. This was legitimate; it would have been legitimate also for CBS to buy time on the air, from its own or other stations, to make its point. I am convinced that the F.C.C. never intended to prevent broadcasters from defending their own interests on the air, although the Mayflower decision may have had this additional effect. The intent of the original ruling was to prevent the broadcasters from using their channels and their prestige to influence people on matters of public debate in which the stations and networks were *not* specifically involved: as on new tax laws or immigration laws or locally on new bond issues. Broadcasters might feel themselves concerned with revisions of the Taft-Hartley Act or new corporation taxes—but editorializing or propagandizing on these subjects, the F.C.C. originally had said, was improper. As no network took advantage of the reversal until the subject of access to public hearings came up, the question of access and the question of editorializing became entangled. Some time later General Sarnoff (speaking extemporaneously in a reply to a question) agreed completely with Stanton's position on access to hearings, and then dissociated this question from the editorial problem:

"What is a network editorial? Is an editorial only an editorial when it talks about the interest of the network, or is an editorial an editorial when it talks about any public questions that may be controversial and vital? If it be the latter—and I assume it must be included in the definition—then I want to distinguish between the right of a network to editorialize, which I think it should have, and the execution of that right, which is a matter of policy, of wisdom, of importance and circumstances at a particular time. A policeman should certainly have the right to carry a loaded pistol, but the execution, the firing of that pistol, is quite another matter as distinguished from his right to carry it. . . .

"It is not enough to say that [the broadcaster] will give 'the other side' an opportunity to answer because the question is, what is the other side? . . .

"And who is to select the exponent of the other side? And how often will that right to editorialize be exercised by a network? Will it be a daily editorial as in a newspaper? And if so, is it practical to give 'the other side' an equal opportunity to answer daily?

"If the right to editorialize is not confined to the interest of the network itself or the interests of the radio art and industry, in which the network or its owner also has an interest, but is extended to other public or political questions—that is, if the network is to have the same right as the newspaper has to editorialize—it follows that it must have the same political rights. Thus a network could be a Republican network or a Democratic network, or the network of some other legally recognized political faith. It so happens that now there are only four TV networks, and it is conceivable that all four networks could become Republican, or all four might become Democratic networks. Surely this cannot be anyone's intention, for such a condition would be highly undesirable. . . ."

General Sarnoff then noted that daily replies to daily editorials would be impractical, and announced that NBC would not now abandon its policy, which is not to editorialize. He made a distinction between network and local stations, holding that the latter "might well exercise their right in their local communities; especially when a great many of them served one region, an independent partisan station would not be improper." He did not approve in any way of a network imposing its editorial views on a local station.

The unimplemented CBS policy is to editorialize on any subject it considers suitable. Prepared for submission to the F.C.C. during the argument on the matter were sample editorials on subjects rousing acute partisan feelings, such as the use of public funds for bus service to religious schools. The disuse of the right is perhaps the fullest commentary on the obstacles to free discussion on the air. I have alluded to the argument that the answer to a network editorial would have the same value as a letter to the editor has on a newspaper. The disparity in influence between an editorial (especially if printed on page one) and a letter to the editor is manifest. When President Stanton of CBS went on the air to defend a company policy, he announced that the distinguished jurist Harold L. Medina would answer him a week later. But the assumption that a protesting voice, admitted to the air by a network, has the power and the prestige of the network itself or the grateful allegiance of the audience, is sheer nonsense.

A minor point in connection with rights and freedoms is that the networks apparently have no status, not being licensed by the F.C.C. I have referred to this anomaly in another connection on page 123. The special point here is that the public has no redress, through the F.C.C., if a network fails in its duty because the present system allocates portions of the air to stations only. A network usually owns some stations and has arrangements with others, its affiliates, but as a corporation it does not put programs on the air. It creates them, but it can get to the air only by way of one of its "owned and operated" stations or, less commonly, through an affiliate. It is a link between sponsors and stations, between stations and the public, but the network itself does not use the fundamental element which the F.C.C. allots and in return for which the F.C.C. exacts promises from broadcasters: a part of the frequency waveband.

To require the networks to be licensed by the government is to subject them to conditions that can amount to restraint in their operations. As one of these operations is the supply of news to the citizens, licensing might become a harassment leading to limitation on free speech and free publication.

If networks had created a forum for the discussion of their public problems, they could now bring their case to the people—a strong case. Without this continuing forum, every time a network speaks, it appears as a special pleader. In the matter of licensing, which is of vital importance, no appeal to the people has been made. So far the proposal has not been embodied in a Congressional bill, but it was discussed in connection with fairly open threats from a Congressional committee to the broadcasters—a veiled warning to "clean house" or else. (The specific instance was the one I have mentioned—the appearance of more tipplers in dramatic programs than some committee members felt was desirable.)

28

RIGHTS AND DUTIES III:

THE LIMITATIONS OF FREEDOM

The movies encountered censorship when the handling of sexual and marriage problems and the presentation of seductive women offended organized sections of the public. The TV screen is not at present a good medium for voluptuous charms, and sex is filtered out. The demand for censorship concentrates on a single phase of broadcasting—programs of crime and sadistic violence—and on these only because they can be seen by children.

There is a double problem here: whether these programs are so numerous as to be harmful is the first; the other is what to do about them, harmful or not, in view of a rising sentiment against them. The second of these questions is the more involved and the more important, and I shall treat the first summarily to provide background for an examination of the second. There is not, in fact, sufficient data for a thorough study of the influence of horror programs on children, and the arguments adduced for and against them are the same as the ones met in the parallel field of the horror-comic book. The position has been taken that in order to develop a realistic view of the world, children must know about crime and cruelty, and that seeing such programs is the present-day equivalent of reading dime novels, affording the child a desirable excitement and some kind of psychological satisfaction as well.

No defender of these programs has set a limit on the number of hours a child should spend with them before the law of diminishing psychological returns sets in. No one has discussed the difference in impact between the illustrated magazine and the acted-out event on the home screen, or the difference in effect of the movie Western with the Westerns now made for viewing at home. On these questions also a lack of information invalidates most of the argument.

Outside the argument stands the fact that a quarter-hour devoted to one type of program cannot be devoted to another and that if several types of programs are available at the same time, the viewer can observe only one. These truisms become significant by multiplication. At one time programs based on crime took up about one hour of every seven in the metropolitan area of New York and on some stations crime and Western programs together ran from a fifth to a third of their total time on the air. Although energetic protests had been made, the number of crime programs *increased* in a year by fifty per cent.

One consequence of the popularity of these programs is that so little effort is made to produce anything of positive value. A few programs for very small children, keeping them pleasantly occupied while mother makes the beds, have been presented, and of these, *Ding Dong School* has become the exemplar. A few programs bow to literature and the arts, also. But the need for bold imaginative creation for children will never be acutely felt while the standard of acceptability remains what it has been in broadcasting from the start: as long as no positive proof of harm is presented, the program may be transmitted. It is as meager an ethical standard as can be imagined.

This is far from convicting the broadcasters of anti-social action, and it is also far from providing any grounds for the various moves proposed to improve the situation. My own ground is that, no matter how beneficial and inspiring these crime programs may be, no matter how essential to the development of a mature outlook, room should be provided for other types of programing even if they are less socially useful. I hold to the principle, expounded elsewhere in this book, that variety is even more important than excellence, and this must be particularly true in regard to children who are forming their interests. The preponderance of one kind of entertainment prevents them from getting to know others that are at least as suitable to their years, and this becomes even more effective when the technical excellence of this single type is by far superior. In a study made of all children's programs by the National Association for Better Radio and Television, some twenty programs were listed as desirable, and it was noted that the budget of a single (un-desirable) Western was larger than the budgets of all the twenty other programs put together.

It was, I believe, this concrete bit of evidence that brought the 1954 report of this organization so much publicity. The vast disparity between the two sets of cost figures dramatized the difficulty of penetrating through the crime barrier to the mind of the child. As it happened, investigations of crime books were going on at the same time, and the consequent outcry revealed an almost panicky state of mind in which proposals to nullify the First Amendment were often heard, and the mildest proposals were for a self-censorship harsher than that of the Hollywood Code. The same Senate committee which had seen a "czar" set up over the publication of crime books heard its chairman (in what he called an "offhand" way) suggest that government policing might be the alternative to self-censorship (with a czar to keep it active) in television. It also received testimony as to the incidence of violence in children's programs: there were about fifteen separate instances per hour, more than twice as many as appeared on programs intended primarily for adults. (These figures are for 1953–1954, several years after the percentages given above.)

This is the background of the agitation that sporadically flares up, a little more urgent each time, a little more likely to influence Congressional committees. In the public mind, a ratio between crime programs and delinquency begins to be accepted as demonstrated fact—which it is not—and as parallel implications about horror books and crime movies become part of a single argument, the call for action is louder than the voice of reason. Two of the more responsible proposals can be compared because, with the same end in view, they are opposite in approach. The first comes from Walter Lippmann's newspaper column.

Noting that the crime rate of youths of eighteen and under has been rising four times as rapidly as the crime rate for adults, Lippmann suggested three lines of action. The first two concerned parental responsibility and the disciplinary power of the schools. "The third is to intervene to protect the country, and particularly the adolescents, against the morbid stimulation they now get from comic books, and much of the movies and of television." Of this he then says:

"There can be no real doubt, it seems to me, that the movies and television and the comic books are purveying violence and lust to a vicious and intolerable degree. There can be no real doubt that public exhibitions of sadism tend to excite sadistic desires and to teach the audience how to gratify sadistic desires. Nor can there be any real doubt that there is a close connection between the suddenness of the increase in sadistic crimes and the new vogue of sadism among the mass media of entertainment.

"Censorship is no doubt a clumsy and usually a stupid and self-defeating remedy for such evils. But a continual exposure of a generation to the commercial exploitation of the enjoyment of violence and cruelty is one way to corrode the foundations of a civilized society. For my own part, believing as I do in freedom of speech and thought, I see no objection in principle to censorship of the mass entertainment of the young. Until some more refined way is worked out of controlling this evil thing, the risks to our liberties are, I believe, decidedly less than the risks of unmanageable violence."

Arthur H. DeBra, an executive of the Motion Picture Association (the Will Hays, and then the Eric Johnston, Office), replied to Mr. Lippmann's strictures as they concerned the movies, and Mr. Lippmann then wrote:

"Mr. DeBra does not deny that the movies, for which he speaks, are purveying violence, lust and sadism. He contends, however, that it is 'a confusion of cause and effect' to say that such movies incite to violence, lust and sadism. Mr. DeBra's opinion is that the presentation of these movies is 'a reflection of the *concern* of the public with these things and a desire to see them dramatized in the mass media.' . . .

"Mr. DeBra's argument makes it difficult to believe that the Motion Picture Association is willing and able to exercise adequate control over anti-social motion pictures. If these are the theories of the voluntary censors, it is easy to understand why when one goes to a movie theater one sees so often what one sees, a calculated and deliberate exploitation of violence, cruelty and lust. Mr. DeBra's theory will either have to be revised so that the voluntary control is greatly improved or the law will have to be invoked. . . .

"As a matter of fact no one, and that includes Mr. DeBra, can believe that young people, and for that matter adults, can watch the enactment of scenes of violent lust, of extreme cruelty, of roaring brutality, and be unaffected by them. . . .

"The Production Code Administration is deluding itself if it thinks that 'the sympathy of the audience' is turned against evil by . . . an ending in which the wicked man is punished. The sadistic scenes are far more compelling than the scenes of moral retribution. For in them we experience without civilized restraint the play of the most powerful underlying impulses and passions of human nature. The effect of this experience is to make these impulses much harder to restrain. In juveniles who for one reason or another are weak, neglected, unloved, disoriented, there is no denying that the experience of evil makes for evil."

Those familiar with the usual line of argument will see both the strength and the weakness of Mr. Lippmann's final paragraph. He has spoken earlier of the effect of scenes of violence on "young people, and for that matter adults," and here at the end he speaks of the particular segment of the young who are more likely than others to experience evil effects. The reason for this, I take it, is the basic defense, implicit or explicit, the numerical fact that crime books and pictures and programs are seen by millions of children who do not become delinquent. This is offered as proof that these entertainments are in themselves incapable of causing crime. Otherwise, and more cruelly expressed, the defense is that the delinquents were predisposed (blessed word!) to crime. There they stop, not having the courage to call these children predestined sinners, as Jonathan Edwards might have put it, nor do they dare to assert that the books and the pictures and the programs were only the instruments that an angry God deliberately put in their hands to encompass their downfall. "Predisposition" is as ill-documented as any other portion of the argument, but it has to be acknowledged, as Mr. Lippmann has done; it does not invalidate the bill of complaint against the effect of the horror merchandise on the *entire* community.

The singular merit of Mr. Lippmann's presentation does not, however, lie in the second of these articles, but in the final lines of the first. Here we have, for the first time in my knowledge, a man genuinely concerned with our liberties who faces the consequences of the decision he feels forced to make, chief of which is "the risks to our liberties." He recognizes a slight weakening of the guarantees of the Bill of Rights, weighs it against other dangers, and decides that temporarily ("until some more refined way is worked out") we must risk it. We have all, I believe, heard legislators propose bills to license the press and declare that they were not breaching the First Amendment. We have even heard the Supreme Court refuse to grant the movies the protection of this cardinal law (and witnessed also the reversal of this opinion). The truth is that a kind of panic overtakes legislators, as it does other people, at times, and they do not see what their proposals involve until it is too late, at which time they conveniently deny that they are doing anything more than invoking the police power. I have myself been so pressed in debate on the horror books as to say that I believed some legislation would have to be passed. My motives were of the best—I wanted to get something done before outraged feelings of a large number of people, supported by a sudden reaction against some book-inspired crime, would lead to legislative lynching. But I stammered around the consequences, being unable then, as I fear I still am, to accept even the limited restriction that Mr. Lippmann can face. Within three months after Mr. Lippmann wrote, the producers of many of the crime books promulgated a Draconian code, depriving themselves, among other things, of the privilege of using ghoulish words in the names of their magazines and vampires and werewolves in their stories. It remains to be seen whether the producers of children's programs in television will be so self-denying.

If they are not, a proposal superficially more attractive than the appointment of a "czar" or policing by the F.C.C. has been made—originally, I believe, by John Crosby of the New York *Herald Tribune*. It is simply that the networks take away from sponsors and their agencies the right to create programs for children, reserving it to themselves as they reserve the right to prepare and present the news. Mr. Crosby feels that the parallel is close enough, that news is too essential a commodity to be left in the hands of people who cannot be called to account for any tampering they may do and that children's programs are equally important. The effect of false news reports is a sort of corruption of the body politic; the effect of bad programs is a corruption of the health of children. A mild and sensible proposal it appears to be—and it is as good an example as any of the complexities of the broadcasting business. It is also a good test case for working out principles.

We have to start with the differences in raw materials and proceed to the final consumption of the product. At every point we see essential differences. An area of ascertainable fact is the first thing we recognize about the news—there is no such area about fiction of any kind. News may be slanted or items omitted (and both of these may be defended as matters of judgment), but falsehoods can be denounced, and, in fact, the F.C.C. appears to have ample authority to punish even undue prejudice in handling news.

A SHOCKING IDEA

Programs for children on the BBC, according to Enid Love, who is its assistant head of School Broadcasting, "must be planned and produced by men and women with a genuine concern for the well-being of children as well as a feeling for the medium with which they work."

This is respectfully submitted to the manufacturers of fare for our own little ones.

But of course these English tolerate do-gooders, people genuinely concerned with the well-being of others. We do not. We have a few nasty phrases to characterize those who dare to criticize *anything* our free-enterprisers put on the air, summed up in the classic: "To criticize radio—why, that's un-American." One reason is that reformers and do-gooders are the first to criticize.

They are no doubt tiresome people, and you can go back to H. L. Mencken and find a treasury of abuse for them. They saddled Prohibition on us, didn't they?

Still, the next time the nasty word is used, I wish someone would ask: Would you rather leave everything in the hands of the do-badders?

The preparation of the news almost always begins with the factual reports transmitted to broadcasting stations by the news services. Certain programs for children may also start from fact, but if fiction is admitted, we have to begin with the creative act. In the nature of things, no standards comparable to those of the Associated Press and the United Press exist for workers in the imagination. It becomes slightly tedious for the reader, I am sure, to note these uninteresting differences, but the proposals made to govern any portion of broadcasting are of vital importance, and the failure of any man, with access to the public, with influence on the business, to analyze the essentials of a proposal is as dangerous as the panic flight to legislation.

The practical difficulties can always be circumvented. The Crosby system would virtually compel affiliates of a network to use its programs whether they liked them or not, the alternative being to create programs of their own, which few small stations are capable of doing. Perhaps the flagship station or the few owned stations that are the center of the network could create a variety of programs for children, and, since no others would be available, sponsors would have to buy them. There remains the enormous area of the independent stations. For these, not under the moral domination of Mr. Crosby's virtuous networks, packagers and Hollywood entrepreneurs will create one series after another, and they will not have to be too gory because the network series, by definition, will be anemic. Nothing in the world prevents stations (even stations with network affiliations) from carrying these independent productions, and if the history of broadcasting in its first thirty years is any criterion, nothing will prevent some stations from carrying any program, however repulsive to the sensitive judgment of a small portion of the community, provided a sponsor pays for it and the majority of citizens either accept it with pleasure, or are indifferent to it, or simply have not heard about it. Individual protests are impressive only if they get into print. Otherwise, protests are considered as coming from the "lunatic fringe." Any *organized* protest to sponsors, any threat from considerable groups of parents that they will prevent their children from viewing certain programs and from buying the sponsors' products, has a chance of success. But so far the protesting groups have been able to muster only the tiniest memberships. The sponsors know that they can count on apathy, neutrality, and positive enthusiasm to outweigh criticism a thousand or ten thousand times.

It is therefore not at all certain that forcing the networks to create their children's programs will keep inferior programs off the air. The net result may be that the most popular stations will for a time carry programs that are conceived by the networks, blessed by child psychologists, and possibly quite popular. The question remains whether there is any justification for putting this burden on the networks and whether the networks have any right to say that they will not allow any other agency to create programs for children.

No one has yet suggested legislation (with penalties) to compel the networks to create their own programs for children—only a kind of moral imperative for which a hidden justification actually exists. When Congress passed the first act setting up the radio commission that later became the F.C.C., including in that act the famous phrases about public convenience, interest, and necessity, *all* programs were created by stations. No one else was in the business—no advertising- or talent-agencies, no sponsors. So it can be argued that Congress meant stations to be licensed to carry on their business of *transmitting programs that they had themselves created*—and nothing else. This will not stand up before the F.C.C. or the Supreme Court, I am well aware, but it provides a background of intention which clearly justifies the public in saying to the broadcasters, "When any part of your business touches us in a peculiarly sensitive area, make yourself directly responsible to us— not outside agencies, not someone we cannot immediately hold to account."

While this would be only a moderate burden to put upon the stations and networks, it would be an intolerable interference with the business of others, for in effect the broadcasters would be saying, "No matter how good your programs may be, we will not allow you to put them on the air." It is true that this is precisely what they say in respect to the news, and, for the sake of principle only, I should like to see this position challenged; the arguments on both sides might clarify the whole issue, still clouded, of the broadcaster's rights—particularly the right to refuse programs. The simple fact is that stations and networks have always asserted this right, but in varying degrees. When they have been prosperous, they have laid down rules for sponsors to obey; when prosperity waned, rules were relaxed—the connection between wealth and the luxury of high moral standards, which Bernard Shaw among others observed, has been beautifully demonstrated. The network's right has been more fully exercised in regard to programs than to commercials. There was the celebrated case of "Lucky Strike Green Has Gone to War," a slogan irritating to many people and possibly disruptive of morale in the anxious days of the war, since it injected a tone of mystery, a kind of promise of good news when the mystery would be unveiled. CBS had positive proof of the irritation and begged the sponsor and his agency to abandon the slogan, but it was not dropped until George Washington Hill, the president of the American Tobacco Company, was convinced that it had done its work for Lucky Strike. On the other hand, the sponsor of an inexpensive and undistinguished program lying between two popular shows on a Sunday evening was ordered to provide better entertainment or give up his time.

In self-defense, networks and many stations have their own censors— usually a small department on the lookout for inadvertent slander, for which they, rather than a sponsor, might be held responsible, as well as for blasphemy, smut, and sly double meanings. This department (Continuity Acceptance is one name under which it operates) has the power, if backed by the executives, of rejecting a script on the grounds of public policy, as it would a play glorifying pacifism in wartime, a talk urging armed rebellion at any time. The limitations have never been set down, but a station refusing to broadcast a series of programs because it is too vulgar, tasteless, or dull would probably find that very series on a rival station, and unless other, better programs with equal profit came along, the high-minded broadcaster would soon be compelled to lower his standards. The power to reject programs—not because someone else has made them, but simply because they are no good—remains with the broadcaster and must remain with him because he—not the sponsor—is answerable to the F.C.C. and to the public. It is the failure to exercise this right—not the lack of other rules and regulations—which has let our air become polluted (according to the critics) with crime programs for children which (according to the critics) do incalculable harm.

I have suggested that more data is needed about the effect of these programs, but one point should be made clear: The burden of proof is not on the public. They need only say "We do not like this program." When they say this in sufficient numbers, the program will disappear. It is only when we begin to talk about laws and action from the F.C.C. *compelling* broadcasters to follow certain rules that proof can be demanded.

Motion-picture exhibitors in the United States have constantly fought against a rating system for pictures which identifies those suitable for adults only. There are good arguments for both sides. When broadcasters meet this problem, they reach for their time-zone clocks, on the assumption that children go to bed at nine or ten o'clock in whatever zone they may be. A coast-to-coast network program designed to escape the attention of little ones could therefore not be presented before midnight in the East. A safe (ten o'clock) crime in New York would still catch the young on the banks of the Mississippi.

These young, according to a fairly popular view, are to be deprived of the pleasures of crime by their parents, who will send the brats to bed. This is parallel to the argument for depriving all citizens of the right to complain about programs because "they can turn it off, can't

---

TURNABOUT

So much is said about the effect of television on children and so little of the effect of children on television! A research bureau reports that "70% of the kids ask their parents to buy products advertised on television. And 80% of the parents *do it!*" Reported elsewhere and not verified is the case of a child who compelled his mother to buy a certain brand of dog food although they had no dog.

Another bureau reports that households with children watch television from eight to ten hours more per week than those composed of adults only, that children are more than half of all the viewers from three to six P.M., and that even after the presumed bedtime of the little ones, they constitute more than a quarter of the entire audience—up to midnight.

The first-mentioned study is charmingly entitled "And a Little Child Shall Lead Them—to YOUR PRODUCT."

they?" I have dissected the latter bit of sophistry elsewhere and my position has in turn been analyzed and rebutted, but I am forced to stay with it: Not what anyone can turn *off*, but what nearly everyone turns *to*, creates the moral and intellectual and emotional climate in which we live, and we can no more escape the consequences of a powerful series of broadcasts than we escape the consequences of an atomic bomb by going underground. We shall perhaps survive, but not in the world we thought we were making.

The authority of parents over children has been undermined by many institutions in our time. Reactionaries, conservatives, and some radicals blame the progressive school; the churches are blamed; the wars we have gone through and the statesmanship we have suffered are blamed; our writers are blamed. The mass media, I am happy to say, are seldom, if ever, called to account. For fifty years the movies, for thirty years broadcasting, have steadily belittled parents, steadily made the mature and the intelligent into the butts of comedy; and in the past twenty years advertising has gone over the heads of parents to use children, setting them against parents if need be. It is not an irreversible trend, but as long as it continues let no intelligent person say that if parents do not like a program they can prevent their children from seeing it. They can, at home, at a fearful price in domestic disharmony; they cannot, without reverting to an autocratic system of parental authority, keep their children from seeing programs elsewhere. A little realism here is required.

And perhaps a little philosophy for grownups. For if we should ever be able to *prove* that harm comes to adults from some of the programs they see, will the precedent we have set for children apply? It is not so remote a possibility as it may seem. It is certainly a warning to us not to be too ready with laws and rules for the young, lest we find ourselves bound by them in all our maturity.

29

PROBLEMS OF POWER I:

THE POLITICS OF COLOR

It is not possible to make a neat separation between the rights of the broadcaster and his duties to the public, but the problems discussed in the foregoing pages center on the networks' assertion of existing rights, whereas those which follow are concerned with services that can be rendered to the public in the future. They involve power in different ways: color television is a vital element in the struggle for supremacy between the networks and questions the right of the networks to provide programs more useful to themselves than desired by the audience. The two technical items—broadcasting in the ultra-high-frequency range, and broadcasting by some system of collecting fees from the audience—can both be considered as breakdowns of the commercial monopoly in broadcasting. Educational broadcasting is, in a sense, the problem most clearly involving public service—but this also can lead to a change in the structure of the whole industry by bringing into existence a network dedicated to education and thereby competing with the commercial broadcasters (and the pay-TV broadcasters if they exist) for a portion of the audience.

We are now actually in the second phase of the color politics. In the first, CBS developed a rudimentary color system and immediately asked the F.C.C. to keep commercial television off the air entirely on the ground that the public should not be allowed to buy sets which would so soon be obsolete (plus the prediction that a public accustomed to the movie's Technicolor would not look at television in monochrome). At that time CBS had no manufacturing interest in television and foresaw endless deficits for itself while it paid out huge sums for transmitters and studio equipment to its chief rival, RCA. The effort to hold back television for five or ten years failed. While CBS was spending two or three million dollars propagandizing for color, RCA was spending some fifty million dollars perfecting black-and-white to the point where the F.C.C. found it technically good enough to be offered to the public. This ended the first phase, and an interlude of considerable technical significance followed during which something very like statesmanship was exhibited or forced upon the broadcasters: CBS gave up the fight for its color system as a whole, and arrangements were made to protect the public from the chaos of two receiving-systems operating in different ways. Essential to the approved system, and preparing the way for the second phase of the battle of color, was the requirement that whatever was sent out in color could be received in acceptable black-and-white on the thirty million sets already bought by the public. The technical name for this was "compatibility," and it was a good name because the lack of compatibility is in many communities grounds for separation if not for divorce.

The moment compatibility was achieved, the broadcasters could begin making their experiments publicly, and the F.C.C. did not withhold permission to send out commercial programs in color. For a year this privilege was used with tact and discretion. Short and simple programs, many of them in the afternoon, were the first test cases, programs redesigned for color or those in which a perceptible inferiority in the black-and-white picture would not be too objectionable. The producers understood that they were in for a long study and slow and careful experimentation. For one thing, they had before them the history of Technicolor, which was so prematurely launched, so ill-managed, it might have faded from the screen for a generation. It was saved by the genius of the great stage designer Robert Edmond Jones, to whom Kenneth Macgowan, producing for Pioneer Pictures, entrusted the handling of color for the short subject *La Cucaracha*. The picture was so successful that the finances of the Technicolor company were almost immediately restored. Jones never had a free hand again, and from *La Cucaracha* to the Olivier *Henry V*, almost every picture in Technicolor was "a pot of paint flung in the face of the . . . public." Electronic color is in itself more delicate than Technicolor and more true to life; when the system goes wrong, the picture becomes laughable and the effect is all the worse because the right picture had been so amazingly right. And, to be sure, the pervasive sense that television is "real" makes sea-green faces and red butter too disturbing. To make the system work and to develop a group of scenic designers, costumers, and makeup men, to work with lighting experts and electronic engineers, was a large undertaking, and the most intelligent move was the decision to proceed slowly, testing each combination, doing as little to disturb the audience as possible.

Not one of the problems had been solved when NBC announced a series of elaborate programs, lasting ninety minutes each, to be done in color and costing a sponsor between $250,000 and $350,000. They were to be variety shows or musical comedies or revivals of Broadway hits; they were to have many stars. When CBS followed this lead, its product was substantially the same. The first few shows were marked by two phenomena: bad judgment on the part of the producers and rebellion on the part of the public. In a rare manifestation of the old pioneer spirit, millions of Americans walked all the way over to their television sets and tuned out the programs they did not like. This show of independence so disturbed the broadcasters, long accustomed to docile obedience, that the president of NBC referred to his customers as "the great lethargic American masses." He was annoyed because, he indicated, people did not tune in these occasional programs but, he implied, stayed in their old ruts, preferring the programs they were used to. He was wrong on one count: all the evidence indicated that they did give the unusual programs a chance and simply did not like them. He was fatuous on one count, also: of all people, the head of a network ought not to upbraid people for doing exactly what all the networks had been training them to do for a generation. The bad manners of calling one's customers a lethargic mass is remarkable only because for once, apparently, a broadcaster was provoked into saying exactly what he meant.

What happened with color has a direct bearing on the entire future of television. It is part of the context in which the major problems of educational and subscription TV must be considered, and has some bearing on the future of Congressional control of broadcasting. So the precise point of divergence between the public and the two networks should be identified. It was not that the black-and-white picture received from the color transmission was actually too low in quality to be acceptable. The public had taken television to its bosom five years earlier with pictures lower in quality, tearing themselves to pieces, slipping out of the frame of the screen—*but* those had been the best pictures available at the time, the best pictures the broadcasters could transmit to the public. The color picture was simply the best picture the broadcasters could transmit to the sponsor of the program, a few dozen critics, and a few thousand individuals who somehow had got hold of color receivers. The picture was intended for *them*. Every announcement stressed the color, and all through the introductions and the commercials the color values were emphasized. Moreover, it became clear that the choice of material and the methods of production were those which showed color off to best advantage. The thirty million black-and-white sets were not considered; their owners could pick up the leavings —or do without. They chose to do without. In front of a color set one saw perhaps twenty girls in lovely costumes ranging from the lightest to the darkest blue—when it came off well, it was an astounding demonstration of the critical power of the color system; but on the black-and-white screen there were twenty girls in light or dark gray, the figures far too small to be interesting, their separate movements indistinguishable without the separation of colors. Hearing again and again that the programs cost from $250,000 to $350,000, the audience, deciding that most of it went for color, turned back to the programs made for them, with their requirements paramount.

Eventually the black-and-white reception of color transmissions improved and several programs of good entertainment quality were produced. Eventually President Weaver of NBC got over his fit of pique, and a large number of people were looking at the "spectaculars," as he had named them. He had reason to be pleased: NBC had been able to charge several million dollars' worth of experimentation in color to sponsors instead of to itself, and what had seemed merely a piece of fumbling publicity was soon forgotten.

Actually, it was the worst case of betrayal of the public interest in the history of broadcasting, an aggressive assertion of a philosophy of broadcasting totally opposed to the American system, against the spirit of the basic law—and unrebuked. For the assumption was that NBC (and CBS followed) had as much right to put on a series of totally unacceptable broadcasts, serving one-hundredth of one per cent of the public, as Ford had to produce a passenger car with caterpillar treads or Wrigley to make chewing gum that tasted of bananas. The assumption was that NBC could operate in the interest of RCA when that interest conflicted with the public interest. The company was taking a risk, wasn't it? The risk of alienating the public. If NBC was willing to take the risk, who had any right to complain?

The answer is that, by law, the people have the right to complain, and that, by law, the F.C.C. is the people's agency. In its proper anxiety to get color experiments made, the F.C.C. had placed no restrictions on the transmissions of programs, and what NBC did was therefore technically legal; it offended against the "public interest" clause, but the F.C.C. took no notice.

So ended the second phase of color. By this time RCA, the parent company of NBC, was well on its way to spend its fifty million dollars to "put color over." As the third phase approached, virtually everyone was convinced that the technical problems had been or soon would be solved; although several manufacturers withdrew their color receivers from the market or stopped making them, RCA was full of confidence and improvements were announced by CBS (which had gone into the manufacture of tubes as well as of receivers). The conversion of the thirty million existing sets so that they could receive broadcasts in color would cost the public between one and two billion dollars, spread over a longish period of years. The only reason this is worth mentioning is that the broadcasters were perfectly willing to have the public spend this sum.

30

PROBLEMS OF POWER II:

THE ULTRA-HIGHS

The willingness of broadcasters to make the public spend billions of dollars for color receivers is legitimate business and is only remarkable because the same broadcasters are doing everything in their power to prevent the public from spending any money whatever on another little mechanism that can multiply many times over the satisfactions television can bring. This is, in itself, a highly prejudiced statement, representing the views of those who are in favor of utilizing a portion of the air now virtually unused. A good deal of self-interest appears on both sides, and the situation is aggravated because the subject is complex and bristles with technicalities. As these are not in my own field, I have been at pains to have them simplified for me in the hope that I can transmit the simplification without reconfusion setting in.

The system of television familiar to most of us is represented on our receivers by a knob that can be turned to thirteen positions, each representing a channel. There is another system with seventy additional channels, and, technically, these systems can operate side by side. This is the central fact in the battle of the frequencies—or perhaps this and the fact that they are not both in common use and that some broadcasters hope they never will be.

No community in the United States is served by all of the existing channels. Seven stations exist in New York, but the average receiver gets no more than four of these stations clearly. The prospect of having seventy more stations to choose from is appalling, and that is one reason why "multiplied many times over" is deceptive; in the average community only two or three stations would be added if the entire frequency band useful in television were being used. In small communities, now served by one or two stations, the full-range system might double the total number of stations. This does not tell the entire story. If a community is served by three railroads, the satisfactions of travel would not be tripled by adding half a dozen more lines; but if all three of the original roads covered the same territory and the added six went to forty new places, the multiplication of satisfaction would be incalculable—there is no slide rule for pleasure. The proponents of full-range operation believe that in the competition between the old and the new systems, in the increased number of stations and networks looking for public approval and the advertiser's dollar, more *different kinds of programs* will be produced—the trains will not only offer more speed and comfort, but will go to many places people would like to see, places kept off the map of our interests because no one (on the limited number of stations now available) has told us about them. The enthusiasts for full-range television would not accept the implications of "limited number." They are openly the enemies of the present network system, and they would say that under that system all the stations in a community are compelled to do more or less the same thing, like all the major trunk lines in the United States which are on the single East-West axis. They say that people live North-South also and should be allowed to travel in a thousand diagonals and arcs and tangents. They believe that competition and free enterprise, under which the present networks were established, are still valid and that it ill becomes the beneficiaries of our economic system to prevent others from using it.

It is hard to say which is more complicated, the complexity of the wave-band problem or the intricacies of network operations. There are moments when the natural phenomenon of sound seems transparently simple compared to the mazes and the obscurities of the contracts, the division of profits, the assignment of time periods, and all the other details of a station-and-network affiliation. One aspect of this relationship, a fairly elementary one, can be understood if we carry the analogy of the railroads a step further. Stations on the trunk lines do a lot of business, stations on spurs do little, and a railroad entirely off the main line, operating between two towns all by itself, is likely to be supplanted by a bus-and-truck system in short order. In broadcasting, the networks are the trunk lines, and—more so in television than in radio —they have a life-and-death power over individual stations. Unaffiliated with a network, a station has nothing to transmit except movies (which a rival affiliated station also can do), and it cannot build up a loyal audience for whatever meager programs it can afford to produce, because the great network shows are seen on the competitive outlets. There are at present two dominant networks, NBC and CBS; one aggressive competitor, ABC; and Dumont, which in 1954-1955 began to reduce its network activities. The power of the networks to give *and to withhold programs* is cited in connection with the Army-McCarthy hearings (on page 235), and it should be noted that in the course of those hearings certain stations broke away from their usual affiliations and picked up the transmissions from ABC and Dumont—but, as far as I know, they did this only when they could cancel their contracts with local sponsors; they could not get out of network commitments. At the same time, the power of the networks to accept a station's request for affiliation is virtually unlimited, and its right to reject such a request is absolute; it can also supply or refuse to supply programs, and a network program not carried by its own affiliate may be lost to a community because an independent station, in the same area, cannot buy it.

Observing this concentration of power in three or four corporations without responsibility to the Commission that represents the public, Frieda B. Hennock, a member of the Commission from 1948 to 1955, proposed a complete reversal of those policies which, she said, gave the networks a stranglehold on the stations and, as a consequence, gave them irresponsible control over television as a whole. As her last significant official act, she asked the Senate's committee investigating the broadcasting industry to recommend a law compelling networks to apply to the F.C.C. for licenses, as stations do. She found the existing situation unrealistic—a practical application, to be sure, of the mystical network qualities I have already described. Miss Hennock had long been known as the only woman on the Commission, but she had an even higher distinction as other members resigned or were replaced when their terms ended: she was the only Commissioner who protected the public interest in advance. Whatever remains of a good prospect for educational television is to her credit because she insisted upon holding some channels out of commercial assignment; she seems also to be the only active dissenter from the Commission's policy in the UHF controversy. She is active and she is urgent, and her desperation rises from the unsated appetite of the American people for television sets. They buy them at the rate of some twenty thousand a day. And every million sets added to those already in use makes more and more difficult the task of widening the area of television service. For these sets are almost all of the limited type. Full-range sets, receivers for all the possible stations, are on the market, but the public has little incentive to buy them, and UHF stations providing programs in the hope of stimulating sales have gone off the air. Licensees of such stations, observing the fate of the pioneers, have turned back their franchises unused, and educational stations, uniformly successful in the rare instances of operation on the commonly used channels, have sickened and died in the higher levels. And not only educational programs are affected, for the most popular of events now unavailable to television might be brought to the air if receivers for the new channels were coming into use: championship prize fights and new movies, for instance. They are promised if we ever have any system of pay-TV, and the solution of that vexing problem might be made much easier if the UHF channels were in general operation.

We have, then, more than an abstract question of anti-monopoly or the protection of the free-enterprise system; we have the very concrete business of getting as many kinds of desirable and popular programs on the air as we possibly can. We have seen that the networks are pushing color, asking the public, in effect, to invest several billion dollars or miss the best that is on the air. Yet the conversion to color cannot bring new kinds of programs to the public (except for the very small number that are, in a sense, about color itself, such as the techniques of oil painting or of fashion-designing). Color will actually be another obstacle in the path of full-range television because the investment in limited-range receivers will be all the higher; in that sense, color will add to the near monopoly enjoyed by the two major networks.

This is the situation into which the Senate was asked to inquire in the middle of 1955. Before the committee was a report which suggested, in effect, that nothing could or should be done because thirty million sets, bought and sold in good faith, would become only half useful if UHF channels were favored. Of these sets, some nine million were manufactured and sold *after* the basic problems of UHF had been publicized. Miss Hennock holds that by prompt action the F.C.C. could have encouraged the sale of full-range receivers and so cut down the dimensions of the problem. Actually, the Commission was aware of the possibilities of full-range reception as far back as 1945, when it declared that "in the present state of the art the development of the upper portion of the spectrum is necessary for the establishment of a truly nationwide and competitive system of television broadcasting." Since that time most of the rules laid down by the committee have not only favored the lower frequencies, but have in many instances reduced UHF stations to the position of satellites, re-broadcasting whatever the mother-station in the familiar very high frequency range sends out, initiating no service to the public.

If the Commission has been overly sensitive to network pressure and derelict in its duty to the public, the trouble it has laid up for itself may be punishment enough. For it has been compelled to discuss, at least, the best method of unscrambling its eggs. As if recognizing the implausibility of the situation, the interested parties have given the process a self-destructive name: de-intermixture. In essence, it means turning over certain areas to UHF stations alone, others to VHF. The outraged citizens of those communities that have enjoyed everyday television and are now to be told they cannot have it any more (unless they buy converters) will be an excellent indication of the public feeling about television as a whole. That feeling is one element in the related problem of metered or subscription or pay-as-you-go television.

31

PROBLEMS OF POWER III:

PROGRAMS FOR PAY

The problems of television are recurrences of those of radio. The one we have just discussed parallels in detail the history of frequency-modulation, a system of radio so impressive in 1941 that the industry expected it to take first place after the war ended (allowing time for television to perfect itself). The F.C.C., however, gave it no encouragement, and took away some of its space on the air to help television. FM languished until about 1950, when it became clear that the commercial broadcasters were going to do little or nothing for that part of the audience which was no longer satisfied with the banalities of radio and not yet willing to accept the parallel experiments in television. Since then it has had a steady growth, but it remains tangent to the great circle of broadcasting, and the competitive networks it might have created never came into being. And parallel to the problem of paying for television programs is the effort made several years ago by Muzak and other suppliers of recorded or transcribed music to get from the F.C.C. a portion of the air waves on which their commodity could be transmitted to subscribers only. The networks protested against this "narrowcasting" as an alienation from the public of part of its domain, and the F.C.C. refused to give its permission. Muzak became familiar in restaurants and elsewhere, coming through leased wires—and it should be noted that television has already been sent to paying customers in the same way, by cable to theaters, the programs never being on the air at all. No technical obstacle prevents the transmission of programs by wire to the home receiver, but the cost of leasing the wires from the telephone company staggers even the promoters who expect the public to invest billions of dollars in machinery that will carry programs they will not be able to see unless they pay billions more.

The polls taken on this subject and the quality of argument it brought forth seemed to me interesting as reflections of public feeling about broadcasting in general and the broadcasters' concept of their place in American society, and I have noted the salient facts and ideas on page 204, but the heart of the matter, as everyone knew, could not be reached by statistics or invective. The center of the argument is at the core of every discussion of broadcasting: Is the service supplied the best we can get? And it must be understood that the broadcasters constantly deviate from this center to the tangent question: Is the service what the public wants?

If the answer to the central question is, as in all human enterprises it must be, that there is room for improvement, the following question is: Can the broadcasters improve in all the desirable ways or must we go to another system in addition to or (to follow the question to its logical end) in place of the present one? Pay-TV is, of course, not the only alternative to commercial broadcasting: the British, the Canadian, and the Soviet Union provide other models. But pay-TV is in itself a commercial enterprise, willing to subject itself to Federal regulation but not to Federal interference with programs, and it is therefore in our tradition and in our style. As long as we focus our interest on the result—programs—we can avoid the abstractions that cluttered up the special pleading of both sides and we can observe the separate ways in which each avoided the central issue. The broadcasters did not say that they could provide the programs their rivals offered; the broadcasters said that no one could get those programs or enough of them, or they said that the alternative system would have disastrous results. The spokesmen for the various pay systems, while they promised almost everything to almost everybody and made the usual obligatory bow to culture, did not for a moment make the one offer that could guarantee the public a real variety of programs. They did not say that, in return for being granted the use of part of the public domain of the air, they would accept the position of any public utility and let the government regulate its rates and set up standards of quality for the service rendered. This would be inviting the F.C.C. to interfere with program content, for pay-TV could be required to transmit not only more, but more skillfully produced Shakespeare, with better actors. The prospect of a Federal bureau discriminating between two schools of ballet or the quality of the camerawork in competing productions is pleasant to think about, but is not entirely relevant; in practice, the F.C.C. would need only to look over the production schedule of an applicant, approve it or suggest changes, and then refuse renewal of the license if the promised had not been, within reason, fulfilled.

This is not what the F.C.C. does for commercial stations. It gets from the applicant a general statement of policy—how much time he will take from the network and how much he will fill in response to regional needs. If these intentions are matched by good character, the license is granted; *no specifications are given*. Whether this is desirable or not is an abstract question; the F.C.C. cannot change its rules now. But the applicants for frequencies to be used for pay-TV are in a new category. They are proposing to take away a portion of the public domain and then charge the public on a metered basis—so much per program, as a local gas company charges so much a cubic foot or a national railroad charges so much per mile. Even if we accept all the verbal arguments proving that commercial broadcasting is not "free," the hard fact is that the customer does not pay by the program; he pays a few cents more a month (for power and for use of his tubes) if he watches his set more than his neighbor, and he gets the programs put on by ten cigarette companies whether he smokes one brand or all or none.

The networks failed to come to grips with this central problem, not feeling too certain of their own ground, for a Congressional investigation (friendly in intent) was getting under way in 1954. With all the talk of licensing the networks, the danger was that an uninstructed Congressman would say "Why aren't the networks public utilities?" and the only answer would be that the public does not pay for its entertainment directly. If the public were convinced that broadcasting had become a "monopoly" or a "duopoly," this answer would hardly be satisfactory, and one of the most skillful pleaders on the side of pay-TV has undermined the position in advance. As a former general counsel to the F.C.C., Telford Taylor naturally is familiar with the laws governing

broadcasting and holds that the present situation—"a wholly artificial
. . . restriction on the economic and cultural base of broadcasting—a
limitation known to no other mass medium"—was never intended by
Congress and is "the accidental result of language drawn long ago and
wholly without reference" to the present question. In a letter to the
New York Times he wrote:

"It has been too soon forgotten that radio-broadcasting was a rapidly
growing though chaotic industry for a number of years before advertising was coupled with it. Had the technical means existed in the late
Twenties to exact a fee from the listener in order to meet the costs of
programing, surely this would have been done. The other mass media
—newspapers, magazines, books, motion pictures—depend in varying degrees upon the consumer's as well as the advertiser's dollar. It was only
for lack of any practical way to collect the radio listener's dollar on a
per-program basis that advertising emerged as the sole economic base of
broadcasting, and that Federal regulation developed within that framework.

"Opponents of subscription TV, therefore, are under the heavy burden of justifying a governmental prohibition against doing in broadcasting what has always been done in the other mass media; of justifying
what amounts to a monopolistic privilege—that the radio frequencies
shall be available for commercial exploitation exclusively for advertising purposes. This is a strange outcome, especially in the light of the
Congressional declaration of policy that the channels shall be available
'to all the people of the United States.' "

Mr. Taylor's lumping of radio and television with "the other mass
media—newspapers, magazines, books, motion pictures" is a little too
lighthearted. As soon as a would-be manufacturer of printed matter or
motion pictures finds the money, he can go into business, subject to
the laws governing other business, without receiving a license to operate
from the Federal government; but, with all the wealth and good will in
the world, a new broadcasting business cannot come into existence if
all the frequencies are taken up or if the Federal government (the
F.C.C.) thinks that the business would not be properly managed. As
long as paper and celluloid can be bought in the open market, there is
no legal restriction on the quantities of books or newspapers or films

produced; the raw material of broadcasting—its paper and celluloid
—cannot be bought in the open market because it belongs to the people, it is the air. And because the broadcasters get from the people the
privilege of using part of the air, they report to the people and are
subject to penalties—not, as the other exploiters of the mass media are,
for such crimes as libel or dissemination of pornography, but for failing
to be as diligent in serving the public as they should be. And because
they subject themselves to regulation by the Federal government, the
broadcasters are allowed to make money through the use of the people's property, but without charging the people for the service.

The technical means for making the public pay did exist in the late
1920s, not on a "per program" basis, but on an annual basis. Two
methods were widely used—the Canadian, which placed a big sales tax
on receivers and used the proceeds to finance the Canadian Broadcasting
Corporation, and the British, which imposed a direct annual tax on receivers and so paid for experiments in television as well as for radio
service to the public. Neither of these would have suited us; nor did
the system proposed by David Sarnoff—contributions from the manufacturers of radio receivers forming a pool to be drawn on by broadcasters and, if this should prove insufficient, endowments from public-
spirited citizens and foundations. The Act that started Federal control of
broadcasting was passed before any commercial message had been uttered on the air. When it was passed, the holder of the license was creating his own programs, and it is unlikely that Congress would have considered broadcasters who became merely merchants of time on the air
as operating in the public interest. On the other hand, through all the
changes of political complexion, Congress has never challenged the position of the F.C.C. which is that broadcasters *can* operate in the public
interest while permitting programs to be dominated by advertisers.

Yet, in spite of these defects, Mr. Taylor's argument has the singular
merit of going to the heart of the question: the added competitive
system would put an end to the real monopoly in broadcasting, which
is a monopoly of purpose. With exceptions that grow less and less important, the frequencies of the air are used to transmit such programs as
will sell goods. The pay-TV system would share some characteristics
with the commercial system: it would be a profit-making enterprise that
must please large segments of the public. But it would not necessarily
advertise commodities for sale (and probably this would be written

into the license by stipulation). Like the movies, pay-TV would need to sell nothing but itself. It is not necessary to say that this is a better or a worse motive than selling gasoline or toothpaste—the important thing is that it is a different motive and might consequently result in different programs. There are programs that attract large audiences but are not adaptable to hard-selling commercials; they are used for prestige, for institutional advertising, for single individual "special events." Full-length plays, and more generous portions of Shakespeare than can be crowded into an hour, and grand opera, and a considerable number of cultural and educational programs are in this category. While the more profitable sports events and new musical shows would still be preferred (by the public and by the management of pay-TV), the less popular programs would occur more frequently simply because they would pay for themselves. If several stations broadcast paid-for programs at the same time, this would be inevitable; and if the F.C.C. required these new broadcasters to select their programs with due regard to those transmitted by the commercial broadcasters and regard also for the interests of all substantial groups, something like a balanced schedule would appear on the air—for the first time in broadcasting history.

The commercial broadcasters say that if any portion of the air were given over to pay-TV, the whole air would presently be absorbed into the system because the pay-TV managers would outbid the present sponsors of the Lucys and the Gleasons; they say that if only five per cent of the families now watching the Ed Sullivan program paid fifty cents to see it, the producers would get $375,000 (roughly 2½ times as much as the program now costs). And they say or imply that, with these profits to be made, the chances of programs of limited appeal would be no greater than they are today. It is an additional argument in favor of strict supervision by the F.C.C., because if this should occur, we would again have one kind of broadcasting—as mercenary as our present system, with the stakes higher than ever and the tendency to lower standards correspondingly more marked. The prospects of an enriched program structure would be dim indeed.

32

PROBLEMS OF POWER IV:

THE EDUCATIONAL NEXUS

It is at this point that the last of the public problems in broadcasting joins the questions of color, of the ultra-high frequencies, and of pay television. It is the problem of separate channels for educational programs. For in the maze of uncertainties in this field, there is at least one certainty. Whenever an educational station has operated on the common frequencies, it has prospered; when it has been pushed into the UHF, where no commercial station operated and where, consequently, no receivers were available, the educational station has by itself been insufficient to persuade people to buy converters. The old maxim of broadcasting applies here as elsewhere: the commercial broadcaster creates the audience and turns it over to the statesman, the teacher, the minister, the philosopher. If the present managers of the business had encouraged UHF transmissions, education would move into the field with a potential audience. If pay-TV is restricted to UHF, it will have to create this audience, broadcasting to small audiences for a time and making itself so attractive that sets will be bought. When this has been accomplished, educational television will become a practical possibility.

But whether education should lead a separate life, isolated in the distant channels, or coexist with the entertainments and the cultural offerings of commercial television is not to be summarily decided. On the two material questions—Can television be used for education? Will people care for educational television?—our information is meager. Almost all the answers indicate that the experiment should be made, although no conclusive data can be expected for some time. We know that in an experiment conducted in Canada the same class work was given to groups of students in three ways: directly by the teacher in the school-room, with textbooks; by radio; by television. The television group got its lessons best, understood the work best, and remembered longest. As for getting people to use what television offers, when commercial stations in Detroit and other Michigan cities carried the state university's programs, educational in the strictest sense of the word, they developed an audience of sponsorable proportions. Within a short time after it went on the air the educational station KUHT in Houston could say that "some 800,000 different people view at least one of our programs per week"—it is on Channel 8 in the frequency band of the commercial stations. On the other hand, the well-financed station in Los Angeles, working on the higher frequencies, had such a limited public that the moment its backer withdrew his support, it went out of existence. This was in contrast to WQED in Pittsburgh, in the commercial lower-frequency range, which had nearly a hundred thousand subscribers to its monthly program schedules at two dollars a year (providing four-fifths of its annual production budget); in competition with the usual violence of children's hours, WQED put on shows of magic and music and some straight pre-school education and received as many as three thousand letters a week. One can at least say with confidence that good educational programs have one thing in common with good (and bad) commercial programs: if they are on the air, they will attract an audience.

That audience is bound to include many people who have been dissatisfied with television, many who have *wanted* to continue their education in maturity. (I omit here the other uses of the channels—transmissions to the schools during school hours and later programs intended to support the school curriculum.) If programs are provided for beginners in various subjects, as well as for advanced students, the process of accretion will bring in numbers of people who had not been aware of their wants—the kind of people who would have been sure that a college professor talking about Shakespeare was not for them; when the professor was Frank Baxter, they discovered it was very much for them.

Yet I think it is fair to ask whether this is the full duty of educators using the public air, whether this does not come down to re-educating the educated (with a small fringe of newcomers), whether in some way the air cannot be used more effectively. I must even confess that separate channels for education have seemed to me self-defeating, and I have become a reluctant convert to their principles only because the commercial broadcasters so specifically refused to meet the challenge of the educators. They tried to reverse the F.C.C.'s decision allotting special channels; they issued statements and filed a lengthy brief that (in addition to the usual identification of "the American way" with commercial broadcasting) went into minute details of the crimes educational channels would commit, one of them being transmission of college football games; but not for one moment did the broadcasters suggest that they could do what the educators wanted to do. They did not say, as they might well have said, that if you provided separate channels for education, you might be giving a free hand to pedantry on one side and on the other to vulgar commercialism relieved of all responsibility to the general culture of our society because that was taken care of on Channel 65. They did not say—and they, more than most people, should have said—that in a democratic society we want diffusion of education, not concentration. They did not say that commercial entertainment had an audience which might be persuaded to accept education and that entertainment and education each needed the other, that they must be close to each other, not separated, so that cross-fertilization could occur. All they said was that they wanted all the channels for themselves.

This was an intellectual low-point for the industry, which then made a brilliant recovery. Locally and then nationally, the broadcasters began to use the materials of education for entertainment. They gave spectacular proof that they had been wrong and the educators right—education was entitled to a place on the air. With all their wealth and skill and experience they set a standard few educational stations could approach, and the rough going later when educators asked for special channels was a direct consequence. Why have educational channels, taken away from the public, when the commercial channels gave glimpses of metallurgy and medicine and ballet and philosophy? To be sure, the ballet bit might be five minutes on Kate Smith's program on Tuesday afternoon and no more ballet until a week from the following

Friday at 10:45 P.M. The effort to get some education into all commercial programs might end up with a melodrama about the eye bank (Who can identify the killer with the transplanted eye?). But there was always *Omnibus*, which arrived in triple armor, being endowed and educational and sponsored all at once—or so it seemed.

When the first announcement was made that the Ford Foundation would establish and support a radio- and TV-producing "Workshop," the usual cry of dismay was heard. The most influential of the trade journals noted (after the obligatory defense of the American way of life) that over a period of ten years the Foundation could buy up every station in the United States without even touching its capital, and the "radical" associations of many of the executives of the Foundation were duly pointed out. All was forgiven a little later when it developed that the principal TV program of the "Workshop" would be sponsored (hence not subversive) and would differ from other commercial programs chiefly in that the sponsors would not create the program or have any direct control of its materials. (One of the most successful advertising men in the business, James Webb Young, was adviser to the Foundation at the time these arrangements were made.)

Legitimate as the program was, it again appeared revolutionary because the materials it used and the general air of the presentation were like those of *Look* or *Life* rather than those of the Sunday tabloids. The title; the offered explanation that *Omnibus* would have something for everybody; the pleasant statement by its MC, Alistair Cooke, that it was directed to the middlebrow; the mocking air with which Mr. Cooke accepted an award to *Omnibus* for "the best educational program"; even the contemptuous criticism that *Omnibus* was selling its experimental soul to become popular—all of them put together could not counteract the powerful impression that the program is highbrow, intellectual, and educational. It is indeed educational in the way that an intelligently edited magazine is educational, not as a textbook is. It is the Chautauqua circuit compared to a course at a university. A small number of sustaining programs, almost all of them presented on Sunday afternoon, come closer to the educational standard; they explore a single subject, using drama or discussion as well as demonstration—but they use these more popular methods for enlightenment, to clarify a subject rather than to belittle it. *Omnibus* does not pretend to be educational and cannot because it has an obligation to attract sponsors;

an educational program cannot have such a secondary commitment. To say this is not to impute the slightest lack of integrity. *Omnibus* would, in fact, be less significant if it did not have sponsors, for its special value lies in the demonstration that the principle of the lowest common denominator is not absolute in the entertainment business. Indeed, the plight of anyone attempting to create an intelligent sponsorable program would be grimly serious if *Omnibus* ("with all the Ford Foundation money") had failed. The faults of the program are its fluctuations and uncertainties, the feeling that it can take no pride in its failures because these failures are not distinguished. These faults diminish, but do not destroy, its prime value. The relative success of attracting five sponsors to divide the cost of a program that costs less than many single-sponsored shows is as much a condition of its existence as the relative freedom from interference by these sponsors. The program would be going against its own grain if it changed into a wholly experimental workshop and had to retreat to its parent Foundation for support. There is need for an entirely experimental program; there is no ground for asking *Omnibus* to be that program.

In this, *Omnibus* parallels the entire relation of the broadcasting industry to educational programs. The atmosphere in which broadcasters and educators debate is charged with recriminations, probably because both sides are aware of guilt in the past. The assumption has always been that the broadcasters *ought* to put on educational programs although it is abundantly clear that nine-tenths of the people engaged in the business cannot possibly create educational programs and should not be allowed to do so if they could. A sponsor has no right to use his time on the air to "educate" anyone in anything except the qualities of his product; a local station living on its share of the proceeds of network programs cannot possibly afford to produce educationals. The networks can do this, but in the present state of our knowledge it would seem best to ask the networks to support, rather than to create, true educational series, to keep up a constant cross-reference to such programs on the educational stations, to prepare the ground in which the educator will plant the seed. This is not so slight a task as it seems, and it involves an even harder one: network programs should not belittle education and educators, should not constantly present the educated intellectual as a prig and a fool, should not consistently demonstrate the superiority of the oaf to the intelligent man. (There are moments when it seems that nine-tenths of TV comedy depends on the themes I am asking the broadcasters to abandon.)

What I have written is a transparent device for evading the major duty of solving the problems of educational television. About them I have only a single conviction: the method of special channels should be tried, and the educators should have as fair a chance as commercial broadcasters—they should be allowed to make as many mistakes, to try as many different techniques. At the same time, my suggestion is not totally beside the point I wish to make, which is that the commercial and the educational programs (wherever they occur) should nourish one another. I see no possible point of origin for real educational programs except stations out of the commercial field, producing and transmitting programs corresponding to the college or high-school curriculum and general cultural programs, the equivalent of *certain parts* of the sustaining hours of radio in the early 1930s or of the Third Program of the British. The italics represent the haunting fear I have always had of the pedant, the excellent scholarly type who wrecked more than a hundred educational radio stations and who still makes life difficult and programs heavy-going on educational TV stations. An educational station that did not take advantage of the techniques developed in commercial radio because they were not blessed by the high priests of pedagogy has no place on the air and should exist only as a laboratory experiment. For, while broadcasting must be taken as an extension of the classroom, it is such an extension in time and space as to require totally new methods or, as a minimum, readaptation of the old.

We already know that the oldest method of all—Mark Hopkins at one end of the TV system and a student at the other—will work if our Mark Hopkins is pleasant-spoken and unpedantic and is content with the first phase of teaching: to stir the imagination, to arouse curiosity. It is too early to be sure about the methods that will not serve, because the actual schoolroom scenes and the carefully planned seminar discussions that pretend to be spontaneous, dreary as they are, may yet turn into something better. As far as methods go, indeed, we should be as generous as we have been to the commercial program-makers who have put their trials and errors on the air. The educational broadcaster, spending public moneys, will be under attack, he will be denounced as a failure if his first attempt falls short of some artificial standard imposed from the outside, some configuration of costs and audiences and comparisons with other enterprises. Partly this will represent rancor against the smug air of superiority found in some academic circles; partly it will be impatience with the faults of teachers as remembered from schooldays and now appearing bigger than life in television: pedantry and its opposite, condescension; the teacher as the remote, the almost sacred Master—and the teacher who belittles his knowledge and is all too chummy. But all these are insignificant and can be overcome as surely as the vulgar banality of a hundred commercial programs has been overcome.

The essential thing now is that the road to experiment must remain open. Badgered and shamed and morally bullied by Miss Hennock, the Commission of which she was then a member finally set aside a number of channels for educational stations—with an implied threat. Applications had to be made before a certain date, after which channels not applied for would again be available for commercial use. The showing until the final date was meager (the inertia of educators and the indifference of state legislatures were the chief obstacles), and, theoretically, the present situation is that no channels are being specifically withheld from commercial use. The fact is that few commercial broadcasters are applying; experience with the ultra-high frequencies, where most of these channels lie, has discouraged them. But new rules by the F.C.C. have already aroused considerable network interest in these frequencies (as satellites of their regular stations); pay-TV may use them and make them desirable properties; and at any time a new invention may make receivers for UHF cheaper and better than our present ones. In those circumstances the educators would find their potential stations pre-empted by commerce.

Usually the desirability of educational stations has been discussed in relation to television. It needs to be considered in the context of all our other educational problems—the lack of adequate buildings, the shortage of teachers, the known demand for adult education, the deficiency in certain areas of trained personnel (highly advertised when our military establishment is affected, but equally significant in other places). The arguments against educational television may all turn out to be valid, but the argument that it should not be tried is not in keeping with our tradition. In particular, the idea that the State as educator-by-television is more socialistic than the State as educator-in-the-class-room is preposterous; yet precisely this argument was used to kill the sensible experimental project of the New York Board of Regents—a decision that left to the "socialistic" state of Alabama the distinction of having the first educational network in the country.

33

A NEW APPROACH

The most notable triumph of the broadcasting industry is this: it has made itself indispensable to public discussion, so that the entire nation turns on its sets with absolute confidence when information without prejudice is wanted, or the clash of opinion on any conceivable subject. There is only one exception. On public health and the virtues of jazz, on the causes of delinquency, the consolations of religion, the merits of public housing, or the subversive implications, if any, of modern art —no field of human interest or enterprise has been denied its moment on the air, except the vast enterprise that affects all the others—broadcasting itself. In 1955, terrified lest they lose their monopoly and share the air with pay-TV, some network executives stated their case to the public and allowed the contrary position to be argued, but full and continuous discussion of the public interest in broadcasting has never taken place.

Some years ago William C. Benton proposed that the Senate, of which he had once been a member, appoint a committee of distinguished citizens (outside of Congress) to observe the workings of radio and television and make a report as a basis for legislative action. It seemed to me that such a group, not elected but with quasi-official powers, would be highly improper. The more distinguished the group, the more influential it would be, so that it could become a sort of public lobby which our elected representatives could not resist, and the half-dozen active (and possibly fanatical) members of the group might, in effect, be writing the laws governing the air. The only merit I could see in the proposal was that the findings of such a committee would naturally be reported and the broadcasters would in self-defense be compelled to open their channels to public discussion of themselves.

This merit I attempted to save in a counter-proposal that the public appoint its own watchdog committees. I thought that out of labor unions and Chambers of Commerce and the D.A.R. and the Republican or Democratic Club of every Congressional district, out of university alumni and Rotarians and fraternal orders and parent-teacher groups and leagues of bowlers and undergraduate societies and the Sons of Iowa in Tampa, Florida, and out of each of the multitudinous fraternities and groups and organizations in which Americans congregate for pleasure or for business, we should get a few people (chosen by their fellow members) to watch and listen and report. It would be easier in towns and villages and small cities, but it would not be impossible in New York or Chicago, and the errors made by one group would be canceled out by others. In the end we should have truly representative reports from the widest possible cross-section of the public, and these reports joined to others (by counties, by states) would eventually become a national report on the admirations, the fears, the passions for and against, which people have about the entertainment they are getting.

And at this point I suggested that the broadcasters would certainly offer their facilities for the propagation of the report, would answer criticism, would bask in the favor of the people and promise amendment where they felt criticism justified. It seemed to me that such an annual report, getting vast publicity in the newspapers, would force its way to the broadcasters' channels and that the more graceful thing would be for them to invite the critics in advance. Inasmuch as any fair report would be heavily in favor of the broadcasters, the risk taken would be slight, the advantages incalculable. Above all other benefits, the broadcasters would have from the audience a continuing vote of confidence, for it is the essence of this plan that discussion should begin locally, at the invitation of single stations, and should continue until all minor matters had been canvassed and only basic issues of policy remained to be discussed on the networks. In this final discussion the distinguished men and women of the Benton proposal would appear, not appointed by Congress, but as members of the great community. Among these distinguished men and women would be the heads of the broadcasting business, too.

Neither the Senator nor myself was successful, but in 1955 Frank Stanton, president of CBS, announced a plan that, in the old phrase, combined the best features of both. It was, in essence, an invitation to the public to participate in those decisions of the broadcasters which directly affect the public. CBS, Stanton said, was providing a fund to finance a study "of the most difficult, vexing or perplexing questions on which public opinion of all degrees should be solicited as to the role of television in our society. . . ." A committee of men and women distinguished in all relevant fields would decide what these questions were, and they would then be turned over to a professional researcher for "a field study to collect the answers the public gives back." (The distinguished committee and the researcher it employs are totally independent—CBS completely retires from the field after it has established the original fund.)

"We have need of these answers," said Mr. Stanton, and proceeded:

"I cannot guarantee that the study will provide all of the answers, because the approach is too novel, but *we owe it to our audience as well as to ourselves to try to establish some systematic method of inviting the public to participate in shaping what we do.* Such a thoughtful and conscientious probing could well provide a newer and far better set of navigation charts than anyone in the broadcasting industry—or in any area of mass communications—has ever had.

"Most emphatically, this would not be—and the reputation of the Committee would be such that it *could* not be—a study of 'what the public likes' in the way of programs, so that the public could just be given more of it. The Committee would take all pains that its report could not be used as a shelter for complacency, or as justification for continuing in a series of well-worn ruts, or persisting in a habit known to be bad merely because a majority of the public seems to have only mild opinions about it.

"What our industry would gain from such a national study, embracing every social and economic level from top to bottom, is something very important indeed. I believe it would serve as a catalyst to start the reaction of *a true two-way communication between television and the great society it tries to serve,* whereby society responds to television in terms deeper and more important than any popularity ratings could ever reflect, and in terms far more meaningful than is provided by the selective process of reading a typical mail that comes to the broadcasters, the legislator, or the F.C.C. The temper of the public on many important issues and problems before us could be made unmistakably clear.

"A passive society is death to television in any long run, as much as it is death to any other institution. *As I see this public inquiry, it would create a great deal of active controversy,* and make a large fraction of our society think, as it had never been asked to think before, How can I make a positive contribution to the television broadcasting art of the future? And therein we could find the strong beginnings for the new next decade of television progress—and suggestions for the true Role of Television in Our Society. . . ."

In spite of Mr. Stanton's specific disclaimer, John Crosby suspected that the whole apparatus of committee and researcher was only another way of making "the listeners' likes and dislikes . . . the arbiter of what goes on the air." This he properly rejects, on the basic principles that the broadcasters must make the final decision, putting on the air what their judgment tells them ought to be on the air, and that "giving the people what they want" is insufficient excuse for inferior programs. Mr. Stanton's reply to Mr. Crosby revealed the moral ambiguity of the broadcasters' position. He reasserted his original statement: the broadcaster would not be bound to continue the supply of routine programs merely because of a vague popular acceptance. He was looking for the deeper sources of audience reaction. Then he gave an example: through this inquiry the broadcasters could discover "whether the public is receptive when it turns . . . to . . . 'straight enlightenment' . . . or do they regard the television set as a home entertainment center . . . and resent . . . an intrusion of a teacher." With all the banalities of television to choose from, Mr. Stanton was wondering whether Frank Baxter on Shakespeare was "an intrusion"! It was the same occupational blindness that had led him in his original statement to speak of the deep responses of society to television and not of television's responses to society, and to stress the fatality that a passive society would bring to his business, unaware that passive broadcasting can create a passive society.

Nevertheless, the Stanton plan, which has been put into action, is of great significance. For the first time a broadcaster has committed himself to the principle of consultation with the entire public instead of being content with measuring the size of that portion of the public which constitutes an audience. For the first time the public has, by implication, received freedom to use the air frequencies in order to criticize those who hold those frequencies. (The passages I have italicized in Stanton's remarks can have no other meaning.) In a sense that his fellow broadcasters may not like, he has suggested that broadcasting is, in some ways, more than a public service and very like a public utility.

There have been no symptoms of public resentment against the broadcasters—only sporadic discontent with a few programs. The stations and networks have been enterprising, giving the public many things before the public asked for them. Discussion of the whole system of broadcasting will probably turn out to be ninety-per-cent favorable to the present status, and the malcontents may strengthen the position of the broadcasters by being, as they were in the matter of radio commercials, so completely out of touch with the vast majority. So the broadcasters have much to gain by coming into the open with their problems. They may have to drop a few obnoxious programs, but they will gain the inestimable prize of complete public confidence. They may even escape from some of the conditions of servitude which they themselves abhor, for the stations and networks are as often victims as villains. They cannot openly denounce those who corrupt their innocence—not so long as they enjoy being kept in luxury by their seducers. At a meeting of NBC's television affiliates, General Sarnoff discussed network responsibilities and, among other things, said:

"There are stations that are not affiliated with any network, who do things that sometimes displease some people in Washington. . . . And affiliates have minds of their own and are free to exercise their own judgments. . . . There are talent agents who do things with their artists . . . and who compel practices that are beyond the control of the networks. There are even some sponsors, God Bless Them! who sometimes do things that they ought not to do. . . . And as for advertising agencies, they too, occasionally kick you around a bit and make you do some things which you wouldn't do if you weren't living in a highly competitive situation."

I submit that it is to the interest of the broadcasters to let the public know these things before they are put on the defensive. For several years the F.C.C. and Congress have both been conspicuously friendly to the broadcasting interest, but the ways of politics and, in particular, the ways of investigating committees are not to be trusted. The gravity of the public problems I have listed is enough to show how carefully public opinion must be consulted; and the broadcasters can perform the greatest service to themselves while performing the greatest service to the public—by sharing the air with them in discussion of our common problems.

34

THE TRINITY OF THE ARTS

Whether we think of our public arts primarily as entertainment or as communications, we recognize in them certain qualities setting them apart from the parallel arts in other countries. The tempo of a Swedish movie, the topic of a French song, the political structure of British broadcasting are, in the proper sense of the word, foreign to us. And, although our jazz and our silent movies profoundly influenced jazz and movies abroad, significant differences exist, particularly in what these entertainments mean to the people, how important entertainment becomes to them, and how entertainment is used to create public sentiment or influence public judgment. The special values we attach to these arts rise from the unique situation of the United States among the nations. I was not myself aware of this until, a few years ago, I was asked to "situate" these arts for Europeans. Taking advantage of the perspective imposed on me, I wrote a description that, corrected for recent changes, is the basis of the following.

The way this country was populated, the way our institutions were developed, made it impossible for us to have either classic or folk arts of our own. They are imports. Whatever came to these shores and, particularly, whatever crossed the Mississippi has been profoundly altered; our domestic architecture, our painting and sculpture, our grand opera, and our literature have their origins elsewhere. Where we do have a tradition, another tradition, usually European, is behind it, and, with the exception of a small and neglected contribution from the Indians, the same thing is true of our folk art—it is a transplantation and transformation of a score of European, Asian, and African folk arts. Fusing several traditions, we have created something new, but the special quality of uniqueness which comes from the past and governs the future— a quality that a Frenchman, a German, an Italian instinctively feels about the major and folk arts of his own country—is bound to be lacking.

The popular arts, consequently, are the only ones which give to the American a sense of ownership; these are the forms of expression he has made here. He knows that ragtime and jazz music can be traced to the jungles of Africa and the synagogues of Cracow and Kiev, but they were created by people who had *become American*. He knows that the mechanisms of the motion picture were invented in several lands and that the art of acting did not begin in Hollywood, but he feels that the special tempo of the American movie and the substitution of "personalities" for actors correspond to something American, not European. He has for the popular arts the same feeling that he has for other manifestations of his national character: for the development of the motorcar as a means of universal, not limited, transportation; for the construction of Boulder Dam and the whole socio-economic evolution of the Tennessee Valley.

Only in the skyscraper and in jazz does the essential American spirit manifest itself in areas related to the classic arts—and how architecture and music are transformed by becoming American! (In 1927 George Santayana listed the "good things" in America: "football, kindness and jazz bands.")

I do not pretend that the vast popularity of the lively arts can be traced to any conscious feeling that they, more than any others, are our own, but I think it is in the psychological background. In the foreground are other factors—some of them the capital events of American history. In the first half of the nineteenth century the prime event was the taking-over of a continent, making it into a nation. It was not a time for the classic arts to flourish, and the poets and sculptors and novelists—the Freneaus and Coopers and Storeys—left America for Europe or stayed behind and jeered at the rude pioneer, finding only in his womenfolk any appreciation of the translations and copies they made from the European originals.

In the next phase of our history the country became more industrial than agricultural, and the huge immigrations began. In a kind of psychological speed-up, everything that recalled European origins was brushed aside so that the newcomer could swim, without the impedimenta of the past, in the national current. Just as the first era had separated the people from the major arts, the second was unfavorable to the preservation of the folk arts. A kind of vacuum was created, and into it the popular arts naturally flowed because in a special way they were in the spirit of the country. The fine arts, it can be said, express the soul of a people (the eternal), and the folk arts reflect earthly experience over the centuries (the past). The popular arts express the present moment, the instant mood. A nation born of revolution, moving across the face of a continent, socially fluid, breaking with its past, erecting material satisfactions into a supreme good, had to find some expression of itself. It is interesting to note that the characteristic American variations of the fine arts—the music that began in New Orleans and the architecture in Chicago which foretold the skyscraper—both began to manifest themselves when the era of consolidation was coming to an end, after the frontier (which meant good free land) ceased to exist in the early 1890s. The nation was establishing itself as part of the world—within less than a decade we were engaged in our first war with a continental European power and had forced our way into an international banking consortium. And as we began to feel our strength, the first of the mechanical inventions for duplicating sounds and images came in, the phonograph record and the motion-picture film. Mass production, a traditional American method since the time of Eli Whitney, began to take over the arts, to produce them for everyone—big business and the democratic ideal appeared in a perfect fusion. Between the time of Thomas A. Edison, who had so much to do with these first inventions, and Lee De Forest, whose photoelectric cell is the central device of mass entertainment today, new characteristics were acquired by the popular arts, so that they could be called at one time, in one aspect, the lively arts, in another the mass media, and in other aspects what I call them now, the public arts.

In the last chapter of this book I propose to collect all the descriptive terms and all the specific qualities of the public arts, so as to define their special character. I am now trying not to isolate, but to connect them, and the essential connection is this: they are a cross-section of the classic, the folk, and the fine arts, and you may think of this cross-section as fanning out from a narrow base in the classics, widening in the folk arts, and almost as broad in the field of the popular arts as the field itself. The frieze along the pediment of the Parthenon and Shakespeare's plays at the Globe Theatre were manifestations of public art, and so were the ballads hawked in the streets of London after an execution; *Madame Bovary* was prosecuted as an offense against public morals. You might say that the most scholarly or abstruse or esoteric of works, once they are committed to print or canvas, once they are made available in any form to anyone, become public and in that sense all our distinctions are matters of degree: how public, to how big a public, and so on. We are not, however, dealing with abstractions here, for if forty million angelic men and women and children dance simultaneously on the head of a pin representing one television program, the consequences may be different in essence, not in degree, from the consequences of four men singing a lewd lyric in close harmony.

By so much I anticipate the definition of the public arts in order to make clear that this is a category of action, not of aesthetics. Whenever any art, because of specific circumstances, takes on the quality of a public art, it has an effect on us and, in principle, invites or requires an action on our part—acceptance, criticism, rejection. As this is most conspicuously the case when the popular arts enter the phase of the public arts, I will "situate" them now, not in relation to our cultural history but in relation to the immediate past.

There was in the 1920s a tremendous outburst of creative energy in the popular arts. It manifested itself in many different ways—in the movies it was a consolidation of all the skills known before, in dancing it was a phenomenal breakdown of the almost classic onestep into the Charleston and the Black Bottom, and this went along with the rising tide of jazz on one side and on the other the creation of a new sweetness and gaiety in musical shows. There were exciting things in the comic strip, and writing in the American vernacular suddenly moved from grotesque exaggeration of dialect to genuine use of the rhythms of our speech. A typical phenomenon is the simultaneous appearance of first-rate work by Berlin, Porter, Kern, Gershwin, and Rodgers in the musical theater; they were not alone, but I mention these because more than a generation later the old and new works of those still living and the great works of Kern and Gershwin were at a high point of critical and popular success. Another indication was this: of the talents in vaudeville and musical shows and the allied arts, almost all who lived long enough managed the transition into movies, then radio, and later television—they had the essence of the matter in them. It was the cresting of a huge wave, and it carried me and my recognition of its significance to an appropriate success—the acceptance of "the lively arts" not only as a convenient name for a group of entertainments, but also for an attitude toward them.

I was not, of course, the first or the only critic who was aware in the fermentation around me of something of extraordinary interest—I happened to arrive at exactly the right moment and caught the fancy of the reading public. *The 7 Lively Arts*, published in 1924, restored a good conscience to people who were enjoying "Kitten on the Keys" and "Gasoline Alley"—but with an uneasy feeling that they *ought* to be hearing Puccini and looking at the murals of Puvis de Chavannes. It is not at all difficult for me to recapture the enthusiasm with which I recorded my gratitude to the men and women who had given me pleasure, but I cannot be so certain of motives. It is possible that the major criticism of the book was right, although I resented it at the time: I may have given the impression that I uniquely had discovered the peculiar excellence of those talented people whom everybody (except the critical intellectuals) was enjoying. I know that I wanted to be effective, I wanted to prove my points, and I probably exaggerated the indifference of some intellectuals and the hostility of others, as if there had been a conspiracy of silence which I had to break into. Of one thing I then felt certain: my enemies were not the college professors and the pedants; they were the bright younger generation ready to accept any novelty in the arts provided it was not native to America and not popular among the lowbrows.

All this has, of course, changed, and not chiefly because *The 7 Lively Arts* was published, but because the flowering of talent to which I have referred was brilliant enough to persuade even the most reluctant. I had supplied a convenient pivot on which a change in opinion could turn. That it may have turned too far is possible.

In a discussion of the attitude of intellectuals toward popular entertainment in the 1950s, Denis Brogan ascribes it to "egalitarian national-ism . . . asserting or implying, that there is something fresh, new, admirable in the most popular success that gives them a claim on our attention. . . . It is smart, for the smart, to make . . . Gershwin equal Richard Strauss. And these assertions are made, not only because these popular art forms are popular, but because they are American. . . ." (I interrupt the quotation here because I think Mr. Brogan is slightly off the beam. The patriotic approach is not, I believe, a species of cultural jingoism; it is only an assertion that these arts say something about us which we wanted said, which George Gershwin could express in the idiom we understand and which Charles Loeffler could not, no matter how distinguished Loeffler's utterance may have been. And why that is important, in relation to the popular arts and to American life as a whole, will be suggested later in this chapter. I resume the quotation, with a bow, because Mr. Brogan's perceptions and his failure to perceive are relevant to the present discourse.)

"This affection of the eggheads (then known as highbrows) for 'the seven lively arts' had a good deal of justification when Gilbert Seldes launched the phrase and the crusade. America was just emerging from the grasp of the genteel tradition. Pressed against the flat and rigid bosom of academic taste, the lusty young *enfants terribles* of the first postwar period were ready to do anything to escape from the schoolmarms, the dominies, the National Academy of Arts and Letters. There were the movies, there was jazz! while the last vapid runnings of the not very strong New England brew were being issued to the no longer docile young. It was better to plug *The Garrick Gaieties* than read the works of the epigoni of Emerson or Howells. The era of beautiful nonsense talked a lot of nonsense and this was part of it but it was only partly nonsense. Today it is much more like a *trahison des clercs*."

Now what impresses me most (after the pleasure of being handsomely received by a good critic) is the odd feeling of being told something about myself which does not seem exactly right, and this sense of groping in the dark of my own professional past is all the more disturbing because Mr. Edmund Wilson, for whom also I have a profound (and affectionate) respect, connects *The 7 Lively Arts* "with everything that was newest in Europe (at the time it was published), the jazz rhythms of Stravinsky and Edith Sitwell, the ballets of Jean Cocteau, and the premeditated delirium of the Dadaists. . . ." Mr. Wilson himself has always been something of an enthusiast for the popular arts and has an extraordinary gift for calling up the special quality of performers—the way they stand or move or talk—and this is rare among critics of the more serious forms of art and literature. As managing editor of *Vanity Fair* he published some of the essays out of which my book developed, and there exists (as a token of his devotion to vaudeville) a photograph of him, Joe Cook, and myself in the stance of a three-man team of acrobats. I cannot therefore quarrel with him seriously. He knew what I was trying to do, "which was to show that the popular arts in America were remarkable for vitality and imagination and that the best they had produced was to be preferred to the '*faux bon*' of our respectable arts." If he thinks I had, at that time, a trace of "the upsidedown snobbery of the cafe-chantant and the music hall," he also says that I took part audaciously in the "liquidation of genteel culture" which was going on in the 1920s.

All this is probably true, although I should certainly not have said at the time that I was aware of doing anything so significant. The people to whom I addressed my reproaches had broken with the old tradition years before, they had been excited by the Armory Show in 1913, they had rejoiced in the splash and noise of the Russian Ballet a year or so later, they knew their Secession and Stieglitz and the imagist poets (the first anthology, *Des Imagistes*, was published in 1914), and in the theater they had not only heard of, but practiced, expressionism. The decisive period of rebellion against the genteel tradition in America was between 1910 and 1925. By the latter date Mencken and Nathan had done their hatchet work in the *Smart Set* and were going on to the *American Mercury*, and the *Dial*, as a mediator between the avant-garde and the progressive (giving little quarter to the classic), was five years old. The *Little Review* had been in trouble with the authorities for printing Joyce, and *Ulysses* had seeped into the country and been saluted as a masterpiece in many places. Indeed, one of the shocks of surviving that era is to find that so much of the literature and art of the '50s was already well established in the first half of the '20s. Among the American poets we published in the *Dial* before 1925 were E. E. Cummings, William Carlos Williams, Wallace Stevens, and Marianne Moore—all of whom won special honors in the 1950s. Eliot and Pound were among our foreign correspondents. Stravinsky and Schoenberg were the great figures in music, and Picasso and Braque in painting.* It seemed to us on the *Dial*—as, indeed, it seemed to the far more chic and successful *Vanity Fair*—that only a fringe of heavy-minded people were still interested in Brahms and Sargent and Howells. *Vanity Fair* gave its readers some of the same people we did with a copious dosage of whatever was smart from month to month, and it was in *Vanity Fair* that the idea of the popular arts as arts actually began to take shape, for Frank Crowninshield approved of the hospitality that his editors John Peale Bishop and Edmund Wilson extended to my series of reports on current attractions which eventually suggested the book (to Henry Seidel Canby and, through him, to me). To be sure, we had hit on something smart—but again it was not so much against the scholars and the pedants of our time that we reacted. It was against the avant-garde and the intellectual and the sophisticated critic who were for everything modern, provided they could think of it in the framework of the fine arts.

Obviously, the judgment of two responsible critics is not to be rejected without considerable thought. After writing the preceding pages, I did a little field work on my own reputation and discovered that I was wrong and Messrs. Brogan and Wilson right. One of the durable satisfactions of my professional life has been meeting men and women who read *The 7 Lively Arts* when they were in college or of college age. By presenting a brief questionnaire to a dozen or so of them who have become my friends, I am able to report that it was precisely as an attack on the stuffy older tradition that my praise of the popular arts seemed most important to them. I still have the feeling that a large number of my contemporaries felt in 1920 that the genteel tradition (so identified by Santayana, who was heard at Harvard for the last time in 1913) had been annihilated before the end of the first World War. We were lucky to think so, but we were in error, according to the next age group—the young people who survived the war and were, for a brief time, known as the "lost generation."

Aware of this error, in emphasis if not in total judgment, I must approach with caution the relation of critics to the public phases of the popular arts. A tiny minority of ultra-conservatives still exists, and, al-

* The *Dial* was well aware of, but did not publish, O'Neill and Hemingway, both of whom were warmly recommended to the editors by subordinates.

though Brogan is not entirely one of them, he says that mass culture is "shallow, evasive . . . and performs no more important cultural function than does tobacco. . . ." By creating a habit, it "excludes the possibility of other . . . superior forms of culture." This absorption of our habitual attention, this concentration on creating only those appetites which the managers of the mass media can satisfy, are among the dangerous features of the mass media, to be sure. They persist because the countervailing power has not yet made itself felt, because those who have a vested interest in the satisfaction of other appetites are disorganized, at cross purposes, and dreadfully insecure. There are the educators who alternately shrink from television or go into it "selling culture" like commercial announcers; there are publishers who publish sensational biographies or cover pictures of the second- as well as the first-rate talents in order to increase circulation; there are critics of the popular arts who feel compelled to prove (to someone, perhaps to themselves) that they are boys in the back room just the same as anyone else, no better, perhaps not so good. The critics have experience in these matters and are paid to be critical, to discriminate between the better and the worse; yet they constantly capitulate, saying that no one knows what is good and bad, and, after all, in the long run, the public, etc.

In the long run the public does accept a lot of third-rate stuff that it does not particularly care for, any more than it cares for shoddy goods in dress materials, or paper instead of leather in shoes, or food without taste or nourishment. People do buy all these things, but that is no proof that they will not take anything better, and it is the job of the critic to assay whatever is presented to the public and to distinguish between the better and the worse. The critic who so earnestly insists that he is no surer in judgment than the untrained public is failing in his job or being patronizing, in a sort of inverse snobbery, and a little hypocritical. He seems at times to be begging people to remain ignorant, threatening them with a loss of aesthetic virginity if they eat of the fruit that grows on the tree of knowledge.

We are all familiar with the pedants who cannot enjoy music if there are only nine oboes instead of ten in the orchestra, and who see only pigments in *La Grande Jatte* where others see a picture. Between them and total ignorance of any art there are a hundred degrees, and it is nonsense to say that our capacity for pleasure is diminished if we learn something about the way a work is made. The keen relish with which even the average person enjoys a great work in fiction, in music, in painting, not the first time, but the second and third and tenth, is in part a recognition of the fact that whatever the work of art says to us is effective because the saying itself, which is the structure or organization of the work, gives us satisfaction. These are the satisfactions that some trained critics ask us to keep from "the people," assuring us that we cannot gain insight by knowing what the artist is doing. The best they can offer is Somerset Maugham's statement that this sort of knowledge is neither more nor less important than calling a headwaiter by his first name—a sentiment bonhomous and coarse at the same time, and to be expected from a writer who cares so much about his trade and so little, naturally, about his art.

The concept of the audience as boobs is satisfying to hucksters and to highbrows. It is not accurate, nor is it permanently acceptable to democrats. We might as well remember that the great frauds in medicine, the most appalling superstitions about witches, the wildest social and economic panaceas, and the foulest delusions about the nature of man were all accepted by the learned and well-bred long before they reached "the common people." We might remember, too, that all the generalizations about "the mob" were created in self-defense by aristocrats or their satellites; they were fixed before the days of universal education and political democracy, and they are not binding on us if we have the courage to test them and reject whatever is false.

The critics in America, particularly of popular entertainment, need to make up their minds about the audience, and to make it up with the foreknowledge that, substantially, the audience is unaware of the critics. When the big-circulation dailies in New York and Chicago began to use pictographs to indicate their opinion of a movie, they recognized the fact that even their down-to-earth way of writing needed illustration for the readers and that ***½* was the simplest way to say "You'll love this picture." But this did not release the critic from the prime obligation—to say also "This is a great picture" or "This is pretty third-rate stuff with some amusing bits." The number of stars accorded to a picture should have represented, in fact, a compromise between what the critic thought of it and what he thought the public would think.

There grows up in critics a contempt for what the public likes, and this contempt is itself contemptible, for it is part of the duty of the critic to guide the public taste. I would say that it is also part of the critic's duty to fight against the cynical contempt for the public which corrupts the makers of entertainment. The producers loudly proclaim that the public is never wrong, but that is part of their cynicism, because they fervently believe that *they know* what the public will take, and when the public refuses, they are disappointed not in themselves and their formulas, but in the public taste. They blame the New York critics for the failure of a picture in Wichita Falls, and they say that the "artistic picture" (one in every five hundred made in Hollywood) has ruined the box office. They think the public is wrong-headed beyond redemption because it prefers television to badly made movies. They will not face the consequences of their own actions. They have treated the public like cattle, coaxing and driving them into any corral where a double feature could be shown. The public kept drifting away, but the managers stubbornly went on. Although their own accountants showed that they were losing more people each year than they were gaining, they still believed they could hoodwink the stupid public with another bit of sleight of hand. Several times they did, and prolonged their tenure of office by another few years. At the end of 1955 they were happy to point out that they were still in business—using more raw film to make TV programs than to make their own features!

This cynicism about the public touches the broadcasters, too—the makers of programs, the sponsors, the management of networks. We are not talking about the notion that people set out deliberately to make bad programs. Not the intention to make a bad show, but weakening of the desire to make a better one, is the problem—the feeling that we can put this over on a public which has already accepted that and the other. The public does not always respond the right way, and the producers get sore—as, for instance, in the case of color TV programs cited on page 256.

All the more, the critic should understand his place between the producer and the consumer. He has a vital function. In the theater it can be expressed in dollars and cents: the critic is always aware of the cost of tickets, he knows that his readers can afford to go to the theater only a few times a year, and it is his job to help them not to waste their money on trash. By his destruction of trash he helps (in theory) to give the best shows a chance to survive. Neither he nor any book critic worth his salt ever pretends not to know the difference between solid work and silly twaddle; his standards may be low, but they are his instruments of judgment and he does not throw them away if he pans a play and it becomes a success. The situation of the critic of broadcasting is different only because the audience does not pay in cash for each separate program—it pays in the time given to the program, and it pays also if the program has an adverse effect on the emotional integrity or the clearness of mind of those who witness it. The critic has no business imposing his standards as the only ones appropriate for broadcasting, but he has to *use* his standards and make sure the audience gets a true report. For the critic to do less is the real "treason of the intellectuals" to which Mr. Brogan refers.

If we do not have to whisper in the presence of any work that has been called a classic nor swoon before all the primitives, we can come to a kind of general agreement about the third group, the popular arts that more and more in our time are mass arts. We can agree that they often debase the classics, and that there is even within themselves a tendency to degradation which runs side by side with the happier function of diffusing what is good, making millions of people aware of their own capacity to understand and enjoy the creative power of genius and the intellectual power of great talents. Examples of both functions are easy to find. Of the first, there is *The Gioconda Smile*, by Aldous Huxley. The dramatization was made by Huxley himself, and he provided a trick ("happy") ending, hardly more satisfactory than the "all-a-dream" trick of lesser writers because it diluted the bitter irony of the story and some of its intensity went with it. The story remains a favorite in television: it has sex, mystery, and the trick. And each time it is done, less of the original quality remains. On the third time in two years, the essence of each of the three principal characters had been altered out of all recognition, and the pivot of the play, the morbid woman who invented for herself the role of sympathetic intellectual friend to the man whose wife she poisoned, was transformed into all that was desirable in a healthy and attractive American young woman of the station-wagon set.

Beside this is the other constant: the honorable use of great classics and the effort to find the legitimate way of bringing difficult material to the TV screen. In the nature of things, this cannot be so common as its opposite—even in the arts the descent to Avernus is facile and the upgrade is a strain. The notable successes in radio were in symphonic music and the discussion of international affairs, with poetic documentary a not fully realized attempt at original creativeness. We have not yet seen anything so sure in television, but we have seen the effort continue. It will not end, we may be sure, while competition between sponsors and also between networks continues, for the very forces that lead them so often to imitation compel them in the end to strike out on new paths, and a moment comes when people can no longer be held by third-rate imitations of the second-rate. One consequence of competition is the technical excellence of our popular arts—the glossy surface and the dynamics of a good production are a pleasure to our visceral senses, parallel to the pleasure we take in our motorcars or the mechanical dependability of our telephones. This does not atone for the spiritual and intellectual thinness that is also a consequence of competition—but as long as the competitors have to reach upward as well as down, as long as they have standards that can be altered, we need not despair.

The danger point in this field is the moment when the routine becomes so much more the pattern of production than experiment that the flow toward the safe-and-same is irreversible—a situation reached more than once in the movies, where the unexpected accident of a new mechanism provided a new life—sound, color, three dimensions, wide screen—just as television provided a new life for the owners of radio stations and networks. When a program becomes a vested interest (when ten or thirty million dollars are invested in a single comedian and his works), the capacity of a network to operate in the public interest is imperiled. When it becomes of prime importance to purveyors of entertainment to prevent their audiences from thinking, the managers must attempt to robotize the mass—but it is not to the advantage of a free society to let itself be robotized.

The present is a critical situation, marked by an increasing awareness of the problem among thoughtful people, marked by some deference to intelligent opinion on the part of the managers, and marked to a high degree by the energy and strength of the lively arts themselves—which may be the most hopeful element of all. Most urgent, if we are to take advantage of a situation which constantly threatens to deteriorate, is the recognition that these arts have, in addition to their essential qualities, a special relation to society which makes them properly "the public arts."

35

THE PUBLIC ARTS

"This country, with its institutions, belongs to the people who inhabit it," said Abraham Lincoln, and as he was then facing the possible dissolution of the United States, he added, "Whenever they [the people] shall grow weary of the existing government, they can exercise their Constitutional right of amending it or their revolutionary right to dismember or overthrow it."

I am suggesting that the cultural institutions of a country also belong to its inhabitants, and, not having the courage of Lincoln's radicalism, I do not insist upon the revolutionary right of the people to destroy whatever wearies them. Moderately I propose the idea that the people have valid rights over those cultural institutions which can be properly called "the public arts." In the previous chapter I have indicated that the quality of being "public" inheres in various degrees in all the arts, that oratory and drama in ancient Greece were more public than the art of history, just as in folk arts ballads were more public than pottery, and, although the lively arts are most affected with the special public quality, the movies are more public than dancing. I now propose to bring together from various sections of this book the identifying characteristics of these public arts, knowing that to some degree the identification is shadowy, that by definition no communicative art can be totally private. I am, on the other hand, convinced that in some instances the degree

of difference is so great that you can no longer compare the effect of the
public and the non-public art, as if quantity—the mass of material offered or the mass of people accepting it—had resulted in a change in
essence, a quality change. Also, in one single respect the public arts differ absolutely from all others. The major marks of identification are
these:

¶The public arts are popular to the extent of being almost universally
acceptable.
¶They tend to be more and more professionalized, less and less to be
practiced privately.
¶They are often produced by teams rather than by individuals. They
are commissioned, the patron-sponsor-executive providing the pattern.
¶They are by intention ephemeral, paying well initially, but not increasing in value with the passage of time.

These are I think entirely self-evident.

¶The public arts are offered to the public as a whole, not to any segment of it.

This is, I believe, a new thing in the world, because these arts solicit the
favor of the entire public (excepting the highly intellectualized fringe
that turns its back on whatever is popular). This was not the case when
a mural, commissioned by a ruling family, was exposed in a Renaissance
church or when Shakespeare's plays were presented in the presence of
"the groundlings."

¶Physically, the public arts have mass or velocity or both, and they
tend to outstrip or displace all the other arts.
¶They touch large numbers of people simultaneously, and their effect
is not limited to those whom they directly touch.
¶They interconnect and support one another, thus causing a sort of
reverberation.
¶They are, to an extent, habit-forming, and their effect is contagious.

The social reverberation produced when millions of people follow the
same entertainment or receive the same communication at one time is
something different from the imitation of a royal mistress's hairdo—the
diffusion is immeasurably greater, the penetration deeper. The physical

reduplication of comic books and phonograph records, the velocity of radio and television, the availability of the motion-picture film, and the way the various entertainments support one another create another kind of contagion: the public mind is crammed with details about them, so that the true significance of "the mass media" becomes, not their appeal to the mass audience, but their own dimensions, the size and weight and speed and force that the mass media possess. Among these physical properties is the simple one of occupying a certain space and thus preventing any other body from occupying that space. As the public arts occupy more and more of the public mind over longer and longer periods, they are an obstacle to the extension of the other arts.

❨The public arts popularize the classic arts.
These classic arts they diffuse without substantial alteration, as in the broadcast of a symphony, or they adapt with respect for the original (Shakespeare, for instance), or they degrade. Whether this degradation is inevitable is a prime question. Are the public arts an illustration of "nature's tendency to degrade the organized and to destroy the meaningful"? I am not sure. In *The Human Use of Human Beings*, Dr. Norbert Wiener notes that in control and communication we always fight this entropic tendency, and he adds: "While the universe as a whole . . . tends to run down, there are local enclaves . . . in which there is a limited and temporary tendency for organization to increase. Life finds its home in some of these enclaves." I am not sure whether the parallel I observe is more than verbal. It appears to me that the degradation of the highly organized corresponds to the observed tendency of the popular arts to go steadily to lower levels of general intelligence and emotional maturity; and the enclaves would correspond to those experiments which oppose the tendency toward routine and try to bring individuality back to the mass media.

❨The public arts create, refuse to create, or destroy their own audiences.
❨They are, in varying degrees, governed by public law.
❨The unique element: broadcasting uses a portion of the public domain.
These social factors are obviously connected with the physical items previously noted. Granted that there are no *wholly* private arts, we still

perceive a difference between a poem printed on a page of a mass-circulation magazine and a song presented a dozen times a day by singers of intense popularity. There is a difference in effect between "D'ye Ken John Peel" and the singing commercial for Pepsi-Cola, which uses the same tune and whose diffusion is now so great that the original song has virtually ceased to exist. We will not understand *I Love Lucy* in the terms of Walter Pater on the Mona Lisa, nor Disney's Davy Crockett if we think he is "merely" a contemporary version of Leatherstocking.

The physical properties of the public arts give to their managers certain social powers, but the managers do not generally accept responsibility for the creation of audiences; they say they satisfy public demand. To abridge a long argument, let us say they cannot pretend, as they do, that they create audiences for Shakespeare and symphonic music but do not create an audience for crime serials. Public demand is diffused and generalized: for diversion, for escape, for excitement, for something like an emotional spree; it is not specific. The makers of entertainment satisfy demand in the ways they find most profitable—just as the processors of food satisfy a demand. It is not the only way, and it may not even be the best way. In turn, the demand must be stimulated and made specific: the public must be made to *want* split-pea soup and panel shows if the makers of these commodities are to prosper. It is, moreover, demonstrable that the producers suppress those demands which they cannot advantageously fulfill—as when programs, even popular ones, are dropped or shifted or supplied to one part of the country and not to another, to correspond to the marketing requirements of the sponsor. This power to create audiences and to manipulate demand is the least understood element in the structure of the entertainment business.

That the public arts are subject to law is well understood, but it is hard to discover a fixed principle in the shifts of opinion about censorship in the movies, pre-publication licensing of comic books, and programs for children in television. The position taken by Walter Lippmann, whom I have quoted on page 245, reflects a willingness (which I suspect is common) to compromise the principle of absolute freedom of expression if necessary—but the necessity does not have to be demonstrated by any clear and present danger. The unproved but suspected link between horror books and delinquency is always available for headlines, and a quick hysterical reaction can get laws on the books which it may take years to revoke.

The last characteristic of the public arts—that they use part of the public domain—applies to the broadcasting arts only and is without complexities. The Federal government lends part of the air to a corporation—obviously it can impose conditions. If the conditions are too harsh, the broadcasters will return their franchises, as they have done recently—the requirement that they transmit programs on the UHF channels in order to hold their rights, even though receivers for these frequencies do not exist in their area, is too harsh. On the other hand, if the conditions are too easy (as in the case of broadcasting, taken as a whole), the public may be short-changed until competitors (e.g., backers of pay-TV) offer better service when a station applies for a renewal of license. The only hidden factor in this special case is that the public seems totally unaware of its legal rights—and the broadcasters are not in any hurry to enlighten them.

But the concept of the public arts to which, I am confident, we must eventually come is not drawn from this single characteristic of the entertainment-and-communications enterprises. The base of this new concept is that, by their own nature, these arts are matters of public concern, subject to public opinion; that even *outside of law* the public has sovereign rights over them, since these arts, no less than the institutions of government, belong to the people.

They belong to the people and consequently the people have certain rights and duties in respect to them. I have not put this down as one of the prime characteristics of the public arts because it seems to me highly subjective—and a matter of morality. Here the bearing of the Innis approach (which I have discussed on page 229) becomes most significant. Because the moment we see that a transformation in the way we live is taking place, the right and the duty to direct that change become self-evident. This is not only an appeal to the self-interest of the intelligent, the mature, and the educated—like the appeal the Federalists made to "the rich and wellborn" to support a strong Federal government when the structure of our country was shaped. There is a self-interest, obviously. But in the end I must fall back on the simple moral ground that no good citizen, no good man or woman, has the right to abandon ship while there remains a reasonable hope of steering it into safe harbor if all hands do their work. If we knew that our whole system of free education was being undermined, or the right of every citizen to vote, would any citizen have the moral right to indifference? Would any citizen have the right to remain silent if he knew that a vast power was—inadvertently or not—attempting to destroy that system?

I do not assert that either of these things is happening. I note that either or both may happen without our knowing it, that people using power, often enough unaware of the consequences of their actions, may preserve the *forms* of our educational or political system and nullify its *effects*.

I suggest that, as the fundamental values of our lives and those of our children will be affected by the revolutionary change in entertainment and communications which I have described in this book, we have an obligation to control the speed and direction of this change. Our *right* has been a thousand times established in law and custom. What we lack is the will.

In my own mind, the defect of all attempts so far to influence the mass media has been an almost snobbish dislike for them and an exaggerated fear. We have to recognize a possible danger. We have no right to panic in front of an imaginary one. The next step, after a realistic appraisal of the incalculable social values of the public arts and of the ills —avoidable or not—they bring, is to gather together all those whose livelihood, whose freedom, whose peace of mind are threatened if substantially *all* communications are used for a single purpose. Fortunately, some extremely skillful users of mass communications are in this number: the publishers of the Luce and Cowles magazines have a stake in intelligence only slightly less than that of the publishers of *Harper's* and the *Atlantic*; within the broadcasting business are groups and individuals who are more secure if the level of intelligence in the audience rises slowly and steadily. The makers of nonfiction movies require a high degree of intelligent attention in their audiences, but Walt Disney also needs something above the lowest common denominator. Beyond these groups are the educators, the publishers of fiction and nonfiction and textbooks, the producers of plays and the managers of concert tours, the museums and art galleries and the manufacturers of reproductions of works of art. Also, the scientists and the great corporations who need scientifically trained personnel, our diplomatic service, and, finally, our statesmen. In simplest terms, all these need citizens of good habits of mind and emotional maturity, and already the lack of these—of teachers and of scientists in particular—is proof that you cannot devote the great part of our communications systems to trivialities and be secure in a world as complex and divided as our own.

I do not know what form the pooling of interests will take. The natural turn is toward the rich foundations for research, for organization, and for publicity. They are, in many cases, already under suspicion as being too intellectual and not patriotic enough, but they can still fight for intelligence and for the kind of patriotism that protects the fundamentals of our national life. One aspect of our common genius is our capacity to organize for action when the necessity becomes clear. It is clear now because the moment we see that the public arts are bringing about social change, the right and the duty to direct this change is in our hands. Between those who are not aware of the effect these changes can have on their inalienable rights and those who do not know that they have the right to control the changes, the managers of the public arts have had almost unlimited freedom. They are not entitled to it.

I have suggested on page 279 that awareness can start with the people themselves, in small units, combining into greater. Parallel to this, I now suggest that the managers of all our cultural institutions enter into an open conspiracy to *use* the public arts in order to protect our heritage of national culture. They can command the attention of the public and can bring the discussion of our basic problems to those very channels which now are used to dissipate our intellectual energies. As long as the means of communication are not available for criticism of themselves, as long as we are prevented from thinking about the process by which we are hypnotized into not thinking, we remain at the mercy of our simplest appetites, our immediate and almost childish sensations, and these can be exploited—for the arts most useful to the public are essentially those which can be most effectively turned against the public good.

To know this, to know that we have the right to put them into our service, is the beginning of an intelligent approach to the problems and to the opportunities of the public arts.

ABOUT THE AUTHOR

GILBERT SELDES *added a phrase to the language a quarter of a century ago when he wrote* The Seven Lively Arts. *He had been a Phi Beta Kappa graduate of Harvard, a music critic, a theater critic, a foreign correspondent, and managing editor of* The Dial. *That book was followed by a series of others, including* The Years of the Locust, Mainland, The Stammering Century *and, in 1950,* The Great Audience, *a book that summed up what he had learned as a practitioner of the arts. Between 1937 and 1945 he was director of television programs for CBS. Now, in* The Public Arts, *Mr. Seldes writes as a practicing radio and television critic, a teacher and possibly the most distinguished commentator of his generation on the blessings and the responsibilities that the electronic revolution has given to modern men.*

VEGAS
HEAT

FERN MICHAELS

VEGAS HEAT

Kensington Books
http://www.kensingtonbooks.com

KENSINGTON BOOKS are published by

Kensington Publishing Corp.
850 Third Avenue
New York, NY 10022

Library of Congress Card Catalog Number: 96-077850
ISBN 1-57566-138-1

First Printing: March, 1997
10 9 8 7 6 5 4 3 2 1

Printed in the United States of America

*I'd like to dedicate this book to those nearest and dearest to my heart:
Cynthia, Susy, Patty, Michael, David, Kelly and Billy. And for the four
legged creatures who warm my heart, old and new; Fred, Gus, Harry,
Maxie, Rosie, Lily and Lennie, Buck, Weenie, Spanky, Pete, Zack, Tinker,
Einstein, Izzie and Bennie. I love each and every one of you.*

PART ONE

1980

1

Those in the know said Babylon was a one-of-a-kind gambling casino. Those same people said the Thornton family, owners of the casino, had overextended themselves. The big question on the Big White Way was how Ash Thornton, a man confined to a wheelchair, a man whose body was racked with pain twenty-four hours a day, could hope to operate Babylon.

The windowless counting room, an inner sanctuary where the money washed through daily, bore testament to how well the wheelchair-bound man managed. For Ash the ultimate thrill was being immersed in the sight, smell, and touch of money—tons of money, stacks and bundles of coins so heavy he had been forced to buy a hydraulic lift to move it all around the counting room.

It was amazing to Fanny that rather than counting the money, Ash had the cash bundled according to denomination and *weighed*. Her daughter Sunny had told her a million dollars in $100 bills weighed 20 1/2 pounds; a million dollars in $20 bills weighed 102 pounds. A million dollars in $5 bills weighed 408 pounds.

There was even a name for the electronic coin-weighing scale, the Toledo Scale. Sunny had laughed, a tinge of hysteria in her voice, when she said a million dollars in quarters from the slots weighed twenty-one tons. A fortune passed through Babylon every day of the year, so much money that it had to be weighed instead of counted.

What *was* she doing here? *I'm trying to justify my mother-in-law's faith in my ability to safeguard the Thornton family fortune,* Fanny told herself. *I'm trying to help her family and to keep my own family intact.*

Fanny Thornton hated the opulent, decadent casino. Today, she should have called ahead to arrange a meeting someplace else, made a luncheon reservation as far away from this fool's paradise as possible. She knew that floor Security had announced her entrance the moment she walked through the door. Ash was probably watching her from one of his top-secret peepholes. Birch and Sage were probably on their way to intercept her while Sunny sat with her feet propped up on an open desk drawer, awaiting her arrival. She, too, would have been notified that Fanny Thornton was in the casino. The big question to all of them would be, why?

Knowing what was ahead of her, Fanny quickened her step, refusing to look at the acres of slot machines and banks of poker tables. Directly in her line of vision, striding toward her, were her handsome twin sons, dressed in dark suits and pristine white shirts. They could have posed as Wall Street bankers. They were smiling, but only Sage's smile reached his eyes.

"Mom! What brings you down here? Try and work up a smile or the customers will think Babylon hasn't been kind to you." Birch leaned over and kissed her lightly on the cheek.

"Mom, it's good to see you." Sage hugged her as he gave her a smacking loud kiss. "Do you have time for lunch or at least a cup of coffee?"

"I have the time. How's your father?" Her voice was polite, nothing more.

"Is that one of those questions that doesn't require an answer or is it one of those questions whose answer doesn't matter?" Birch asked as he cupped her elbow to lead her through the casino.

"Both."

Sage laughed, a sound of genuine merriment. Birch's features tightened.

Fanny looked from one of her sons to the other. The twins were like night and day. Sage was loving, open, warmhearted, and always the first one to ask "what can I do to help?" He was so much like her he scared her at times. Birch was cool, noncommittal except where his father was concerned, selfish, and arrogant, possessing all the same traits his father was known for.

Fanny shook off her son's hand, a motion that caused Birch's lips to tighten. She didn't care. She had every right to expect loyalty from her children. "If it's your intention to lead me to your father's office, forget it. This may surprise you, but I don't require an escort."

"Mom, why are you always so difficult when you come here?" Birch asked.

Fanny stopped in mid-stride. "That's a very amusing statement, Birch. I've been to this casino exactly twice in eighteen months. The first time was at the grand opening. The second was when Sunny fainted and Sage called me. The first time I was here I spent so much time smiling I thought I would end up with TMJ. My second visit was spent putting cool cloths on Sunny's forehead. Perhaps you have me mixed up with someone else."

"Mom, Birch didn't mean . . ."

"Yes, Birch means exactly what he says. I don't like this place. I have never liked it, even when it was on the drawing board. Those feelings have not changed. The only reason I'm here is because of business. Now, if you don't mind, I can find my way to Sunny's office by myself. Fetch your father, please."

"Mom . . ." Birch watched his mother walk away, her shoulders stiff, her ears closed to whatever he wanted to say.

"When was the last time you called her just to say hello, how are you?" Sage asked. "She hasn't forgiven us for choosing up sides two years ago. I can't say that I blame her. It was the worst kind of betrayal. You know it, and I know it. We're damn lucky she even talks to us."

"This is bullshit. We're running a business here. There's no room for 'he said, she said, I don't like this and I don't like that' crap. What's the point in calling, she's never home. She's always off somewhere with Simon."

"*Uncle* Simon, Birch. Show some respect. Mom can do whatever she pleases. She doesn't owe us explanations. She's fifty-four and she's independent. She makes more money than this casino does. Go ahead, defend that one."

"I don't have to defend anything. I don't kiss ass and take names later like you do, Sage."

"Where the hell did that come from? Mom walks in here and she has every right to do so and that invisible alarm goes off. Dad gets in a flap, Sunny goes white in the face, and you look so damn brittle it wouldn't surprise me to see your face split wide-open. Am I the only one who's normal around here? Scratch that, and add our sister Billie to the normal list. Don't forget for even one minute where the money came from for this fancy-dancy casino. Or is that what's eating you?"

"Let's not get into this now, Sage. I'll get Dad and meet you in Sunny's office. Where do you suppose *Uncle* Simon is? Dad calls him *her* shadow. He says they're joined at the hip. Actually, he didn't say hip."

"I know what he said. I was there. That crap is getting really old, Birch. Why can't you accept things for what they are? You're turning into Dad's clone. I just want you to know I hate what I see."

"Ah, the good son. Mom's good son. I'm the bad seed, is that it? Because I hate it that our uncle has taken over Mom's life? Dad hates it too. He still loves her."

"That's about the biggest crock I've ever heard. You're even more stupid if you believe it. You need to start lining up your ducks, Birch, before it's too late."

"Jesus, Sage, that almost sounds like a threat."

"It's whatever you want it to be," Sage said, turning on his heel. "I wouldn't make light of this to Dad. Whatever it is that brought Mom here must be serious. Hey, isn't that our little sister making her way in our direction?"

"What the hell! Is this a family reunion?" Birch demanded.

Sage grinned. "I think it's one of those things that's going to require a family vote. Billie, you're lookin' good!" He hugged his sister. Birch did, too, but not with the same enthusiasm.

"You handsome devil! You still beating the women off with a stick?" Billie teased as she tweaked Sage's cheek. "If you'd wipe that scowl off your face, Birch, you'd be just as handsome. What's up? Mom just said to be here at noon."

"Your guess is as good as ours."

"How's our little mother to be? I can't believe Sunny is going to have a baby."

"Dad can't believe it either," Sage said. "He's taking it personally. He thinks Sunny is having this baby to embarrass him. He won't allow her out on the floor."

"What?"

"You heard me. You wouldn't believe the crap that goes on here."

"Sure I would. Sunny takes it?" Billie said, her eyes wide with disbelief.

"She doesn't want to make waves. She says she learned her lesson that time when we all turned on Mom. In addition, I don't think she's feeling all that good. Tyler asked me to keep a close eye on her. I worry about her. If she doesn't shoot off her mouth, something is very wrong. Birch . . . Birch seems to take some kind of perverse pleasure in baiting her. It's taking a toll on her, Billie. So, enough about us, how are you doing? You still seeing that guy?"

"Yes, and don't ask me any more questions. My love life is my own. Tell me about yours."

"Her name is Iris. She said her mother named her after her favorite flower. She reminds me of Mom. Really down-to-earth, wants a family. She just got a professorship at the university. She's so smart she makes me look like a dummy." Billie hooted with laughter. "Sunny says Rainbow Babies is making so much money you guys can't count it fast enough."

"Kid clothing sells. We're doing well. Why does it have to be us guys versus you guys? I hate that, Sage."

"Because that's the way it is. This family has always been divided, and it will probably remain that way as long as Dad calls the shots around here. I don't see any changes on the horizon."

"Is there anything I can do?"

"Sure, have dinner with me and Iris over the weekend. I'd really like you to meet her. Bring along what's his name." Sage dropped his voice to a whisper as they approached the door to Sunny's office. "Billie, I want out of here. I gave it my best shot, but it isn't good enough. This was supposed to be a four-way operation, but Dad and Birch call the shots. Sunny and I are just their flunkies. I hate getting up in the morning knowing I have to come here."

"Then do something about it. The Dutch have a saying, Sage. If you can't whistle on your way to work, you don't belong in that job? Do you whistle?"

"Hell no, I don't."

"There you go. Is there anything I can do?"

"If there is, I'll call you. I just know this is going to be one of those spill-your-guts things. Everyone is going to say things they'll regret later on. The wedge will become wider. One of these days we're going to be strangers to one another. Wanna bet?"

"No thanks."

The door to Sunny's office opened. Billie said, "Mom, you look wonderful. Sunny, you look terrible. Are you taking your vitamins?"

"Of course I'm taking my vitamins. I'm married to a doctor. I just called down to the conference room to get it ready. We're going to need to spread out. The kitchen is sending up coffee and sandwiches. How's what's his name?" Sunny asked, leading the way out of her office.

"What's his name is just fine, thank you. So, Mom, what's this all about?" Billie asked as she linked her arm with her mother's.

"Family business. Serious business. I'm going to stop by the offices later. I haven't seen Bess in three weeks."

"Sunny's Togs and Rainbow Babies aren't the same without you. Bess misses you, Mom. She's just like you and Aunt Billie. You really are lucky to have such a good friend."

"I know that. We're like sisters. Actually, we're closer than sisters. I'm worried about Sunny, Billie. Has she said anything to you?"

"Only that she's taking her vitamins. Get her out of here, Mom. There aren't any windows, she's indoors all day, sometimes for twelve hours. It doesn't look to me like she gets any thanks for all her hard work either. Wouldn't it be something if she had twins?"

"Bite your tongue, Billie," Fanny said.

"Are you going to give us a clue as to what this meeting is all about, Mom?" Sunny asked. "Pop's smack in the middle of winding up all the details for the World Series Poker Championship. The emperor of Las Vegas as he's called these days, will view this meeting as a thorn in his side."

Fanny snorted. The World Series Championship was what Wimbledon was to tennis—the oldest and most prestigious of all the tournaments. Players came from all over the globe to compete. For three straight weeks, twenty-four hours a day, people would line up and play, right up to the main event, the $10,000 buy-in no-limit tournament that would last four days until a new champion was crowned.

"Fanny, what a pleasant surprise."

Fanny stared at the man in the wheelchair, the man who had once been her husband. She felt her shoulders straighten. There were no regrets. Not now, not ever.

He was impeccably dressed, manicured, and coifed. "Whatever this is about, Fanny, can we make it quick?" he said, not looking at her. "I'm up to my ears with the final details for the championship. There aren't enough hours in the day." His voice was syrupy, the way it always was when he thought he could charm her, wheedle her into doing what he wanted.

"Dad, I offered to help," Sunny said. "Sage . . ."

"Forget it, Sunny. The customers don't want to see your big belly. It's a turnoff. Men don't want reminders of home and hearth when they come to paradise."

Fanny sucked in her breath when her daughter's eyes filled with tears. "That was unnecessarily cruel, Ash, and you need to apologize to your daughter."

"It's okay, Mom." Sunny said.

"No. It is not okay. It wasn't okay when your father said the same things to me years ago and it's not okay now. This is not *your* casino, Ash. It belongs to the Thornton family enterprise. Sunny has a role here, and if you forgot what it is, I can have my attorneys refresh your memory. I also don't give a damn about your championship gambling tournament. Now, I came here to discuss something very important."

"You're really trying to stick it to me, aren't you, Fanny? Where's Simon? Shouldn't he be here?"

"Why is that, Ash? He doesn't belong to this immediate family even though he is your brother. But, to answer your question, I don't know where he is. Before we get down to the reason I'm here, outline what Sunny can do to take part of the burden off your shoulders. *Now*, Ash."

"Mom, it's okay. Really it is."

"Ash? Birch? Sage?" Fanny said. The three men stared at Fanny, blank looks on their faces. "I see, no one knows what's going on. Well, we'll change that right now. Sunny, you are in charge of the championship. You will report to Billie and me at the end of each workday. If it's too much for you, hire some help. Now that we've settled that little matter, let's get on with it."

"Just a goddamn minute, Fanny. You can't waltz in here and tell me how to run this business."

"I just did. We've moved on, Ash. What part didn't you understand?"

"You're deliberately screwing this up, Fanny. The minute you get your fingers on something it goes to hell."

"I made a decision, Ash. When I do that, I don't look back, and I don't back down. If I did, I wouldn't be in business, and you wouldn't be sitting here in this . . . this obscene den of opulence. As I said, I came here for a reason. I'm giving you all the courtesy of asking your opinion. I'll weigh what you have to say very carefully." Fanny drew a deep breath as she stared at the faces of her family.

"What is it, Mom?" Billie asked gently.

"Billie Coleman needs our help. As you know, your grandmother Sallie bought into Coleman Aviation years ago. The stock has been holding its own until now. Ash, I know Moss talked to you about the plans for his new plane before he died. I also heard you say you would help in any way you could. Simon also agreed. The Colemans are tapped out. They have nowhere else to turn. They've come too far now to let it all settle in the dust. I think we should do all we can to help Aunt Billie bring Moss's dream to life the way we all worked to make this dream possible for you, Ash. I'd like to hear your thoughts."

"Charity begins at home, Mom. What have the Colemans ever

done for us? Uncle Seth didn't give a damn about Grandma Sallie. His own *sister*. I don't plan on forgetting that," Birch said.

"What happens if they go belly up?" Ash asked. "Where does that leave us, Fanny? What exactly do you want from us? Our cash flow isn't that strong. Or are you saying you want to mortgage everything. That's it, isn't it? Jesus Christ, Fanny, we could lose everything on some cockamamie dream of Moss's."

Fanny's heart hammered in her chest. She waited.

"Aunt Billie is family. Families stick together. If this is a yes or no vote, then I vote yes," Sage said.

"Me too," Billie said without hesitation.

The score was two to two. If Sunny didn't vote, it would be up to Fanny to break the tie. The turmoil on her daughter's face tore at her heart. Once before Sunny had taken a stand and made a decision she couldn't live with.

"What are you waiting for, Sunny?" Ash demanded, his eyes boring into his daughter.

Fanny shivered at Ash's tone as she too waited for her daughter's response.

"I love Aunt Billie. I love all the Colemans. I say what's ours is theirs. I know in my heart Aunt Billie would do the same for us. I'm voting the way Grandma Sallie would want me to vote. I vote yes."

"That's just dandy. And when that plane doesn't get off the ground and we're hiding out from our creditors, where will you all be?" Ash snarled, his wheelchair burning rubber as he pressed the electric control.

"You're a jerk, Sunny," Birch said. He followed his father out into the hall.

"No, you are not a jerk," Billie said as she wrapped her arms around her sister. "I know what it took for you to do that." This last was said in a hushed whisper.

"So, what's the game plan?" Sage asked.

"I'm going to talk to Simon. He's our investment man. I don't think he's going to agree. This could go either way. Sage said it best. Families need to stick together. It's possible we could lose our shirts."

Billie's voice was flippant. "The sign on my door says I'm the head designer of Sunny's Togs and Rainbow Babies. If we lose our shirts, I'll design us new ones."

"Attagirl," Sage said, pounding her on the back. "C'mon, Sunny, sit down. You don't have any color. Are you sure you're okay?"

Fanny's head jerked upward at the concern in Sage's voice. "I'm taking all of us to lunch at Peridot. Billie, call Bess and ask her to meet us there. Sage, ask Birch if he wants to join us. There's no point in asking your father, but do it anyway. I'll meet you at the front door. I want to call Billie and tell her the good news."

The moment the door closed behind her children, the phone was in Fanny's hand. She would call Billie, but first she was calling Sunny's husband.

"Dr. Ford here."

"Tyler, it's Fanny."

"What's wrong?"

"That's what I want you to tell me. Sunny looks like death warmed over, and that's a kind statement. Aside from morning sickness, a pregnant woman usually has a wonderful sparkle in her eyes, color in her cheeks. She's a happy woman. This is not the case with Sunny. And another thing, she shouldn't be working twelve hours a day."

"You're right about everything, Fanny. Were you ever successful in changing Sunny's mind or getting her to do something she didn't want to do? I've spoken to her doctor, and he tells me she's fine. He said if she wants to work, she should work. She eats well, she exercises moderately, she takes her prenatal vitamins, and she sleeps through the night. She tells me she takes an hour nap in the middle of the afternoon. She makes sure she takes breaks and walks outside. She didn't have morning sickness. She's never been one to complain. My personal opinion is she's under a lot of stress at the casino with her father and brothers. Did something happen or did you just call to ask me questions? Whatever we say, Fanny, will go no farther."

"I know that, Tyler." Fanny told him about the brief meeting and Sunny's vote. "She looks so . . . fragile, so washed-out. She appeared a little wobbly to me. If she's willing to come up to Sunrise for a week or so, would you have any objections?"

"None at all. I've suggested the same thing to her, but she's married to that casino. I hate that goddamn place."

"Not as much as I do. Maybe I can work a little mother magic." She told him about the vote to help the Colemans. "How's everything going otherwise, Tyler?"

"Reconstructive surgery is not glamorous, but it is rewarding to make someone feel whole again. I love what I do as much as Sunny loves what she does. So, you see, I'm the last person who should even make suggestions where her job is concerned. I'm being paged, Fanny. Call me if you think there's something I can do. Not that my vote counts, but I think you're doing the right thing. Tell Billie I said hello when you talk to her."

"I'll do that, Tyler. She adores you, you know. She said you remind her of her son Riley."

"That's one of the nicest things anyone has ever said to me. Look, you do what you feel is right and don't let anyone make you back down. Families need to stick together. We'll talk again."

Fanny's fingers drummed on Sunny's desk. She should be feeling better after Tyler's reassuring words, but she didn't. Her motherly intuition was telling her something was wrong. She dialed Billie Coleman's number in Austin, Texas.

"Is everything okay?" Billie asked, breathless. She had picked up the phone on the first ring. "Every time I hear the phone the word disaster rings in my head. Before you can ask, we're facing a brick wall. Money just pours out of here. I don't know what to do. If I don't finish this project, then Riley's death and all those other boys who died in Coleman aircraft will have been in vain . . . how can I live with that? As sick as he was at the end, Moss worked tirelessly to perfect this plane. How can I do less?"

"You can't. The Thorntons are going to help, Billie. I'm at Babylon right now. We voted and the money will be on the way by the end of the week. If it isn't enough, we'll go back to the drawing board. Please, Billie, don't cry. Be thankful your granddaughter Sawyer is the aeronautical engineer on this project."

"We're all obsessed with this plane project, Sawyer more so. My own children . . . Fanny, how is it possible for a mother to be estranged from her two daughters? I never, ever thought such a thing would happen to me, how my daughters can fight me on this plane. All they want is the money they say we're wasting. They say a new plane won't bring Riley back, and they're right about that. He was their brother, and I know they loved him. On a more pleasant note, I just know Sawyer is going to explode when I tell her about your offer. That child has worked for months now, getting by on three hours' sleep a night. She eats, sleeps, and dreams about her grandfather's dream plane. She's going to get it off the ground too, thanks to you. Fanny, I wish there were words . . ."

"Words aren't necessary, Billie. We're family."

"We could lose our shirts."

"Well, guess what? Your namesake said if that happens, she would design us new ones. You can't beat an offer like that."

"No, you can't. How are things going on the Big White Way? How's Sunny? Is Birch still giving you heartache?"

"I'm in the conference room here at Babylon, Billie. I'll call you this evening. I'm taking the kids to lunch at Peridot."

"That place where you and Sallie got blitzed at your first meeting? When I told Thad how Devin took you two home in a hearse because no one had gas, he laughed until he cried."

"Drunk or not, that is one of my fondest memories of my mother-in-law. Oh, Billie, I miss her so much. She had such faith and trust in me. I hope I can live up to her expectations. I know in my heart she would approve of what we're doing. Family, Billie, is what life is all about. Sallie always said our families' destiny was in your hands and mine. Together, we'll work toward that end."

"We won't fail, Fanny. You can take that to the bank. Do I dare ask about Simon?"

"Tonight, Billie. Give everyone my love. Now, take a nap, okay?"

"At ten o'clock in the morning?"

"Why not? Aren't we independent women? If we are, then we can take a nap anytime we want. Actually, we can do *anything* we want. Both of us have earned that little perk. Talk to you tonight."

The Peridot restaurant was as old as Las Vegas itself. It was also Fanny's favorite restaurant for the very reason Billie Coleman had mentioned earlier.

"I love it when my brother finally acts like a grown-up and holds our chairs out for us," Billie said.

Sunny's voice was blunt yet sad when she said, "You're leaving, aren't you, Sage?"

"I want to. I'm willing to stay until you have the baby and get back into the swing of things. We're just flunkies, Sunny. You know it, and I know it. I glide around the floor trying to look important. I'm not sure what you do behind those closed doors. I don't know if you're aware of the latest developments. Is anyone interested?" The women nodded just as Bess Noble, Fanny's second-in-command, joined them.

"I heard that," Bess said as she kissed everyone before taking her seat. "Now, tell us what the latest development is."

"Dad and Birch want to buy riverboats in Biloxi, Mississippi, for gambling. He planned to apply for a mortgage, but you beat him to it, Mom. At least I think you did. Dad and Birch can be secretive at times. Those riverboats are a great big can of worms. I spoke up and said it had to be put to a vote, but they ignored me. At the risk of repeating myself, what the hell kind of family is this? Tell me, Mom, what you want us to do to help Aunt Billie."

"I'm going to call Simon this evening and discuss everything. We'll sell off all our shares of Rainbow Babies and Sunny's Togs. Simon never sold them. He fibbed to us about that transaction. Thank God he did. We're going to move our offices out of Sallie's Bingo Palace. It will go on the market tomorrow. It's prime real estate so it should fetch several million. I'm going to mortgage Babylon. By tomorrow the news will be on the Strip and the sharks will start to gather, so be prepared. I'll empty out that monster safe in Sunrise. I'll *mortgage* Sunrise. I'll sell all the jewelry Sallie left me. That's already in the works. I'll borrow what I can to make up the difference. The only monies we'll have coming in will go to make the mortgage payments. I did have a thought, though, and I'd like your opinions. Sallie never raised the rates for the other casinos to tie into her sewage and electrical systems. It's time for a hefty increase. Those fees, I believe, will keep our heads above water."

The sighs of relief could be heard around the table. "Good thinking, Mom," Sunny said.

"It's about time," Sage offered.

"This might be a good time to unveil my latest creation," Billie said as she dug into the voluminous bag she was never without and pulled out two soft dolls. "Meet Bernie and Blossom. I showed them to a few of our salespeople who took them on the road. Guess what! We already have orders for ten thousand. The big question is, how are we going to market them? The next question is, where do we get the money? Do we form a separate company or do we license them under Rainbow Babies or Sunny's Togs? I thought we could hire the Bernsteins to get our publicity started. We can have a million of these on the market by next Christmas."

Sage stared at his sister, his face full of awe. "Just like that! Where are you going to manufacture them?"

"Made in the good old U.S. of A. Forty bucks a pop or $39.95. People like to walk away with change even if it's only a nickel. We learned that in marketing class."

Fanny held the soft fabric doll in her hands. As always, she marveled at her younger daughter's abilities. "The scraps from Rainbow Babies, right?"

"Yes, but each face is different. I know eight people that come to mind who will be willing to work on the faces. The doll itself and the garment can be made for under a dollar if mass produced. The faces are what will cost, and labor of course. Sign on, Sage, we can use your expertise. You said you want out of Babylon. So, what do you all think?"

"I think this is one of your best ideas," Bess said, a calculator in hand.

"Billie, these dolls are priceless. I wish I had your talent. Can I have the first one off the line for my new baby, Bernie if he's a boy? If I have a girl, I'll take Blossom. They are so adorable. Raggedy Ann and Andy will be passé."

Billie reached into the bag again and withdrew two tissue-wrapped bundles. "I already made them for you. I wanted something special for you. That's where I got the idea. Think about it, Sunny, you have a clothing company named after you and now you're the inspiration behind these two dolls. I don't think we're headed to the poor house just yet."

"This calls for a celebration," Fanny said.

"Let's have some of that same wine you and Grandma Sallie had that famous day you first met. Tell us the story again, Mom," Sage said.

"It was wartime and I was meeting your grandmother for the first time . . ."

The moment the door closed behind Ash Thornton, he went into a rage. "Now, do you see what your mother is capable of? She undermines every single thing I do. If she'd keep her nose out of the casino business, things would be just fine. Do I interfere in her business? No, I do not. Your mother has to dabble in everything. She's not content to own two of the biggest clothing companies in the country, she has to make her presence felt in everything that concerns me. I'm not going to let that happen. We're going to go ahead with those riverboats. I want you in Mississippi tomorrow. Get everything under way. She won't stop us. If she does . . . I'll deal with it then and there. When Sunny comes back from lunch, send her in here. She's out of here until that kid arrives. I have enough problems without her jinxing me. Why are you looking at me that way, Birch? Business is business. We're on top, and I plan on staying there. So I already took a mortgage out, so what? I got a good interest rate and cut Granger's markers to half. That's how you do business in this town. I love bankers who gamble. Hell, the governor was in here two weeks ago, and he shot a load that made me blink. You suck up to these people and you can get anything you want. You have to know how to play the game. Your mother doesn't know the *name* of the game much less how to *play* it. I even know what her next move is going to be. She's going to raise the rates on the sewage and electric plants. That won't endear us to the rest of the owners. The dark stuff will start to fly. Anything can happen in this town and take my word for it, something will happen as soon as those rate hikes go into effect. Your mother talks a good game about tightening our belts and all that crap. Don't kid yourself, son, it's what Fanny wants when Fanny wants it. Thanks for sticking up for me. They'll eat our dust yet."

"Dad, this is all wrong. The past is past. Can't we let it die and make things better? I know you can't go back, but you can go forward and make it better than it was. Sage is going to walk. I could see it in his face."

"Sage is not a team player. Neither is Sunny. You and me now, we have the same goals. We'll make those goals, too."

Birch watched as his father swallowed a handful of pills. He could feel his shoulders slump. Sage was his twin, his other half. He never felt quite whole unless Sage was close by. He adored Sunny, always had. It was all getting away from him, just like the last time when they sided with their father against their mother.

"You can't tell Sunny she isn't needed right now. If we do that, Mom will shut this place down so fast we won't have time to blink. She'll do it, Dad. I'd hate to see you make the mistake of pushing her to the edge. She won't jump over the edge, she'll plow you right under. She takes her commitment to Grandma Sallie and this family very seriously. You're wrong about Sage, too. Sage has the charisma to make this place work. He works the floor like a pro. Any casino on this Strip would hire him and pay him five times what we pay him. He'd be worth every dollar, too. Don't mess with Sage, Dad."

Ash eyed his son, his one remaining ally. His mind was scrambled with the pills he'd just taken. His chaotic thoughts reeled back in time to when he was Birch's age. He'd been just as tall, just as good-looking, just as virile, just as mobile. He stared at the replica of himself and wanted to cry. "Sage is weak," he mumbled.

"You're wrong. Sage has more guts than the two of us put together. I'll walk out of here before I let you put Sage down."

Ash stared at his son and knew he meant every word. He waved him out of the room. When the door closed behind Birch, great wrenching sobs tore at his wasted body. "I hate your goddamn fucking guts, Fanny," he sobbed.

In his office, Birch sat down behind his desk. His head dropped to his hands. He wished he could turn back the hands of the clock to the day he and Sage left for college with Simon behind the wheel.

He knew the story behind his father and his Uncle Simon. He'd heard his father's version, his grandmother's version, Simon's version, and then his mother's version. Somewhere in between was the *real* story. Late at night in the college dorm, he and Sage had put their own spin on the story and came up with one they could both live with. Now, eighteen years later, history seemed to be repeating itself. He was his father and Sage was Simon. He remembered how his Uncle Simon had come out the winner in all the different stories, even their own. That meant Sage was a winner and he was . . . his father all over again.

It was three o'clock when Birch closed his briefcase. "Biloxi, Mississippi, here I come," he muttered. The knock on his door startled him. "Come in," he called.

"Nah. I don't think so," Sage said from the open doorway. "I stopped by Dad's office to drop this off, but he was asleep. He'd just tear it up anyway. You can do whatever you want with it. It's my resignation. You going somewhere? Let me guess. Biloxi, Mississippi, right? Big mistake, Birch."

"Come on, Sage, we go through this at least once a week. You always back down. This thing is going to blow over the way these things always blow over. This is our business. We need to pull together."

"That's really funny coming from you. I've had it. What we voted for was right for all the right reasons. I don't have any regrets. All I want is a life, and I'm damn well going to get one. Uncle Simon walked away and got his life. I've got the guts to do the same thing."

"Let's not forget that good old Uncle Simon walked off with the queen of this parade. Our mother."

"Mom's personal life is none of our business. Justify what happened with Sunny, Birch. Don't tell me nothing happened either. I know how you and Dad do things."

"Sunny belongs at home taking care of herself. Mom stayed home and took care of us. Why isn't that good enough for her?"

"The why of it doesn't matter. It's her choice. We made a pact early on. You can't blow Sunny off. You're gonna do it, aren't you? I refuse to be a party to anything that hurts one of us. What the hell happened to you, Birch? For months now we've been at opposite ends of the spectrum. I miss the old Birch, my buddy and my pal. Where'd he go?"

"Get your ass in here and stop telling the world our business. What about Dad?"

"Ah, the emperor's son has spoken. The queen's son is speaking now, the son who is his own man, and he says, fuck you, Birch." In a dramatic gesture, Sage threw his hands high in the air. "Jesus, do you have any idea of how good I feel right now? Because I'm in such a good mood, I'm going to give you some advice for free. Forget those riverboats, they're going to sink to the bottom of the Mississippi River. Give some thought to buying a gondola. Isn't that what emperors ride around in or sail in . . . ? Whatever. See you around."

"Sage, wait. We need to talk. Sage, get in here. What the hell is bugging you? Come on, we can talk this through and make it work."

"Sorry, Birch, not this time."

The sound of the door closing behind his brother sounded ominous, final. Birch cried then for what he'd allowed himself to become: the emperor's son.

2

Fanny waved good-bye to her children, then frowned as she watched Sage and Billie link arms with Sunny. She turned to Bess. "I'm worried."

"I know. Why don't we take a walk, just you and me, Fanny? Remember the old days when we traipsed around this town? Two young girls who never in their wildest dreams thought they would be where they are right now."

"I had such dreams back then. I thought I had a marriage made in heaven. Hell would be more like it. I tell myself there must have been some good years. If there were, why can't I remember them?"

"It's over. You can't look back. You told me that a thousand times or more."

"That's because Sallie always said it to me. I miss her so much, Bess. A day doesn't go by that I don't think about her. She was my best friend. The mother I never had. I try to do things the way I think she would want me to do them, but I'm never sure I'm succeeding."

"Maybe you need to stop doing that and do what *you* think is best. Sallie isn't here anymore. She trusted you. That means she trusted your judgment. Lay her to rest and live your own life. It's time for you to crawl out from under her shadow."

"Oh, Bess, it sounds so simple. I can't turn it off. I envy you and your nice normal family. You and John were meant for each other. Doctor and Mrs. Bess Noble. I love the way that sounds. You and John got the brass ring, my friend."

"We've had our ups and downs, Fanny. Every married couple does at one time or another."

"You came out stronger, though. We're to the half century mark, Bess. Actually, we're past the mark. I'm divorced. My family is divided. No one is happy. Sunny's ill, I feel it in my bones. My eyes see things I don't want to recognize. Yes, my businesses are successful. Yes, I provide jobs for a lot of people, including my children. When is it my time in the sun, Bess?"

"Whenever you decide to make a commitment to Simon. You could get married tomorrow at a Las Vegas wedding chapel if you wanted to. You could do it the minute you pick up Simon. It's a choice, Fanny. You have to get rid of all that guilt you're carrying around. So what if Simon is Ash's brother. So what, Fanny! You're divorced for God's sake. Ash no longer has a hold on you. His accident wasn't your fault. Let it die already." There was such exasperation in Bess's voice that Fanny laughed aloud.

"I think you care more than I do."

"That's a bald-faced lie if I ever heard one. You love Simon. He loves you. Carrying on an affair is what Sallie did. That's not who you are, Fanny. You're a home and hearth person. If you deliberately *choose* to pattern your life after Sallie's that's one thing. If you let circumstances dictate to you, that's something else. Sallie has a hold on you from the grave. You need to shake it loose."

Fanny stopped walking to stare at her friend. "Is that what I'm doing, Bess?"

"Yes." The single word was an explosion of sound from Bess's mouth. "I want to see some backbone. Starting right now!"

Fanny hugged her friend as people walked around them, smiles on their faces. "What would I do without you, Bess?"

Bess shrugged. "We need to start scrounging for money for the dolls. You can put John and me down for $75,000. I know the kids will kick in with their savings. Your kids, that is. Mine don't have any savings."

"Don't you have to ask John?"

"Nope. That's why we work so well together. He knows I wouldn't do anything to put our lives in jeopardy. We have other savings. If he knew the situation, he'd offer before I could get the words out of my mouth."

Fanny recognized the truth of the statement. "Isn't it strange, Bess, how Billie managed to save the day? She did it once before with Rainbow Babies. The truth, Bess, am I doing the right thing where Billie Coleman is concerned?"

"Absolutely. When it comes down to the wire, Fanny, when everything else is shot to hell, family is the only thing you can count on. In the end family always comes through for you. Trust me on this."

"My own family . . . Birch . . ."

"Birch is torn, Fanny. All you can do is be there for him when he finally comes to terms with his role in his father's life. Birch isn't a kid anymore. You always said because he was minutes older, he was the leader and Sage was the follower. That changed somewhere along the way. Sage is his own person and has been for a very long time. I think Birch knows that and doesn't know how to get back on even footing. He'll figure it out, and when he does, he'll come back to the fold and you'll be there because that's what mothers do."

"But, will I feel the same way about him? Right now I love him, but I don't like him. Does that make sense? He hates it that I'm considering marrying Simon."

"No, Ash is making him hate the idea. Birch always adored his uncle. He has to deal with that, too. He has a lot on his plate right now. The minute Sage is gone, he's going to start soul searching. We'll just wait and hope he sees the light. By the way, how is your ex?"

"His debonair self as far as I could see. If you're asking me if he's still taking all those drugs, my answer would be yes. His eyes appeared glassy to me, but he wears tinted glasses indoors. Sage told me once the fluorescent lighting bothers his eyes. I don't want to know, Bess. All I want is what Sallie wanted, a simple life with a man I love and who loves me. I want my family."

"Then tell Simon you'll marry him and don't change your mind this time. No matter how much he loves you, he won't wait forever. Neither one of you is getting any younger."

"I have loose ends in my life, Bess. I hate loose ends. I know life doesn't come in a tidy little box with a ribbon on top. I have the box and the ribbon, but I can't tie it into a bow. I still haven't found my mother. My instincts tell me she's out there somewhere. I'm ashamed that I didn't do more to find her. I could have half brothers and sisters, a whole other family I know nothing about. I need to do something about that. Then there's Jake and his money. I've borrowed on that money so many times I've lost count. I need to lay that to rest, too. It's been thirty years, Bess, since that bus holdup when Jake gave me his money to hold. I wanted to give the money back, but I could never find him. He must have a family somewhere. I never did tell Ash about that money. Simon invested it time and again. It's a small fortune."

"Fanny, with all the new technology out there today you can hire the best of the best. It might take a while, but I think you'll be able to lay those two matters to rest once and for all. Now, didn't we have a nice chat? Time for you to be getting ready for the drive to the airport. Isn't Simon due in soon?"

"How do you know he's coming in and that I'm picking him up?"

"Because you're wearing your yellow dress. You always wear yellow when you pick Simon up. Sometimes you are very transparent, Fanny."

"Obviously," Fanny sniffed. "I didn't lie back there at the meeting when I said I didn't know where Simon was. I didn't know *precisely* what city or town his plane was flying over at that moment." Fanny grinned and hugged her friend.

She would have known him anywhere, even in a dark room, this love of hers. She wanted to jump over the barrier and run to him. Instead she held out her arms and smiled. "I missed you. I thought about you every minute of every day. The moment I open my eyes in the morning my first thought is, is Simon awake yet?"

He kissed her while the world on the tarmac watched. Neither one cared. "It doesn't have to be this way," he said against her lips.

"I know," she whispered. "For now it is what it is. I do love you, more than I loved you yesterday and not as much as I will tomorrow. So there!"

"How's everything?"

"Some things are good, some things are bad, some things are indifferent. Nothing much changes around here. We'll talk later. Let's just enjoy each other. It's been two whole weeks, Simon!"

"Three hundred and thirty-six hours or twenty thousand one hundred and sixty minutes. Damn, I can't calculate the seconds in my head."

"Who cares? You're here and that's all that counts."

"Fanny, let's get married. Right now. I'm willing to keep it a secret if you don't want the family to know. I see something in your eyes I've never seen before and it scares me. *Now,* Fanny."

Fanny slid into the passenger side of her car. Simon always drove when they were together. Her heart started to flutter in her chest. Simon's words sounded like an ultimatum. The hard set of his jaw frightened her. Bess's words rang in her ears. "Simon won't wait forever."

Fanny's voice was squeaky, jittery-sounding when she said, "By now, do you mean on the way home or *soon?*" Simon's demand coupled with what had transpired earlier left her feeling drained. She needed to say something positive, something light and funny to take away the harsh look on her beloved's face. She couldn't find the words. Was it possible they weren't in her vocabulary? Was it possible she wasn't meant to marry Simon? The thought was so devastating she could feel her eyes start to burn.

"Fanny, did you hear what I said?"

"Yes, Simon, I did. I'm thinking."

The disbelief in Simon's voice was total. "You're *thinking?* That doesn't say very much for us, Fanny. What in the name of God do you have to think about?"

"Everything, Simon. Everything."

"That word sounds ominous. I don't think I care for that explanation. Would you mind explaining?"

"Can we have this discussion when we get to Sunrise?"

"It doesn't look like I have a choice. What's happening to us, Fanny?"

Fanny's voice was a tortured whisper. "I don't know."

"I thought what we felt for one another was rock solid. You and me against the world, that kind of thing. Am I wrong, Fanny?"

"No. I never thought I could love someone as much as I love you. I didn't know I could feel like this. I don't want to lose you like I did the last time, Simon. If you recall, I asked you to marry me and you turned me down flat. Those were the longest, the most miserable days of my life. We'll talk over cocoa, and a nice warm fire. It's still chilly on the mountain in the evenings."

"Okay, Fanny. So, how are the kids? They're always going to be kids to me no matter how old they are."

"We'll talk about that tonight, too. I am worried about Sunny. Tyler said he spoke to her obstetrician and he said she was fine. She is not fine. Something is wrong, but I don't know what it is."

Simon sighed. Maybe it wasn't him after all. Maybe Fanny's eyes were filled with sadness because of her children. The invisible load on his shoulders lightened. However, the wariness stayed in his eyes. "How's Ash?" His voice said he didn't care one way or the other. The expression in his eyes was a direct contradiction to his words.

"As arrogant as ever. I've only been to Babylon twice since the grand opening. I don't think I'll ever get used to seeing people gamble before breakfast. I wish we had never built that damn place." Fanny's voice was so vehement, Simon's eyebrows shot upward.

"It wasn't the answer you were looking for, was it?"

"It was the answer for Ash. He's breaking all the rules. All the agreements we had. He thinks I'm going to go along with his shenanigans because of the kids. He deliberately baits me, deliberately pushes me to the wall. I hate his defiance and it has nothing to do with his accident or with him being in a wheelchair. He hates my mobility and my feelings for you. He hates my father and my brothers for finishing *his* casino. They call him The Emperor on the Strip. Somehow he managed to get this poker tournament for Babylon. People have to pay ten thousand dollars to play. That just absolutely, totally, mystifies me. Ash says it's a real feather in his cap."

"I'd say so. He'll clear a few million for the Thornton coffers and it will only enhance his image in Vegas. The Emperor, huh?" A storm began to build in Simon's eyes that Fanny couldn't see. "What do you suppose that makes the rest of us?" Simon threw his head back against the headrest and laughed so hard tears rolled down his cheeks. Later, when he dried his eyes, Fanny was startled at how angry his eyes looked. The deep belly laugh sounded forced to her ears for some reason. She shrugged off the feeling. If Simon was angry, he had a right to be angry. She couldn't let little things like that mar her happiness.

Fanny didn't mean to laugh. Nothing her ex-husband did was funny. But they both started to laugh until they were giddy. The tense moments were over. For a little while.

They made the rest of the drive to Sunrise in comfortable, companionable silence. From time to time Simon squeezed her hand.

The moment he pulled the car into the courtyard, Fanny said, "Now I can *breathe*. I need my daily sagebrush fix. Smell it, Simon, isn't it wonderful? The air up here on the mountain is so clean and pure. Down in town I always feel like I'm fighting to breathe. Ten years from now Las Vegas is going to be as crowded as New York City. I'll be sixty-four then. Do you think I'll care, Simon?"

"I hope not. I want us to retire and go off together someplace. A new place because new beginnings should have new surroundings. Just you and me, Fanny. We're never going to need anyone else. I'm selling my brokerage house, my client base, the whole ball of wax. All my real estate is on the market. My plan was to put on a blindfold and stand in front of a map and stick a pin in it. Then I was going to have you do the same thing, at which point we'd pick somewhere in the middle. Whatcha think?"

"Oh, Simon, do you really want to do that? I've never lived anywhere but Pennsylvania and Nevada. I need to think about this, Simon. You're selling *everything?*"

"Everything. I'm ready for a new beginning. I've paid my dues."

"Is that another way of saying you're going to stick the pin in the map with or without me?" She wondered if the fear she felt showed in her face.

"I'm afraid so, Fanny." The intense angry expression was back in Simon's eyes.

Fanny felt her knees start to crumple. "That's . . . that's an ultimatum."

"No, Fanny, it's a statement of fact. I'm going to do this. I want *us* to do it together. It's what we said *we* both wanted for our lives. I'm doing my best to stick with the plan."

For the second time in one day, Fanny Thornton's world turned upside down. "Let's go down to the studio, Simon. I need to let Daisy out. She's going to be so happy to see you. Daisy is the nicest present anyone ever gave me. She's all the more precious because you picked her out."

Simon sucked in his breath. The studio was Fanny's place of refuge, her port in any storm that crashed into her life. They'd made love there so many times—wild, uninhibited love and sweet, gentle love. Only in that safe haven did either one of them feel free. He was starting to hate Sunrise and the mountain it sat on. He was even beginning to hate the studio, viewing it as a shackle tying Fanny to the mountain, to the house she'd shared with Ash. They wouldn't be coming back here again, he'd make sure of that. He shivered in the bright sunshine as Fanny inserted the key in the lock.

Daisy slammed her small body against Fanny's legs, yipping her pleasure now that her mistress was home. Fanny rolled on the floor with the little dog, her skirt hiked up past her thighs. "Join in, Simon," she gasped as she rolled over and over, Daisy hopping from her to Simon.

And then he was on top of her, staring down into her flushed face the minute Daisy scooted out the door. "I don't think there's another human being in this world who can tear at my heart the way you do, Fanny." His heart thundered in his chest as Fanny returned his ardent kisses and embraces. He thought he would choke on his own desire when her rich sound of pleasure curled around him.

How wonderful she smelled, a delicious womanly scent that was all her own. A warm, sunshiny smell mixed with flowers and sagebrush.

His lips left the sweetness of her mouth, seeking the softness beneath her chin where her throat pulsed and curled into her shoulder as he worked the straps of the yellow dress down over her shoulders. Fanny helped him, wiggling and sliding until she was naked beneath his hard body. Her own hands were feverish as she worked at the buttons of his shirt, the zipper of his trousers.

His hands traveled the length of her as he sought those places that gave her the most pleasure, a taut breast, a welcoming thigh. He fought to harness his growing desire as he waited for her own greedy passion to match his own.

A sound escaped his lips, a moan, a plea, as he crushed her mouth to his. When he at last broke free, he stared down at her, at the tawny luster of her breasts that summoned him, their rosy crests erect and tempting. Her slender waist curved into his hands, her rounded haunches grinding into his thighs.

Simon's lips touched her everywhere, his thirst for her deep and raw as he sought to quench it. He felt her body cry out to him as her slender legs wrapped themselves around him. She offered herself completely as their lusty passions met and were satisfied, again and again, until they lay back, their breathing ragged gasps, their slick bodies molded to one another.

A long time later, Simon said, "Can you even begin to imagine what it would have been like if we were doing this when we were *twenty?*"

There was something in his tone, something she should be picking up on. She'd worry about whatever it was later. "Absolutely wonderful," Fanny sighed. "I'm glad we didn't know each other when we were twenty. We wouldn't be here now, at this, the best time of our lives."

"Is it the best time, Fanny?"

Fanny sat up, oblivious to her nakedness. "It's supposed to be. I want it to be. I feel it is. There are some loose threads . . . I love you, Simon, more than I can ever put into words, and I know you love me in the same way."

Simon handed Fanny her clothing and watched as she struggled with her thoughts. "Then why do I feel like an old sleeve that's unraveling a little bit at a time?"

Fanny walked into the bathroom, her buttocks jiggling for his benefit. "Life isn't easy, is it, Simon? Life just gets in the way of so many things. I wish I knew how to deal with it."

Ten minutes later, Fanny was back in the living room sitting on one of the deep red chairs that she loved, Simon across from her in a matching chair. He handed her a cup of coffee.

"You were saying."

"That life gets in the way of so many plans. I think, Simon, that unknowingly, unwittingly, I have been trying to emulate your mother. I said I wouldn't do that, didn't plan to do it, but there it is. In my desperate desire to do what Sallie wanted, at least what I thought she wanted, I reacted. You know the old saying, for every action there is a reaction. Like now, with us. We're a reaction to something I did or said. Sallie was right about a lot of things and she was wrong about a lot of things, too. Bess said it best earlier today. She said I chose to pattern myself after Sallie because I loved her so much. I want to run away. What I *really* want to do is pick up my purse in one hand, Daisy in the other, and walk out the door and not look back. I want you to be waiting on the other side of the door when I make my grand exit."

"Then let's do it!" Simon said, rubbing his hands together, his face gleeful at the prospect of what Fanny had just said. The same look was back in his eyes. Fanny felt a chill race down her spine.

"I can't, Simon. Life got in the way this morning. I made promises and commitments and I have to honor them. That's what life is all about. At least my life. It's tearing me apart, Simon, but I have no other choice."

"One always has choices, Fanny. Tell me straight out what it is you're trying to say."

In a flat monotone, Fanny told him everything, starting with the Colemans, Sunny's health, young Billie's newest brainchild. "Then there's my mother to find and the old business of Jake that has to be brought to closure. You promised to put an investigator on finding Jake. I keep forgetting to ask you if you found out anything."

"The last report was a big zero. The man dropped off the face of the earth. I did try, Fanny. You need to chalk it up as one of those little mysteries in life that will never be solved. As far as I'm concerned, Jake's money is yours." Simon sucked in his breath and let it out with a loud *swoosh* of sound. "You're making a mistake, in my opinion, in regard to Billie Coleman."

"No, Simon, I'm not. Maybe this is something only a mother understands, then again, maybe not. Billie's son was flying a defective Coleman plane when he died. The Thorntons own the controlling interest in Coleman Aviation. What kind of person would I be if I turned my back on Billie now? Her son died! Other mothers' sons died in planes of ours that were defective. That has to be made right, and the only ones who can make it right are Billie, her granddaughter, and me. Sawyer is as committed as we are. It's almost as though God put Sawyer on this earth to finish Billie's husband's plane. Maybe it really is a mother thing. I know the monies I'll be giving her won't be enough, but we'll worry about that later. We're family, Simon. Sallie would want me to do what I'm doing. Me, Fanny Logan Thornton wants it, too. This is who I am, Simon, and I can't change. I will not turn my back on Billie. Right now I'm all she has, and I know what that feeling is like."

Fanny felt her insides cringe at the coldness she saw reflected in Simon's eyes. "Why do you ask my opinion on things if you have no intention of following my advice?" he asked. "You could lose everything, Fanny. Have you thought about that?"

"Yes. That's all I've been thinking about. We put it to a family vote this morning. Birch and Ash are against it, but then they have an ulterior motive, they want to buy riverboats in Biloxi, Mississippi, for gambling. Ash never liked Billie Coleman. He blamed her for my independence. I heard him tell Moss Coleman he would help in any way he could when it came to building this new plane. With Moss dead, he's reneging. I don't like that. In my eyes, a person is only as good as their word. I can, and I will, live with my decision. You're to sell everything off, Simon, and wire the monies to the Coleman account by the close of business on Friday."

"With all that you could still walk out the door. You can lose your shirt here or somewhere else, somewhere where we're together." His voice sounded too cool, too practiced to Fanny's ears. He was upset.

"My daughter is going to need me. I want to be here for her."

"Sunny could come and stay with us for a while. This isn't working for me, Fanny."

"Sunny wouldn't agree to that. She has a husband she loves and who adores her. We aren't talking about a rash or some hair loss. Whatever it is, it's serious. I'm the first to admit this is all in my head, but I know I'm not wrong. Ash is going to do . . . something. Birch is going way out on a limb. I need to be here when the limb comes down. I've made up my mind now that I will leave no stone unturned in finding my mother. I'm going to do this, Simon. You're being obstinate."

"Where does that leave me? I do not care for the word obstinate at all. Do you *ever* plan on marrying me?" His voice was icy cold when he said, "It always comes back to Ash."

"Oh, yes, Simon. Yes, yes, yes. I just can't give you a time or a place. What we have right now is working. Isn't it? You need to take Ash's name out of your vocabulary."

"Not for me. You made your decisions. I made my decisions, too. What we're faced with is a stalemate. You won't or can't budge and neither can I. *I don't like to lose, Fanny.*"

Simon's voice was so strange, Fanny started to cry. "You're making this sound like a . . . contest of some kind, you against me. Then you throw Ash into the same pot. Please, Simon, try to understand."

"Fanny, I do understand. I understand, but I can't accept it. I want a life. There's no point in rehashing this. I'll leave now, but I have to borrow your car. I'll call you and tell you where it is at the airport. I'll take care of your business before I leave."

"Simon, wait . . . we're grown adults, surely we can work this out and come to a decision we can both live with. It can't be your way all the time, Simon. It just can't. I need you."

"And I need you. I'm walking out that door, Fanny, and I'm going to close it. Daisy is right here. There's your purse on the table. Your choice, Fanny, your call."

Go! Go! Go! Fanny's mind shrieked when the door closed behind

Simon. Daisy was in her arms. She picked up her purse from the table, her eyes going to a framed picture of herself with her children under the cottonwoods. She stared at it for a long minute before her shoulders slumped. Daisy jumped from her arms the same moment her purse thudded to the floor.

Simon waited on the other side of the door, but not for long. She wasn't going to open that door. He turned and walked up the path to the courtyard where the car was parked.

Inside the studio, Fanny watched from behind the curtains. "Come back, Simon, please come back." The sound of the car's engine turning over drove her to one of the big red chairs. "Good-bye, Simon."

His shoulders rigid with anger, Simon floored the gas pedal as he started down the mountain. He found himself blinking as he tried to dispel the rage that was rivering through him. Where in the hell had he ever come up with the idea that Fanny would bow and bend to his will? For some reason he'd thought her pliable, with a sapling strength. She was proving to be a goddamn three-hundred-year-old oak that would outlast him and anyone who crossed her path.

Simon's foot pressed harder on the accelerator. He was being stupid, this mountain road was something he needed to respect. His foot eased up a little. He changed his mental gears. Ash and the kids. That's what it came down to. It would always be Ash and the kids versus him. Fanny didn't need to hit him over the head with a sledgehammer. Everything she said or did involved Ash in some way or the kids. "I can't and I won't accept that."

Simon rolled down the window before he turned on the radio. The music blasted through his head and on out the window to ricochet down the mountain. He flicked the radio off before he maneuvered the car around a murderous curve in the road.

"We'll just see about that. I told you the truth, Fanny, when I said I don't like to lose."

He set the controls to cruise, turned the radio back on, then lowered the sound. Soft, mellow music filtered through the car.

It was a game. It was always a game. The kind of game he and Ash used to play. As in all games, there was a winner and a loser. The secret was patience. *Wait it out, Simon,* he cautioned himself. *You'll win because you always win.*

Simon Thornton smiled. It was so true.

3

Simon Thornton stood, his eyes sweeping around the comfortable office where he'd spent the major part of his life. Months ago he'd separated his life into three stages; first, his years in the military, where he'd used someone else's identity just so he could get away from his parents and his brother Ash. The second part was heading for New York where, with his nose to the grindstone, he'd carved out a business that made him a millionaire a hundred times over. The third part was Fanny. His reason for getting up in the morning, for living, for *being*. The time was finally here when he could stick it to Ash once and for all. It was supposed to be the best day of his life. The day he'd separated his life he'd decided his pie was to be cut in thirds because Fanny was the final slice. Now all he had was a pie with no topping. There was no reason to get up in the morning, no goal to shoot for in the living department. As for being . . . well, he was tough, he could exist with the best of them. He knew how to go through the motions. If he wasn't happy who was going to notice? No one. Not one single person. Maybe Jerry.

He opened all the drawers in his desk, prolonging the moment when he would walk through the door and then close it. Jerry, his friend since childhood, along with all his employees, would have balloons, a cake, some champagne, and probably a present that everyone chipped in to buy. His eyes would burn when he shook hands, clapped others on the back, and then, finally, the bear hug for Jerry. Thirty minutes out of his life. After that he'd head uptown to his apartment to pick up his luggage, at which point he would be completely homeless for the first time in his life.

The urge to smash something, preferably Ash's handsome face, was so strong that Simon clenched his fists, then stuck his hands in his pockets. He was smart enough to know anger didn't solve anything. All he had to do was fall back and regroup. It wasn't supposed to be like this. Fanny was supposed to be here with him when he walked away for the last time to start their new life. His clenched fist hit the wall just as Jerry opened the door slightly and angled through it.

"That bad, huh?"

The pain in Simon's hand matched the pain on his face. "I suspect I'll get over it in about a hundred years."

"Is there anything I can do, Simon?"

"If there was, you'd be the first person I'd ask."

"I feel like I did the day we cooked up that scheme for you to use my cousin's identity. I bawled for days when I realized you were finally gone. Now I'm gonna bawl for weeks, maybe months or years. Simon, do you know what the hell you're doing? You waited this long for Fanny, what's the harm in waiting a little while longer? Ultimatums never work for the person issuing them. We both know that. What in the hell ever possessed you to do that?"

"I could see it all sliding away, little by little. I figured it was better to get on with it. I don't like parts of things, little bits of this or that. When two people love each other they should be able to work together to make a good life. Like you and your wife. Fanny had her mind made up before I got up to bat. I don't want to talk about this, Jerry."

"You still haven't told me where you're going. You're going to write and call, aren't you?"

"Sure."

"You really are going to stick a pin in the map. Jesus, Simon, that's not romantic at all. It's stupid. Why don't you just get in the truck and drive till you run out of gas? That makes a little more sense. Simon . . ."

"Don't fall apart on me, Jerry. Right now I feel like I was put together with spit and chewing gum. I need . . . I need to walk out of here all in one piece. We'll always be best buddies. We both know that. I'll be in touch. Finish up Fanny's business for her. All the wheels are in motion. She wanted it all done by the close of business today. Get rid of the damn map on the wall. Okay, buddy, let's get this show on the road."

The banners and streamers were colorful, his employees shouting, "bon voyage" as champagne corks popped. Shrill whistles and hoots of "You're going to hate retirement," rocked against the walls. "Speech, speech!"

"C'mon, I'm not a speech maker. Thanks for your loyalty and for the good job you've done all these years. I'm going to miss all of you. End of speech."

Someone said, "Jerry went to get something for you."

"It better fit in my Rover."

"Oh, it will fit," Jerry said, leading two small dogs into the room. "This is Tootsie and this is Slick. They've had all their shots. They're hale and hearty. Total weight is a little over six pounds. Slick's the heaviest. Tootsie, as you can see, is delicate. We were going to get you one of those man dogs so you could call him Duke or Spike, but these little beauties beckoned. They're called Teacup Yorkies. They're trained and both have been neutered. They understand one command; freeze! They're seven months old. Say something, Simon."

"I guess they'll fit in the Rover," Simon said as he nuzzled the tiny dogs under his chin. "This wasn't in my game plan."

"I know," Jerry said. "I put their gear in your truck. You might have to pile your stuff on the top. Listen, I gotta go," Jerry said with a catch in his voice.

Simon bit down on his lower lip. "Yeah, yeah. Thanks, everyone. I'll send a postcard."

The clock in the lobby said it was 1:10 when he walked toward the doors that led to the underground garage. At 2:20 he drove onto the New Jersey Turnpike, heading south, Tootsie and Slick nestled in his lap.

Fanny slipped from her bed, her eye on the digital clock on the nightstand. Her suitcase stared at her like a single malevolent eye. Last night she'd pulled it out and then replaced it in the closet seven times. Then she'd cried herself to sleep. She'd woken at 2:30 and called Bess and said, "I'm going. I'll be in touch." At 3:05 she'd called her again and said, "I changed my mind." It was now 4:25.

Fanny's eyes were wild as she looked around her studio. Her little corner of life. Empty. Daisy whimpered. "As much as I love you, Daisy, you aren't enough. Get your stuff and pile it up by the door. We're going to New York! I'm not giving up Simon for anyone."

She was a whirlwind then as she stripped off her clothes while dialing the airport to have the Thornton plane readied for her trip. "Don't even think about telling me it can't be done? You do it!" She showered, dressed, gulped a cup of yesterday's leftover coffee before she snatched Daisy's gear and stuffed it into a shopping bag. The last thing she did was scribble a note that she left on her drafting table.

Fanny burned rubber, something she'd never done in her life, as she careened down the mountain. An hour later she was running toward the Thornton plane, the shopping bag slapping against her leg, Daisy jostling up and down in her arms.

"Fanny!"

"Bess! Oh, Bess, this is the right thing, isn't it? How did you know? I called back and said I wasn't going. It feels right. Tell me it's right."

"It's right, Fanny. I'm glad you came to your senses. I know you better than you know yourself. You love Simon, and he loves you. Call me and let me know where you are and what I can do. Give Simon a big hug for me. I want to be your matron of honor, and I don't care if it's in Zamboranga. Promise."

"Oh, Bess, I promise. Thank you for . . . being you. Thank you, thank you, thank you. Gotta go. Life is wonderful," she called over her shoulder as she climbed the metal steps. She turned and waved and then blew her best friend a kiss.

In less than twelve minutes she was airborne. In just a few hours she would be in Simon's arms. In her bag she had a map and two pins. "I love him, Daisy, so much it hurts. They don't make bandages big enough to cover that kind of hurt." She leaned back into the depths of the cushioned seat.

The Thornton jet set down at 12:30 Eastern Standard Time. Fanny barreled down the steps and ran across the tarmac to the terminal where she looked around wildly for a sign that would direct her to the transportation area. She ran again, jostling people in her hurry to get to the taxi area. "Wall Street," she gasped as she tossed the shopping bag onto the backseat. "Soon, Daisy. Hurry, driver."

Fanny leaned back against the cracked leather seat. Why was she in such a hurry? Close of business meant five o'clock. The market closed at four. She had plenty of time before Simon walked out of his office building at five-twenty. Her breath exploded in a loud sigh. So close yet so far away. I'm coming, Simon, I'm coming.

Fanny thrust a twenty-dollar bill at the cab driver. She ran to the door, Daisy whimpering at these strange circumstances. She woofed once when she picked up Simon Thornton's scent near the elevator. "Shhh," Fanny said.

Fanny burst through the doors of Simon's offices, her hair in wild disarray, the dog yipping in her arms to see a sea of faces staring at her. She was aware instantly of the balloons, the cake that hadn't been cut, Jerry's tortured face. She could feel the scream starting to build in her throat. "Where is he, Jerry?"

"Fanny . . ."

"Jerry . . . did . . . is he gone, Jerry?"

"I'm sorry, Fanny. He left ten minutes ago. I know he was headed for his apartment to pick up his luggage. Then . . . he wouldn't tell me where he was going. He said he'd write . . . he said that once before and I got two letters in . . . maybe you can catch him. Try, Fanny."

"Call him, Jerry, tell him I'm on my way. Tell him to wait. Please, Jerry."

"I can't, Fanny. His phone was disconnected yesterday. He dumped all that stuff he used to carry around in a Dumpster and he ripped out his car phone."

Fanny started to cry.

"C'mon, we'll take the express elevator. I'll drive you, my car's in the garage. If he hit traffic or if he stops to say good-bye to the doorman or something, we might make it."

"Drive a hundred miles an hour. I'll pay for the tickets. Oh, God, this can't be happening to me. Pretend you're Mario Andretti, Jerry. Can't you go any faster?"

"Fanny, this is New York. It's impossible to . . . try and relax."

"What will I do if he isn't there? Are you sure you don't know where he's going?"

"I'm sure. I wish you had come yesterday. Yesterday he was lower than a snake's belly. I don't know what you'll do, Fanny. I guess you go on the way he's going to go on. Right now there don't seem to be many options for either one of you." His voice was strained and fretful-sounding.

Fanny started to cry again. Daisy curled deeper into her arms. "It's my fault. I'm turning out just like my mother-in-law, and Simon saw that. Can't you go any faster?"

"I'm trying, Fanny."

When at last Jerry pulled his car to the curb, his tires screeching, Fanny bolted from the car. "Simon Thornton, is he here?" Fanny demanded of the doorman.

"He's gone. He left about fifteen minutes ago."

"Did he say where he was going?" Fanny asked.

"All he said was good-bye and he was on his way to a new life. He had two little dogs with him. I'm sorry."

"I'm sorry, too," Fanny said, wiping at the tears dripping on Daisy's head. In the car, Fanny broke down completely. Jerry stared at her helplessly.

"What do you want me to do, Fanny?"

"Take me back to the airport. I can take a taxi if you have something to do."

"If you want the monies wired into the Texas National by the close of business, I'll have to hail you a taxi. Simon was adamant about everything being done by five o'clock today. I gave him my word it would be taken care of. He did everything you wanted, Fanny."

Fanny nodded miserably as she exited the car to wait for a taxi. "Thanks for everything, Jerry. You'll call if . . . ?"

"Of course."

"Tell him I came. Tell him . . ." Fanny opened her purse and pulled out the map and the two safety pins attached at the corner. "Tell him . . . I brought the map and the pins. He'll know what you're talking about."

"I'll tell him, Fanny. Here's your cab. You take care of yourself now, you hear."

"You too, Jerry. Simon is very lucky to have a friend like you."

Fanny was back on the mountain by midnight. She garaged the car and set Daisy down on the ground. Instead of going to her studio, she walked down the path to the small private cemetery. She raised her eyes heavenward. "It's me, Sallie. I screwed everything up. I hate this helpless feeling. I don't know what to do. I can't seem to think straight. I was so close. I missed him by minutes. I don't know how to handle this. How did you manage to go on when Devin died? How did you get through the hours and the minutes? How did you manage to smile? You just went through the motions. Inside you were as dead as Devin was. I think I knew that, but I didn't want to dwell on it. I don't want that to happen to me. I don't want to be like you. I just want to be Fanny Thornton. I want to feel, to love, to cry and laugh. I can handle this. You just watch me. I'll say good night, Sallie. You probably won't be hearing from me for a while, so give my regards to Devin." As an afterthought she said, "And to Philip, too."

Daisy woofed softly, begging to be picked up. The little dog in her arms, Fanny walked around the small cemetery. Overhead the heavens were star-spangled, the three-quarter moon casting a silvery glow over the ageless cottonwood in the middle of the cemetery. The sweet smell of sagebrush engulfed her as she made her way down the small path that led back to her studio.

Inside the studio, Fanny headed straight for her drafting table and the telephone. Bess picked it up on the first ring. "I missed him, Bess. By fifteen minutes. No one knows where he is or where he was going. I guess he stuck his pin in the map and didn't look back. I feel so empty and lost. Why didn't I listen to you that day in the parking lot? I didn't listen because I'm stupid. Stupid, stupid, stupid. I just wanted you to know I'm home. Good night, Bess, and thank you for being my friend."

The connection broken, Fanny changed her clothes and made a pot of coffee. Life was going to go on and there was nothing she could do about it. As of today, this very minute, Simon Thornton was somebody she used to know. Somebody she loved with every breath in her body. The sad part was, Simon didn't love her in the same way. She lifted her coffee cup high in the air in a toast. "Be happy, Simon." Daisy howled, an earsplitting, heart wrenching sound that matched the high-pitched keening wail that escaped her own lips.

The following morning Fanny was up, dressed and ready for whatever the day would bring before the sun climbed over the mountain. It was barely light when she let herself into the corporate headquarters of Sunny's Togs and Rainbow Babies—Sallie Thornton's old bingo palace.

Fanny was hard at work packing up the contents of the rooms when her children and Bess appeared at seven-thirty. "We're relocating to the mountain. It will cut down on our overhead. Chue's cousins, nephews, and nieces are ready to start on Bernie and Blossom tomorrow. Here's our schedule . . ."

"Attagirl, Fanny," Bess said, hugging her. "I didn't say anything to them. I wanted to wait to hear from you."

"Thanks, Bess. I don't think I could handle my children's pitying looks right now. We need to have some letters made up for our customers."

"I took care of that yesterday, Fanny."

"A truck to move this stuff up the mountain?"

"Taken care of yesterday, too. I knew the mountain was our only option. They'll be here by noon."

"The material for the dolls?"

"The mill is shipping it directly to the mountain. Delivery is scheduled for tomorrow. The scraps are on their way as we speak."

Fanny nodded. "Has anyone heard from Sunny?"

"I passed her on the way in this morning. I guess she's at Babylon. She likes to get up when Tyler does so they can have breakfast together, and she gets a few quiet hours in the casino before all hell breaks loose. She waved, so I guess she's okay," Sage said.

Fanny looked at her watch. "I'm going to the bank and I have a few other errands to run, so I probably won't be back till noon. If I have time, I want to stop and see Sunny. Carry on, troops," she said lightly.

Fanny walked through the Nevada Savings and Loan, the Thornton family's bank, down a short corridor where her personal banker, Bradford Tennison, sat behind a polished mahogany desk. They were old friends now, thanks to Sallie Thornton's intervention years ago. "Fanny, what brings you to the bank so early in the morning? Ah, I see, it's serious. Close the door. Can I offer you a cup of coffee?"

"No thanks, Brad. Has Simon been in touch with you?"

"Several times. There's a problem, Fanny. Your ex-husband applied for a mortgage on Babylon. The board approved it three days before I received Simon's call. The paperwork was in order. If this means anything, I voted no. Gambling boats on the Mississippi are risky ventures in my opinion."

"What are you saying, Brad? Ash can't . . . I have to approve any . . . Two signatures, Brad."

Tennison's faced turned pale. "We had two signatures, Fanny."

"You didn't have the one that counts. Mine. I sat here for three hours over a year ago when all this was settled. You and I talked about this. You even said it was a wise decision on my part. Did Simon know about this?"

Tennison's face went from pale to stark white. "I don't know, Fanny. I was in Carson City on bank business. I'm sure one of the bank officers told him. I'm sure we didn't do anything wrong."

"If you're so sure, why is your face so pale? I'll pull everything from this bank, right down to the last penny. I'm almost afraid to ask, how much did Ash . . ."

"Sixteen million dollars."

"Sixteen million dollars!" Fanny watched as the banker's forehead beaded with sweat. She could feel the moistness on her own forehead. She wiped at it with the back of her hand. "Tell me this is just in the works, tell me you didn't cut the check."

"I wish I could tell you that, Fanny, but I can't."

"Then you damn well better stop payment. If you tell me it's too late, I am personally going to wreck this bank. That's not a threat, that's a goddamn promise. Get your people in here, Brad. Now!"

Fanny was so furious she could barely focus on the furnishings in the room. How could this have happened? How dare Ash do this to her? Fanny stopped pacing long enough to place a call to Sage. Her voice was hoarse with rage when she questioned her son.

"Mom, I don't know anything about it. One of us has to sign along with you. That's all you ever told us. Nothing like this has ever come up before. Maybe Birch signed and . . . I don't know, Mom, I'm just speculating. For whatever this is worth, Dad is holding some very impressive markers that have Ryce Granger's name on them. He's second-in-command at ye olde bank. How did that get past Uncle Simon? I can be there in five minutes with all the account folders. Everything is spelled out. They gotta make good. Wait for me before you start wrecking the place."

Fanny's shoulders started to shake as she broke the connection without bothering to answer her son. Yes, how did it get past Simon? She needed to calm down, to get her thoughts in order. The bank was responsible if Ash pulled a fast one. She wondered what the word "impressive" meant to Sage. She had to admit she didn't know how much money the casino would hold in the way of markers. Obviously a lot.

"Fanny, come with me, we're going to one of the boardrooms where we won't be interrupted."

His face was still pale, Fanny noticed. She followed him, her back stiff. She thought her jaw was going to crack any second.

It was a windowless room with only a long conference table and a sideboard. A telephone and several manila folders sat on one end of the sideboard. Nine ashtrays and a silver service containing steaming coffee sat in the middle of the long table. The table was amazingly shiny, Fanny thought as she looked down to see the reflections of the white faces of the men standing at attention, yellow legal tablets in hand.

Fanny slammed her purse on the table just as a knock sounded on the door. The palm of her hand shot upward and then out. "I'll get it."

Sage stood in the open doorway to hand his mother a thick yellow folder. "Thanks, honey, I can handle this," she said in a low whisper.

"You sure?"

"I'm sure."

"Do what I do, kick some ass and take names later," Sage whispered. In spite of herself, Fanny smiled.

"I can do that."

"I know. I ain't your son for nothing. Good luck." He squeezed her shoulder reassuringly.

Fear, Fanny thought, had to be the single most debilitating emotion there was. It was everywhere in the room, swirling and circling her like a deadly fog.

"Someone explain to me what happened." Fanny's eyes swept the table and came to rest on Ryce Granger.

"It's like I said, Fanny. Ryce called the main office and was told he needed two signatures on the application. Ash and Birch signed all the forms. I was in Carson City, not that that makes a difference. Ryce had full authority to put the wheels in motion."

Fanny leaned into the table, her eyes unwaveringly still on Ryce Granger's face. "Was that before or after he cut a deal with my ex-husband to wash some, if not all, of his markers at Babylon? Don't insult me, Brad, by pretending Mr. Granger didn't know it was my signature that was required, not my husband's. The way I see it, this bank is out sixteen million dollars. You will return sixteen million dollars to the Thornton Family Partnership account within forty-eight hours. I have no interest in knowing how you will do this. You will do it or I'll have the banking commission down here so fast your heads will spin off your necks. It is not my responsibility to help you get your monies from Ash. Nor can you foreclose on the casino. If I were you, I think I might look into riverboat gambling. You own those boats now. You and Ash Thornton. You made a deal with the devil, gentlemen. Oh, and one other thing. The Thornton family will no longer be banking with this establishment. Good day, gentlemen. Remember, forty-eight hours from this minute, not one second longer."

Outside the bank, Fanny looked upward at the pale blue sky, a sky that looked more fragile than the finest porcelain. *Where are you, Simon? Did you know about this?*

Fanny drove to Babylon, her thoughts everywhere but on the matter at hand. What would Sallie have done? Did she handle things right? How was the move coming? *I'm going to kill you, Ash Thornton. Oh, Simon, I need you. Please, please, come back.*

Fanny parked in the underground parking lot in a reserved space next to Sunny's car. She exited through the emergency stairwell to come out on the second floor where Ash maintained his suite of offices.

Fanny burst into Ash's offices, slamming the door behind her. "You better hope these walls are soundproof, Ash!"

"Fanny, how the hell did you get in here!"

"I sneaked in. I took a page out of your book. Your surveillance stinks. I'm here, and that's all that matters. Where's Birch?"

"I don't have to account to you, Fanny. If you want to know where Birch is, you should call him. I'm busy."

"You're going to be a hell of a lot busier when you have to deal with the banking commission. They're going to get you on forgery, and I'm not stepping in on your behalf this time. You made Birch, your own son, a party to all of this. You got away with it, too. The big question is, how are you going to repay sixteen million dollars plus interest? Those riverboats belong to the bank now, and since you wiped Granger's markers, you're left holding the proverbial bag. How did you think you were going to get away with this? Do you think I'm really that stupid? Yes, I guess you do," Fanny said sadly.

"You screwed up my deal! Damn you, Fanny. Jesus, I hate your fucking guts. I must have been crazy out of my mind to marry you. This is a dog-eat-dog business and you know it. I'm a cripple, locked in this stinking chair, and all because of you. If you'd just die, we'd all be happy."

Fanny backed up a step, her face draining of all color. "It wasn't my fault that you fell off that girder."

"The hell it wasn't. If you'd given me the money, my own money, Thornton family money, I wouldn't have had to be up there to begin with, trying to keep my eye on things so costs would be down. Oh, no, you give it to me after. *AFTER* I'm sitting in this chair. It was your own guilty conscience that made you go ahead with Babylon. When it was too late, when I had nothing left. I sit in this chair twenty hours a day, full of painkillers while you're out there fucking my brother. The whole town knows about your affair. The kids know, too."

"I didn't try to keep it a secret, Ash. I can do whatever I want. I'm not your wife any longer. As for the town, do you think I care? I made a promise to your mother and I'm doing my best to keep it. I'm sorry you feel the way you do. I refuse to get into the name-calling and the backbiting. Family business behind closed doors is one thing. You've taken it public now. I have no control over the bank. In a week's time their doors will be closed, and you're responsible. All those people will be out of jobs. You have to take responsibility for that, too. The Gaming Commission won't let you work here any longer if you're convicted. This is about as serious as it gets, Ash. Were you ever going to tell me?"

"Shut up, Fanny."

"Is it that you don't want to hear my words, or is it my voice?" Fanny asked, looking around at the opulence of Ash's office. Top-of-the-line stereo system, hidden bar and refrigerator, private wall safe, recessed television, leather chairs and couch. Black-marble bathroom complete with Jacuzzi, priceless paintings on the walls, subdued lighting, perfect for those late-night assignations. All the trappings of the good life. She thought about her tiny studio with the faded red chairs, the fieldstone fireplace, and the narrow twin beds. There simply was no comparison.

Ash's voice was vitriolic, full of hatred when he said, "You wormed your way into my mother's life. You turned her against me and Simon, too. You got it all, the money, the land, the jewelry, the gold, the stock. You stole what was Simon's and mine. My father told me you would do it, too. He knew what was going on. My mother the whore. You're just like her, Fanny. She wheedled that money out of Cotton Easter just the way you wheedled it out of her. You're a cheat and a thief masquerading in a mother's body."

Fanny grew light-headed at the ugly words. He was getting to her, pushing her buttons, jerking her strings. If only Sallie hadn't put her in this position. If only she hadn't agreed to take care of the Thornton monies. If only . . . if only.

Fanny's voice was colder than ice. "My conscience is clear. I will never forgive you for the position you've put Birch in. The headlines will probably read EMPEROR AND SON INDICTED IN BANK FRAUD."

"Then help me, goddamn it."

"Not this time, Ash. Not this time."

"What about Birch?"

"Like father like son," Fanny said.

"You'll help Billie Coleman, but you won't help your husband and son? I hope you rot in hell, Fanny."

"Billie is taking responsibility and trying to correct a terrible wrong. If I were in her place, I'd do the same thing. Birch knows right from wrong just the way you know right from wrong. What's that saying, you play you pay?"

Fanny's legs felt like wet noodles as she made her way to Sunny's office.

Sunny looked up from her cluttered desk. "Mom! Twice in one week? No one told me you were on the floor. Is something wrong?"

"I came in through the garage. I wanted to . . . surprise your father. Do you happen to know where Birch is?"

"Biloxi, Mississippi. Mom, what's wrong?"

Fanny told her.

"Mom, they could go to jail. You can't let that happen. You can do something, can't you?"

"No. If Birch is in Mississippi, it's a done deal. Ash wired the

money. I don't know the ins and outs of that, but it has something
to do with federal regulations, state lines, and things like that."

"Pay the money back."

"It isn't that simple. The owners of the riverboats are already
spending their money. I suppose it's possible for your father to cut
some kind of deal with the bank. Forty-eight hours from now we will
no longer be banking at Nevada Savings and Loan. The Nevada National Trust bank will be handling the Thornton accounts."

"Mom, the bank will shut down if you pull out."

"There is that possibility."

"I hate to say this, Mom, but Grandma Sallie wouldn't let all
those people lose their jobs."

"That's your father's responsibility. Your father should have
thought ahead to what could happen down the road. Pure and simple, he did not think he'd get caught. If I hadn't agreed to help Billie Coleman, we still wouldn't know what he'd done. I'm not Sallie,
Sunny. I have to do what's right, for us, for me."

"Dad and Birch won't be able to work in the gaming business
if . . ."

"I know. How are you feeling, Sunny?"

"Tired at times, other times I feel like scrubbing walls and floors.
Mom, aside from all of this, is there something else bothering you?
You don't look right to me."

"Your father said some very ugly things. I just have to come to
terms with it all. I guess I'm tired, too. I have a hundred things I have
to do. Why don't you and Tyler come up to Sunrise over the weekend?"

"Can't. I have a mountain of things to do before the championship. With Birch gone, Dad piled it all on me. I'm not complaining. I'd rather be busy than just sitting here. Is there anything I can
do?"

"If there is, I'll call you. You might want to take Birch aside when
he comes back and present a clear, concise account of what's going
on. Your father's version won't . . . be as accurate. It's up to you,
though. If you don't want to get involved, I understand."

"I'll talk to him. I think he'll be back in the morning."

When the door closed behind her mother, Sunny sighed deeply.
Who was that cold-eyed person who just walked out of her office?
Certainly not the mother she knew and loved. Did she dare walk
down the hall to her father's offices? And say what? Hey, I heard
you're going to jail. She rummaged through the mess of papers and

schedules on her desk for the number Birch had given her when he left. In case of an emergency. What could be more of an emergency than this? She dialed the operator and placed a person-to-person call. Birch's harried voice came over the wire. Sunny started to babble the moment she heard her brother.

"Jail, Birch. Bars, striped suits, the whole works. Did you hear what I just said?"

"Mom won't let that happen," Birch said.

"Perchance are you talking about the mom you turned your back on? You could never take that one to the bank. In the old days it might have been true. Not this time, Birch. You need to come back. What's the point in staying there? It's all falling apart anyway. This is going to be one of those snowball things," Sunny said in a jittery-sounding voice.

Not this time. Sage had said those same words to him just days ago. "Okay, I'll get the next plane out."

It was six-thirty when Sunny cleared her desk in preparation to leaving the casino. She sensed him before she actually saw him. "Lock the door," she ordered.

Birch locked the door, his face full of questions. "He's acting like a one-man Gestapo unit. He's fired seven people in the past few hours. Twenty others have threatened to quit. The kitchen is in an uproar. The pool overflowed around three o'clock and five ceilings are ruined. Some high roller out of Cincinnati and his retinue says he's pulling out of the tournament and he wants his money back because we didn't come through with the satin sheets his girlfriend requested. The phones aren't working on the seventh floor. There's some shady parasite hanging out in the garage who insists on talking to Dad, and Dad won't go to the garage. The gears on the hydraulic lift in the counting room are stuck. Some guy walked out of here with $96,000 of our money. A pretty routine day if you ask me. What the hell were you thinking of to sign those loan applications, Birch? You know Mom has to sign off on everything."

"Dad said things switched up. I just figured she was so caught up in Uncle Simon she didn't want to be bothered with the casino since it was doing so well. Maybe I should have questioned it, but I didn't. Jesus, it never occurred to me that Dad would lie about something so important. I swear to God, Sunny, I didn't know."

"If Dad backs up your story, then I guess you don't have anything to worry about."

"What do you mean, *if*? I'm telling you the truth. Where is he?"

"Today he's like a spook. He's everywhere. I'm going home. This isn't my problem."

"I could use a little help here, Sunny."

Sunny ignored the pleading tone in her brother's voice. "From me and my big belly? When I could have used a little brotherly intervention with *him*, a few kind words, where the hell were you? Not this time, big brother."

"Sunny, it wasn't like that."

"The hell it wasn't. What you need right now is a Popsicle. The only problem is, Mom isn't here to give you the magic cure-all. I bet she installs those iron gates at Sunrise again to keep us out. See you tomorrow."

Rage, unlike anything he'd ever experienced, coursed through Birch. The moment his body ceased to shake, he headed for his office, where he sucked down two long swallows of his father's favorite whiskey. His eyes murderous, he then headed for the floor, his eyes raking the happy throngs of people parting with their money. The moment he spotted his father, he weaved his way through the narrow lanes of slot machines and the merry sound of coins dropping into the trays.

A tight smile on his face for the benefit of the customers, Birch leaned over and whispered in his father's ear. "Put the goddamn thing in gear or they'll be peeling you off the ceiling."

In Ash's office with the door closed and locked, Birch swung the wheelchair around until his father was facing him. He snorted in disgust at his father's glassy eyes. "You fucking lied to me. You said things switched up. I should have checked, but I didn't think my own father would lie to me. Damn you, why?"

"Why? That's a pretty stupid question. I'm sick of the way your mother handles things. She doesn't know anything about this business. We could make a fortune off those riverboats. She's not going to do anything. Fanny's all talk. She's got this thing about families sticking together. Do you think for one minute she'll let our asses go to jail? Come on, Birch, get real."

"Yeah, that's exactly what she's going to do. Guess what, I'm not going to jail, not for you, not for anyone. I believed you, I trusted you because you're my father, and you fucking screwed me over the way you screw everyone over. It will be up to Mom who she believes, and I don't think it's going to be you. If I were you, I'd give some real serious thought to what you're going to do."

Ash stared at his son. "Come on, Birch, we're talking business here. You gotta do a lot of things that are stomach-turning, but in the end it works out. We can pull this off. I know how to deal with Fanny. I'm counting on you, Birch."

"Not this time."

Ash stared at the door for a long time before he swallowed his second handful of pills in an hour. When his body grew lax, he slipped from his chair, whimpering and mewling like a kitten.

4

Fanny stared at the stack of legal documents piled up next to one of the big red chairs in her study. Her gaze swept sideways to the family picture on the table between the red chairs. Tears puddled in her eyes. A family divided.

Four months of legal hassles, bills, ugly phone calls from her ex-husband, and pleas from her son Birch to make it all come out right. As if she had magic in her fingertips. Legally, Birch was out of the woods, but Ash was swinging in the wind, cutting his own deals with the bank and the Gaming Commission. The money had been put back into her account and then transferred to her new bank. It was business as usual now. She absolutely refused to think about where Ash had managed to get another sixteen million dollars.

Fanny sighed. She had her own business problems to contend with, plus worrying about Sunny. And always, her thoughts were on Simon. Where was he? What was he doing? Did he think of her the way she thought of him? Had he been in touch with Jerry? Fanny shifted her thoughts to her corporate books. A headache started to hammer behind her eyes. With money so tight, everyone was jittery. They were overextended at the bank, their mortgage payments were late, and no one was drawing a salary. Even Bess had agreed, saying, when it's there, you'll pay me. I can wait. They were all waiting for Billie Coleman to make a payment on the monies that had been loaned to Coleman Aviation.

She would never, ever, believe she'd made a mistake in lending Billie the money. Somehow, she'd find a way to keep the businesses going. If she had to sell Sunrise, she'd do it. Sunrise was a place—wood, brick, mortar. People, family, meant more than a structure. If she sold the Thornton family home, she could stay afloat a little while longer. Perhaps the new owner would lease space to her. If not, they had to set up operations in Bess's three-car garage. "I'm sorry, Sallie, I have no other choice," she muttered. Fanny dropped her head into her hands. She really had to stop talking to her mother-in-law as though she were alive.

The phone rang just as she was about to dial the real estate agent's number. "Billie, Billie, slow down. What do you mean you're in Japan? Why? You have a grandson! A grandson you never knew about! Slow, Billie, slow down, the connection is bad as it is. Yes, yes, Moss knew about your grandson but because he was half-Japanese, he never told you? My God, what kind of man would do a thing like that? And a daughter-in-law! I'm sure she's wonderful if your son married her. I am so happy for you, Billie. Who's giving you all the money you need? Ah, I see." Fanny listened, her heart thundering in her chest when Billie told her a payment would be on the way to Nevada the minute she returned to Texas.

"I'm bringing my grandson back with me for a visit. His mother Otami, too, if she's willing to come. Sawyer wants to move everything over here. It's just so hard for me to believe my granddaughter is this *wunderkind* aeronautical engineer. Moss would be so proud of her even though he didn't have much use for women. She's going to get his dream plane off the ground and flying. To say she's the marvel in marvelous is an understatement. We're contemplating the move here to Japan and weighing the cost. Fanny, we could never have gotten this far if it wasn't for you. We all owe you our lives for your kindness and generosity. You are the only one who understood what getting Moss's plane in the air means to me. I'll never be able to thank you. Would you listen to me babble on? I'm sorry I didn't tell you I was leaving, it happened so suddenly. Tell me what's going on. Have you heard from Simon?"

They talked for a long time, two old friends who shared the same values, the same commitment to family. "Say hello to your family, Fanny. Never give up, Fanny, never. When things are the darkest, when all the doors seemed closed, you'll find a light. I'm the living proof."

Fanny smiled. She wanted to say she'd just seen the light with Billie's promise of a payback. Instead she said, "I can't wait to meet your new grandson and daughter-in-law. Call me as soon as you get back to Texas."

Fanny took a deep breath as she gathered up the corporate books and stack of bills. She stared at Daisy for a full minute before she tossed the papers in the air. "C'mon, Daisy, we're going for a walk. I need to say a few thank-yous."

She was a pretty young woman, plainly but neatly dressed. She could have been anybody; no one paid attention to her as she walked about the casino floor, her eyes taking in the furious whirring of the slot machines, the drink girls, the money changers with their carts, and the excited squeals of winning customers and the groans and moans of the losers. Suddenly she felt conspicuous and didn't know why. Maybe if she put some money in the machines, she'd feel like she had a right to be here. She dropped a dollar in the slot and pulled the handle. Twenty silver dollars dropped into the tray at the bottom of the machine. She blinked as she dropped in a second dollar. Fifteen silver dollars dropped to the tray. She blinked again.

"Would you like to trade in the silver for paper money, Miss?" one of the money changers asked.

"Yes, thank you. Can you tell me where the office is or where I can find Mrs. Thornton?"

"We don't have a Mrs. Thornton. We have a Mr. Thornton senior and a Mr. Thornton junior. You can't go to the offices, but I can call and have someone come out here to talk to you."

"Would you do that please?"

"Which one do you want, the older or younger one? Who should I say wants to see him?"

"My name is Lily Bell and I think I'd like to speak with . . . the young Mr. Thornton."

"You wait right here, Miss. It might take ten minutes or so."

In his office, Birch picked up the phone. "Did you tell her my mother doesn't work here? Did she say what she wanted? Where is she exactly? Okay, I'll be out in five minutes." He finished what he was doing, buzzed Sunny to tell her he was going out to the floor.

He saw her from a distance and knew in his gut that she wasn't a customer. He stared a moment longer. She was dressed simply in a plum-colored dress with a matching handbag. Her hair was a cluster of dark curls that capped a face almost devoid of makeup. He could see small pearls in her ears but no rings on her fingers. He drew a deep breath when he saw her smile at someone who spoke to her. In the time it took his heart to beat twice, Birch Thornton knew he wanted to get to know this young woman better.

Up close, he was surprised to see how tall she was. Incredible dark eyes behind heavily fringed lashes stared at him. He was right about the makeup. She didn't need it. "I'm Birch Thornton, can I help you?"

"I hope so, Mr. Thornton. I'm Lily Bell," she said extending her hand. "Is there somewhere we could talk? What I want to discuss is a personal matter."

Birch hesitated for a bare second. Her serious expression said this is important. "How about some coffee in our private dining room? No one will bother us there."

Lily nodded as she walked alongside the tall, immaculately dressed man. He smiled at her as he ushered her into the small, elegant dining room reserved for family and the chosen few who were invited from time to time. "Please, sit down. I'll call the kitchen for the coffee. It won't take long. I also have to let my sister know where I am so I can be paged if necessary.

"It's very good coffee," Birch said, his tone light, his eyes twinkling.

"I'm sure it is. I'm just nervous. I'm not sure I should be here. Sometimes I do things without thinking them through. What that means is, I reacted to . . . something. I was sure I had thought it through, but maybe I didn't. I really wanted to see Mrs. Thornton."

"Mrs. Thornton is my mother. She rarely comes to the casino. Can you tell me what this is about? We can always call her."

"I would rather see her in person."

"You're making this sound very mysterious. Why don't you start at the beginning? I'm a very good listener."

Lily rummaged in her purse and withdrew a snapshot. She slid it across the table toward Birch. "Do you recognize the woman in the picture? Study it very carefully."

Birch reached for the picture and studied it as Lily requested. "She looks familiar, but no, I don't know her. I don't think I've ever seen her."

"Does she remind you of anyone?"

"Sort of. Who is she?"

"My father's second wife. My . . . stepmother. She's very ill."

"I'm sorry, but what does that have to do with my mother? Do you think she knows her?"

"I think she's your grandmother, your mother's mother. Look at the picture again and tell me if that's who she reminds you of now."

"There seems to be a resemblance. My mother's mother abandoned her family. My grandfather raised my mother and her brothers all by himself. He did a good job of it, too. No one ever heard from her. My mother tried to find her, she hired detectives, but she was unable to locate her. What kind of woman does something like that? What is it that you want exactly?"

"To reunite mother and daughter. I told you I don't know if coming here was right or wrong. I did what I felt was right. If this is your grandmother, your mother is the one who has to make the decision. I saw a picture of your mother and your other grandmother a long time ago, in one of those Sunday family sections. I just happened to be watching my stepmother when she saw it, and she burst into tears. It said your mother's maiden name was Logan and she came from Shamrock, Pennsylvania. That's where my stepmother was from. We live in Bakersfield, California. She was very good to me. I have a half brother and sister, Paul and Anna. And before you can ask, we don't want anything from your family. Paul and Anna didn't want me to come here. They wanted to let things be. I'm not like that. I think families should stick together. When my own mother died, my father really was mother and father to me. When Harriet came along, she treated me like her own child."

Birch leaned back in his chair, his eyes speculative. "What do you want me to do?"

"Arrange a meeting with your mother. I want to talk to her. In the end, Mr. Thornton, it will be her decision. She has a right to know. If for some reason you don't want to arrange a meeting, I'll have to find another way to meet her. I've come too far now to back down."

"Do you want to go now or will later on or tomorrow do?"

"Time is of the essence. Harriet doesn't have long."

"Let me clear my decks. Drink your coffee, have another cup, and we'll leave. There's a lavatory at the end of the room in the corner in case you want to use it. I won't be long. It's a forty-five-minute ride up the mountain. I think, Miss Bell, you did the right thing."

"Do you really, Mr. Thornton?" Lily smiled. It was a smile that wrapped itself around Birch, the kind of smile that tugged at his heart.

"Yes, I do." He returned her smile. Lily grew light-headed and thought about things like moonlight, stardust, and then more earthy things like holding hands and walking through flower-scented meadows. With someone like Birch Thornton.

His stomach churning, Birch strode through the casino, unaware of the admiring glances following him. Somebody was watching over him. Lily Bell had given him the reason he needed to go to Sunrise to see his mother. He'd apologized for the fiasco at the bank, grateful to his father for backing up his denial. He'd taken his lumps by accepting his mother's stern, cold attitude, somehow managing to slink off with his head bowed, his heart quivering in his chest. Now, he had the one thing his mother craved more than anything in the world: entrance into his grandmother's world, a world denied his mother since birth.

Birch slowed his footsteps as he approached the door to his sister's office. He loved Sunny. From the time they were little he'd been her staunchest supporter. He hated seeing the disappointment in her eyes where he was concerned. He'd apologized to her, too, and all she'd done was nod her head. She'd cut herself off from him and his father, doing her job, staying out of sight, crying quietly when she thought no one was around. Sunny had the same kind of guts Sage had, the kind that counted. He listened for a moment before he tapped lightly on the door. The faint sound of the computer keys stopped. "Come in."

"Sunny, do you have a minute?"

"I have lots of minutes, Birch. Sit down."

"How are you feeling?"

"Is that one of those polite questions to make conversation or do you care?"

"Jesus, Sunny, every time I talk to you you have a burr in your undies. I care, or I wouldn't have asked."

"I feel like a pregnant woman. You didn't stop in here to ask me how I am. What's up?"

Birch told her.

"Wow! Where is she?"

"In the private dining room. Do you want to meet her?"

"Surely you jest. One minute you want me to stay hidden because of my big belly and the next you want me to walk out on the floor where customers can actually *SEE* me. Or do you want me to go down through the garage and come up by the service elevator? If Dad sees me on the floor in the monitor, this place will be in flux for three days." This last was said so bitterly, Birch cringed. He pretended not to see the tears in his sister's eyes.

"I want you to walk with me. That means at my side. I don't much care what Dad does or says these days. I'm doing my job just the way you're doing yours. God, Sunny, how did you handle your estrangement from Mom when you two went at it? It's killing me."

"You were wrong, Birch, just the way I was wrong. Mom taught us to take responsibility for our actions. That was the hardest lesson I ever learned. I chipped away a part of her heart. I don't think I can ever repair the damage I did to her. I hold back now because I don't ever want to see that awful look in her eyes again. You sold out, Birch."

"I didn't know, Sunny. Dad lied to me."

"That was my excuse, too. It isn't good enough. Have you spoken to Sage or Billie?"

"I call, but they don't call back. I'm not going to force myself on them."

"Do what I do, get in their face and go on from there. Refuse to accept their attitude, and if that doesn't work, beat the shit out of Sage."

Birch snorted. "Jesus, Sunny, you have to stop talking like a truck driver. Sage would deck me. Billie would kick my ass all the way down the mountain."

"You deserve both. Betrayal is a serious business, and no, I will not intervene."

"I didn't ask you to."

"You were thinking about it. I know you, Birch. Do you ever think we'll be a real family again?" Sunny's voice was so wistful, Birch put his arm around her shoulders.

"I like to think so, but I wouldn't bet the rent on it."

"What's *he* been doing?"

"I have no idea. I try and stay out of his way. He's up to something, though. He's got more schemes than a wizard. I gotta tell you something, Sunny. I'm scared shitless about that sixteen million dollars. I think we both know where he got it. When the other shoe falls I hope I'm not around. I pray to God every day that he can keep all those deals he cut straight in his mind. Another thing, he's got everyone in the world looking for Uncle Simon. It's like he dropped off the face of the earth. Guess he had it with this family, too."

"He's part of this family. Don't think for one minute Uncle Simon isn't hurting. He's out there somewhere thinking of us every hour of the day. That's the way he is. I don't know what happened between him and Mom. If ever two people were meant for each other . . ."

"Dad said . . ."

Sunny was a whirlwind. She was out of her chair and across the room, backing her brother up against the wall, her face almost touching Birch's face, her eyes spewing sparks. "When in the damn hell are you going to learn you can't believe anything *he* says? When, Birch?"

Undaunted, Birch blustered, "Uncle Simon had all the right breaks. He's not in a wheelchair."

"Uncle Simon made his own breaks. All he ever did was give. He never took."

"Except Mom."

"Yeah, Mom. Not until it was all over between her and Dad, though. You have a long way to go, Birch, before you belong in my little circle. I've had enough of this crap. All we do is spin our wheels. Let's go meet the charming Lily Bell. Let's see what she has up her sleeve. Everyone wants something."

"And you have the nerve to say I'm cynical!" Birch snorted. "She said she doesn't want anything."

"If I told you that, would you believe me?"

"Coming from you, yeah, I would."

Sunny smiled. Her grip on her brother's arm tightened. It was her way of showing approval.

"What's she like?"

"She kind of reminds me of Mom. The way I remember Mom when we were growing up. She's pretty. Her smile is . . . nice. I liked her."

"Aahhh."

"Get off it, Sunny. Smile. We're on camera."

Sunny stuck out her tongue as she let go of her brother's arm to do a deliberate duck walk, her stomach protruding for all the world to see. In spite of himself, Birch laughed aloud. He reached for Sunny's arm and for the benefit of the customers watching, said, "We're getting married this afternoon." Sunny howled with laughter.

"That's going to make *him* nuts for a whole week. I'm glad to see you haven't lost your sense of humor."

"Okay, we're here. Try not to be obnoxious, Sunny."

In his office, his eyes on the monitors, Ash seethed with rage. He buzzed Security, barking his order, "Bring my daughter and son here. Now! They're headed for the private dining room. I want to know who they're meeting."

The head of Security raced down the hall toward the private dining room, reaching it just as Birch was about to open the door. "Sunny, Birch, hold on. Your father wants to see you right away." The head of Security's voice was flat. His eyes looked worried.

"Tell my father we're both too busy to join him right now." For the benefit of the security camera, and Neal Tortalow's job, Birch jabbed a finger in the man's chest to make his point.

"He isn't going to like this, Birch."

"Ask me if I care, Neal."

Birch closed the door behind Sunny, and locked it. In the blink of an eye he had his jacket off. He tossed it over the security camera attached to the wall overhead.

"Well-done, big brother."

"I'm Sunny Thornton Ford, Birch's sister," Sunny said, holding out her hand. Lily Bell's handshake was every bit as firm as Sunny's.

"It's nice to meet you, Mrs. Ford. Do you want me to tell you why I came here?"

"Birch told me. I'd like to see the picture. Growing up we only knew one grandmother. Oh, yes, I can see the resemblance. I don't know how Mom is going to take this, Miss Bell. It's been so long and she never knew . . . her brothers, my uncles might remember."

"Brothers?"

"Uncle Daniel and Uncle Brad. My grandfather is still alive, too, but in frail health. I don't understand, didn't she tell you any of this?"

"No. She doesn't know I'm here. I made up my own scenario and checked it out as much as I could. I don't know this for sure, but I suspect, from things she said from time to time, that she didn't feel she had any right to appear in your mother's life. During her last operation she did a lot of muttering when she was coming out from under the anesthetic. That's how I was able to piece things together. There was this article in the paper about your mother and the elder Mrs. Thornton. Harriet kept it, and I saw her reading it many times. She almost wore out the paper. It didn't say anything about your uncles." Her voice was fretful now, the cornflower blue eyes sad, tears gathering in the corners of her eyes.

"Let's have some lunch!" Sunny said. She pressed a buzzer and spoke quietly. "A double pastrami on rye, two pickles, a glass of milk and a side order of potato salad. Birch? Make that two. Miss Bell?" She nodded. "Three of everything. Hurry up. I'm starving. Oh, bring it in from the side door."

"Are you hoping for a boy or a girl?" Lily Bell asked politely.

"It doesn't matter."

"Your baby will make Harriet a great-grandmother."

"What's she like?" Sunny asked.

"She treated me like a daughter. She was there for me when I needed someone. My father loved her, and she loved him. My own mother died shortly after I was born. Together, my father and Harriet had a son and daughter. They didn't want me to come here. Maybe I shouldn't have, I don't know. I was at the hospital sitting there for my shift with Harriet, and I thought about all the nice things she'd done for me, and I decided maybe, just maybe, I could . . ."

"What will you do if my mother and uncles don't want to . . . meet her?"

"I'll go home and put this behind me. I'll know I tried. I'll tell Harriet about the visit. She hates lies, so I'll tell her the truth. I wish I could tell you why she left her family, but I can't."

"Leaving three little kids for a man to raise is pretty shitty in my opinion," the outspoken Sunny said. Birch nodded in agreement.

"I agree with you," Lily Bell said.

Their lunch arrived at the same moment Ash Thornton banged on the dining room door. "Open the goddamn door, Birch!"

Birch bit into his sandwich as did Sunny. Both pretended they heard nothing. Following their cue, Lily crunched on a pickle. "Let's not mention this to you know who," Birch said as he gulped at his milk.

"I'm way ahead of you," Sunny replied as she trundled over to the service door to lock it. "This is a good sandwich. I'm going to have heartburn all afternoon."

"That means your baby is going to have a lot of hair," Lily said. "What's your mother like?"

"One of a kind," Birch said.

"The best," Sunny said.

"I'm looking forward to meeting her. I'd like to know all about her in case she decides not to go with me to California. I want to be able to tell Harriet what a wonderful daughter she has."

"No thanks to her," Sunny blurted. "I believe she's the person she is because my grandfather Logan and my uncles raised her. If your Harriet had a hand in it, I doubt she'd be who she is today."

Birch kissed the top of Sunny's head. "You don't know that, Sunny. Stop being such a hard-ass."

"Your sister is probably right, Mr. Thornton. Harriet often said she wasn't the same person she was in her youth. But then, who is? Isn't that what maturity is all about? I'm also certain Harriet shouldered all the blame. If it were otherwise, she would have gone back to her family in the later years in an attempt to make things right."

"I'll have Security break down this door if you don't open it this damn minute," Ash Thornton bellowed from the other side of the door.

"I think, Miss Bell, this might be a good time for us to leave."

"If you aren't going to finish that sandwich, can I have it, Birch?"

"Take it with you, Sunny. You look tired. I'll give you a ride home."

"Very good idea. Tyler can drop me off tomorrow morning."

"If I were you, I'd take a few days off. With pay of course."

"I like that idea, too."

Lily Bell's face flushed at the ripe curses filtering through the door. She allowed herself to be ushered out the service door and didn't question why they were going through the kitchen to an alley leading to Birch's reserved parking space.

"I'd say that was a very clean getaway," Lily said.

"I'd say so," Birch said, volunteering no other information.

"I'll take care of things, make a few calls," Sunny said as she got out of the car in front of her apartment building ten minutes later. "Take as much time as you need, Birch. It was nice meeting you, Miss Bell."

"You too, Mrs. Ford. I hope you have a little girl that looks just like you."

"That's what my husband said. With my luck it's going to look like Birch. He's quite good-looking when he's spiffed up. He's a twin, you know."

"You can go in anytime now, Sunny. Don't you have to take a nap or something?"

"Birch, give Mom a hug. A really big one. I know for a fact she has a whole box of cherry Popsicles in the freezer. She's dying for us to ask for one."

"No kidding! How do you know that?"

Sunny smirked. "I was with her when she bought them. She said she was getting in practice again for when this little guy of mine makes his entrance. Ask for one, Birch."

"My dad always gave me a licorice stick. It made all the bad things go away," Lily volunteered.

Birch smiled from ear to ear. He was starting to like this young woman.

"Nice meeting you, Miss Bell," Sunny said. She offered up a jaunty salute in her brother's direction.

The ride up the mountain was made in companionable silence. From time to time one or the other would say something that brought a smile to the other's face.

Birch thought he was being devious when he blurted, "Are you and your half sister and brother married with families?"

"No. I came close once, but he wanted different things from life than I did. My sister is engaged. Paul says he's going to remain a bachelor. He's a forest ranger, and he loves the outdoors. Young women want bright lights and people. Anna will probably marry in a year or so. They want to save money so they can buy a house and not have to pay rent. I have a good job, and I inherited my father's house. We all have a nice life. I want you to know that so you understand we don't want anything from your family. How about you, are you married? Your sister said you had a twin. Are you look-alikes?"

She wasn't married. She had a good job. The urge to reach out and touch her hand was so strong, Birch's knuckles grew white on the steering wheel. "You're going to like my mother." The words blurted out of his mouth so fast, Lily smiled.

"I'm sure I will."

"Thanks for not asking about that ruckus back at the casino."

"Do you want to talk about it? I'm a stranger, and I never betray confidences. Sometimes it helps to talk."

He wanted to unload, to confide, more than anything in the world, knowing instinctively this young woman wouldn't judge him. "It's one of those family things that doesn't bear repeating. That's just another way of saying this, too, will pass. Tell me about you."

"I live in a world of books. Growing up there were no children my age in the neighborhood, so I read a lot. Books became my best friends. I was a librarian for a few years until I opened my own bookstore. There's a small café attached to it. No one was more surprised than I when I made a profit. Not right away, of course. I like being independent and not having to account to anyone. Do you know what type book sells the most?"

"Thrillers?"

"Yes. Mysteries, high-tech thrillers. I read them all. They're my favorites. Do you read?"

"When I have the time. Sage, my brother, is the real reader in the family. When do you plan on returning to California?"

"Tomorrow morning."

"If my mother decides to go with you, I can fly you in the company plane. I think I might like to meet my grandmother. I wish I could tell you Mom will go, but I really don't know. If she decides not to go, I will."

"That's very nice of you, Mr. Thornton."

"Can we be Birch and Lily?"

"Sure. What do you do at the casino? I had no idea what a gambling casino was like. I just don't understand how people can gamble away their money. I could never do that. I work for my money."

"You sound just like my mother. She feels like you do. We grew up in the gaming profession. To us it's like any other business. Some days it gets away from you, but it works out in the end. We have thousands of employees who make sure things run smoothly."

"I don't know if I could work in a room with canned air all day. I like to look out a window. I read somewhere that people who handle money all day get sick a lot. Is that true?"

Birch laughed. "I'll have to check that one out. Off the top of my head I'd say our absentee level is about normal. We're almost there." Again, he had the urge to reach out for her hand. "Will you have dinner with me this evening?"

"Well . . . I didn't plan . . ."

"You have to eat."

"I didn't bring any . . . I just brought my overnight case. I don't have anything fancy to wear."

"I'm not into fancy myself. What you have on is beautiful, and it will fit in anywhere I take you. I like to go to out-of-the-way places where the food is good. Places the tourists don't know about. Are you a meat or fish person?"

"I like everything. Yes, I would like to have dinner with you. It doesn't matter where. I adapt."

"Ah, a girl after my own heart," Birch said lightly. This time he did reach out to touch her hand. He withdrew it quickly, a huge smile on his face.

"That's Chue's house on the right. My grandmother Sallie brought him and his sister up to the mountain when they were children. Chue looks after things here and is responsible for the hanging gardens at the casino. Su Li, his sister, is a famous doctor. She's retired now, though. We consider them family." Birch slowed the car at the bend in the road so his passenger could admire the gardens Chue had planted.

"It's lovely."

"My grandmother lived in a little house right in the middle of the garden. She had it built specially so she could take care of my grandfather. When she died, my mother burned it down. At my grandmother's request. Her ashes are scattered over the mountain. Look. There's Daisy." Birch slowed the car again and opened the door. Daisy hopped in and snuggled in Birch's lap. "Here comes Mom!" He turned in time to see a startled expression on Lily's face.

"She looks just like Harriet." Her breath exploded in a loud sigh of relief.

"Mom, I brought someone to see you." He hugged her and whispered in her ear. "Hear her out, Mom, this isn't as crazy as it sounds. Mom, this is Lily Bell. She came from California to see you." His whispered voice dropped even lower. "I like this girl, Mom."

"Miss Bell," Fanny said, offering her hand to the young woman. "It's a pleasure to meet you. Why don't we go into the studio and have some coffee?"

"Why don't I make the coffee while you and Lily talk?"

Puzzled, Fanny agreed as she led the way to her studio.

While Birch clanged and banged in the kitchen, Fanny listened to Lily's story. From time to time he poked his head out of the tiny area to see his mother's expression. Her face was whiter than chalk. Her hands trembled as she held the small photograph at different angles to view it.

"I don't know what to say."

"I imagine it's a terrible shock. I don't blame you if you don't want to see her. I didn't know you had brothers until your son told me. I wish I had more to tell you, but Harriet didn't talk about her old life. I'm so sorry."

"Birch?"

"I can see the resemblance in the picture, Mom. Why don't you call Uncle Daniel and Uncle Brad and see what they say? I can fly you up there in the morning, Mom. It will be a day out of your life. If you don't go, you'll always wonder if you made the right decision."

"I'll call my brothers and see what they say. Birch is right—if I don't go, I'll always wonder. I need to think for a minute. Birch, show Miss Bell around. Introduce her to Sage and Billie. I hear Bess's car. Would you ask her to come over to the studio?"

When the door closed behind her son, Fanny let her emotions loose. Her clenched fists banged at the arms of the red chair. Tears trickled down her cheeks as she tried to see the numbers on the phone to call her brothers. Somehow she managed to blurt out Lily Bell's story. "I'm going, Daniel. You and Brad have to make up your own minds. Miss Bell said time is of the essence. You could take the red-eye and be there before me. We can meet in the hospital lobby. I don't know if you should tell Daddy or not. I'll leave that up to you. Do you think this is some kind of omen, Daniel? Why now after all these years? We have a brother and a sister we never knew about. That has to mean something to us. I'm going! You will? All right, Daniel. Give Daddy my love, and I'll see you in the morning."

Fanny turned. "Did you get all that, Bess?"

"You found your mother. That's wonderful, Fanny. It is, isn't it?"

"Yes and no. Why don't I feel something?"

"You will. I see the resemblance," Bess said as she held the picture up to the light.

"I see Daniel and Brad more than myself. I look more like my father. I know it's her. I just know it. What in the world will I say to her? She's dying. What if I say the wrong thing?"

"I don't think you need to worry about right or wrong. You say what you feel. Stay as long as you need to stay. We can handle things here. I picked up the mail, and the good news is Billie Coleman sent us another check."

"Bless her heart. I need to call her tonight. I keep forgetting about the time difference in Japan. Was there any other mail?"

"If that's your way of asking me if there's a letter from Simon Thornton, the answer is no. Fanny, why don't you just write him a letter and pray the post office forwards it? I'm sure Simon has personal mail. If it isn't forwarded, where does it go? He has no home. He sold the business. Mail goes somewhere. Just do it."

Fanny bent over to pull a shoe box out from under one of the red chairs. "Should I mail all 120 of them? I've written one every day since I got back. I used to write to Ash like that. Every single day. Look what it got me."

"Four great kids, a wonderful business, one-of-a-kind friends, this lovely mountaintop home, and now your mother. If you hadn't met and married Ash, you could be clerking in a dimestore and I'd still be serving egg salad sandwiches at the counter in my father's drugstore. You and I might never have met. Everything happens for a reason. We both know that. I say mail the damn letters. I'll take them down the mountain tonight when I go home."

"Okay."

"I love it when one of us makes the right decision."

"Oh, Bess, I'm finally going to see my mother. I swear, I never thought it would happen. Say a prayer that I feel something when I see her. I don't want her to die without knowing us. We had so much love to give her, the boys and me. How could she just up and leave us like that? I need to know why. I want to know what it was that made her walk away. Maybe if she tells me something I can believe, I'll feel something. Oh Bess, what if she says she never thought about us, never wondered how we turned out?"

"She isn't going to say that, Fanny."

"But what if she does?"

"Then you'll tell her you're sorry she felt like that. You'll tell her you and your brothers thought about her every day of your lives. Stop worrying, mothers don't say things like that. Is there anything I can do, Fanny?"

"No."

Bess let herself out the door. She looked through the window to see Fanny curled up in the red chair, the picture of her mother in her hand.

"Oh, Mom, I have so much to tell you," Fanny whispered to the picture.

5

The hospital had a hushed quietness in the early hours of the morning. The sickening smell of flowers waiting to be delivered permeated the small lobby. Fanny gagged at the overpowering scent. Flowers and hospitals led to funerals and more flowers, eulogies and tears.

She saw them then, her two older brothers. They looked like tired little boys as they paced between the gray plastic-and-chrome chairs, their hands jammed into their pockets. The relief in their eyes when they saw her brought tears to her eyes. "I'm so glad you came," Fanny said.

"Dad insisted. We would have come anyway, Fanny. I don't know what I'm supposed to feel or what I should say," Daniel, the oldest, said in a weary voice.

"I think we'll know when we get there. If it's any consolation, I feel the same way. I'd like you to meet the young lady who . . . Lily, this is Daniel and Brad."

Lily acknowledged the introduction. "I'll go up first, and if Harriet is awake, prepare her. I'll come back for you. The coffee shop is open and the coffee is quite good." Fanny nodded.

Birch ordered coffee that no one drank.

"I think I wish this wasn't happening. Our lives are going to change now," Daniel said. "I don't think I want another brother or sister. You guys and your families are all I need or want."

"I agree," Brad said.

The bitterness in both her brothers' faces tugged at Fanny's heart. "We need some closure to this part of our lives. Our children have a right to know about our side of the family. Everything happens for a reason. Sometimes the timing isn't quite what we would like, but you have to deal with it. Right now, it's the only game in town. If it wasn't for Miss Bell, we still wouldn't know. We have the right to know the whys of it all. I want to know. Please, let's try not to be bitter. We all have good lives, wonderful children, and our families are intact. More or less."

"As usual, Fanny, you're right," Brad said squeezing her shoulders.

Birch watched the interaction between his mother and uncles, his heart thumping in his chest. The more or less pertained to him and his father. It always came down to family. Would he be as charitable as these two giants towering over him if he was in their position. They'd come here with bitterness in their hearts because a member of their family asked them to. And now, that member, his mother, had somehow managed to wipe away the bitterness. All he could see in their faces was sadness.

Lily Bell walked over to their table. "She's awake. It's difficult for her to talk, but she wants to see all of you. She . . . she wanted the nurse to fix her hair and put one of her own gowns on her. Another five minutes and we can go up. Anna and Paul are on the way. Is there anything you want to ask me?" The question was directed at Fanny's brothers. Both men shook their heads.

They waited.

The door to the coffee shop opened suddenly. Fanny was aware of movement, of hushed whispers. She looked up to see Sunny, Sage, and Billie. She cried then as her children circled around her. Out of the corner of her eye she saw Sage draw Birch into the tight little circle. "You belong here too, big brother. Sunny took up two seats." It brought the desired smiles Sage was looking for.

"We can go up now," Lily said, her eyes on her watch.

If the frail woman in the bed had ever been pretty, it wasn't evident now, but there was an alertness in her eyes Fanny hadn't expected. They circled the bed, uncertainty on their features.

"I'm Fanny, Mom. This is Daniel and this is Brad. My children are here too, Birch and Sage, they're twins. This is Sunny, who's going to make you a great-grandmother, and this is Billie. I want to be honest and tell you none of us knows what to do or say. I think we want to know why you left us. We have a right to know that. We can go on from there."

"Your father was a good man. Solid, dependable, hardworking. I wanted something different. I tried to tell him that, but he didn't *hear* me. When you were born something happened to me. All I did was cry. I couldn't eat or sleep. Three children in diapers overwhelmed me. I tried, but I couldn't make it work. I left knowing in my heart your father would do a better job of raising you three than I ever could. I was right. Many times I wanted to call or write, but I told myself I gave up that right. I have no excuses, and I don't ask your forgiveness because I'm dying. I'm grateful that you came. I always wondered how you turned out."

"Pretty damn good," the outspoken Sunny blurted.

"I want you to leave now. Go back to your families and lead your own lives. Mine is over, and I take full responsibility for all the things I should have done and all the things I shouldn't have done. I have two children who will mourn for me. I don't know if I have a right to say this or not, but I'll say it anyway. I'm very proud of the way your father raised you."

"Just a damn minute here," Sunny said.

"Hush, Sunny," Fanny said.

"What will you name the child?" Harriet asked, her voice little more than a raspy whisper.

"It's not going to be Harriet, that's for sure."

Strangled sounds came from the frail figure. "I like that. There's one in every family. Brad was like that as a little boy."

"He still is, Mom," Fanny said. "Is there anything we can do for you?"

"Say a prayer once in a while. Not for me, for your father. Goodbye."

There was nothing for them to do but leave.

More strangled sounds came from the bed. "What did she say?" Fanny asked Lily.

"She said you weren't to stay for the funeral."

Sunny waddled back to the bed and leaned over. "Well, guess what, *Grandmother*, we aren't staying. We all came here because of our mother, not because of you. You're right, you don't deserve us. When you get to your final destination say hello to our *other* grandmother." She leaned closer and kissed the dry sunken cheeks. "That's for my mother."

"Take care of her."

"You bet we will. You have a good trip now, you hear."

The old woman's tortured laughter followed them from the room.

"If you weren't pregnant, I'd lay you out right here," Sage said. "What the hell got into you? Have a good trip? Jesus."

"She laughed, didn't she? I didn't want her to think we're like her. I wasn't being mean-spirited, Sage, I was trying to lighten the moment. She knew that, I saw it in her eyes."

"It's a damn good thing Mom didn't hear all of that."

"Is that a threat you're going to hold over my head?" Sunny asked.

"If I thought it would get me anywhere, I would. Just shut the hell up and let's go. This family is going to breakfast *to talk*."

"About what? I am hungry. I'm always hungry. I eat all day long. I'm actually starving."

"Miss Bell is going to bring . . . what do I call them, aunt, uncle, what? Anna and Paul, I guess," he said answering his own question. "After we talk I assume we'll leave. It was a good idea of yours, Sunny, to come here. I thought Mom was going to faint dead away. Are you okay?"

"If you feed me, I will be. Now do you understand about family, Sage? This is all so sad. Mom must be devastated. I don't know what to say to her or if I should say anything. Sometimes I think this family is jinxed. I saw that little thing with Birch. You're a nice guy, Sage, and if I say so, it must be true."

"So, how are you *really* feeling?"

"Real shitty. I think there's something wrong with me aside from my pregnancy. I've had every test in the book and nothing shows up. It's something I feel, something I just know, if that makes sense."

Sage felt his stomach lurch. He wanted to say a prayer right then and there for his sister and didn't know why. He closed his eyes for a second, trying to imagine life without Sunny in it. "I'll tell you what. If you don't feel better after you deliver, we'll go to New York. They're supposed to have the finest hospitals and the best doctors. I'll go with you. I think it's your pregnancy, though."

Sunny stopped. "No. It's something else. I'm afraid, Sage."

He was afraid too. "Don't go spooking me now, Sunny. I bet you're having twins and that's why you feel like you do."

"I hope you're right, Sage."

To Sage, his sister's voice had an ominous ring. "You know me, I'm always right. Hey, did'ya see that guy driving by? He looked just like Uncle Simon."

"What guy?" Sunny asked as she looked up and down the road.

"He's gone now. It looked just like him. I guess today isn't the best of days. Maybe I wanted to see him to make sense out of all of this. Uncle Simon always had the answers to everything. If Mom ever needed Uncle Simon, it's now."

"Dad ruined that. He's at the bottom of it all," Sunny said. "God, can't we talk about something pleasant once in a while? I think Birch likes Lily Bell. I think he likes her a lot. So there."

"Long-distance romances never work. So there yourself."

"Birch can fly here every other day if he wants to. I see something brewing right under our noses."

"You need to mind your own business. Try and keep that mouth of yours shut over breakfast. This is Mom's gig, so don't go screwing it up. We're here. Behave yourself and don't embarrass us."

"Up yours, Sage."

Sage grinned. Sunny was never going to curb her tongue or her actions. Sunny was a what-you-see-is-what-you-get girl. His eyes were worried, though, as he held the door open so his family could enter the restaurant.

Lily Bell declined breakfast, saying she would wait outside for her half brother and half sister. Birch joined her. Sunny smirked in Sage's direction as she ordered a breakfast large enough for three people.

"We have to do what she wants, and she wants us to leave," Fanny said.

"I don't have any problem with that," Daniel said. Brad seconded his brother's words.

"It's sad. She was our mother. I wanted to feel something, I really did, but she was a stranger. I watched her eyes and I don't think she felt anything either. Do we just leave and not look back? That seems cruel. She said nice things about Daddy. Miss Bell said she was a nice person."

"Let it go, Fanny," Daniel said. "We have our closure now. Oops, here come our new siblings." He stood to extend his hand and introduce himself. Brad and Sage did the same.

"Please, sit down. Would you like some coffee?" Fanny asked.

Anna and Paul sat down but declined the coffee. An uncomfortable silence fell around the table. Fanny waited until Anna spoke. "I think things should be left as they are. We'll go on with our lives and you'll go on with yours. We have nothing in common even though we share the same mother. Paul and I are glad you got to see Mom for your sake. I don't know what happened before, and neither Paul nor I want to know now. It goes without saying that we won't make any demands on your family. Now, if you'll excuse us, we want to go to the hospital."

Fanny nodded. The men stood again, but this time there were no handshakes.

"Cold-hearted bitch," Sunny said. She bit into a blueberry muffin slathered with soft butter.

"My life won't be torn asunder if I never see those two again," Billie said.

"They're holding themselves in tight control. They lost their father, and now they're going to lose their mother. I don't think they knew what to do. We have no other choice but to abide by their wishes and respect their grief. Daniel? Brad? Do you have anything to say?"

"You're right, Fanny. It's behind us now."

"I want to thank whoever's paying for this wonderful breakfast," Brad said as he looked pointedly at Sage. "There's an eleven o'clock flight to Pittsburgh, and we'll make it if we leave now. I'm sorry things didn't turn out better, Fanny."

"I'm okay with this, Brad. I got to see my mother. I never thought that would happen. The truth is, I gave up a long time ago. I'm just sorry it's under these circumstances. Give Daddy a big kiss and hug for me."

"Birch and Lily are driving them to the airport. We'll meet up with them there," Sage volunteered.

"That's nice," Fanny said.

"You okay, Mom?" Billie asked.

"I think so. I feel like I should have . . . said something meaningful or . . . something. I didn't even kiss her or touch her hand."

"Mom, if you were meant to do those things, you would have done them. She didn't expect it, and I don't think she wanted it. If you want the truth, I think we interrupted her dying schedule. That's my opinion." To the waitress she said, "I'll have an orange and a blueberry muffin to go."

Fanny smiled at her daughter. "I think you might be right. *Exactly* how much weight have you gained, Sunny?"

"You don't want to know, Mom."

"Tyler calls her two-ton Lizzie." Sage guffawed. "I'm telling you, she's having twins."

"If I do, I'm naming them Daniel and Brad. If I have a girl, I'm calling her Polly."

"Really, Sunny. That's wonderful. They'll be so pleased if it comes to pass."

"Sure, those guys are so generous I know they'll cough up a really good trust fund for their namesakes. They're such mushy pushovers. I just love them to death. Pay the check and let's get out of this town. It's depressing," Sunny said.

Across the street from the restaurant a tall man dressed in khaki slacks and rumpled tee shirt climbed from his car and entered a small market attached to the gas station. The two little dogs hopped up on the shelf behind the backseat to stare out the window. On the other side of the street the Thornton family climbed into Sage's rental car.

In her struggle to get comfortable, Sunny found herself staring across the street at the small black car. "Did you see those two cute little dogs? I think I'm going to ask Tyler to get me one. I always wanted a dog. That's the same guy, Sage, the one I told you looked like Uncle Simon. Shoot, he's going the other way. I'll tell you, he was the spitting image of our uncle."

"She's always seeing strange things," Sage said to his mother, who was busy craning her neck to look where Sunny was pointing.

"I do not *see things.* The man looked *exactly* like Uncle Simon. He was even wearing khaki pants and a tee shirt. It's the same guy we saw before. I'm not making this up, Mom."

"Turn around, Sage, go back to the gas station," Fanny ordered. Sage slammed on the brakes and made a U-turn in the middle of the road. The moment the car stopped in front of the little market, Fanny was out of the car, running inside. She fumbled with her wallet and withdrew a picture of Simon. She held it up to the young clerk. "Was this man just in here?"

"Yes, ma'am, not five minutes ago. He bought some dog food, dog treats, newspapers, and cigarettes."

"Has he ever been in here before?" Fanny thought her heart would thunder right out of her chest.

"I've never seen him."

Fanny ran back to the car. "It was Simon. Sage, take this road and see if you can overtake him. It was Simon!"

"Mom, he could have turned off anywhere. He's got ten minutes on us. I'm doing it, I'm doing it," he said at the anguish on his mother's face.

"No one ever pays any attention to me," Sunny said, biting into the muffin she'd taken to go.

"Can't you drive faster, Sage?" Fanny demanded, her head out the window as she tried to scan the highway.

"Mom, I'm going eighty now. Get your head in here before someone going ninety clips it off. He could be anywhere, Mom. There were five turnoffs and all those side streets he could have turned on. Let's stop at a gas station and see if he's listed in the phone book. We can check with the utility company, too."

"Just keep driving, Sage. It was him. I can't believe this."

"I can," Sunny chirped from the backseat. "Things like this happen in the movies all the time. Picture this, we find him and I go into labor and deliver twins. Everyone lives happily ever after."

"I wouldn't blame Tyler one bit if he divorced you. You need a muzzle."

"You're just ticked off because I saw him twice, and you didn't believe me either time. I bet he's living on some mountaintop. All by himself with those two little dogs. He only comes down off the mountain for dog food, cigarettes, and newspapers. He's probably living off the land, thin as a rail, unhappy, wondering where it all went wrong."

"That's enough, Sunny," Fanny said. Her voice was as shaky as her insides.

"The interstate is up ahead. What do you want me to do, Mom?"

"Pull over to the side of the road. I need to think."

The occupants of the car remained silent as Fanny squeezed her eyes shut. So close and yet so far away. Sage was right, he could be anywhere. Better to go back and hire a private detective to locate Simon. At least now she knew the general area he was in. Sunny was probably right about Simon living on a mountaintop. Simon loved the mountains. How like Simon to get two dogs.

"Go back to the airport, Sage. Birch will be waiting for us. I can always come back here when we aren't so pressed for time."

"Are you sure, Mom?" Sage asked.

"I'm sure. None of us needs this today on top of everything else."

"Mom, can I say something?" Sunny asked.

"Of course, Sunny."

"I remember Uncle Simon talking about a place called Stallion Springs one time. I think it's somewhere in the Tehachapi Mountains. He said he owned some land there and one day he was going to build a cabin. We were little when he said that. I don't even know why I remember it."

"He never mentioned it to me. It's a place to start. We'll find him."

"Only if he wants to be found," Sunny muttered under her breath.

Simon Thornton threw down the newspaper he'd been reading. The two little dogs at his feet immediately dragged it off. In ten minutes it would be in shreds and then one or the other would poop in the middle. Normally he'd just shake his head and laugh. Not today. Today he was out of sorts. Today he was seeing his nieces and nephews everywhere. He'd had his usual nightmare about Ash three times in the past week. He was thinking too much, and he hadn't slept well since the day he walked out of his New York office.

"Cabin fever," he muttered to the dogs who ignored him. They were on the financial page now, growling playfully at one another. Maybe it was time to move on. The question was, where? "I always wanted to see Oregon," he muttered again. He hated it when he muttered to himself. If he didn't watch it, he'd become a wilderness recluse. Like he wasn't one already. What he should do was go into town and call Malcom and maybe Ash and maybe Fanny. Just to say hello. Then again, maybe he wouldn't do that. What would be the point?

The point was . . . he was tired of fishing, tired of hunting, tired of sitting here on the front porch of someone else's cabin doing nothing. Actually, he was goddamn sick and tired of things not going his way. He should be building his own cabin so he could freeze his ass off in the winter. He was drinking too much, too. Drinking so he could sleep. When he did sleep all he did was dream about Fanny and Ash. When he wasn't dreaming about them he was dreaming about his mother and his youth.

One phone call. What was the harm in making one phone call. Enough time had gone by so it wouldn't seem like he was backwatering. Who should he call, though? Fanny, Malcom, Fanny, Ash, Fanny. It wasn't right that he wasn't staying in touch. Things could be happening, things he should know about. Ash's condition could worsen and the boys wouldn't know where to locate him. *That* he needed to know about. Fanny could be sick, Sunny could be having her baby. Malcom could be in trouble at the company.

Five minutes later he had himself convinced he needed to go back to town. He piled the dogs in the car, his shoulders lighter. He whistled because Slick liked to join in by howling at the top of his lungs. Tootsie usually slept through the whole ordeal.

Simon drove steadily, the miles ticking off slowly as he ran different conversations over and over in his mind. He'd call Fanny first. He'd say whatever came into his mind. Then he'd call Malcom. Ash would be last on his list.

Two hours later, Simon pulled into a Mobil station, where he asked the attendant for ten dollars in change. He was breathing like a long-distance runner when he placed the call to Fanny and got her answering machine. He hung up. His second call was to Malcom whose secretary said he was out of town. He felt his shoulders start to slump. What the hell, Ash was better than nothing. Instead, he placed a second call to Fanny and told the operator to stay on the line, that he wanted to leave a message. He listened to her sweet voice say, "I'm not here, please leave a message and the time you called."

Simon cleared his throat twice before he could speak, his heart jumping crazily inside his chest. "Fanny, this is Simon. It's around two o'clock. I just wanted to call to say hello and to let you know I'm fine. I've been moving around quite a bit and will probably grease up my sneakers and move again by tomorrow. I think about us all the time and what we had and what we could be having now. You know how much I love you, but I need to tell you again. Perhaps someday when things are right . . . will that day ever come, Fanny? I feel sort of foolish talking to a machine. I guess I'll say good-bye. I think about us every single day. Oh, I got two dogs. Tootise and Slick. They're great company. Daisy would love them. I'll call again when the loneliness gets too unbearable. Good-bye, Fanny."

Ash's voice boomed over the wire. "Simon, is that really you? I've got everyone in the world looking for you. Listen, I got myself into a bit of a mess. I need some help here. Fanny put the squeeze on me, and I'm lucky my ass isn't in jail. Where the hell are you?"

"Does it matter, Ash? I'm talking to you now. What is it you think I can do for you?"

"You can loan me about fourteen million dollars is what you can do for me."

Simon threw his head back and roared with laughter. "Ash, if I had fourteen million dollars, I wouldn't be standing here in a phone booth talking to you. What did you do this time?"

"I told you, I didn't do anything. Fanny squeezed me out. I bought these riverboats in Biloxi, Mississippi. She went through the roof because the bank gave me the money on my signature without hers. She threw a fit and the damn bank had to close down. A whole bunch of other shit went down, too. I was swinging in the wind, little brother, so I had to cut some deals, and I can't make good. How much can you loan me?"

"Zip. Squat. *Nada*. How could you do such a stupid thing? Did you involve the kids? You did, didn't you?"

"Birch went along with it." Ash's voice was whiny, full of self-pity. "Are you refusing to help me? You owe me, Simon."

"Where's Fanny, Ash?"

"Jesus, you aren't going to believe this one. Some chick waltzes in here saying she knows where Fanny's mother is and they all took off and left me here to run things. Ungrateful snots. Do they give a shit about me? No they do not. Birch just up and took the damn plane and didn't even ask my permission. This is not a considerate family."

"Fanny finally found her mother," Simon said, his voice full of awe. So that's where she'd gone.

"Yeah, the old lady is dying. It's just like Fanny to rush there to hold her hand."

"Yeah, Ash, that's just like Fanny," Simon said softly.

"Where the hell are you, Simon? I need a little help here. I thought we were brothers. Hell, you're marrying my ex-wife. That has to count for something."

"Who told you that?"

"Get off it, Simon. Everyone in Las Vegas knows. What I don't understand is why you left. Did Fanny pull one of her famous stunts on you, too? If she did, you know what I've had to put up with. I'm desperate here, and you aren't making it any easier. Do you want me to beg?"

"Ash, what's the money for?"

"To pay back the loan. The interest is killing me. They'll kill me next. You know what those people are like. Do you want my death on your conscience? Mom wouldn't like this, Simon."

"Ash, you aren't a stupid man. Why did you go to those thugs?"

"It wasn't like I had other choices, Simon. In my condition prison was not an alternative. You know they'll kill me. You have the money; I know that, too."

"You know what, Ash, no matter what this family does where you're concerned, it's never enough. All you do is demand. We give and give and give and all you do is take and take and take. I will not give you fourteen million dollars to pay to gangsters and thugs. If you needed it for your own well-being, I wouldn't hesitate. If you needed a kidney, an eye or a lung, I'd be the first in line." That had to be the biggest lie he'd ever told in his life, he thought smugly. "Sell the goddamn riverboats to someone else and get your money back. I'm surprised you didn't sink them to collect on the insurance. Oh, Jesus, don't do that, Ash. Insurance companies are like cops—they can and will find out you did it and you'll get into some really big trouble. You're on your own this time."

The curses were so ugly Simon could only smile in satisfaction. He hung up the phone and got into his car. Tootsie and Slick were all over him, sensing his unhappiness. He shifted gears, his thoughts far away. "I hope meeting your mother was everything you wanted it to be." Tootsie snuggled in his lap while Slick leaped up to wiggle around on the back of the headrest.

The ride back to the cabin was made in silence.

Cuddling with Daisy, Fanny listened to Simon's message over and over again. Each time his voice sounded more dear, more wonderful. She thought she was playing it for the ninety-ninth time when the phone rang. She recognized her ex-husband's irate voice immediately. She knew she should hang up, but even Ash couldn't bother her today. Today Simon called and said he would call again. Her world was right side up.

"Okay, Fanny, I'm going to cut right through to the quick of it. God help me, but I need your help. I'm only going to say this once. If you don't help me now, you'll be attending my funeral in a few days. Are you listening to me, Fanny?"

"You're screaming in my ear, Ash. Of course I can hear you. Aren't you going to ask me about my mother?"

"No. I don't care about your mother, and I'd be a hypocrite if I said I did. Why you care about someone who left you as a baby is something I don't even want to pretend I understand. I need fourteen million dollars in three days or they'll be delivering my body parts to your front door. That's the sum total of why I'm calling you. Simon refuses to help me. He called a few hours ago and flat out turned me down. There's nowhere else to turn. You have to help me."

"No, Ash, I don't. Aren't you being a little dramatic?"

"Maybe you should read the newspapers more often in that ivory tower you live in, Fanny. I am not being dramatic. I admit I made a mistake. Put yourself in my position. I wouldn't have done well in prison in my condition. You hung me out to dry, Fanny, and we both know it. Do you want my death on your conscience?"

"Of course not."

"Then give me the money. I'll find a way to make it up to you. Those riverboats are going to make a fortune."

"Sell them, Ash."

"I don't have time to sell them. I have three days. It was pure dumb luck that Simon called today. I've been trying to find him for months. He owes me his life, and this is how he repays me. I hate his fucking guts."

Fanny swayed dizzily. "Ash, I don't have fourteen million dollars. Everything we own is mortgaged to the hilt. And before you can bring it up, Billie Coleman has already paid two installments on the money she borrowed. We're just getting by."

"Then tap the kids' trust funds. You have the power to do that. Fanny, I'm desperate."

"They've been tapped already, Ash. Get it through your head, there's no money. I'm not a magician, I can't pull it out of a hat. This is your own doing, Ash. You got yourself in this mess because of your greed. Stop and think now, what would an emperor do in your position?"

"Will you be serious? I'm scared, Fanny. I don't think I've ever been scared in my life except when I had the accident. I'm totally helpless now. Please, you have to find a way to help me."

"Ash, I don't know what to say. I don't know how to help you. I would if I could. You know that. That's the reason you called me. I need to think. I'll call you back in the morning."

"In the morning! That cuts my time down to two days. I'm sitting on a ticking time bomb, and you tell me you'll call me in the morning! Jesus Christ, Fanny, that's not what I need to hear right now."

"It's the best I can do at the moment. Are you going to be at the casino this evening?"

"It's the only place I'm safe. All right, I'll wait for your call."

Fanny didn't think she had the strength to hang up the phone. She felt the beginnings of a headache as her stomach started to churn. She'd wanted to go out to the cemetery and talk. She needed to look upward and speak to Sallie so she could try and understand her feelings. Now, she couldn't do that. Now, she had to think about Ash and his impending dismemberment. She wished she could cry, for her mother, for Simon, for Ash. She knew if she gave in to that particular weakness, her strength would be gone.

She had to do something, but what? What would Sallie have done? Forget Sallie. Sallie had lived in a make-believe world for too long at the end. As sweet and as wonderful as she was, she wouldn't have been able to handle this either. Or would she?

Fannie dropped to her knees and pulled out the jewelry box that had once belonged to Sallie. Helter-skelter she dumped everything on the floor until the false bottom fell out. Thank God the folded piece of paper was still there. What was it Sallie had said so long ago? If you're ever in trouble, call this number and speak to the person who answers the phone. Just tell them who you are. No name, no address, just a phone number. Fanny sucked in her breath. Should she call now or should she wait? Maybe she should play Simon's message again. Maybe she should go out to the cemetery. Maybe she should read a book on dismemberment.

Fanny stared at the phone for twenty long minutes before she could gather up the courage to pick up the receiver. Her hand trembled so badly she could barely dial the numbers from the paper.

The phone was picked up on the second ring. The voice was harsh and cold. "State your business quickly."

Fanny flinched. "This is Fanny Thornton and I need to speak with you and I need to do it now. Not later, not tomorrow. I can be in town in forty-five minutes, and I can meet you at Sophie's Cafe. Yes or no?"

"One hour, Mrs. Thornton."

Fanny stared at the pinging phone in her hand. To calm herself she played Simon's message five more times.

Fanny walked into Sophie's Cafe with three minutes to spare. She sat down at a table in the corner and ordered a cup of coffee. Her gaze settled on the door. She waited. When the door finally opened, the two people sitting at separate tables got up and left. The waitress disappeared. She heard the snick of the lock and then the shades over the door being rolled down. It was like a scene in a bad movie. *I can do this. I really can do this.*

He looked so normal, so clean and pressed, that Fanny relaxed. He wasn't a youngster, but he wasn't that old either. *It's the white hair that makes him look older,* Fanny thought. *He's waiting for me to say something.* "I don't know who you are but my mother-in-law left me your phone number and said if I ever found myself in trouble, I should call and speak to whoever answered the phone. I, myself am not in trouble, but . . . I . . ."

"I'm aware of your problem."

"I rather thought you would be. I need your people to reduce the interest on my ex-husband's loan. Bank rates will do nicely. Will you agree to that?"

"Impossible."

"Then let's try this on for size. Tonight, I shut off the power and the city goes black. After I do that, I turn my water valve and your people don't flush. I can keep the electricity and water on at Babylon. You lose. We win. All night. Tomorrow night and the night after. Is it still impossible?"

"Yes."

"That's a very foolish response. In one night your casinos will lose millions. We pick up millions, but we do have an occupancy problem. Shall we try it for one night? By the way, who are you?"

"Just someone who was indebted to Sallie. My name isn't important. Wait here, Mrs. Thornton. I'll return in one hour. They serve a very good goulash. By the time you finish I'll be back with your answer." He snapped his fingers and a bowl of spicy goulash was set in front of Fanny. She barely heard the door close.

Fanny looked around for the door to the ladies' room. Inside, she leaned against the door, her body shaking uncontrollably. She struggled to take long, deep breaths that exploded out of her mouth like gunshots. When she felt calm enough to walk, she returned to her table. She stared at the goulash and then at her watch. The minutes ticked by. She nibbled on a piece of French bread and thought about her mother. Was she still alive? "I need a phone."

Fanny dialed the operator and placed a call to the hospital. She asked for the floor nurse on Harriet's floor and was told her mother had passed away at twelve minutes past noon. She placed a second call to Shamrock, Pennsylvania, and spoke to her brother Daniel. "Tell Brad and Daddy. We'll talk tomorrow, Daniel."

Fanny's third and fourth calls were to the water company and the electric company. To both she said, "Stand by for my call. I'll call you either way once I've made my decision."

More minutes crept by. Fanny placed money next to the phone for her long-distance calls. The money and phone were whisked away so fast, Fanny barely saw them disappear.

Her headache was alive now, banging inside her skull. She needed to be hard and strong and not let these people intimidate her.

Five minutes to go.

The goulash was cold now, the French bread dry and hard.

Three minutes to go.

"I need a telephone."

Two minutes to go. One minute.

Fanny stared at the doors of the café, at the green shades drawn to the bottom of the glass.

One minute past the hour.

Two minutes past the hour.

Fanny picked up the phone, her back stiff, her jaw tight. Water or power? Power of course. She dialed the number, announced herself just as the door opened. "Six points above the bank rate."

"No deal."

"In five minutes, Mr. Secore, turn off the power. You understand the power is to stay on at Babylon. I'll stay on the line."

"Five points."

"Four minutes, sir. The answer is no."

"Four points."

"My answer is the same."

"Three and that's as low as I'm authorized to go."

"I'm sorry. Bank rates. It's dark outside. Aren't the lights pretty? I don't think there's another place in this country that has as many lights as this town. *Thirty seconds.*"

Fanny watched sweat bead on the chiseled features. He was scared.

"Pull the switch, Mr. Secore."

"Wait."

"Too late, Mr. whatever your name is." Fanny dialed again.

"Mr. Quincy, this is Fanny Thornton. Turn the valve. Make sure there's water at Babylon. Thank you."

"Mrs. Thornton . . . please, wait."

"Why?"

"Let me go back to my people. Four points isn't that unreasonable."

"To me it's very unreasonable. Bank rates. The power and water stay off all night. Another thing, Mr. whatever your name is, nothing had better happen to my ex-husband. If it does, I will call in the FBI and they'll be all over your people . . . what's that expression that's used so much these days? Oh, yes, like fleas on a dog. Sallie would be very disappointed that you didn't come through for her. I think she honestly thought you people had a code of honor. Obviously she was wrong. Another thing, if anything happens to any member of my family, and that includes me, there will be no water or power until everything is probated, and our affairs are so complex it could take *years.* Think about that when you go back to report to your people. I'll call you tomorrow morning at nine o'clock."

Fanny walked out the door, her back stiff, her eyes watering with the headache pounding inside her head. She had to drive to Babylon now through the dark city. God in heaven, what had she just done?

Twenty minutes later, Fanny walked into her ex-husband's office. Birch was standing next to his father, his face ashen. Ash's face was gleeful.

"By God, you did it, Fanny! You shut down this town! You

brought them to their knees. I'll kiss your feet, Fanny, if you want me to. You came through for me. I knew you would."

"At what cost to the rest of us, Ash? At what cost?" Fanny whispered as her son wrapped his arms around her.

6

His arm tightening on his mother's shoulder, Birch said, "I don't think it's a good idea for you to drive up the mountain tonight, Mom. I'll call the desk and get you a room."

"He's right, Fanny. The dark stuff is going to hit the fan in about thirty minutes. Forget what I just said, it's happening now," Ash said, his eyes on the monitors. His excitement was palpable.

"Stay here, Mom. Keep the door locked. Dad, are you going out to the floor?"

"Damn right I am."

The moment the door closed, Birch said, "Turning off the power and water is about the stupidest thing we've ever done. What the hell got into Mom?"

"I didn't tell her to do it if that's what you're thinking. I asked her to bail us out and she said we're tapped out. You heard what I heard. Jesus, we're over occupancy. We have to do something."

"You do it, Dad. I have to get Mom a room."

"Take a look at the registration desk. We were probably sold out five minutes after she had the switch pulled. We need more help. Start calling around. Give Sage a call. Billie, too. Everyone we know. This is a golden opportunity, and we can take in some serious money this evening. Don't just stand there, Birch, get to work!"

"What about Mom?"

"She can stay in the penthouse with me. There are two bedrooms, you know."

Birch raced back to the office. "No rooms, Mom. You'll have to stay in the penthouse. Don't worry. He'll be on the floor all night. It's jamming out there. I have to get some help here."

"Can I do anything, Birch? I'm willing."

"I think it would be better if you went upstairs. I don't want to have to worry about you." He buzzed the head of Security. "Neal, come around to the office and take my mother up to the penthouse. If you can spare anyone, have them hang out in the hall. After you do that, call in everyone who's off tonight. Cut whatever deal you have to to get them in here."

"She really pulled the switch, huh?"

"That's not the half of it. They can't flush either."

"I didn't know your mother had that kind of guts. I don't mean that in a . . ."

"I know what you mean. I never thought she'd do it either. I think she's in shock that she did it. Keep checking on her all night, okay?"

"Sure, Birch."

Birch walked over to a secluded alcove and picked up one of the phones to ask for an outside line. He dialed, the breath rushing from his mouth when he heard Sage's voice. "Sage, Mom pulled the switch and turned off the valve. The town is pitch-dark. I need you to come in and help. Call Billie and anyone else you can think of. This is going to be one very long night."

"Why?" Sage gasped.

"Because those . . . hoods have Dad on the ropes. I've got her safe in the penthouse, and Neal is watching out for her. Listen. I don't have time to chat. Call Sunny, but tell her to stay home. She could get hurt if she's on the floor. Some of these people can act like animals when things get out of control, and, trust me, things are out of control. Tell Tyler to come over if he's free. Bess, too, and John if he isn't at the hospital."

"I'm on my way. I'll call from the car. What's The Emperor doing?"

"Holding court. What the hell do you think he's doing?"

"For some reason I thought he'd be counting his money. I'll see you in a bit."

Birch trotted out to the floor, his eyes raking the room for a sign of his father. Every table, every slot machine was filled to capacity. The noise was deafening. He thought about calling the police when he saw the guards at the huge front doors. He'd never seen people clamor and bang on plate glass to get into an establishment to gamble away their money. In another hour or so it was going to turn ugly.

"Mr. Thornton, the switchboard is going berserk. We can't handle the calls coming in. These messages seem like the most important. I thought you might want to see them right away as some of them sound . . . disturbing."

Birch shoved the stack of yellow slips into his jacket pocket. He could just imagine who the calls were from and what they said.

It took Birch thirty-five minutes to cross the room. On the way he broke up two tussles with patrons fighting over slot machines. "Do it again and you're out of here, and you won't be permitted back in. This is the only game in town so think carefully."

Smiling and jostling his way through the packed room, Birch finally reached his father, who was speaking with a reporter from the *Nevada Sun.* "Dad, I need to talk to you." Ash excused himself, turned his chair around to follow Birch.

"This is what I like, a full house. The tournament was nothing compared to this. So, what's your problem, Birch? Aside from wall-to-wall people, things are running okay. I saw Sage a moment ago, and Billie was handling drinks. Bess is changing monies. That's Tyler over there with Neal, so I guess he'll be handling the money, too. I called Wells Fargo and they're going to pick up money on the hour. I haven't seen any of the other owners, have you?"

"I haven't seen them, but I heard from them." Sage pulled the stack of crumpled messages from his pocket. He rifled through them. "All present and accounted for. What's your next question?"

Ash's eyes were so gleeful Birch felt sick to his stomach. "If your mother hangs tight on this, I'm home free in three days. It's time those sharks took a hit. Not only will they be willing to give me bank rates, they'll pay us to turn the power and water back on. I can either go with the bank rates and pay the loan off the way I wanted, or I can pay it off and walk away. I also have the option of banking all this money we're raking in to get those riverboats operational. Three days, Birch. Customers will be bouncing off the walls and hanging from the ceiling to give me their money."

Birch's stomach rumbled. "What about Mom?"

"One of a kind. She always comes through," Ash said magnanimously.

"That's not what I meant. They'll meet her demands tomorrow and she'll turn everything back on. She'll never go for three days."

"She will if they threaten her. That's the next step. Intimidation is how they get to you. Fanny won't tolerate it. She'll extend the days each time they do or say something she doesn't like. Your mother is a woman of principle. I'm counting on her staying that way, too. She won't let me down."

"That's funny as hell coming from you, Dad."

An ear-piercing whistle sounded across the room. Birch craned his neck to see Sage motioning to him. "Enjoy it while it lasts," Birch said to his father.

"I am. This is my night, kiddo. I can't wait to see the morning papers. I can see it now, three-inch headlines." Ash waved his arms expansively. "EMPEROR TAKES OVER CITY!" He shrugged at Birch's retreating back.

Tonight, Las Vegas was his alone.

"This is a zoo. We better start clearing out some of these people before the fire marshal shuts us down."

"If you think that's going to happen, you're nuts. No one in this town is going to mess with Mom. The threat was always there, right out in the open, but no one, and that includes me, ever thought this night would come to pass. Mom is the most powerful woman in this town, probably this state. If you were the fire marshal, would you take her on?"

"Probably not, but there's danger here. I say we go to the stockroom and pull out all those portable fire extinguishers and keep them handy. You have to keep all the exit doors clear. We need some more people, Birch. Hell, I'm willing to go out on the street and recruit if necessary. I guess you know the switchboard is jammed."

Birch waved the stack of messages under his brother's nose. "And, on top of these, let me tell you what our father's thinking is on all of this . . ."

"I hate this goddamn business," Sage muttered as he struggled through the crowds of gamblers.

Upstairs in the penthouse, Fanny stood in the dark staring out at the town that was just as dark. She shivered. She wanted to go home and play Simon's message again. She needed to hear his calm, sane voice. Needed to hear him say he loved her, needed to hear him say he would call again. She wanted to sit in her big red chair with Daisy in her lap.

"I'm going home." She scribbled off a note and left it on the dining-room table.

Thirty minutes later, wearing Ash's jeans, windbreaker, and baseball cap, Fanny slid behind wheel of the junk car Sunny kept in the garage for emergencies. She gunned the motor and then roared up the ramp and out to the main road. She didn't take a deep breath until she was out of town and on her way up the mountain, her high-beam lights leading the way.

A long time later, after disconnecting the phone, when she was ensconced in the depths of the old red chair, coffee cup in hand, Daisy in her lap, she burst into tears. "Oh, Simon, I need you." Fanny fell asleep, Simon's name on her lips, his message playing over and over until Daisy, too, drifted into slumber.

Simon woke, showered, shaved, and brewed a pot of coffee he carried out to the porch. He propped his feet on the railing, staring off into the distance. His left hand dropped to the portable radio next to his chair. From long years of habit he listened to the early-morning news and the late news. He adjusted the volume and waited to see what had gone on in the world overnight. He listened, his thoughts far away until he heard the commentator say, *"Last night just as darkness fell, the Big White Way in Las Vegas turned black and dry. Stories, none of which can be confirmed, range from Russian spies blowing up the electric company to squirrels chewing up the circuitry. One has to wonder how and why squirrels would turn off the water, though. The smart money is saying the man known as The Emperor of Las Vegas turned off the power and water in a fit of pique. Ashford Thornton, the owner of Babylon, couldn't be reached for comment. Babylon is the only casino to have power and water in the town of Las Vegas. We invite any listeners who have additional information to call us here in the news room. This is Sam Le Roy signing off. Stay tuned for Maxwell Minton and the latest Top 40 hits to start off your day."*

The legs on Simon's chair hit the porch with a thud. Tootsie and Slick woke up, stared at him, then went back to sleep. Simon cursed his lack of a phone, civilization and anything else that came to mind. "C'mon, you guys, gather up your gear. We're going to Las Vegas."

Simon didn't bother to pack. He gathered up his clothes and possessions, making nine trips to his car throwing everything in the trunk any old way. He emptied out the coffeepot and carried a cup to the car, where he set it on the console. "Hop in." Tootsie and Slick climbed into the backseat, their chews, toys, and blankets spread around them. If he was lucky, he could make Las Vegas by eleven o'clock and Sunrise by noon.

It wasn't until Simon stopped for gas at the halfway point that he realized Ash didn't have the authority to turn off the power and water in Las Vegas. Only Fanny could do that. "Son of a bitch!" He threw money in the general direction of the gas station attendant, slid into his car and peeled rubber, his tires leaving long black skid lines on the concrete.

Fanny connected the phone at one minute to nine. It rang almost immediately.

"Mom, where have you been? We've been calling all over the place. There was a busy signal at Sunrise. We thought someone snatched you and forced you to leave that note. Are you okay?"

"I'm fine. Tell me what happened."

"It would be easier to tell you what didn't happen. We made a barrel of money. Sage, Billie, Bess, and Tyler came to help out. Sage went out on the street and recruited bouncers. We needed to keep the exits clear in case anything went wrong. We were seriously over our occupancy rate. The cops and fire department were out in force, but nothing serious went awry. The casino is still jamming. Wells Fargo takes money out on the hour. Dad just took about ninety pills and is sleeping. Sage is eating breakfast, Billie is catnapping, and Tyler went to the hospital. Sunny just walked in a minute ago. Our rooms are booked solid, and Dad raised the rates by a hundred percent. Nobody complained if you can believe that. All the headliners from the other casinos left town this morning. At least that's what the news said. This stuff is going to make a hell of a scrapbook. Mom, why'd you do it?"

"Your father said those people would kill him. He was frightened out of his wits. I had to do something. Where could I possibly come up with fourteen million dollars in three days? I had to do what I did. I gave them a choice, they chose not to take it. All I asked for was bank rates on the loan. They came down to three above the bank, and I said no. Three percent of fourteen million dollars compounded daily is a lot of money. We played hardball. They blinked. Did I say that right, Birch?"

His mother the hardball player. His mother going up against gangsters. It boggled his mind. "I couldn't have said it any better. What are you going to do now?"

"I told them I'd call them at nine o'clock. It's after nine. I don't want to seem eager. Maybe I won't call them."

"Dad wants three days. Can you handle it, Mom?"

Three days. Fanny's stomach started to gurgle. "I'm just going to . . . what I'm going to do is . . . wing it. I want to hear what those people have to say."

"Every single one of them called the casino last night. The switchboard finally blew out around four this morning. It's being fixed as we speak. I'm calling you from a phone booth out on the street. We didn't return any of the calls. I'm going to try and grab some sleep. Sunny is going to watch the monitors. Call me when you know something. Mom, be careful."

"I will. I have Daisy right here."

"I don't think that powder puff is going to be much protection if anyone comes looking for you."

"They won't do that, Birch. They know the alternative if they do. Get some sleep, honey. I'll talk to you later."

Fanny replaced the phone and reached for her coffee cup.

The phone rang again just as Fanny poured more coffee. She let it ring five times before she picked it up. "Mrs. Thornton? You said you would call at nine o'clock. I waited for your call."

Fanny sucked in her breath. She would recognize that voice if she was in a cave full of screaming bats. "I was washing my hair at nine o'clock," Fanny lied.

"Washing your hair?" Fanny could just imagine the stupid look on the man's face.

"Uh-huh. What can I do for you this morning?"

"Two above the bank rate."

"Be serious. This is not negotiable. I have things to do today so I need to know if you're going to be calling me back."

"We're not your husband's personal bankers, Mrs. Thornton. We made the loan in good faith and your husband signed the necessary papers."

"Ex-husband. Ash was heavily medicated when he signed those papers. I told you, the matter is not negotiable. I have to roll my hair now or it will frizz up. Good-bye."

Fanny gulped at the coffee in the heavy mug. "Either you're stupid, Fanny Thornton, or you have no brains," she muttered to herself.

When the phone rang again, Fanny let it ring eight times before she picked it up. She listened to the cold, angry voice, a voice she matched perfectly when she said, "I told you this is not negotiable. You know my terms. You're starting to irritate me. Either you agree now or just for pure orneriness on my part I'll leave the switch and valve off a whole day as punishment when we do come to terms. You can't win, Mr. whatever your name is. Tell that to your people. Now, get the hell off my line. Someone important might be trying to call me."

"Mrs. Thornton, you're being very foolish. I cannot control my employers. Things happen in this town that are never spoken of again. Please, you need to reconsider and allow my people to save face here. In addition you are restricting the rights of my employers to earn a living. They can sue you."

"You just threatened me. I will not tolerate that kind of behavior. Is it your intention to cut me up in pieces and stuff me in a paper bag? The switch and valve stay off for two days. Each time you call me I'll add another day. Sue me. The case will be in the courts for years. All your dirty laundry will be aired. The Feds will take over this town, and we both know it. One hundred percent interest is ludicrous. What I will negotiate are the monies you pay me to turn the switch and valve back on. You're dark for two more days. Don't . . ." Fanny grappled for a word her daughter Sunny would use under the circumstances to make her point. "Don't *piss* me off." She wasn't sure, but she thought she heard a chuckle on the other end of the phone as she was hanging it up.

Fanny looked around her small, comfortable studio. Would they kill her? She needed to do something. Scrub the kitchen floor. The small bathroom needed to be cleaned. The windows should be washed.

Fanny looked down at herself. She was still dressed in Ash's clothing, the jeans rolled up six times around her ankles. The tattered sweatshirt that said U.S. Navy on the front, Ash's prize possession, seemed fit attire for the work at hand. A red bandanna tied around her hair completed her outfit.

Fanny was hard at work, the kitchen floor covered with soapy water when Chue burst through the front door. "Miss Fanny, a parade is coming up the mountain. Five long black cars like . . . the ones at Miss Sallie's funeral. Another blue car is behind them. What do you want me to do? Is this trouble?"

"Oh, yeah." Fanny could feel bile rise in her throat. "When they get here, escort them in and then go to your house and call the boys at the casino."

"I will stay. I know jujitsu."

"It's all right, Chue. This is going to be a verbal battle."

"They are here."

"Let them in, Chue."

Fanny dipped her rag into the soapsuds and was industriously scrubbing the tile floor when she noticed two rows of shiny black shoes out of the corner of her eye. She leaned back against the cabinet on her haunches. "Welcome to Sunrise, gentlemen. Humph," she snorted. "Where are your chain saws? That's how you do it, isn't it?" When her heart exploded would her chest cavity just burst or would her heart tear itself loose and come up and out through her throat?

"Do what, Mrs. Thornton?" a soft cultured voice asked.

"You know, slice and dice, rip apart my joints, that kind of thing. I'm not afraid of you," she blustered.

"You have no reason to be afraid. Concerned, yes. I think perhaps you watch too many movies. We're legitimate businessmen. These gentlemen, myself included, are here to conduct business."

"You mean you're here to negotiate. Let's tell it like it is." Fanny ignored the outstretched hand. Through the sea of shiny black shoes she saw a pair of worn sneakers with frayed shoelaces, the kind of laces dogs chew on. Suddenly her cozy kitchen was lighter, brighter. The sun seemed warmer as it sliced through the venetian blinds and across her neck. She jerked her head. The rows of shiny black shoes faded before her eyes until the worn sneakers found their way front and center. "Move!" she said irritably. "Simon! Oh, Simon, is it really you? Move, move," Fanny yelled as she scrambled to her knees on the wet floor to get to her feet. "Oh, Simon, you're here. How did you know? Sit, sit," she said to the men. "Make some coffee, finish the floor, do whatever you want. I'll be back in a little while."

She was in the air swirling about the small room, her lips pressed against Simon's as he tried to whirl both of them out the door, three yapping dogs at their feet. "Oh, Simon, you came back. I followed you that day and missed you by fifteen minutes. Fifteen minutes. I wanted to die. Where were you? Sunny saw you in Bakersfield and we tried to follow you. Oh, Simon, I have so much to tell you. I found my mother. I actually saw her. Kiss me, hold me tight and don't you ever let me go again. God, I love you, Simon. I want to get married. Today."

"You came after me! I didn't know, Fanny. I never should have left. It was stupid of me. I heard the news this morning. I'm ready to get married right now," Simon said, kissing her eyes, her nose, her ears.

"I have to finish scrubbing the floor first and find a dress to wear. What color, Simon?"

"That blue flowered one. All my clothes are in the trunk and they're wrinkled."

"I'll iron them for you. I love you, Simon. So much I ache. I want to carry lilies of the valley. I love the way they smell. Should it be private or should we invite people? That's all nonsense, all I want is you. I can carry plastic flowers."

"Whatever you want, Fanny. What the hell is going on? Are those men the other casino owners? Why are they here, Fanny? Do you have any idea of how much danger you're in?"

"I don't want to talk about that. I want to talk about us. We're finally getting married. Introduce me, Simon." Fanny dropped to her knees to fondle the little dogs' ears. "Oh, look, they like Daisy. This is so wonderful. We're a family, Simon. Us and the dogs."

"Forever and ever. Let's get rid of these guys. Can you get rid of them or are they . . . ?"

"I have to make some deals here. How much should I ask for?"

"Push them to the wall." Simon's words left him giddy when he saw the smile on Fanny's face.

Fanny cleared her throat. "Gentlemen, sit down. When a man stands over a woman, it's for the purposes of intimidation. Fine. This is fine. Now, have you agreed to bank rates? You have. All right, now we have some place to start. The town is dark and waterless for two more days. You had a choice and you chose not to exercise that choice. Last night I did some calculating on my adding machine and the numbers were so high they ran off the roll of paper. That tells me you want to return to business as quickly as possible. This is what I propose. Forgive the debt to my ex-husband and we'll lease the riverboats in Biloxi, Mississippi, to you at the same rates you were charging him. What is power and water worth to you for the next two days? Tomorrow and the day after it will be worth more than it's worth today. While you huddle, I'm going to finish my kitchen floor because I'm getting married today, and I have to get ready. Even though I'm in a wonderful mood right now, that could change if your numbers aren't . . . acceptable."

Inside the studio with the door closed, Fanny hissed, "I think I finally figured out who that one guy is, the one I met last night at the café in town. Do you remember your mother's friend Jeb? She gave him a job and took care of his family? There were four boys and they all looked like Jeb. Sallie bought him a house and sent his boys to college. She paid all the bills when Jeb's wife got sick, and then she paid the medical bills for Jeb after he passed away. Sallie said Jeb used to feed her and Cotton and the other miners when they were broke. I'm almost positive the man I met last night is one of Jeb's boys, and if you look really closely at three of the others, they look like him, too. I don't know if it means anything or not."

"Fanny, what the hell are you talking about?"

"I'm just trying to make sense of all this. I want out of here, Simon. We can talk driving down the mountain. There are no words to tell you how happy I am to see you. The perfect ending to a nightmare. Ash . . . I don't want to talk about him either. There, the floor is dry. Let's take a shower together." She was babbling, but she didn't care.

"Fanny!"

"I just wanted to see what you would say. Hold the fort so I can get dressed. I was so afraid, Simon."

Simon followed Fanny into the tiny bathroom. "I don't know what's going on and *I'm* afraid. You have the edge on me by knowing. Hurry up, Fanny, I want out of here."

In the tiny kitchen Simon filled to overflowing with his presence, he poured himself a cup of cold coffee, his eyes on the men in dark suits outside the window. What were they saying? What were they agreeing to? Would they buckle under to Fanny? *Ash, you son of a bitch, I'd like to strangle you for putting Fanny in this position.* If he was lucky maybe they'd still kill Ash to make a point. He wouldn't grieve.

"Simon."

Simon turned at the sound of his whispered name. She was more beautiful than he remembered. He stood still, certain he was dreaming. If he didn't move or speak, he could preserve the dream.

"Simon?"

"Fanny," he said in a strangled voice.

"I'm ready to get married now. I'm wearing something old, something new, something borrowed and blue. I think that's the way it goes."

"I love this dream," Simon said.

"I thought it was a dream, too. Should we pinch each other?"

"I'd rather hold you and kiss you till you yell for mercy. I really like this dream."

"I do, too," Fanny said, advancing one step, then another until she was standing nose to nose with Simon. "I can feel your breath on my cheek and feel your heart beating next to mine. We aren't dreaming, Simon. I'm going to need a ring."

"We'll get one in town."

"Just a plain gold band. Thick, a little wide. Very plain. I love you so much. Oh, Simon, don't start something we can't finish here and now." Fanny nibbled on his lip, his ear, the side of his neck.

"Mrs. Thornton."

"Hmmmm," Fanny said.

"My associates would like to speak with you. Outside if you don't mind."

"I don't mind at all. Do you mind, Simon?"

"Yes, I mind. Get rid of them, Fanny. They're cluttering up our dream."

Fanny giggled. Simon loved the sound. He said so.

"I'm not a bit afraid. I thought they'd come here with guns and . . . you know, chain saws and . . . suitcases full of money to try and . . . bribe me. I didn't pack anything."

"Good idea. We'll buy everything. I have a feeling you're going to be very rich when you walk out of here."

"I don't want their money, Simon. I wouldn't take it if they gave it to me."

"That's a pretty stupid attitude, Fanny. Then what is this all about?"

"It's about Ash paying out one hundred percent in interest. He can only handle a legitimate bank loan with regulated interest rates. All that stuff I said before, those were just words. I wanted them to be on the receiving end of things for a change. They were bleeding him, threatening and intimidating him. I will not tolerate that. They said they were legitimate businessmen. Legitimate businessmen don't charge one hundred percent interest. Get Daisy's stuff, and I'll meet you by the car. Lock the door, Simon."

Simon's gay mood changed suddenly. "It sounds to me, Fanny, like you're still shackled to Ash. I don't want him in our lives. Cut him loose."

Fanny stared at Simon. "I can't do that, Simon. I told you once before there is a small part of my life that will always belong to Ash. It's the way it is. You have to accept it." She watched as a veil dropped over Simon's eyes. He nodded curtly before he turned his back on her.

"When will the power and water be turned on, Mrs. Thornton?" the spokesperson asked.

"When we come to terms. What have you decided?"

"We've decided you drive a very hard bargain. We aren't fools as you must realize. Every day our casinos are shut down we lose millions of dollars. We have no wish to repeat last night's disaster. As it stands now even though you turn on the power and water, we are still losing money. Our headliners left last night and early this morning. Contractually, we still have to pay them. Our food spoiled, our sewage system backed up. We also had several serious accidents because of the darkness. Many of our customers relocated to your casino and will undoubtedly stay there for the length of their visit. It's a domino effect. What all this means to you is, we agree to your terms." Fanny thought she saw grudging respect in the man's eyes.

"In writing, sir, in town, at my attorney's office." Fanny looked at her watch. "In ninety minutes. You might want to think about wearing gray flannel. Black is ominous. Then again, if that's your intent . . . gray is so much more business-like." Fanny smiled wickedly. Power was wonderful. She wondered if she would become addicted to it. Never.

The moment Fanny settled herself she heaved a mighty sigh. "Simon, if Ash wasn't wheelchair-bound, do you think he would have done the same thing?"

"Yes, but it would be worse. Ash marches to his own drummer." Fanny blanched at the coolness in Simon's voice.

A second later, Fanny was asleep. Simon smiled as he stretched out his arm to gather her close to him. The release of fear was better than any sleeping pill.

He was getting married. Finally. All because of Ash and his damn riverboats. The big question was, where should they go? What should they do with their lives? By agreeing to marry him, Fanny must be willing to do whatever he wanted. The only thing he knew for certain right now was he didn't want to spend one second longer in Las Vegas than he had to. He had to get Fanny away from her damn family. Fanny always had ideas. Maybe they could travel, see the world together. Maybe Fanny would want to buy a farm or move to a small town like the one she grew up in. He would agree to anything Fanny wanted to do as long as she didn't allow Ash and her family to invade their lives.

A prickle of fear rippled up Simon's back. Would Fanny leave her children and move away? Now that Sunny was about to deliver, would Fanny walk away from her first grandchild? Did he have the right to expect her to say good-bye to her family? She would be giving up her businesses, too. It wasn't going to be simple after all. Why couldn't two people just fall in love and live happily ever after? Because life gets in the way, he answered himself.

He drove on, Fanny's head on his shoulder. She didn't wake until he pulled into Babylon's underground garage. "Are we here already,

Simon? I fell asleep. I'm so sorry. I think it was all that anxiety and then the outcome. Simon, I played your message over a hundred times. What should we do first?"

"Fanny, I don't want to get married until this is over and done with. When we drive away from here I don't want to have to worry about Ash's enemies. Make no mistake, they are his enemies. No man is a law unto himself in this town even if his wife can turn switches and valves."

"You're scaring me, Simon."

"That's good, Fanny, because I don't want you thinking those hoodlums in their three-piece suits were telling you the truth when they said they were legitimate businessmen. They aren't. They caved in because you had them by the short hairs. They aren't going to forget it. They won't mess with you, but they will mess with Ash. Perhaps not right now. They'll wait until things quiet down, and it's business as usual. That's when they'll do something. Just be aware. I think we both need to talk to Ash. He won't listen to either one of us, but I want to know I did everything I could to warn him. First it was the poker tournament. He aced them out on that. There was this little episode. That makes two. Three will not be Ash's lucky number. I don't know, maybe we can get through to him."

"Don't count on it, Simon. Ash doesn't listen to anyone. I don't want him to spoil this for us. Are we going to tell anyone, or are we just going to *do it?*"

"I say we just go off and do it. We'll call when it's a done deed."

"Okay, Mr. Thornton. We have time to go upstairs to the office and tell everyone what's going on before we walk to the attorney's office. I'm sure the kids are worried."

"Lead the way, Mrs. Thornton."

"Talk about red letter days," Ash's voice boomed when Fanny and Simon walked through the door, his anger at his brother forgotten. His mood was expansive as he waved his arms about, his smile affable.

His eyes were so glassy Fanny could see herself in their depths. She could feel her insides start to churn. "Relax, Ash. Everything isn't over yet. I'm on my way to the lawyer's office to finalize everything. At that time I'll have the water and power restored. I made a deal, Ash. Me. Not you. And you damn well better live up to it. You have bank rates on your loan. I suggest any monies above the norm last night and today go toward an up-front payment of your loan. Your riverboats in Mississippi are going to be leased to those people at an appropriate rate of interest. You're ahead of the game, Ash. You're alive. If you want, give them the riverboats and we'll make it a wash and you won't have that tremendous debt staring you in the face every day. I think I can make a deal on that. It's your decision."

"Fanny, Fanny, Fanny, you brought them to their knees. You cut deals like a pro. They have to respect that. I told you I wanted the power and water off for two more days. You don't listen to me. Now, why is that, Fanny?"

"Because, Ash, you never say anything that makes sense. It's always me, me, me. You never think about anyone else. Did you for one minute think about all those people who aren't working because I shut the town down? Everything has its own ripple effect. I did what I did for you because I believed you would be killed. That's what you told me. I will not do it again. This advice is free, Ash. Stay where there are people and don't go anywhere alone. I have just enough time to get to the lawyer's and then I'm leaving town for an indefinite period of time. I'll say good-bye to the kids on the way out."

"Wait just a damn minute, Fanny. What do you mean you're going out of town? What if I need you?"

"What part didn't you understand, Ash? I did what you wanted. You're alive and well. You have the business to occupy you night and day."

"You gave away my damn riverboats. You just up and gave them away. That's just like you, Fanny. Your way or no way. Go ahead, take your lover and get out of my casino. Who needs you anyway?"

Fanny's shoulders sagged. "Have a nice day, Ash." *I will not cry. I absolutely will not cry. I refuse to cry. He cannot make me cry. He's to be pitied.*

"If crying makes you feel better then cry, honey," Simon said. "Ash was always a greedy horse's patoot. Come on, it's getting on toward ninety minutes. Are you comfortable with all your decisions?"

"Yes."

"Then, say your good-byes so we can take care of business and get married."

"I don't think I've ever heard anything that sounds more wonderful. Do you think the dogs are okay in the car?"

"They're sleeping like babies curled up together. They know we're coming back. The windows are partially open and the garage is cool, not to mention the fact that the attendant is keeping his eye on them."

Fanny's children hugged her and Simon both. "You're getting married, aren't you?" Sunny whispered.

"Uh-huh. *I'll call every day*," Fanny promised. "Take care of yourself, Sunny, and keep those boys in line."

"Be happy, Mom," Birch said, a catch in his voice. "We'll all miss you."

"Call Lily Bell and invite her for the weekend."

"He already did that," Sage said. "Have a good trip wherever it is you're going."

Fanny waved good-bye. "Why do I feel like I'm deserting them?"

"Because you've never gone away from them before, and the trip to Hong Kong doesn't count. They know you aren't coming back, and you know it, too. They have their lives and you have yours. I've waited all my life for this day, Fanny, and I want to get on with it before it's over. I'm giving you fifteen minutes in that lawyer's office and that's it."

"Okay, Mr. Thornton."

"Wait, Mrs. Thornton, I don't understand. What you're saying brings things to a wash. What about the . . . ?"

"You're Jeb's son, aren't you?" At the man's slight nod, Fanny said, "I thought so. The power and water are being turned on as we speak." She eyed the metal suitcases on top of the desk. She knew they were full of money. Money they thought she wanted. "I hope I never have to do this again. I want you to know I meant every word I said back on the mountain. What's it going to be?"

"We'll lease the boats. We'll pay three points above the bank rate. Is that satisfactory?"

"Yes." To the lawyer she said, "Whatever those three points amount to moneywise, give it to the Thornton Medical Center and the Thornton Pediatric Unit every month." Fanny scribbled her signature in six different places. She dusted her hands dramatically. "Done."

The man from the diner extended his hand. Fanny looked at it for a long moment before she held out her own hand. "I think Sallie and Jeb would approve," she said quietly. Fanny raised her eyes to see a smile tug at the corners of the man's mouth.

Fanny had to strain to hear the words, "You have nothing to fear from my people, Mrs. Thornton."

Fanny smiled. "I can't say the same thing . . . sir. Stay on your toes and you'll probably never see or hear from me again. There is every possibility that sometime in the future you might . . . *need* my help. I'm going to give you a number to call if that should happen. We'll use the name Sallie as a reference." The man nodded slightly.

Outside in the fresh air, Fanny took several deep breaths. "I'm ready, Simon."

"Where are we going to do it?"

"At the first wedding chapel we come to. They sell rings and flowers and everything. I want a veil. I can't get married without a veil. Oh, Simon, I forgot about you. What are you going to wear? Simon, Sage whispered something in my ear I want to share with you. He said, and this is a direct quote, 'Mom, *I think* Uncle Simon is the wind beneath your sails.' You are, my darling, Simon."

Simon's throat closed tight. In the whole of his life no one had ever said anything to him as wonderful-sounding as those few words. He smiled from ear to ear. He finally managed to say, "I don't care what I wear. Does it matter to you?"

"No, Simon, it doesn't matter in the least. I love you just the way you are and I'd marry you in your skivvies."

PART TWO

1983–1984

7

Fanny stood on the front porch doing what she did every day at this hour: she surveyed her domain. She looked at the lush green grass in front of the house. At the straggly shrubbery, at the wilted pots of flowers. In the early morning, just as the sun was coming up, the lawn looked like a carpet of emeralds sprinkled with diamonds, thanks to the morning dew. She loved sitting on the front steps with her cup of coffee when the weather permitted. Simon preferred to sit at the kitchen table in his bathrobe.

A frown built between her brows. Once, in the early days of her marriage, she'd thought they were alike, preferring the same things. She'd been so wrong then. They didn't even like the same food. Every day, seven days a week, she prepared two separate dinners, one for Simon and one for her. In the beginning it was fun, a challenge. Now, with the business going full steam, it was work. Everything was work. What she needed was a housekeeper, but Simon didn't want anyone living in the house with them. She'd given in on that point. The truth was, she always gave in.

Fanny finished her coffee. Today was their anniversary. She'd washed her fine china, polished the candlesticks, had Ash send her a magnificent bottle of fine wine that was supposed to be a surprise, ironed her best linen tablecloth. Tonight she would make only one meal, Simon's favorite, rare prime rib. She liked her meat well done. She would eat the ends.

Fanny set her empty cup on the steps. Her shoulders felt tense. A walk around the small yard might ease the tightness a little. She walked slowly, aware of the silence. It was so quiet here in Stallion Springs. She had no neighbors, no friends. Simon said they didn't need any, they had each other and the dogs. Days were spent with the dogs they bred and her evenings were spent sewing, since Simon monopolized the television set.

I'm not happy. I haven't been happy for a long time. She knew Simon was aware that something was wrong. So many times she tried to talk to him, to explain that she wanted to go to town, back to Nevada for a visit. His excuse was always the same: When you have your own business, you're married to that business. This business, he would go on to say, deals with flesh-and-blood animals. When we take a vacation, we'll take it together. In three years they hadn't had a vacation. This morning for the first time she realized she was a *prisoner.* She wasn't under lock and key, but she was a prisoner nonetheless. Getting permission from Simon to go into town was a major ordeal. There's no gas, I can't find the keys, there's something wrong with the tires. The list of excuses was endless.

The first months had been idyllic as the house and barns were being finished. Decorating had been such fun. And when the first batch of dogs arrived she had been ecstatic. She loved the tiny Yorkies they bred, and she hated giving them up. She was the one who cleaned the pens, fed them, and assigned them to the different buyers. Simon took care of the paperwork.

She longed for people, for her friends. During the second year she spent a great deal of time on the phone with Billie and Bess until Simon said the bills were too high. He'd sulked for seven straight days when she said she would pay the bill with her own money. She wasn't sure, but she thought he listened in on her phone conversations. He'd sulked for two straight weeks the day Bess showed up unexpectedly yelling "SURPRISE!" at the top of her lungs. He'd been cold but civil. Bess had never come back to visit, nor had Billie.

Fanny stood back to look at the spacious log cabin that was her home. At best it was Spartan. Simon didn't like what he called clutter while she loved knickknacks, family pictures, collectibles. All her treasures were still in the packing boxes. She shaded her eyes from the late-afternoon sun to look around the eleven acres that was now her home.

It was a far cry from Sunrise. Trees were trees, but somehow the trees at Sunrise seemed like they belonged while these trees just stood there, straggly, ugly, barren-looking in the winter. She'd made an effort in the beginning to prune the bushes, to plant flowers, to clear away the brush, but Simon had ridiculed her efforts. Rather than see that cold, blank look in her husband's eyes, she'd given up her gardening efforts. Everything now was overgrown and stragglylooking. The urge to cry was so strong, Fanny bit down on her lower lip.

"Fanny! Fanny!" Fanny looked at the cabin, then at the barn. If she went to the barn, there was every chance her roast would be overdone and her anniversary dinner would be spoiled. "Just a minute, Simon."

"Now, Fanny."

Fanny ran to the barn. "Cissie's ahead of schedule. You need to calm her. Where were you? Don't tell me. You were talking on the phone to Sunny again. How the hell many times did she call today? I thought you were going to tell her to stop calling so much."

"I wasn't talking to Sunny. I was cooking dinner. Just to keep the record clear, my daughter didn't call today."

"It's still early, she will. With a kid and a new baby to take care of, you have to wonder where she gets the time to call you six times a day."

"She never calls more than twice a day. I'm her mother, Simon. I like talking to my daughter. Especially when you don't listen to our conversations," Fanny snapped. She dropped to her knees to stroke Cissie's head. "There are times, Simon, when I think you are trying to drive a wedge between me and my family."

"That's the most ridiculous thing I ever heard come out of your mouth."

"Really. Then why did you object to me putting pictures of my family in the living room?"

"Because they're *your* family, not *our* family. We have our own life now. If you weren't so tight-assed about things, we could have a wonderful life."

Fanny tried to keep her voice on a conversational level so Cissie wouldn't get excited. "You knew I had a family when I married you. My children are your nieces and nephews, so they are your family, too."

"They're Ash's kids, not mine."

"What do you want me to say, Simon?"

"I'd like it if you wouldn't let them infringe on our life. It was fine in the beginning, then that daughter of yours started calling every two minutes because she misses her mommy. For God's sake, Fanny, they're grown men and women."

"I wonder why you married me, Simon. I never pretended to be anything but what I am. What I am is what you said you loved about me. You really should go see about the roast if you want me to stay here."

"I have to get Flossie and Flicker ready and their paperwork done because the Albertsons are coming to pick them up at six o'clock.

That's a thousand dollars, Fanny, and I think it's a little more important than your roast."

"Simon, did you forget, it's our anniversary? I was making a special dinner."

"Did you whine like this with Ash?"

"Why is it everything I do has to tie in with Ash in your mind? I hate it when you do this, Simon. I really hate it. Another thing, the Albertsons called to say they told you yesterday they wouldn't be picking up the dogs till nine tomorrow morning. Mrs. Albertson said she spoke to you. She was just calling today to remind us. So, are you going to look at the roast or not? Personally, I don't care one way or the other."

"If you don't care, then why should I do it?"

Fanny could feel her eyes start to burn. "Suit yourself."

"You aren't happy, are you, Fanny?"

Fanny was tempted to lie. "No, Simon, I'm not happy."

"You compare this marriage to the one you had with Ash, right?"

"Wrong." Fanny felt herself flush with the lie.

"Maybe we should invite him for the weekend."

"Maybe we should," Fanny said through clenched teeth.

"You'll see him at the christening. It's a one-day thing, Fanny. I'm not staying."

"Suit yourself. I'm staying longer. I want to see Billie and Thad. I want to do some shopping with Bess, and I want to visit with my children. I want to get to know my grandchildren."

Simon's steely gaze pierced her. "When were you going to tell me your plans?"

"When it was time to leave. I hate fighting with you. Why should I make myself miserable two days in advance? Simon, what has happened to us? It's all going wrong."

"If you would spend a little more time with me and a little less with your kids, we wouldn't squabble so much."

"I'm really sorry you feel like this. I've given one hundred percent to this marriage to the exclusion of all else. When I go up to the house, since there's no point in trying to save dinner, I'm going to unpack my boxes and I'm going to put out my pictures. I'm going to town tomorrow and buy frames for Jake's pictures. I think you might have given maybe 10 percent. Those aren't very good numbers, Simon." Fanny continued stroking Cissie's head.

"Fanny, what are you talking about? You're making me sound like some kind of . . . an ogre. I just don't see why we need pictures everywhere. I don't like clutter. You knew that when you married me."

"Maybe you don't need pictures, but I do, and I don't think my family should be considered as clutter. I'm sorry I didn't bring this up a long time ago. I hate fighting with you, Simon."

"We aren't fighting. We're having a discussion. Fighting is what you used to do with Ash. I think you have us mixed up."

"You see, Simon, that's where you're wrong. I know exactly who it is that's mixed up, and it isn't me. I've had it. I'm sick and tired of your attitude. I'm sick and tired of hearing Ash's name in every conversation we have. Three's a crowd, Simon, in case you haven't noticed. I was hoping today, because it's our anniversary, that we could have a nice dinner and try to get back to where we were. Our marriage is in trouble, Simon."

"If you'd stop seeing problems where there are no problems, if you'd do as I ask you to do, you wouldn't be causing yourself so many problems."

"For three years, Simon, you've been trying to make me into someone I'm not. I allowed it because I loved you so much. I desperately wanted this marriage to work. I would have stood on my head if that's what you wanted. Nothing I do is good enough for you. I'm sorry. This simply is not working for me."

"What the hell does that mean, Fanny?"

"It's not working. I'm not happy. I'm tired of trying. The only thing I want right now is to pack for my trip back home. I'm counting the hours. Actually, Simon, I'm counting the minutes. Now, be quiet. The pups are coming."

Two hours later, mother and six pups were resting comfortably. Fanny washed her hands, dried them, and left the barn. In the kitchen she removed the overdone roast from the oven and dumped it in the sink along with the pared vegetables and salad. The garbage disposal struggled to grind the voluminous amount of food. She returned the candlesticks and candles to the china cabinet. The last thing she did was to fold her linen tablecloth and put away her good china. The wine bottle stood on the counter in full view. Retail it would have cost close to $200. Ash had told her to consider it an anniversary present even though she'd asked him to send it to her.

Fanny saw Simon's shadow in the doorway before he opened the screen door. She sucked in her breath. Where had it all gone awry? What did she do that was so wrong? How much more could she do? Her eyes sparked as she reached for the wine bottle.

"Where did that come from?"

"Nevada. Surely you realize the liquor stores around here don't stock this kind of wine. I wanted it to be special because I mistakenly thought today was a special day. In a way it was, Cissie had six beautiful pups."

"Did Ash send this wine?"

"Yes, he did. At my request. You can either join me or you can drink your orange, grapefruit, lemon juice. I really don't care, Simon."

Simon snatched the wine from her hands and poured it down the drain.

Fanny stared at her husband for a full five minutes before she got up from her chair. She walked upstairs, tossed her makeup into a small bag along with a nightshirt. She looked around for her purse. She reached for it along with her jacket.

"What are you doing, Fanny? Where are you going?"

"Back where I belong. Get out of my way, Simon." His arm stretched across the open doorway. Fanny ducked under it and ran down the steps. Simon followed her, taking the steps two at a time.

Simon's voice was outraged when he shouted, "You're walking out on me on our anniversary? Isn't that what Ash used to do to you?"

"Shut the hell up, Simon." Fanny turned the key in the ignition. "I'm going to Sunrise. We were both invited. If you want to join me on Sunday, do so. If you don't, that's okay, too. Now get the hell out of my way before I run over you. Oh, yes, happy anniversary."

Simon stared at the back of the Jeep Cherokee as it roared down the driveway. His eyes were cold and calculating when he returned to the fragrant kitchen to pour himself a glass of juice. "This is all your fault, Ash," he muttered as he downed the juice. "Everything that's ever gone wrong in my life is your fault, you son of a bitch."

Sunny Thornton Ford rocked quietly in the comfortable rocking chair, her eyes on the toddler playing with a basket of colorful blocks, her arms warm and full with seven-week-old Polly. She leaned her head back into the softness of the rocker to allow the fear she always felt to take over her body. Fear she always felt when things were too quiet, too serene. She had to do something. Very soon.

Her gaze dropped to the basket of mail at the side of the rocker. She could pull it off if she really tried. Tyler would never stop her from going to her college reunion and she knew for a fact he wouldn't be able to go with her. She had capable household help and her sister Billie said she'd stop by twice a day to play with little Jake and Polly. She could do it. She'd attend the reunion, get her picture taken, take a roll of film herself, sign all the old yearbooks, get hers signed, gather up all the handout materials and stuff everything in one envelope to show Tyler on her return. The moment she was free she would head for Boston and the Leahy Clinic. Three days of intensive testing would tell her what was wrong and if it was possible to correct her condition. She would pay for the tests with cash, so nothing would show up on her health insurance.

Damn, she hated keeping secrets from her husband and her family. She shouldn't even be contemplating this.

Polly squirmed, her face puckering as she prepared to burp. The sound was loud in the quiet room. Jake laughed and Sunny smiled. Her family.

Today was going to be her true test. The family would be here for Polly's christening. She had to get into her cheerful mode, schmooze with family members, pretend not to see the concern on her husband's face, and see that everyone had a good time. How she was going to do that while sitting was still a mystery to her. She heaved a mighty sigh. She was tired of covering up, tired of not feeling well, tired of lying, and tired of the fear that consumed her twenty-four hours a day. Maybe Sage was right and she had a screw loose inside her brain.

Sage was her confidant and she didn't know why that was. She wished now, for the thousandth time, that she'd made more of an effort to socialize with Iris, Sage's wife, and Lily Bell, Birch's long time fiancée. She adored both young women. By her own choice she'd given up her job at the casino, elected to stay home with her children. She was safe here from inquisitive eyes and callous questions. At home she could control her wobbly gait. At home she could drop things and cover up her little accidents more easily. If she bumped into things, the help just smiled when she'd say, "Oops, I'm so clumsy."

Today, though, her mother and Simon would be here. She'd never been able to hide anything from her mother. Her mother would notice. Then again, if Sage could occupy her, maybe not. Fanny would be busy with Jake and Polly. She could plead weariness and sit as much as she could. Although Sage hadn't said, she was certain he'd confided in Iris. Iris would take up some of the slack, too. *What the hell is wrong with me?*

She cried then, her tears dropping on Polly's downy head. What if she had a terminal disease and she never lived to see her children grow up? Now she knew how her father felt, trapped in his wheelchair. Would he show up for Polly's christening?

Jake stopped building his bridge, scrambled to his feet, and ran to the French doors leading to the small balcony. "Pop Pop's here, Mommy. Me go push his chair."

Sunny looked at her watch. "Go ahead, Jake. Bring Pop Pop here, okay?" Her father was three hours early. What did *that* mean?

She heard the sound of the whirring chair before she saw it. She worked a smile onto her face as she shifted Polly so her father could get a better look at the infant.

"She looks like you did when you were born. My God, that was so long ago. We miss you at the casino, Sunny."

"I bet. You couldn't wait for me to leave when I was pregnant with Jake."

"Image is everything, Sunny. Right now I suspect you're more of a pro in regard to image making than I am. I came up here early because . . . look, I know I've been a lousy father, but that doesn't mean I don't care. I do. Sometimes I get so full of self-pity I can't see beyond my own needs. I have a keen eye, though. I know something's wrong. I know you're trying to hide it. I want to know why. You're too young to be going through something like this. I want the truth. I won't betray you, Sunny. I'm not that big a louse."

Sunny could feel the tears start to build behind her eyelids. "I don't know what's wrong with me. I came up with this plan . . . I don't know why I'm fighting it, fear I guess. I didn't want anyone to know. Tyler . . . everyone is worried about me. Hell, I'm worried myself. That's a lie. I'm scared to death. I'm afraid to find out."

"Sunny, hiding from something isn't the answer. You have to look it square in the face, deal with it, and go on from there. I know what I'm talking about. Whatever it is you can deal with it. You have more guts than anyone in this family."

"Had. I have two children now. I came up with this plan. Tell me what you think."

Ash listened, his eyes on his daughter. He stared intently as though seeing her for the first time.

"It sounds like a roundabout way of doing things. There are very good doctors here, and we can bring in specialists. What do you *think* is wrong?"

"I think I have a muscle or nerve disease. I read up on everything I could find and I think it's multiple sclerosis. That means eventually I'll be in a wheelchair like you. I won't be able to take care of my own kids. People . . . *die* with the disease."

"How long have you known?"

"About a year before I got pregnant with Jake. I blamed everything under the sun and refused to see a doctor. I had tests. Nothing showed up. I figured if they couldn't find anything whatever, it would go away. It didn't. I never said I was the smart one in the family."

"No, that spot is reserved for your mother. Does she know?"

"She hasn't been here since Jake was christened. He's three now. We talk almost every day. Actually, we used to talk every day. Weeks go by, and we don't talk. She's too busy with her new life. I think she thinks of me as an intrusion. Sage knows. Birch . . . Birch doesn't say anything. Everyone has their own lives. Billie is so busy with the business we don't see each other that often. I see the worry on her face. I guess they all figure I'm married to a doctor, and I'm old enough to take care of myself. I haven't done a very good job of it."

"Do you want me to go with you, Sunny? It's time for me to get an evaluation myself. But, before we do that, why don't I do some checking and see if there's a specialist a little closer to home. It would be better to start with one doctor and stick with him. If you need treatments, you'll be near home. That's important."

"That's very funny coming from you, Dad."

"I know. Do you want some advice, Sunny? You don't have to follow it."

"Sure."

"Everyone is going to be here today. Let me tell them. Or, you tell them yourself. They all care about you. None of them will turn their backs on you. It's going to take some guts, but you have those by the bushel. Your mother is going to be devastated."

"Hardly. She's so wrapped up in her new life with her new husband there's no time for visits, or . . . anything. I'm the one who does the calling. She does call once a month. I could die in a month, and she wouldn't know. Mom and Uncle Simon with a breeding kennel. From Wall Street to scooping up poop. It's an eye-opener, all right. They're making a fortune and love what they do. I suppose that's half the battle. I'm jealous."

"I understand the feeling, Sunny. I've envied Simon for years. Then he up and marries my ex-wife. It didn't go down real easy. So, what's your answer? I'm here for you. A little late, but I'm here."

Sunny's shoulders drooped. She started to cry.

Ash stared at his daughter, a helpless look on his face. Suddenly he wanted to make things right for this girl of his that he'd wronged for so many years. He maneuvered his chair until he was alongside her. He reached for her hand and smiled. "Hey, we can do anything, we're Thorntons, kiddo. I'm going to be here for you, and that's a promise you can take to the bank. Things are running so smooth at the casino I can take off whole blocks of time. We'll do whatever we have to do, Sunny."

Sunny leaned over to lay Polly in the cradle next to her chair. She slid from the rocker to sit at her father's feet, her head in his lap. She cried silently as her father patted her head.

Ash's heart filled with something he'd never experienced before. He found himself choking up as he talked to his daughter. He knew he had to say the right words or it would all get away from him. "Listen to me, Sunny. I know you're scared. I know what that's like. What's worse is the realization that things might not get better but stay as they are or even worsen. You have to handle the cards that are dealt to you because it's the only game in town, kiddo. You don't even want to think about the alternative. I went down that road, too. I can't begin to tell you how many times I thought about ending it all. I'd start thinking about how I screwed things up, about the mistakes I made. I'd think about Simon and how much I hated him. Then I'd think about your mother and you kids. Every damn night I'd vow to make things better the next day. I never did though. I let other things get in the way. I love life and I know you do, too. That's why I'm still hanging around. Yeah, I take pills and smoke stuff I shouldn't. It's the only way I can cope so that I can be around. Like I said, the alternative doesn't bear thinking about.

"What we're going to do is get a diagnosis. We'll get the best of the best and you will do whatever it takes to get you on the road to recovery. You can handle this, Sunny, because you have two little kids to think about. This isn't just about you anymore. It's about Jake and Polly and your husband and the rest of us. We're going to get you some full-time house help. I know a thing or two about that. Your mother was worn to a frazzle with the twins and my mother stepped in and made things right. We'll lick this together."

"Dad, what if I end up in a wheelchair? I can't walk a straight line anymore, and I bump into things. Tyler won't . . . how's he going to feel about me if that happens? What kind of wife and mother will I be?"

"The best. The same kind of wife and mother you are now. For

starters you have to stop thinking so negatively. The first step is dealing with it. After you tell the rest of the family, we'll go on from there.
Is it a deal, Sunny?"

"It's a deal."

Fanny backed away from the doorway, her vision blurred. She
motioned for Simon to be quiet and to back up and return to the
foyer.

"What's wrong?" Simon asked.

"Ash is in the room with Sunny." She told him what she'd overheard. "I should be the one doing this, Simon. Why did Ash have
to . . . ? Why Ash? I was so damn busy leading this life you and I
made for ourselves I ignored my daughter when I knew something
was wrong. I pretended things were all right. In my heart I knew they
weren't. My God, what have I become? How could I become so selfish? I'm sorry I ever listened to you. This, Simon, is the result."

"For heaven's sake, Fanny, Sunny is a grown woman, and she's
married to a doctor. It's her health, her body. What could you have
done? Dragged her to a doctor? Forced her to do something she
wasn't ready to do? We both know Sunny. If you had done that, she
would have told you to mind your own business and we both know
it. So what if Ash is the one who is finally getting her to do something? He's succeeding, and that's the only thing that matters. If you
stop and think about it, Fanny, he is the right person."

"I find that very strange coming from you. Ash must have an
ulterior motive then. He never does anything without a reason.
He's probably still after Sunny's trust fund. I know he could get
Birch's with a snap of his fingers. I bet you that's what this is all
about."

"Maybe this time it's different. Maybe this time Ash is acting like
a real father. I think you want to believe that. Let it be, Fanny. Let
Sunny handle things her way. If that includes her father helping her
through this, accept it. It's got to be what's best for Sunny. Right now
she's relating to Ash. We have our own lives."

"I should have called more often. You always got so upset when
my children called, Simon. I hated seeing that angry look on your
face. I should have visited. You didn't want me to visit. I'm sorry I
listened to you. Sunny kept saying she was fine. I actually started to
believe I was mistaken. I feel so guilty. What if she isn't fine? What
if this is really serious? How do I deal with that?"

"One day at a time. That has to be Birch. He's the only one who blares his horn all the way up the mountain. Looks like Sage is right behind him. In about an hour this house is going to rock right off the mountain. When do you expect Billie Coleman and Thad Kingsley?"

"Momentarily. I'm so happy for Billie. She's loved Thad for so long. It's strange though, isn't it? Thad was Moss's best friend. They went through the war together and remained friends until the day Moss died. Thad loved Moss like a brother. Thad loves politics, but Billie hates it. Senator Thad Kingsley. It has a nice ring to it. I don't think Billie will like living in the Washington fishbowl when they marry? What will that make Billie?"

Simon smirked. "A senator's wife. Don't you think it a little strange that Billie is contemplating marrying her husband's best friend? How long have they been fooling around?"

Fanny stared at her husband. "No more strange than me marrying you. No, Billie was not fooling around. I resent you even thinking such a thing. There are days, Simon, when I don't know who you are anymore. There are days when I don't even like you."

"I'm the same old me. Being anywhere near Ash brings out the worst in me. Sorry." Fanny didn't think he sounded sorry at all.

"The senator from Vermont. Billie told me how wonderful Thad's farm is. She loves it there. She loves it as much as I love Sunrise. Wait till she finds out how many pups we have. Isn't it strange, Simon, how life has come full circle for us? This should be the most wonderful time of our lives and it isn't wonderful at all. Now this problem with Sunny. I'm feeling cheated and angry, and I don't know what to do about it."

"I don't want to hear that kind of talk. Let's go outside and welcome the young people."

"Why does what you just said make me feel very old? And why isn't there any warmth in your voice?"

"Because we are old. As usual you're imagining things."

Fanny stared at her husband's cold features. Fanny frowned. He was switching up again and acting like the old Simon.

The greeting was everything a family greeting should be. There were hugs and kisses, good-natured hisses and boos because there weren't enough letters and phone calls, more hugs and kisses when young Billie and Bess arrived.

"Where are the presents?" Bess shouted. "We have ours. I don't see any gaily wrapped packages for Miss Polly."

They played the game because, as Ash said, it was the only game in town. The concern and worry in her children's eyes matched Fanny's. It didn't need to be said with words, they all knew that today was a turning point of sorts for one of their own.

"Presents! You want presents! Well take a look at this," Sage said, popping his trunk open. He pulled out a bright red tricycle. "Complete with horn and a banana seat!"

"I can top that," Birch said, opening his trunk. "Roller skates with a key, a scooter with a bell on each handle."

"Ha!" Billie said. "Take a look at this red wagon! Complete with a family of dolls!"

"What did you bring, Mom?" they asked in unison.

"Well I . . . I didn't know . . . I thought . . ."

"This is Dolly," Simon said, taking a basket out of the car. "She's seven weeks old. Polly and Dolly. A savings bond, too," Simon said.

"Dad's here," Billie said. "Wonder what he brought. Sneak a look in the van and see if there's a package, Birch?"

"Yep, a big one too. Where is he?"

"He's with Sunny," Fanny said quietly.

"How's our new little mother?" Billie asked.

"I imagine she's fine," Fanny said. "I haven't seen Tyler."

"He makes rounds early on Sundays. He'll be here soon."

"Let's go inside," Fanny said, "and see what we can do to help."

"This is how we're going to do it. You're going to wash your face and then you're going to get behind my chair and push me out into the family room. After the greetings, you're going to . . . what, Sunny?"

"Tell them everything. What if Tyler isn't there, Dad?"

"Then we'll wait for Tyler. He'll be here any minute. You can do this, Sunny. I'll be right beside you. You made a commitment and now you have to follow through. You have no idea how good you're going to feel once you open up."

"Dad, what made you come up here early? What made you . . ."

"I heard Birch talking to Sage several days ago. You gave up too easy, kiddo, that's how I knew for certain something was wrong. I know how much you loved working at the casino. The bright lights, the noise, the moans and groans get into your bloodstream after a while. I want you to come back. I *need* you, Sunny. Christ, is that a confession or what? I want it to be your goal. If, and this is a big if, you feel it's a worthy goal. This is the eighties, the working woman's decade."

"What if . . . what if . . . I end up in a chair like yours? Will you still want me?"

"Don't you ever ask me a stupid question like that again. Of course I'll want you. After a while the chair becomes invisible to other people. His and hers. Father and daughter. It has a nice ring to it. I know you have ideas, Sunny, and I want us to act on those ideas. I want Babylon to be Uno forever. Together we can do it. You game?"

"Yeah. I really am. Okay, I'm going to wash my face and we'll get this show on the road."

"Daddy's home," Jake said, running from the room, his chubby legs pumping furiously. A moment later Tyler was standing in the middle of the room, Jake on his shoulders.

"Ash, nice to see you. Where's Sunny?" he boomed. Then in a whisper he said, "Did you talk to her?"

"You know women. She's splashing perfume or something." Ash nodded and whispered in return, "It's under control."

In the family room there were more hugs and kisses, more oohs and aahs, as Tyler showed off his new daughter.

"She looks so much like Sunny it's uncanny. Do you agree, Ash?" Fanny said as she reached for her granddaughter.

"It was my first thought when I saw Sunny holding her. I brought a present. Will you get it, Birch? I want you to know I sweated this present, kiddo, but I managed to track it down. It's used, secondhand if you will, but I thought you'd like it."

There was a mild scurry as brothers and sister ran to the court-yard to bring in Polly's gifts. They laughed over the tricycle and scooter. Sunny openly frowned at the puppy in the basket. "I don't think so, Mom. Not now. Jake might hurt it without meaning to and I don't have the time to train a dog. Please don't be offended, but you'll have to take her back. I appreciate the bond. Thanks, Mom and Uncle Simon."

"C'mon, c'mon, open mine," Ash said.

"It's almost too pretty to open," Sunny said breathlessly. "Okay, here goes." She removed the large red bow and the silver foil paper. Nestled inside the large box, amid mounds of tissue paper, was a complete layette.

"Your mother made you one just like this when you were born. I convinced her to make another one for the fund-raiser at the medical center. It fetched the most money in the raffle. A doctor's wife bought it. She saved it all these years. I tracked her down through the medical center and got her to agree to part with it. This layette is what convinced your mom to go into business. Sunny's Togs are the result. The woman said it's in mint condition. Do you like it?"

"Oh, Dad, this is super. What an absolutely wonderful gift. Mom, it's exquisite. I'll save it for Polly's first baby."

Fanny stared at Ash, her mouth dropping open. The urge to put her fist to her ex-husband's face was so strong, she clutched at the puppy until it squealed.

Simon leaned over to take the puppy and whispered, "Easy does it, Fanny."

"Thank you all for the wonderful presents. Listen, there's something I want to tell all of you before the minister gets here. Please, let me say what I have to say and when I'm finished, let's not beat it to death. I don't want any discussions, any advice, or any of that stuff."

Sunny reached for her husband's hand. Ash reached out to take her other hand. He squeezed it.

Sunny talked steadily, her eyes on Bess, who was holding Polly. "So, that's the way it is. Dad's going to go with me. He's going to be my . . . backbone until mine stiffens up a little more. I'll deal with it, and I'll handle it the best way I can. I have the best husband in the world, and I know he's going to be there for me. When whatever it is I have is under control I'm going to go back to work at the casino. I guess that's it and in the nick of time. I hear Reverend Gillespie so let's get Polly christened so we can enjoy the party and just being together. Is everyone okay with this?" Sunny beamed at the smiles and nods.

Fanny could feel her insides start to quiver. All she wanted to do was run from the room and cry. Everyone had to be as aware as she was that her daughter had difficulty looking her in the eye. Her hug had been a mere touching of the shoulders and there had been no kiss, or smooch, as Sunny referred to a real kiss. *She hates it that I got married and moved away,* Fanny thought.

Baby Polly voiced her opinion of the christening with one long, loud wail. She was asleep in Billie's arms a moment later.

For the first time in her life, Fanny felt like an outsider. It showed in the stiffness of her shoulders and the grim set of her jaw.

After the ceremony, the young people moved off toward the kitchen and the patio, Ash and Simon headed for the cemetery. Fanny looked at Bess.

"It's going to be okay, Fanny. All you need to think about now is the end result. It doesn't matter how or why Sunny gets there. Let Ash do the father thing. I saw something in his eyes, Fanny, when Sunny was talking. It was good. Usually you, me, the world, can read Ash Thornton. Today was unlike anything I've ever seen where he's concerned. Maybe that's what's bothering you. This time he might come through all the way for Sunny."

"I refuse to believe that. I know Ash."

"You *used* to know Ash. The puppy wasn't a good idea, but then I guess you know that. If Sunny is feeling deserted, the puppy was just a reminder of that desertion. You cut the strings, Fanny. Don't attempt to tie a knot now to make things better. It is what it is. You're entitled to a life of your own. You paid your dues, and it's your turn now. You are happy, aren't you, Fanny?"

"Actually, I'm not happy at all, Bess. My marriage is . . . was . . . a mistake. I think I'm finally ready to talk about it. I feel like I don't belong here."

"You don't. You're damn right we'll talk about it later. Your kids get their own lives, you get yours, if you're lucky, and everyone gets on with the business of living. Or, moving on if you prefer that term. I like to think of it as my time in the sun."

"Bess, the last time I saw Jake was at his christening. He's three years old. I can't tell you where those three years went. They're gone, and I can't get them back. I don't even know that little boy. What's worse, he doesn't know me. I know in my heart Sunny left him with a sitter when Sage and Iris got married just to keep him from me. Sunny looked right through me. All those calls, every single day. They meant something to her. I . . . oh, Bess, I thought of them as interruptions because that's how Simon viewed it. More often than not I'd hurry her off the phone. My God, what did I do in the name of love that's now sour?"

"You had the audacity to reach out for some happiness with a new life. We'll talk about that new life when you're ready. Stop being so hard on yourself. Mother-daughter love is something that can never be destroyed, no matter what."

"You're wrong, Bess. I feel it here," Fanny said, thumping her chest. "Maybe I'll stay on for a little while. Simon can handle things back at the ranch. I'm not sure I even want to go back there. With him."

"Were you invited?" Bess asked bluntly.

"No. I should . . . don't I . . . I need an invitation?"

"Absolutely. You never take anything for granted where kids are concerned, and it doesn't make any difference how old those kids are."

"This is my house," Fanny said defensively.

"Was your house. Another family lives here now."

"Are you saying I'm not welcome?"

"Fanny, I don't know. So much is going on right now. You could *offer* to stay. Sunny would probably view it as after the fact. That's just my personal opinion. If it were me, I don't think I would even offer. You need to go back home and settle your own life. If Sunny needs you, she knows where to find you."

"You make it sound like I'm forcing myself on my daughter. I don't much care for this conversation. My children are like yo-yos, Bess. They keep switching sides and that shouldn't be. A parent's love is unconditional. A child's isn't. Someday I hope I'm wise enough to understand it all. I'd leave right now if Billie and Thad weren't coming."

"That's something Ash would do, not something Fanny does. Shift into neutral and ... what is it Ash says? Oh, yes, play the game, it's the only one in town. Go join your daughters and daughter-in-law in the kitchen. Just be Fanny."

Fanny walked into her old kitchen. It was Sunny's kitchen now, warm and light with plants and herbs on the windowsill and shiny copper pots hanging from the beams. A colorful rag rug sat beneath the huge claw-footed table. There were baskets of flowers on the hearth and a new red plaid cushion on her old rocker. Bess was right, this wasn't her kitchen any more than the rest of the house was hers.

At some point during her scrutiny of the kitchen she'd become aware of a change in the tone and the conversation.

"Am I interrupting anything serious?"

"Of course not, Mom," Billie said. "We were trying to figure out what it will take to get Birch to the altar with Lily. Bachelorhood isn't *that* wonderful."

Fanny had never been able to warm up to Lily Bell. Secretly she thought Birch could do much better, but she would have cut out her tongue before she voiced such an opinion.

"Birch was always a slow starter. He builds up to things," Fanny said lightly. "How's your family, Iris?"

"Mom and Dad went on a cruise. When they make a port of call

Dad golfs and Mom shops. They're bringing Sage and me grass skirts and Sage swears he'll dance for all of us wearing his. It should be interesting because he has two left feet."

"I would like to see that. He has rhythm though," Fanny smiled. "Do you use the studio much, Sunny?"

"I haven't been in it since the day we moved in. It's not locked if you want to go down there."

"No. I was just curious. It seems a shame to waste the space now that we've moved the offices back to town."

"We can't disturb the shrine," Sunny said as she nestled small baby carrots next to thin slivers of cucumber on a silver tray.

Shrine? She wasn't going to touch that one. Because she was the closest, Fanny reached out to take the tray from Sunny's hands just as Jake charged through the kitchen door, his father in pursuit. The tray fell and skidded across the floor.

"I'm sorry, it was my fault," Fanny said, dropping to her knees to pick up the vegetables. "It wasn't your fault, Sunny."

"If you hadn't dropped it, I would have. I drop everything. Tyler, you need to stand Jake in the corner. He knows better than to charge through the door like that."

"Honey. He's only three. Three-year-olds have the attention span of a gnat." The moment the words were out of her mouth, Fanny regretted them.

"Then why was it good enough for us and not for him? Some of my earliest memories are of 'don't run, walk or you'll get your fanny paddled.' Getting paddled when I didn't listen is another unforgettable memory. Long-distance grandmothering doesn't work these days, Mom."

"I see that," Fanny said as she put the vegetables in the disposal. "I think I'll go outside. If there's anything you want me to do, call me."

"Sure, Mom," Billie said.

"Where's *that* dog?" Sunny asked.

"Simon put her back in her basket in the car. I'm sorry about the dog. I guess neither Simon nor I thought it through." Fanny's tone was apologetic, defensive. The urge to reach for her daughter and shake her made her quicken her pace.

Outside in the bright sunshine, Fanny wandered aimlessly through the garden, stopping to pick a flower from time to time. How many hours she'd spent in this very garden. Once it had been a comforting place to sit and think, a place where she found solace in her troubled marriage. More than once she and Ash had made love on the springy green grass. It was silent now. She looked overhead to see if there were any birds nestled in the trees.

Fanny sat down and reached for a long blade of grass. She placed it between her fingers and brought it to her lips. An earsplitting sound echoed around the garden. Once she'd had a contest with her mother-in-law. She couldn't remember who had won. The little contest had been one of her nicest memories, and now she barely remembered it.

"A penny for your thoughts, Fanny."

"Tyler. I'm afraid they aren't worth even a penny. Where's Jake?"

"Napping. He plays hard and falls asleep on his feet. How are you, Fanny?"

"I thought I was fine until I got here. The truth is I can't wait to leave. I don't feel like I belong here, and I also don't feel welcome."

"I live here, thanks to your generosity, and I feel just the way you do sometimes. These last two years have not been easy."

"Why didn't you say something?"

"Why didn't you ask, Fanny? Sunny's your daughter. We talked about her several times. If there was anyone in the world she'd listen to, it was you. You didn't take the time. I guess I'm blaming you. It isn't right, but it's how I feel."

"Honesty is always good. A person would be a fool not to respect an honest statement of fact. Are you asking me if I'm going to defend myself for the last three years?"

"Only if you feel the need to explain. At this point I really don't care where you've been or what you've been doing. My only concern is my stubborn wife and my two children. Is that honest enough for you?"

Fanny stared at her son-in-law. She saw the torment and anger in his eyes, noticed his clenched fists. She adored this young man with the magical hands, hands that could reconstruct a person's face after a bad accident and make that person whole again. She knew he was a good husband and father. "Of course. Let me make sure I understand this. What you're saying is you're holding me responsible for Sunny's condition. You're her husband, Tyler. You live with her every day. Why couldn't you get her to a doctor? Surely you must have watched her deteriorate. I wasn't here."

"My point exactly. A psychiatrist I spoke with told me women, Sunny in particular, want to be perfect for their husbands. That means no warts, no nothing. When deformities, real or imaginary, show up, the wart holder feels inferior and starts to go into a shell. Confiding in a mother who loves unconditionally, accepts everything unconditionally, is the way to go. That mother gives emotional support. To Sunny you were her cherry Popsicle but you didn't show up to hand it to her. I know she calls you every day because I see the phone bills. What in the goddamn hell did you think, Fanny?"

Fanny felt her insides start to crumple. "I think I thought she wasn't happy. I swear to you, each time she called I asked how she was and asked if there was anything I could do. I invited her to the ranch, but she declined, said she didn't want to come without you and you were too busy. She never once asked me to come here. If she had asked, I would have come. I think you know that, Tyler."

Tyler shrugged. His voice was frosty when he said, "I went to Ash. I have to say he was already on top of it. You have to give the devil his due, Fanny. He came, saw, and did what you should have done."

"That's so cruel, Tyler."

"It's a fact. You can't dispute a fact. I came here to tell you Billie and Thad have arrived and they're on the patio."

Fanny nodded because she didn't trust herself to speak. She watched her son-in-law walk away. She wished she could cry, but her eyes felt dry and hot. The rest of her body felt icy cold.

Fanny straightened her shoulders and strode up the path to the patio. Her smile was warm and all-encompassing when she hugged Billie and Thad.

"Fanny, this baby is so beautiful I never want to let her go. She looks like Sunny. Sit, sit, and tell me what's going on and then I'll tell you horror stories about Washington. I can't wait till we get married. Keeping two residences is ridiculous," she whispered. "I heard about the pup and Thad and I are going to take her if you don't object. He's got her inside his shirt. He's some guy. I didn't think I could ever be this happy, Fanny. You aren't exactly blooming. Do you want to go for a walk and talk?"

"I'd like that. Let me check first to see if there's anything I can do to help."

"Not a thing, Fanny," Bess said. "Be back in an hour. John's barbecuing, and he wants to hear compliments."

"Are you sure?"

"Absolutely."

"That's good because we have to leave right after dinner. Thad rented a plane to make the trip. He has to be back in Washington at the crack of dawn. We'll make it with the time difference. God, I hate politics."

Billie linked her arm with Fanny's. "Now, tell me what's wrong."

Fanny told her. "I want to cry," she said. "I need to cry, but I can't."

They talked, these two old friends who understood family, and who had shared more tragedy in their lives than most people experienced in a lifetime.

"When is it my turn, Billie? Why is this my fault? They're all blaming me. I can see it in their faces. Ash . . . Ash has taken my place. I swear on my children, Billie, I don't begrudge what he's doing as long as his motives are pure. I don't believe they are, and I hope I'm wrong. I'd give up my life for any one of my children just the way you would.

"I was sitting in the garden before and I started to think about Sallie. She knew her children would break her heart. She talked about it so often. It has to be me, Billie. My children keep switching up. One minute they side with me, the next it's with their father. Why can't it just be all of us? They have every right to love their father. That doesn't mean they have to like all the things he does. The same goes for me. They constantly choose sides and smack in the middle of all of this is Simon. If I had married anyone but Simon, things would be just fine. I don't know what to do."

"What did Sallie always tell us? When you don't know what to do, do nothing. That's my advice, Fanny. You want to stay here now, don't you?"

"Part of me does, but as Bess pointed out, I wasn't invited. Simon and I will be right behind you when you leave. Ash will be here for Sunny. If I believed in my heart that there was something I could do, nothing in this world could make me leave. It's a terrible feeling not to be needed or wanted by your own children."

"At this point in time, Fanny, your children love you as much as you love them. This is one of those crises that pop up from time to time when everyone goes off the deep end. Things always right themselves later on. Do whatever feels right to you, Fanny. You can call me any time of the day or night. You know that. When you have more of a grip on things, we can take a vacation together. We could go back to that little house in Arizona that belonged to Sallie and Devin. Or if you feel the need to get away to lick your wounds, you could go alone. Did you ever tell Simon about that little house?"

"No. I don't know why I didn't. Probably because of something Sallie said. You know, never share everything. Some things need to be kept private. When I felt the urge to bolt, I thought about that little house. We probably should be getting back. Bess's husband is a cranky cook. A good one, but feisty. I don't think I can eat anything anyway. Do me a favor, Billie. Eat and run so I can leave. I never thought I'd live to see the day I would say something like that."

Billie laughed. "Next time I get to unload. My granddaughter and my daughter are at it, too. Sawyer absolutely refuses to acknowledge Maggie as her mother. It's eating Maggie alive, and there's nothing she can do about it. It seems to me like we just move from one crisis to the next with barely a breather in between. Take a deep breath now. You can handle this, Fanny."

The next two hours were pleasant enough. Everyone smiled, joked, ate, drank, and cleaned up. Fanny watched Ash closely, her thoughts in a turmoil. As Billie and Thad said their good-byes, Fanny walked over to Ash's chair, leaned over and whispered, "If I ever find out you have an ulterior motive for what you promised today, I swear, I'll make you regret the day you were born. Better yet, I'll shut down Babylon. For good. I have the power to do that. I think it's wonderful that you got Sunny to agree to seek help. Don't let her swing in the wind, Ash." She leaned even closer, her voice more hushed, "You fuck with our kids, and it's all over for you. That's a threat *and* a promise. I apologize for my language. Unfortunately it's the only kind you understand. Did I make myself clear?"

"Absolutely."

"Then I'll say good-bye."

"Leaving so soon, Mom?" young Billie said.

"Yes. You young people can visit. Is there anything I can do before I leave?"

"Not a thing," Sunny said as she hugged her mother. "You're upset with me, aren't you?"

"A little, but it's okay. I understand, Sunny. If you need me or if I can do anything, call me. I can be here in a few hours. Polly is just as beautiful as you were when you were born. Take good care of her. Hug Jake for me and give him a big kiss."

"Okay, Mom."

The chorus of good-byes rang across the mountain as Simon slipped the car in gear.

Fanny was silent for so long, Simon reached over and chucked her under the chin. "Tell me *exactly* what's wrong. How can I help you? What can I do? If my opinion counts for anything, I want you to know that I believe Ash will come through. We had a long talk at the cemetery. For the first time in his life he cares about someone besides himself. In his condition that says a lot."

"Simon, I want to stay here for a few days. I'd like it if you dropped me off in town and went back to the ranch yourself. Just for a few days. I think I need to be by myself for a little while."

"If that's what you want, Fanny. My thinking is you shouldn't be alone."

Fanny thought her husband's voice was whiny and threatening at the same time. She felt her insides start to crunch.

"I *need* to be alone. If you don't or can't understand that, then I'm sorry."

"I do, and I don't. Will you at least call me?"

"No. Alone means alone."

"If you had married anyone but me, this wouldn't be happening, would it?"

"I don't know. What I do know is I cannot allow my children to dictate my life. I would not do that to them, and I will not tolerate it from any child of mine. Just drop me off at Babylon. I want to locate the most strategic places in the casino in case I have to torch it."

"Jesus, Fanny, do you know what you just said?"

"I told Ash I would do it if he didn't follow through with Sunny. I will, too. Yes, drop me off at Babylon."

"Fanny, do you see this developing into a problem between the two of us?"

"We already have a problem, Simon. My family that you're so intent on keeping away from me is now right before me. I will deal with it, and I don't want any interference from you. Now, tell me, is Polly the most beautiful baby you've ever seen?"

"You were probably just as pretty when you were born. I know a secret."

There was such tight control in Simon's voice, Fanny felt her insides start to shrivel. "You can't keep a secret, Simon. Tell me."

"Okay. Thad isn't taking Billie back to Washington. He's taking her to Hawaii!"

"Oh, how wonderful for Billie. When is he going to tell her?"

"When she realizes they aren't landing at Washington National on time. Are we going to be okay, Fanny? I need to know."

"I'll be fine, Simon. I don't know about you. I think I still love you, Simon."

"You *think!*"

"Yes, think. I haven't been happy for a long time. You know that, and you don't seem to care. You are much too controlling, and I do not like the way you try to keep me from my family. I'm having a hard time believing I capitulated where you're concerned. I won't do that again, so be so advised."

"That sounds like a threat."

"Call it whatever you want. It's the way it is."

"Obviously we need to have a long talk."

"We had three years to talk, and it didn't work. Do you know why it didn't work? It didn't work, Simon, because you were too busy listening to yourself instead of hearing what I had to say. I don't care to discuss this anymore."

"Fine," Simon snapped.

"We should be leaving, Tyler. It's after nine and Sunny looks tired."

"It's a good kind of tired, Sage. She loves it when you all come up here and she gets to show off the kids and her homemaking skills. Birch looks like he's had a few too many. Perhaps you should drive him down the mountain."

"I already thought about that and mentioned it to Lily. She's agreeable. We'll say good night then. Guess I'll take the lead. Is Dad staying over?"

"He didn't say anything to me. I don't think so. He said something about wanting to be in town first thing in the morning to get things moving."

"Guess he'll bring up the rear then."

"Time to go, Sage. You're last in line and blocking my car," Birch said.

"Get in my car, Birch, you've had too much to drink. Tyler will move your car to the garage and drive it into town tomorrow. I'll bring him back up the mountain in the evening."

"Telling me what to do again, Sage?"

"You're drunk, Birch."

"Want to see me walk a straight line?"

"Sage is right, Birch," Ash said quietly.

"Am I drunk, Lily? Are you afraid to drive with me?"

"Why don't I drive?"

"Does that mean you think I'm drunk, too?"

"I don't know if you're drunk, but yes, I think you had too much to drink," Lily said.

"Well I don't think any such thing. If you're coming with me, get in the car."

"I'm going first, Birch. Stay behind me and don't even think about passing me on the road. You ride my bumper," Sage said.

"Yes, sir!" Birch said, offering up a sloppy salute.

"Listen, Birch, it's been a long time since I drove this road in the dark. My reflexes aren't what they used to be. Ride with me," Ash said.

"C'mon, Dad, you can do anything. Isn't that what you always told us? Hell, you were a fighting ace during the war. You're single-handedly going to get Sunny on the mend and ride off into the sunset. Get in the car, Lily."

"Ride his ass, Dad," Sage said before he climbed into his own car. "Don't give him any maneuvering room."

"Okay, son."

Sage climbed into his car, fastened his seat belt. He turned to his wife and said, "That's the first time in my life that my father ever called me son. I hope it's not an omen of some kind."

In the few short minutes it took Sage to back up his car and swing it around, Birch roared past him in reverse, swinging his car around in the middle of the road. He blew his horn one, long blast as he careened down the dark mountain road.

"Son of a bitch!" Sage swore.

"Go after him, son. I'm right behind you," Ash said.

Sage needed no second urging. "He's going to do something stupid. I feel it in my gut. I always know when he's . . ."

"Be careful, Sage," Iris said. "He's not that far ahead, and he's not driving that fast. We can see his lights. Lily will talk to him. She said he's afraid to get married because of what happened to your mom and dad. Your dad is right behind us. Please, Sage, don't drive so fast. God, I hate this road. With all the money your family has, why didn't they ever install guardrails?"

"We rarely drive this mountain at night. To answer your question, I don't know. Birch has never been a fast driver. We've always been a cautious bunch. You learn to respect the mountain. It's the curves that worry me. Dad was right, he's been drinking, and when you drink your reflexes aren't what they should be. My father is an expert on things like that."

"I can't see his lights! I can't see his lights! Oh, Jesus! Oh God!"

8

Simon watched his wife drive away in her rental car. He should have pressed harder to find out where she was going. Goddamn it, he should have *demanded* Fanny tell him where she was going. He was her husband for God's sake. His eyes felt moist, which was strange in itself since he was in the desert. He could understand his dry throat and how difficult it was to swallow. He turned to get back in his car when Fanny's vehicle was no longer in sight. His stomach started to rumble and his chest was tight. He couldn't ever remember being this angry. Except maybe when he was a kid and he and Ash were going at it.

Where to go? What to do? Fanny told him to go back to the ranch. As he put the car into gear, he thought he could feel his life slipping away from him. Would Fanny come back? He desperately wanted to believe she would, but would the pull of her family allow her to continue with her own life—her life with him? He simply didn't know. His anger started to build.

Simon made a U-turn in the middle of the road. Just because Fanny said he should go back to the ranch didn't mean he had to do it. If he went back to the ranch without Fanny, it would mean he lost and Ash won. He could stay here, hang out by the car rental agency until her return. So what if the employees thought him a lovesick fool. He knew he wasn't a lovesick fool. He was hanging out to protect his investment. He drove three blocks, made a second U-turn, and headed back the way he'd come. He'd always been a man of his word. Five blocks farther down the road, Simon pulled to the curb. The urge to put his foot through the floorboard was so strong he removed his foot from the brake pedal and turned off the ignition. Where the hell was Fanny going? Maybe what he should do was forget about going to the ranch and drive to his friend Jerry's house. Jerry seemed to have a handle on why women did the things they did. Perhaps he would share his knowledge and offer comforting words. His mood lightened considerably at the thought of spending time with his old school friend who was now retired.

Thirty minutes later, Simon climbed from his car but not before he gave the horn three sharp blasts.

Jerry afforded Simon the first genuine laugh he'd had in weeks when he ran down the driveway dressed in purple-and-yellow lightning-striped shorts, green socks, and red tee shirt. "Yeah, yeah, yeah. I'm painting the kitchen. These are my work duds. You're just in time, Simon. If you help, we can zip it off and drink beer the rest of the day. Later you can tell me what's bothering you. I know something's bothering you because you're standing here. I am in-tu-it-tive as you well know. The best part is we'll have the house to ourselves. Carol went to Georgia to see her sister, who had her gall bladder taken out a few days ago." It was all said with the speed of an out-of-control locomotive. Before Simon knew what was happening he had on a shirt three sizes too big that was smeared with pea green paint.

"Carol said pea green is a restful color for a kitchen. Let me tell you, it's so damn restful she won't cook or clean. I myself almost fell asleep twice while I was painting the ceiling. You take the woodwork and baseboards and I'll finish the walls. How's life in the mountains? Want a beer now, or should we wait till the sun's over the yardarm? Maybe we should eat first. What do you think, Simon?"

Simon pried open a can of semigloss paint. "Fanny went off somewhere to think. She didn't want me along. I'm having trouble dealing with that. I watched her drive off and didn't try to stop her. You've been married a lot longer than I have. Did Carol ever do anything like that?"

"She does it all the time. She goes into the bathroom and locks the door. She stays in there for hours. Once she stayed in there for a whole day. She can't afford to go off to a hotel. Women do things like that when life starts to overwhelm them. To this day I have never found out why she does what she does. When she finally comes out, we don't discuss it. What that means is she came to terms with whatever was bothering her in the first place. You need to stir that paint with gusto."

"I thought you knew everything there was to know about women since you've been married so long."

"No one knows everything about women. I seriously doubt if anyone knows *anything* about women. Maybe if you told me what happened prior to Fanny going off, I might be able to offer some small measure of insight, but don't count on it."

Simon told him. Jerry rocked back on his heels. "That's a motherhood thing. You don't ever, as in ever, mess with motherhood. Listen, let's forget this kitchen and go outside. I have *three* cases of beer and two hammocks. What'ya say?"

Simon slapped the lid on the paint can. He sealed it by bringing his heel down on the top of it. "I'm your man."

"Here we go," Jerry said, climbing into one hammock and indicating that Simon should climb into the other one. "If you want to lie down, you need to position your head just right on the pillow or the beer will dribble down your chin. Watch me so you don't screw up."

"Gotcha. Are you telling me there's nothing I can do or say?"

"The kids are off-limits and sacred. They aren't your kids. The fact is they aren't kids anymore at all. They're grown adults. For some reason that doesn't seem to matter to a mother. Fathers are different."

"Fanny is feeling guilty. Her family has always been her number one priority. She's had to be both mother and father to them all these years because Ash is . . . Ash."

"How is your brother, Simon?" Jerry uncapped two beers and passed one to Simon. "I think we can finish this off before the sun goes down. What's your opinion?"

"Do you have an outside bathroom?"

"Nope. Just aim for the bushes."

"Ash has taken over where Sunny is concerned. If there's anyone who knows about disabilities, it's Ash. I saw his face, Jerry, and this time I think he's on the level. I really think he wants to help his daughter. I want to believe he's being a genuine father this time around, and until someone can prove me wrong, I'll stick with my belief. Fanny is certain Ash is trying to get Sunny's trust monies. Sunny has always blown hot and cold where her father is concerned. She does love him, though, and that's how he got her to agree to seek help. He's going to be right at her side. My feeling, Jerry, is, what does it matter who gets her to go as long as she goes. I think Fanny is seeing it as a betrayal of some kind. The kids resent their mother marrying me on the one hand; the other hand is glad, or was glad that finally Fanny seemed happy. It's all screwed up." His voice was so weary, Jerry handed over another beer that Simon swigged from, almost emptying the bottle with one long gulp.

"Are you afraid Fanny will want to come back here to . . . you know, do that mother thing?"

"I'm not afraid. Hell, I understand that this might be very serious. Sunny doesn't want her here. That's what's bothering Fanny. These past three years we've been so locked into ourselves we didn't go back to Sunrise. Fanny only saw Jake when he was christened. Sunny pointed that out to her. Ash on the other hand has seen the kid a lot, and he genuinely likes the little guy. He did a number on Fanny when he gave Sunny a gift from long ago. I thought Fanny was going to bawl her head off."

"It's wrong to have competition between parents," Jerry singsonged. "If we were painting, we'd be done by now."

"Ask me if I care?" Simon tossed his empty beer bottle in the general direction of the bushes. He held out his hand for a refill.

"What are you going to do next?"

"Stay here with you. Fanny told me to go home. It's not home without her. Everything's under control. I'll buy the next load of beer, okay?"

"Sounds good to me. Carol won't be back till next week. We can throw our wet towels on the floor, not make our beds, leave dishes in the sink and . . . whatever else we want to do. We have to finish the kitchen before she gets back, though."

"Let's call someone to do that. My birthday present to you."

"I accept."

"Jer, who do you think she'll pick, me or the kids?"

"I keep telling you. They aren't kids. Wherever she is, she's probably thinking about how she can combine the two things. She's not going to make choices. Didn't you learn anything about hanging around with me when we were younger? You saw how my mother did things. When Fanny comes back, it will be just like Carol coming out of the bathroom. It will all be under control."

Simon's eyes rolled back in his head. "You must be some kind of saint. I want answers, explanations. How do you stand it?"

"It drives me damn near nuts. I have to stand it because if I don't, she goes back into the bathroom. She honest to God put a dead bolt on the inside and cemented the pins in the hinges so I couldn't take the door off. We have wire mesh on the bathroom window, too. What'ya think of that?"

"Jesus."

"Yeah. I love her though. It will work out, Simon."

"Do you really think so?"

"Yeah, I do. Fanny loves you. You love her."

"Jerry, remember when my father had his stroke and my mother . . ."

"That was different, Simon. Devin and your mother weren't married. You and Fanny are married. Your dad was no kid. It's not the same thing at all."

"I wonder where Fanny is right this minute?"

"She's someplace safe and sound, someplace normal, someplace where she can sit and think. All you have to remember is Fanny loves you. When she does come back, remember the bathroom and keep quiet."

"Okay, Jerry."

Fanny Thornton removed the key from the ignition. She sat for a long moment staring at the cottage nestled in the cottonwoods. The Devin and Sallie house of happiness. Sallie and Devin's retreat from the world—given to Fanny just weeks before her mother-in-law passed on. What was it Sallie had said? "Everyone needs a sanctuary at some time in their life. This will be yours. No one but Billie Coleman and Bess are to know you have this little house. Promise me, Fanny." And she had promised.

Many times over the past years she had come to this tranquil spot on the Arizona border to lick her wounds.

Fanny climbed from the car and knew instantly that Chue or one of his sons had been here recently to prune back the shrubbery and to mow the lawn. She found herself staring intently at the diamond-shaped windows. For one wild, crazy moment she thought she saw Sallie Thornton reflected in the shiny glass panes. A headache started to pound at the base of her skull as she pulled her overnight case and bag of groceries from the trunk of the car. All she wanted was to have a cup of coffee and sit on one of the wicker chairs on the small front porch.

The cottage was immaculate, as though someone had just recently cleaned it. One of Chue's sons had probably done the outside work while a daughter had cleaned inside. Fanny ran the tap water for a few minutes until the residue was gone and the water ran clean and pure.

While the coffee perked, Fanny carried her bag to the bedroom on the second floor that ran the entire length of the house. She sniffed, recognizing the faint scent of sagebrush. She lifted the heirloom spread to see crisply ironed sheets. One of Chue's daughters had definitely been here. Early on, Sallie had expressed a liking for ironed sheets, and Chue's family had obliged.

The small blue-and-white-tiled bathroom sparkled. Fanny washed her face and hands, irritated that she dropped water on the vanity, angry that she was using the pretty cornflower-colored towels. Right now she was angry with the world, with herself. The question was, what was she going to do about it? "I'm going to drink my damn coffee and sit on my front porch. After I do that I'm going to bed and sleep for twenty-four straight hours, at which point I will wake, make more coffee, and sit on the porch again." She burst into tears as she walked down the stairs. As she poured her coffee, she wondered where Simon was and what he was doing. They'd only been apart a few hours, and already she missed him. How lost and lonely he'd looked when she drove away. She knew in her gut it was a *pretend* lost-and-lonely look. She knew her husband too well these days. Was it a mistake to come here to a place with no telephone, television, or radio?

The headache continued to pound inside her head as she made her way to the front porch, kicking off her shoes as she went.

Her feet propped up on the banister, Fanny leaned back into the padded cushions. Now she could think about her family and Simon. And Ash.

"Please, God, in this tranquil setting, help me figure out where I went wrong." A moment later, the intense hammering inside her skull lessened and then was gone. Fanny heaved a sigh of relief as she sipped at the scalding hot coffee. Her thoughts traveled back in time as she gave in to the serenity that was all about her.

Surely in a week's time she would find the answers she was searching for.

"Iris, go back up the hill and call for an ambulance. Hurry! I'm going down the cliff."

Iris needed no second urging. She floored the gas pedal and roared up the steep grade.

Sage yanked at his jacket, tossing it on the ground as he prepared to make his descent down the steep mountainside to where his brother's car smoldered.

Chue's excited Chinese jabbering turned to English when he arrived on the scene. "I brought a rope as soon as I saw what happened. Is it Birch?"

"Yeah, it's Birch. He cut around me and took off. Tie the end of the rope to the tree. I can't see a thing."

"My wife called for an ambulance. It will take some time for it to get here. Go, go, you do not have much time. I will follow you as soon as I secure the rope," Chue said.

Sage was already halfway down the rope, barely feeling the rope burns to his hands. He prayed and he cursed. When his feet hit the ground, he ran to the car and managed to drag Birch away from the smoldering vehicle. There was no sign of Lily. The absence of glass in the windshield told him all he needed to know. How soon would the car explode? He had no idea. In the movies it always took a few minutes.

"Lily must have gone through the windshield on impact. She's not in the car!" he shouted to Chue. "Birch always wore his seat belt. I unbuckled him. Stay clear, it's going to blow."

When the explosion occurred, Sage covered his brother's body with his own. "If you aren't dead, Birch, I swear to God I'll kill you myself for pulling a stunt like that," he sobbed. He looked upward to see his family outlined in the eerie orange light at the top of the road. He could hear their excited voices but couldn't make out their words.

"I can't find a pulse, Chue. You try. I'm too . . . I'm too . . . find his pulse, Chue. Did you find Lily?"

"She's dead, Sage. I do not know this for a fact, but I think she died on impact. I pulled her as far away as I could. He's alive, but barely. His pulse is very weak."

"Tyler!" Sage roared, his voice carrying up the mountain.

"I'm here, Sage. I had to go to my car to get my medical bag. Please, stand back and let me do what I have to do."

"Lily's dead," Sage said.

"Then there's nothing we can do for her. Your brother is my concern right now. Don't go to pieces on me. Your family needs you up there," Tyler said, jerking his head upward. "You need to think about calling your mother and Simon."

"Yeah, yeah. Is he going to live, Tyler? That's all I want to know. Well, is he?"

"I don't know at this time. Let me do what I'm trained to do." A moment later he looked up and said, "I gave you a goddamn order. Obey it! Your family needs you. I'll stay with Birch until the ambulance gets here."

Sage did his best to scramble up the mountain, his leather-soled shoes slipping and sliding as he grappled with the rope for leverage, Chue behind him. The eerie sound of the far-off ambulance rang in his ears as it carried over the mountain.

They were all talking at once, their voices shrill with fear. Sage wanted to cry at the stricken look on his father's face. "I don't know anything. Birch is alive, but he's unconscious. Lily Bell is dead."

"I called the hospital the moment I heard the crash. John will have every specialist in town waiting. They're all standing by. It's going to be all right, Sage," Bess said, putting a comforting hand on his shoulder. In a whispered voice she said, "Your father needs you right now."

"He knows this mountain. I thought he respected it like the rest of us do. How could he have misjudged it?" Ash asked brokenly. "Will he make it, Sage?"

"Dad, I don't know. Tyler is not a man of many words. We need to be grateful a doctor is on the scene."

"Someone has to call Fanny. They should be back at the ranch by now."

"I tried. One of the workers picked up the phone in the kennel and said your mother and Simon aren't there and has no idea when to expect them. I tried calling Billie Coleman, but there was no answer in Washington or at the farmhouse in Vermont. I'll keep trying," Bess said

Sage nodded, his eyes on his two sisters. This wasn't real. He always did dream in color, horrible dreams that woke him up in the middle of the night. During childhood his mother had always comforted him and sat by his bed until he fell asleep. Now, Iris did the same thing. She had the same comforting touch, the same warm smile and gentle eyes as his mother. He wondered if he'd fallen in love with her because she reminded him so much of his mother. *This isn't real. This is just a bad dream and I'm going to wake up and Birch is going to say, "Ha, I fooled you, didn't I?"*

"You aren't dreaming, Sage. This is as real as it gets," Iris said as she reached for his hand. "Thank God Tyler was here."

"Lily's dead. They were going to get married. How's Birch supposed to handle that?"

"One day at a time. Here comes the ambulance. Honey, wheel your father away from the edge. Talk to him. He needs you right now."

Sage didn't know what frightened him more, the white-clad figures carrying their medical equipment or the flashing lights.

"Come on, Dad, we have to get out of the way. Birch is in good hands. All we can do now is pray. Do you know how to do that, Dad?"

The sadness in his father's voice drove shivers of fear up Sage's spine. "I don't know if God will listen to someone like me. He listens to people like your mother. Did anyone reach her?"

"Not yet, Dad. Mom always said God listens to all his children. I think the trick is not to ask for something for yourself. Always pray for others. You can't say things like, if You do this for me, I'll do that for You. I never thought about it too much, but I bet that's why Mom is who she is. She never asks for herself. She always puts other people first. That has to mean something."

"If you call the Highway Patrol and explain the circumstances, they should be able to get Simon's license plate number and put it out on the air. It's possible they stopped along the way. Your mother likes to take scenic routes when she's traveling. Do that, Sage. Fanny will be devastated when she finds out."

"Okay, Dad, I'll get on it as soon as they bring Birch up. I want . . . need to be here for my brother. Are you okay?"

"Christ no. How's Sunny holding up?"

"Billie's with her. Sunny's tough."

"It's all going wrong, Sage."

"You're reacting to the moment, Dad. This family is always embroiled in one crisis or another. Birch is as tough as Sunny. He's going to be okay. Hey, I'm his twin. I'd feel something if . . . you know."

"That's about the biggest bunch of bullshit I ever heard. This is me you're talking to, Sage."

"Do you want me to say I'm piss-assed scared? Okay, I am. That doesn't mean things won't be okay. All I keep thinking about is how Birch and I drifted apart these past years. We used to be joined at the hip. I guess life does that to you."

"Cut the crap, Sage. I'm the reason, and we both know it."

"Why are we having this conversation, Dad?"

"Because you're blaming yourself. I will not tolerate that, son. Birch isn't a kid. When you go out on the road or up in the air you take responsibility for yourself and those around you. If you learned that lesson, why didn't Birch? He liked to hotdog the roads, and now Lily is dead and he's . . ."

The lump Sage felt growing in his throat seemed to be getting bigger by the moment. He nodded, his eyes miserable.

"They're bringing him up! They're bringing him up!" Sunny screamed, her arms flapping every which way. She ran, her knees knocking together, to where her husband was standing. "How is he, Tyler? Is he okay? He isn't going to die, is he, Tyler? I hugged him, but I didn't kiss him good-bye. Say something, Tyler."

"Take your family back to the house, Sunny. It isn't good, okay. Don't upset your father. I'm going with the ambulance."

"We're all going. We'll follow you."

"I want you to stay here, Sunny."

"Do you really think I'm going to do that? That's my brother on the stretcher. We all have a right to know what's wrong. We want to be there, to be close. We can't find Mom, Tyler. What exactly does not good mean?"

"Internal injuries. He took a hell of a blow to the head. He's in shock, and he's unconscious. We'll do the best we can. Trauma units are standing by. I'll see you at the hospital."

They gathered close in a circle as Sunny relayed Tyler's words. "I'll go with Dad. Sage, take Bess and Billie with you and Iris. They're in no shape to drive."

"And you think Dad is? Let's all go in the van, and I'll drive."

"That's good. I'll tell Dad. He has a built-in phone so we can keep trying to call Mom while we go down the mountain."

"I'll go back to the house. Everyone tell me what you need, so we can leave right away. Purses, sweaters, anything else? I'll wake your housekeeper, Sunny, and tell her to sleep in the kids' rooms," Billie said.

"Hurry, Billie."

"Five minutes, Sunny. Get Dad in the van, and I'll be back by the time everyone is settled. Try Mom and Aunt Billie again."

Ten minutes later, Sage started up the van.

Sunny groped for her father's hand. Ash squeezed it reassuringly. "He's going to be okay, isn't he, Dad?"

"Of course he is. Birch is a Thornton. We're hardy stock. He's going to get the best care in the world. Whatever he needs we'll provide. We all need to think positively. We're together, and we're going to stay that way. I don't want to hear a negative word from anyone. Is that understood?"

"That's something Mom would say," Billie said, inching closer to her father. Ash's fingers closed around Billie's. A tear splashed on his hand. He wasn't sure if it was from Billie or himself.

"Your mother still isn't home. I've alerted the Highway Patrol and the local police. They'll alert every police department within a two-hundred-mile radius. We'll find her," Bess said. Under her breath she muttered, "When, I don't know."

"I don't understand Mom anymore. In the old days she never went anywhere without leaving a note or calling someone to say where she'd be in case of an emergency. They should have been home two hours ago. This new life of hers . . . I hate it. I just hate it."

Ash's voice was weary when he replied. "Everyone deserves a life, Sunny. You kids had your mother at your side all your life. Cut her some slack, for heaven's sake."

"That sounds very weird coming out of your mouth, Dad," Sunny said. "She doesn't have time for us anymore. That's what bothers me."

"You aren't children anymore. You're young adults and young adults are supposed to have their own lives and make their own decisions. I don't want to hear any negative talk when it comes to your mother. Wherever she is or whatever she's doing, I'm sure there's a reason for it. Your mother never does anything without a reason."

Sunny's voice turned stubborn and obstinate. "She should be here. If her plans changed, how much time would it have taken to inform someone? She doesn't want to be bothered with us anymore."

"That's not fair, Sunny, and you know it," Bess said. "I think I'll carry that one step farther and ask you why, when your mother and my husband asked you what was wrong with your health, you denied having any problems and told everyone to mind their own business. When a person hears that often enough they back off and don't keep asking. You were the one who didn't want to be bothered. You told your mother more than once that she was stepping over the line where your life was concerned. She did what you wanted, and you still aren't happy."

"It's not the same thing. This is Birch we're talking about."

"If your mother knew about your brother's accident, she would move heaven and earth to get here," Bess snapped.

"Bess is right, Sunny," Ash said. "Your mother is going to be found, and she'll come here as soon as she can."

"What if . . ."

"There are no what ifs. It will be just the way I said it will be. The only thing I cannot give you is the time and the place when it will happen."

"What if something happens to Birch?"

"Shut up, Sunny," Sage yelled from the driver's seat of the van.

"Don't tell me to shut up. Can't you see? It's all falling apart? First it was me. Now it's Birch and . . . Mom. Who's next? What's next, is more like it?"

"Enough!" Sage roared. "One more word, and I'm pulling this van to the side of the road. The next thing I'll do is muzzle you or dump you out. I mean it, Sunny, one more word and that's it." Sunny clamped her lips shut as her nails dug into her father's hand.

They drove the rest of the way in silence.

Sage drove the van to the front entrance of the Thornton Medical Center. He engaged the lift that would lower his father's wheelchair to the ground before the others exited. "The rest of you go in. Iris and I will park the van. We'll meet you inside."

"Smart-ass bastard," Sunny muttered.

"Dumb-ass bitch," Sage muttered in return. He held out his arms and Sunny stepped into them.

"I'm sorry. I'm worried sick. You know me and my mouth. What do you feel, Sage?"

"I don't feel anything. That's because Birch is in a place I can't reach. You gave us too much credit when we were kids. We weren't *that* tuned to one another. We just said we were to get on your nerves, and you bought into it."

"You're telling me this *now!*"

"Timing is everything," Sage said as he drove off.

Sunny straightened her shoulders before she took her position behind her father's chair. "Okay, everyone, it's going to be a long night. I suggest we get some coffee and settle in. First though, I'd like us all to go to the chapel for a few minutes. We need to . . . to make arrangements for . . . Lily. The police are notifying her half brother and sister. Is everyone okay with this?" The others nodded.

Hour after weary hour passed with only one update two hours after Birch was admitted. John Noble offered it on the run: Birch was critical and everything humanly possible was being done to save his life.

Sage paced. Ash dozed, either from weariness or the handful of pills he swallowed. Sunny, Billie, and Bess huddled on a blue-striped sofa that smelled of lemons and mothballs. From time to time Bess used the pay phone in the lobby to try and reach Fanny, with no success.

Time crawled by. Eventually the first violet shadows of dawn could be seen through the windows. "Why is it that terrible things always seem to happen at night when it's pitch-black outside?" Billie whispered. She continued to whisper. "When the sun is out and it's a bright day I feel like I can handle anything. It's been so long. Someone should have come out by now to tell us Birch's condition. God, I wish Mom was here. Lily had no family except her half sister and brother. They were such cold, unfeeling people. Don't pay attention to me, I'm just talking to hear my own voice because I'm so scared."

"We're all scared, honey," Bess said. "If talking helps you, go right ahead."

"I don't want to hear you babble," Sunny said.

"That's too bad. Maybe if you listened to the people around you, you wouldn't be in the position you're in right now," Billie said.

"What's that supposed to mean? That I'm stupid?"

"If the shoe fits, wear it. I don't want to fight with you, Sunny. I guess you had your reasons for playing stupid where your life is concerned, but I fail to see what they could possibly be. Another thing, I'd appreciate it if you'd leave Mom out of your fits of anger and remorse. Everyone in life who has half a brain has to take responsibility for their own actions, and that includes you."

Ash jolted awake. "This is not the time or the place for family bickering. There's no need to pick each other apart out of frustration."

"Dad's right," Sage said.

They heard the tap of John Noble's shoes before they saw him. His eyes were bloodshot, his hair stood on end. His jaw was grim and he needed a shave. He cleared his throat twice before he could speak. "We've managed to stop the internal bleeding. Birch was in surgery for four hours. Right now he's in the Intensive Care Unit. He's being monitored minute by minute. That's the good news. The bad news is he's lapsed into a coma. This happens sometimes. It could be temporary or it could be . . . a while. There is the possibility he won't come out of it. For now that's all I can tell you. I'm not going to lie to you. Birch is in critical condition. It can go either way. I know you want to see him, so you can follow me and look through the glass. Five minutes. Not one second longer. Then I want you all to go home. Get some sleep, eat something, shower, and then you can come back. That's the way we do things here. If there's anything you don't understand, tell me now. Good, follow me."

Bess lagged behind to stand next to her husband as the others pressed their hands against the glass partition. "Is that all of it, John?"

"That's all of it. You have to find Fanny, Bess."

"Is it that bad, John?"

"It's that bad. Right now his chances look like zip. He's young, he's healthy, he could fool all of us. Lily was D.O.A. They've taken her body to the morgue. I don't suppose you know if her half brother and sister are going to claim the body."

"I don't know. The police said they would notify them. I'll check with them later. They say when you go into a coma you go to a deep, dark place. I read that somewhere, John. The article said if you talk to the person you stand a good chance of bringing them out of it. We could take turns doing that. Sunny can talk for hours and hours. Should we do that?"

"Bess . . . everybody has a theory about comas. I'm a medical man. When the time comes . . . if it comes, and you want to talk to Birch, I certainly wouldn't stop you. I've read those same articles. Prayer is good. Concentrate on that right now, and finding Fanny."

"Fanny was so upset when she left. Simon probably suggested something on a whim and they probably followed that whim. What if . . ."

John kissed his wife on the cheek. "Time's up," he said quietly.

"They don't hear you," Bess whispered. "Can't you see? They're all inside that room with Birch? Those kids have always been tighter than feathers on a duck. Each one of them has taken on Birch's pain. Sage is dying inside. That's his big brother by seconds."

"We have to go," Ash said quietly.

"He's going to die. He is, isn't he? Doctors never tell you the truth." A second later Sunny broke formation and entered the room. She flung herself across the bed, sobbing heartbrokenly. "Wake up, Birch. Please, you have to wake up. They're going to yank me out of here any minute. I don't care. I had to talk to you. Both of us can't go down. What will the others do if we both die? This is just a silly old accident. My stuff is worse, I know it is. You know Sage, he pretends to be tough, but he's all mush. He needs you. Billie needs you. Dad can't run the casino without you. Mom won't be able to handle it. Are you listening to me, Birch? Wake up. I want you to wake up right now. Please, Birch, do it for me. I swear I'll never say a cussword again. I'll do everything you say. Damn you, Birch, wake up! Everybody here is pulling for you. You can do it. We need you. Listen to me, Birch, if I go, and I know I have something really bad so that means I'm going to . . . you need to be here for the others. They all think I'm stupid for not going to the doctors earlier. I knew way back then. I know now. You're the lucky one because the doctors can fix you up. People recover from car crashes all the time. What I have can't be fixed. Are you listening to me, Birch?"

"He can't hear you, Sunny," John said as he gently led her from the room.

Sunny shook off his arm. "You don't know that. You can't crawl inside his head. I don't want to hear that. This place is supposed to be a medical marvel. Guess what, you better start doing some marvelous things. Don't you dare let my brother die. Do you hear me?"

"I hear you, Sunny. Now, I want you to hear me. If you ever pull another stunt like that, I'll bar you from this entire floor."

Sunny turned around. "You don't understand. I had to talk to him. I had to. I know you don't understand, and I don't care that you don't understand. I didn't jeopardize my brother's health. I know he heard me. I felt it deep inside me. I don't expect you to understand that either. No, you won't bar me from this floor. I won't allow it. I know you mean well and I mean well, so we're going to have to meet somewhere in between. I own one quarter of this medical center." She raised a shaky finger to point to Sage and Billie and then at Birch's room. "That's the other three quarters. Four quarters make a whole. If it comes to a vote. I know you think your way is best, but you could be wrong. Maybe my way is best because I love Birch, and he knows I love him. That has to count somewhere. That's my brother in there. Just so you know, Dr. Noble. Come on, guys, time to take Dad home. We'll come back later."

"Guess she told you, huh? Would you really bar her from the floor?" Bess whispered.

John Noble looked uncomfortable. "Let me put it this way. I'd try to reason with her."

Bess smiled wanly. "The four of them would shut this place down in a heartbeat just the way Fanny shut down Las Vegas. They are their mother's children, and that's their brother lying in there." John cringed at the reminder. "What in the name of God was she saying in there?"

"You don't want to know, Bess. Take them home and bring me some clean clothes. Toss in an egg salad sandwich, too. Put those little seeds in it, okay?"

"Take care of him, John."

John nodded. "Find Fanny and find her quick. Bess, you know those prayers you say every night on your knees by the bed, say some extra ones, okay?"

Bess nodded as she blew her husband a kiss. "I'll do my best."

9

Simon groaned when he saw the flashing lights of the police cruiser in his rearview mirror. "Shit!" Instead of slowing down, his right foot pressed harder on the gas pedal. He knew it was a stupid thing to do, but he did it anyway. Like he could outrun a police car in his drunken condition. He cursed Jerry for talking him into going to the market for more beer. He knew better than to get into a car when he was drunk. He was about to get out of the car when he heard one of the officers bark an order. "Stay in your vehicle, sir, and roll down your window."

Sir? Simon fumbled in his pocket for his wallet before he realized he'd just taken a twenty-dollar bill off the kitchen counter, change from their last Chinese delivery order. Drunk and driving without a license and vehicle registration. They'd lock him up and throw away the key.

Simon saw himself reflected in the officer's polished sunglasses. He looked like death warmed over, his hair was on end, and he hadn't shaved or showered in four days. He knew he smelled like a distillery

The first officer reached inside the car door and placed both his hands on Simon's shoulders. "Mr. Thornton, there's been an accident and you're wanted at the medical center. Get cleaned up and we'll drive you there."

"Oh, not Fanny. Tell me it isn't Fanny. What . . . who . . . how?"

"It's your nephew, Birch. He was in a serious automobile accident. Do you know how we can locate his mother?"

"I don't know where she is. She said . . . she was going somewhere to think about some . . . family matters. That's why I'm here. I'm waiting. She didn't want me around when she was doing her thinking. How bad is Birch?"

"You need to talk to his doctors. Follow us, Mr. Thornton, while I radio this in."

Simon grappled with his drunkenness as his mind registered the fact that Fanny was safe but her son was injured and in critical condition. He drove carefully, his eyes on the cops' taillights.

At the medical center, the family descended on him like a swarm of locusts. "Where's Mom? Where's Fanny?"

"I don't know. Is there any change?"

"What do you mean you don't know?" Ash snarled. "How can you not know where your wife is, for God's sake?"

Simon's insides started to rumble. "She said she was going off to think, and she wanted to be alone. Do you really think I could have stopped her? She wanted me to go back to the ranch, but I elected to stay here and wait for her because she was so devastated when we started down the mountain. It was what she wanted, Ash, what she needed to do."

"And this is the result," Ash snarled again. "Birch could die, Simon. What's that going to do to Fanny if she isn't here?"

"Ash, you can't blame Fanny. Sage put her rental car plate out on the wire. Someone will see it, and she'll be here before you know it."

"What in the goddamn hell did she have to think about? That's all she ever does, think, think, think. Don't even think about giving me that crap about me getting Sunny to a doctor either. If she was the mother she always claimed to be, she would have dragged Sunny off three years ago. Oh, no, she ups and marries you and forgets all about her children. I'm sorry, Simon. I'm all wound up. Forget all that stuff I just said, okay? Wait just a minute here. If Fanny went off to think, that means there's a problem between you and her. Aha, now it makes sense. So, there's trouble in Paradise, eh?"

"If you weren't in a wheelchair, I'd flatten you right here and now. Once an asshole always an asshole," Simon grated as he walked away.

In the coffee shop, with a steaming cup of coffee that tasted like real coffee, Simon fought the urge to cry. His shoulders started to shake when he felt a gentle hand. "Simon, is it really you?"

"Bess. God, a normal person. Please, sit down. Talk to me in that sane, sensible voice of yours. I just had a go-round with Ash."

"Is Fanny upstairs?"

"I don't know where Fanny is." He repeated his story for Bess's benefit. "Where would she go, Bess? For all I know she could be holed up in any one of the hotels in town. Or, she could be in the mountains sleeping in the car. Sage put her plate out on the wire. I have no clue. You know her, where would she go?"

Bess shrugged as she stared into Simon's eyes. They were so blank she felt afraid. "I've called everywhere. Billie and Thad didn't go back to Washington. I thought the four of you went off somewhere. This is like Fanny, but at the same time it's unlike her. The kids are right, though, Fanny never goes anywhere without telling someone where she can be reached. So, I guess her getting away must have something to do with the two of you."

"Until she married me. Her going away was because of Sunny. Don't make a federal case out of nothing, Bess. Thad took Billie to Hawaii. It was a last minute trip and a surprise."

"Yes, until she married you. Wait a minute! I think I have an idea. I might be wrong, but I don't think so. You wait here, Simon."

Simon stared at Bess's back as she raced from the coffee shop. Five minutes later he saw and heard her car screech out onto the main road. He gulped at the lukewarm coffee, his hands trembling so badly he could barely hold the cup. Had Fanny confided her unhappiness to Bess, to Billie Coleman?

Fanny stared at the bird's nest in the cottonwood. For days now she'd been mentally willing the mother bird to leave the nest. She'd even tried whispering to the mother bird, who stared at her, which was strange in itself. The bird wasn't afraid of her. Maybe it had something to do with the plate of worms she'd dug in the soft earth under the overhang. She thought the babies were ready to fly, but then, what did she know about birds?

"What I do know is if you coddle them too long, they'll never be independent and they'll hang on your tail feathers forever. Just do it and they'll follow you. They trust you. That's what motherhood is all about, you know. Trust is a two-way street where children are concerned. Children trust you to raise them right, to do right by them to the best of your ability, and a parent has the right to expect love and respect and trust, in that order. It's not that way with husbands and wives, though, and I don't know why that is. Another thing, that nest isn't big enough for all of you. Go on, fly. I'll tell you what, I'll go down off the porch and if it looks like they're in trouble, I'll catch them." Fanny didn't feel silly at all for talking to a bird or walking down the steps to see if her intuition was correct. She waited patiently as the mother bird finally perched on the edge of the nest, her wings rustling anxiously in the quiet morning air.

"Do it," Fanny whispered. She watched, hardly daring to breathe as the mother bird fanned her wings over the nest, lifting each little bird with the tip of her wing. Fanny felt the moistness in her eyes as each baby bird took wing. She laughed aloud as the mother bird took to the air, her right wing dipping slightly. Fanny offered up a snappy salute. "Anytime. Your job isn't over yet," she called. "You need to watch over them even if it's from a distance." Would they come back? Probably not. "It's supposed to be this way," Fanny murmured.

Fanny sat for hours on the porch, her eyes scanning the blue sky for a sign of the birds. A wave of sadness swept over her. They didn't need her or the worms she'd dug for them. They were off on their own, soaring high above the trees.

Maybe it was time to go back. Time to join the real world again. Time to call her children to tell them she loved them, time to make decisions where Simon was concerned. It was time.

She could be on the road in thirty minutes once she packed her bag, cleaned out the refrigerator, and gathered up her trash. She could stop at the first convenience store she came to and call Simon to tell him she was on her way. If she hurried and drove the speed limit, she could be back at the ranch by dark.

She heard the car, the sound of the horn, and then she saw a spiral of dust swirl upward. Company? Chue? Who?

"Bess! What are you doing here? How did you know I was here? Something's wrong. Tell me. What, Bess, what happened?"

"Fanny, sit down. We've been looking for you for four days. The police found Simon. He's been staying at Jerry's house. He didn't go back to the ranch the way you asked him to. He waited for you. It's Birch, Fanny. His car went off the mountain the night of the christening. Lily died in the accident and . . . Birch . . . Birch is in a coma. My suggestion would be to leave your car and have Chue and one of his boys come for it."

"Let me get my purse and key to lock the door."

Bess's breath exploded in a loud sigh. Had she expected tears? She knew a thing or two about glazed eyes and shock.

Fanny locked the door. "There were these birds, Bess, a mother and her babies . . ."

Bess listened until Fanny wound down. "Listen to me. Everyone is . . . upset. That's understandable. They're angry with you because you didn't say where you were going. Simon and Ash had words this morning. It isn't going to be easy, Fanny. Even if you'd been there, there was nothing you could do. There's nothing anyone can do. Everything medically that could be done has been done. Birch is in other hands now. Do you understand what I'm saying, Fanny?"

"Yes. How did it happen?"

Bess told her. "Sage pulled him out. Tyler was on the scene within minutes. I'm not going to lie to you, Fanny. It isn't good."

"They're all blaming me, aren't they?"

"In a manner of speaking. They're upset. You can see the terror on their faces. Ash is . . . inconsolable. Sunny flips out on the hour. Billie seems to be holding up fairly well. Sage is just angry. He's so stiff he looks brittle. He's not saying much. He just sits there and I know he's roll-calling every minute of his and Birch's life. You have to be strong, Fanny, and pull your family together before they destroy each other."

"What is John saying, Bess? Were specialists called in?"

"Of course. The best of the best, from all parts of the country. They've all concurred and they've all agreed, nothing more can be done. Your son is in other hands now, Fanny."

"A coma isn't good."

"People come out of comas all the time. Everyone, including John, thought Birch would come out of his after seventy-two hours, but he didn't. He's being monitored minute by minute. Pneumonia looms on the horizon so they're trying to guard against that. It could be turning around as we speak. Medical marvels happen every day of the week."

"I don't think I could bear it if something happened to Birch. How did Billie Coleman handle Riley's death? He was her only son. She told me once that a part of her heart, the part that was reserved for Riley, was missing. Can't you drive any faster, Bess?"

"Of course I can drive faster, but I'm not going to."

Fanny's voice was a low, hushed whisper when she said, "Bess, do you ever wonder, ever question God as to why certain people seem to get so much pain and grief in their lives and other people just go about their business and never experience a moment of anxiety? I've never understood why it's like that."

"Fanny, let's not get into that right now. Let's just say God acts in mysterious ways and let it go at that. My mother always said you never question God nor do you make bargains with Him."

"I find myself wondering what I did wrong. First Ash, then Sunny, and now Birch. Maybe I wasn't supposed to marry Simon. Maybe I'm not supposed to be happy. Why can't I cry, Bess?"

"Because you're numb. Crying just makes your eyes red and ugly. Remember how my mother used to tell us that all the time? It's true."

"I don't feel anything. It's as if someone took away my insides and the rest of me is just a shell. I can walk and I can talk, but I can't feel."

"Why did you go to the cottage, Fanny?"

"I had to do some hard thinking. Mostly about Sunny. I knew if I didn't get it all straight in my head, I would start to cover myself in guilt. I don't want to live with guilt. I had to do some thinking about Simon, too. We didn't have that talk, did we, Bess? I know now I was wrong. I never should have allowed Simon to dictate to me. I stepped over the line where Sunny was concerned. I have to find a way to make it right. At one point, early on, Tyler more or less, without actually coming out and saying the words, implied that Sunny was playacting to get attention. He worked long hours and she was alone a lot and there was trouble with Ash. Three doctors said they couldn't find anything wrong with her. John felt as I did, but we couldn't drag her wherever we thought she should go. Did John ever tell you Sunny told him if he didn't get out of her life she'd get her brothers and sister to agree to remove him from the staff?"

"No, he never told me that."

"Well she did. John backed off just the way I did. I wish you had a phone in this car so I could call the center. Does . . . Birch have a lot of tubes in him?"

"Uh-huh. He's hooked up to a lot of machines. It's frightening at first when you see them until you realize they're keeping him alive. Like John says, Birch is young, he's healthy, and he's a fighter."

"And he's in a coma."

There didn't seem to be any comment to Fanny's statement. Bess drove on in silence.

A long time later, Bess said, "I'll drop you off in front and park the car. ICU is on the fifth floor."

Fanny pressed the elevator button. *Your firstborn son will break your heart.* Fanny whirled around, certain she'd heard Sallie's voice. *You need to be strong, Fanny. Not for the others, for yourself.*

Inside the elevator, Fanny pushed the number 5. When the door closed, she whispered, "Are you here, Sallie? You are. I can feel your presence. Does that mean you're here to take . . . my son? Tell me, please." When there was no response to her plea, Fanny's shoulders slumped, then squared immediately when the doors of the elevator slid open to reveal her family in the small waiting area. No one rose to their feet, no one greeted her except Simon, who held out his hand. *You need to be strong, Fanny. Not for the others, for yourself.*

"Where is he, Simon? I want to see him."

"Ten minutes on the hour, Fanny. It's the rule."

"Then break the damn rule. I want to see my son."

"The second door on the right," Simon said.

Fanny heard the whirring sound of Ash's wheelchair. She turned in time to hear him hiss, "What the hell makes you so damn special? You abide by the rules, that's what makes this place work. We've been sitting here for four days with two and a quarter minutes each every hour. Suddenly the Queen of the Mountain decides to show up and claim the time for herself. It doesn't work that way, Fanny. Sit down."

"You're absolutely right, Ash. I'm sorry. Will they let me look through the glass?"

"No."

"Can I get you something to drink, Fanny?" Simon asked, his hand tight on her arm.

"No. Have you seen him, Simon?"

"For a few minutes. I didn't want to take the time away from the kids and Ash. He looks like he's sleeping. Ash is in charge, Fanny. From what I've seen, it's not a bad thing. I'll go get us some coffee while you talk to him. He needs to talk to you."

Fanny walked over to Ash. "It's twenty minutes to the hour. That gives us twenty minutes. Can we talk? Someplace other than here. The end of the hall looks empty."

Fanny walked alongside the whirring wheelchair. "Ash, I'm sorry about before. I just wanted to see him right away. I want you to tell me the truth. How is he? Has there been any change since the first day?"

"Absolutely no change at all. I don't know how he is, Fanny. The doctors don't say much. You know how doctors are. Tyler and John keep us updated hourly. It's as though he's in a deep sleep. Birch was always a deep, sound sleeper. Remember that time we rang a bell in his ear and he didn't move a muscle?" Ash's voice cracked then. Fanny placed a comforting hand on his shoulder.

"I remember. So many memories. All of them good with the exception of a few, and they don't matter."

"What will we do, Fanny, if he doesn't make it?"

"I don't know, Ash. I guess you go on because you don't have a choice. Just pray that doesn't happen."

"Do you seriously think God's going to listen to me? Give me a break."

"You don't know that He won't. Let's go to the chapel. It's just around the corner."

"I can't remember the words. It's been so long since I prayed."

"I know the words. I'll say them aloud and you can repeat them after me. When it's down to the wire, it's all that's left to any of us." Fanny reached for Ash's hand. He grasped it gratefully.

"Fanny, the kids . . . I want you to know I didn't say a word to them. I told them you'd be here. I tried to do what you would have done if you'd been here. I admit I'm a pretty poor substitute, but I did my best. We pulled together. Sunny went off the deep end for a little while, but she's back on track now. I don't want to see you trying to cuddle up to them. They'll turn on you. You have a right to your life, and I told them so. If they don't understand that or if they refuse to accept it, it's their problem."

Fanny nodded as she guided Ash into the small chapel. She lowered her voice "Ash, about Sunny, I want to thank you for getting through to her. It stung a little at first, but I'm okay with it. I did desert her, and I did neglect her. I'll find a way to try and make it right. I want you to know that."

"Do you think I don't know that? We got down and dirty and pulled it all out. Do you know what her defense is?"

"I can't even begin to imagine."

Ash cleared his throat. "Sunny said she wanted to be perfect like you. She refused to believe her symptoms were anything but, as she put it, pregnancy and new mother pains. Ignore it and it will go away was her philosophy. I don't want you to have regrets, Fanny. You were and still are a wonderful mother. I was and probably still am a lousy father. You can cry in here. Everyone does. I see them when they come out. I come in here once a day and just sit."

"She said that?" Fanny wailed. "Do you cry, Ash?"

"Yeah. Yeah, I do. There was some guy in here the other day bawling his head off. I tried to offer him some comfort. I told him about my accident and about Birch. Turns out he's the top surgeon here. He operated on a ten-year-old boy and lost him on the operating table. When he was leaving, he said something Mom always used to say, God never gives you more than you can handle. I'm ready to pray if you are."

"Our father who art . . ."

Simon quietly withdrew from the doorway. His features were so tormented he didn't see Bess until he bumped into her. "I don't think it means what you think it means, Simon. Parents tend to stick together in situations like this."

Simon nodded. "Do they hold hands and pray together? I'm asking because I've never been in a situation like this before. Maybe I should leave. I feel like I'm in the way."

"Do whatever feels right. There's no protocol in matters like this. I'll take that coffee if you aren't going to drink it." Simon handed over the plastic cup. Out of the corner of his eye he saw Ash and Fanny coming down the hallway.

"You can have my time, Fanny. I'll sit here and talk to Simon and Bess." Fanny flew down the hall.

Inside the dim, cool room, Fanny was only aware of her son. The machines, the tubes, the beeping sounds didn't exist. She reached out to touch Birch's hand, certain the words she was searching for would be forthcoming. Her mouth was dry, her tongue felt as if it were two sizes too big for her mouth. She realized then that there were no special words. In the end all she could do was let the tears roll down her cheeks and whisper, "I'm here, Birch."

"I know. I smelled your perfume when you walked in."

Fanny threw her head back as she bit down on her lower lip. Her tears continued to flow. *Thank you, God.*

"Oh, Birch, you're talking. How long have you been awake?"

"I don't know. Is it important?"

"Probably not."

"I had this bad dream that I was in a deep, dark hole, like a well of some kind and Sunny kept yelling and yelling. She wouldn't stop. Dad and Billie started to pull me out, and I kept slipping back. Then I smelled your perfume so I knew they must have pulled me out and I was okay." A second later he was asleep.

Fanny ran from the room and was almost run over by the team of doctors and nurses. "He's awake. He talked to me. Birch talked to me. He fell asleep again, but he's okay. Oh, Ash, Birch is going to be okay. I know it. I feel it."

"What did he say? Mom, tell us everything," Sunny squealed.

Fanny told them, word for word. "He smelled my perfume. Can you imagine?"

"See! See! I told you if you talk to coma patients they hear you. That's all I did. I yelled at him. I did and said everything I could think of. Sage did the same thing. Birch thought he was dreaming, but he wasn't—he was struggling to come out of that dark place. It worked. Did you believe me? No, you did not. From now on you will all listen when I tell you something. He didn't say anything else, did he?" Sunny asked.

"Only what I told you."

"I think those prayers worked," Ash said as he reached for Fanny's hand. Fanny clasped it tightly in both her hands. Simon left quietly and walked down the corridor to the elevator. He wished he was a kid again so he could crawl into a corner and suck his thumb. For the first time in his life he felt truly displaced.

10

⤳

Fanny looked at the kitchen clock and then at the calendar. It was hard to believe thirty days had passed since Birch's accident. Today he was coming home and tomorrow she was going back to the ranch, back to Simon. Her adrenaline started to flow at the thought of what would happen when she saw her husband again. Struggling to keep the conversation going on the phone twice a day was something she didn't want to think about. She wondered again, and not for the first time, how she'd managed to survive in this chrome-and-glass modern penthouse apartment that was Ash's home. She sipped at her coffee as she looked around. There wasn't one single thing in the kitchen that said anyone actually lived here. There wasn't a fingerprint anywhere on the shiny glass and chrome. There were no colorful chair cushions, no green plants, there wasn't even a window to decorate with curtains. She hated it, hated the bouncy chrome chair and the glass-topped table that tilted if you propped your elbows on it. Nor did she like looking at her feet through the glass tabletop.

Fanny heaved a mighty sigh. Tomorrow she'd be back at the ranch, back in her cozy kitchen with the red-checkered curtains and matching cushions on the worn, scarred oak chairs she'd found in an antique store. She wondered if Simon had watered the plants in the kitchen, the plants that she nurtured so tenderly. Of course he hadn't. Simon never did anything unless it affected him in some way. There would be mounds of dirty dishes in the sink. Her plants would be yellow and wilted. There would be dust on all the furniture. The same sheets would probably still be on the bed.

Right now, this very second, she knew Simon was sitting in his rocker by the fieldstone fireplace with his feet propped on the hearth, reading the paper, the small kitchen television set on the counter turned low. He'd be listening with one ear, muttering about excessively cheerful people at six in the morning.

Today was the most important day of her long stay. Ash and Sunny would be back from Johns Hopkins, Birch would be home, and she'd finally get to pack her bags in preparation to going home. Maybe, if things went well, she could leave later in the day and surprise Simon. Would he be surprised? She dreaded the trip because it was time to make decisions. Time to take charge of her life. Time to tell Simon the way it was going to be from now on.

Fanny wandered into the living room and turned on the television set. She watched an early-morning rerun of *Mannix.* All problems solved in sixty minutes allowing for commercial breaks. Life should be so simple and wonderful.

She hated this place. Truly hated it. She would shrivel up and die if she had to live in this shiny, forever-light place. She snorted when she remembered asking Ash if the windows could be opened. He'd stared at her as if she'd sprouted a second head and said, "Why would you want to open the windows when you have air conditioning?" Maybe the word hate wasn't strong enough. She needed to think of other things.

Her eye fell on the stack of mail on the glass-topped table. A funeral home thank-you card from Lily Bell's half sister and brother. "We appreciate your family's kindness during our bereavement." Signed, Anna and Paul Bell. How sad that there was no warmth, no smiles, no anything. They'd all gone to the funeral, paying for it as well. Sage had ordered the stone, closed the bookstore, and filed all the necessary papers. All Lily's assets would eventually be turned over to Anna and Paul. It had been a bad time for all of them. Birch had been stone-faced when he listened to the details. It was only later that Sage had told his mother what happened the night of the accident. Shy, quiet Lily had instigated a fight the moment they got into the car because Birch had told her he was having second thoughts about marriage and wanted to cool their relationship until he could get a better perspective on his feelings. Lily had grabbed the wheel and told Birch to pull over so they could settle it right then and there. He lost control and the car went over the side.

Birch, Sage said, would carry his guilt for a very long time. He would require several months of therapy, fresh air, and good food. He would mend. Would he ever be the same old Birch? Fanny simply didn't know. What she did know was she'd been there for her son, twenty-four hours a day once he came out of his coma. Not because of some misguided sense of guilt, but because she wanted to be with her son, to encourage him, to be there for him. It had taken its toll on her, though. She was hollow-eyed, and she'd lost eight pounds. Birch was on the road to recovery. She said a prayer that Sunny would be as fortunate. In just a few hours she'd know the outcome of all of Sunny's testing. In one hour the results would be in and then Ash and Sunny would fly home. A celebratory luncheon at Sage and Iris's house was scheduled for noon.

How was she to while away the hours until noon? Maybe she should go shopping and fix this place up. Ash would probably throw a fit if she tried to create a homey atmosphere in the penthouse. She shuddered when she thought of the shimmery, quilted black bedspread. She'd ripped the black satin sheets off in the blink of an eye and added cornflower blue flannel ones because Ash kept the temperature at 60 degrees and threatened to cut off her fingers if she played with the thermostat.

Fanny scratched the whole idea of changing the apartment and opted for a bubble bath instead. She could bring in the portable phone and have a risqué conversation with Simon while she soaked. Provided Simon was in the mood for a risqué conversation, which he probably wasn't.

Fanny walked into Sage's house at ten minutes of twelve. "It's good to see you, Fanny," Iris said, hugging her. Sage kissed her lightly on the cheek.

"Where's Birch?" Fanny asked.

"Drinking a cold beer on the patio. He wants to sit in the sun and get some of his color back. Iris is going to fatten him up in no time. He's a little jittery, and he isn't talking too much. I guess that's normal considering what he's gone through. Can I get you a soft drink?"

"Sure, honey. Iris, can I help?"

"It's under control. I'm just so happy I have the day off. Later I'm going to scrub the kitchen and bathroom. I miss doing all those things, believe it or not. I guess underneath it all I'm just a homebody like my mother. I can't wait to have a baby. Sage and I want a whole houseful of kids," she blurted. Fanny laughed.

"You're sure there's nothing I can do?"

"I'm positive. I'm trying to show off a little for my husband. He thinks of me as a bookworm."

"Then I guess I'll keep my son company for a little while."

Fanny sat down across from Birch. "It's a beautiful day, isn't it?"

"There were days when I didn't think I'd make it. I think I . . . no, I know I now have a healthy respect for what Dad endures every day. I have a long road ahead of me, but I'll make it. I have this guilt about Lily. Everything was fine that day until Sunny said something, and for the life of me I can't even remember what it was she said, and suddenly, everything changed for me. Lily knew it, too, because she got really quiet. What does that make me, Mom?"

"It makes you human. It was a tragic accident with tragic consequences."

"How was the funeral?"

"It was a funeral, Birch. You have to put it behind you and go on."

"I guess so. Mom, I've been thinking about something. Promise me you won't laugh when I tell you, okay?"

"I promise."

"I want to leave here when the doctors discharge me. I need to find my own way. I'm sick of the casino business, sick of never seeing sunlight. Sage found his niche, and now it's time for me to find mine. One of the therapists told me about this place in Oregon where I could commune with nature, and from there work into a trail guide. I think I need to do something like that. At least for a little while. Sage and I drifted apart these last few years. I always thought we'd be inseparable forever. I've learned nothing is forever. I don't think I'll ever take anything for granted again."

"It sounds like you've learned a lot in the past thirty days, Birch."

Birch threw his head back and laughed, a pure sound of magical mirth. Fanny smiled. "Life is just full of surprises."

"How do you think Dad will take it when I tell him?"

"I don't know. You can't worry about that, Birch. Each of us has to find our own way, and each of us has to do whatever it takes to find the right path. I think he'll understand."

"I hope so. I want to thank you, Mom, for staying on. Do you know you gave me twenty-seven pep talks in one day? I counted." It was Fanny's turn to laugh.

Iris set a tray of cheese puffs on the patio table. "Your dad and Sunny just drove up. More glasses and more cheese puffs coming up."

"She's perfect for Sage. I've never seen him so happy and content. He can't wait to become a father. You like Iris, don't you, Mom?"

"I adore her. You're right. She's perfect for Sage."

"Wanna hear something funny, Mom? I never . . . I don't like Tyler. I have a feeling that if Sunny's news isn't good, he's going to bail out on her. Sunny and I talked about it once. She said before that happens, she'd beat him to it. When I wasn't worrying about myself, I was worrying about her. She's going to need a real strong guiding hand. I might go back to school and take some forestry courses."

Fanny looked up at the sound of Ash's chair making its way to the patio. *He looks exhausted,* she thought. She could feel her heart jump up into her throat when he reached for one of the cheese puffs. "Where's Sunny?"

"In the kitchen with Iris and Billie. She pulled up right behind us. She's telling them her version. I'll tell you mine. We have a diagnosis as of seven o'clock this morning. Sunny has multiple sclerosis. They tested her out the kazoo. The doctors arrived at their diagnosis by a process of elimination. Right up front I want to tell you it is not good when a young person gets the disease. For some reason it hits them harder than it would if they were struck down later in life. I believe the confirming factor was the elevation of her gamma globulin. As I said, they gave her every neurological test there was. She has a thinning of the myelin sheath covering the nerves. They thought that was very conclusive. When that happens you don't get flexibility. As I said, the disease is very progressive in young people."

"What . . . what's the treatment?"

"There is no treatment, Fanny. They're working on it, but they haven't got it yet. Dietary changes, fresh air, moderate exercise, that kind of thing. She could go along for years the way she is right now. Each attack seems to last longer and take more of a toll. Eventually she'll be in a wheelchair. She'll be able to do things for herself for now. When that is no longer possible, there's a facility in Texas that helps the more severe patients. The doctors were very blunt because Sunny was very blunt. She wanted everything spelled out, all the T's crossed, all the I's dotted. She handled it very well, so well in fact, she called Tyler and told him she wanted a divorce."

"Ash, don't say that," Fanny gasped.

Ash snorted. "That was the good part. The bad part was Tyler said okay."

"I don't believe this! Tyler was probably just humoring her."

"No, Fanny, he wasn't humoring her. She said they haven't shared the same bed since she got pregnant this last time. She said he's never home, doesn't call, and she told me yesterday he had an offer of a job in New York. He didn't tell her. She went through his mail."

"Didn't I tell you, Mom? If I was in better shape, I'd kill the son of a bitch!" Birch growled. "Sage, you need to have a talk with our brother-in-law, and if you feel the need to beat the shit out of him, give him a jab for me."

"To what end? Isn't it better if she gets rid of him now? Iris said it's important for women to do the dumping. With Sunny's condition, I can understand what she's doing. I will have a talk with him, though. When he walks away, I want him to know that we all know what a shit he is. What about the kids?"

"I don't think they got that far in the discussion," Ash said.

"I don't believe this," Fanny said.

"You keep saying that, Fanny. Why is it so hard to believe Tyler is a son of a bitch?"

"Because I thought you were the only son of a bitch in these parts," Fanny snapped. "Tyler was so good with Sallie when she was sick. He loves Sunny. He told me so."

"Guess he loves his career more. Why are you so surprised, Fanny? Didn't you do the same thing to me in a manner of speaking?"

"No, Ash, I did not. You have no right to even think such a thing much less say it, and you know it. Our marriage was over long before your accident. I did everything I could for you."

"Yes, you did, Fanny, and I'm sorry for shooting off my mouth. You did more than I had any right to expect. I've gotta tell you, Sunny's holding up better than I could have under the circumstances."

"I'm concerned about the children."

"He'll give them up. Trust me on that one," Birch said.

"My God, what's happening to this family?" Fanny said through clenched teeth.

"Hi, everybody! Did Dad tell you everything?"

"Yes. Yes, he did. Is there anything we can do?"

"Not a thing. It's such a relief to finally know what it is. I can handle this. As Dad said, I'm fortunate to be in a position where I can hire help and oversee them. If and when I have to go to Texas for periods of time, I can afford it. Most people can't. I'm blessed in that respect. C'mon, c'mon, this is a good day. Birch is home, he's recovering, we have a handle on me and we're together. Ah, I see Dad told you about Tyler. What can I say? It's better for both of us. He has his career to think about, and I do not want to be a burden to him or anyone else. I am really okay with this. I want you to believe me. Tyler and I have not . . . most of the pain is gone. I'm adjusted to life alone. You guys aren't going to stew and fret about me, are you?"

"Of course we are," Fanny said.

"Then you'll be spinning your wheels for nothing. Give me some credit, Mom, I'm not exactly stupid. So I didn't try to find out what it was earlier. It was my choice. It wouldn't have made one bit of difference. It is what it is."

"That's the right attitude, Sunny," Ash said, reaching for her hand.

"Dad had his tests, too. Unfortunately, his won't be back for another week. Iris is calling us, which means it's time to eat. Eat fast, Dad, I want to get home to see the kids."

"I can drive you home, Sunny. Your dad looks tired," Fanny said.

"No, no, that's okay. I can wait. Maybe you should shower and take a nap before we leave. It might be a good idea for me to do the same thing. Thanks for offering, Mom," Sunny said as an afterthought.

Fanny wanted to cry. She would have if Sage hadn't squeezed her arm. "Sunny's right, it is what it is. Just let it be."

Fanny drew a deep breath. "Okay."

"Sage, hold on a minute," Birch said as he struggled out of his chair. "If you have a minute, I'd like to talk to you." Fanny lingered inside the doorway as Sage walked back to his brother.

"I have as many minutes as you need. What's up?"

"I never thanked you for saving my life. I want to do that now."

"You would have done the same thing."

"Yeah, but you need to say things like that out loud. It kind of cements it if you know what I mean. Jesus, I can't tell you how happy I am that you and Iris found each other. We've had some differences the past few years, but my feelings for you never changed."

"I know that, Birch. All of a sudden we found out we were allowed to think and plan separately. We bought into that myth that twins are supposed to think alike for too long. Spit it out right now. Ah, hell, I know exactly what you're going to say. When you recover you're taking off for the wilds of somewhere, probably to hunt big game or some such shit."

"Close. You okay with that? Can you handle things alone?"

"You know better than to ask. I want whatever is best for you. If it takes you ten years to get your shit together in one sock, so be it. Don't go thinking you're *that* important."

Fanny moved on into the dining room the moment she knew Sage put his arm around his brother's shoulders. All was right in her sons' world.

The luncheon festivities broke up at three o'clock. Fanny and Ash said their good-byes and headed for the door. "I'll pick you up at seven, Sunny."

"Okay, Dad."

"Sunny, I'm proud of you. If you need me or if there's anything . . ."

"Sure, Mom. I'll call," Sunny said interrupting her. "I have to go and do my share of cleaning up, or Billie will do it for me. Drive carefully."

Hot tears pricked at Fanny's eyelids. "I think," Fanny said, "that was one of the neatest brush-offs I've ever gotten. She's better than you ever were, Ash."

"Listen, Fanny, I know you're in a hurry to get back to the ranch, but I'd like to ask a favor. Would you mind sticking around for a few hours? Let me get a couple of hours' sleep and a shower. I need to talk to you about something. I wouldn't ask, but it's very important. I'm dead on my ass. I'd say feet but my feet don't work these days. What do you say?"

"All right, Ash. I'll go shopping. Six o'clock, no later. I don't like driving at night."

"Stay till morning."

"No. I'm packed and ready to go. I want to be around my own things, in my own house. That's where my life is. Drop me off here on the corner. Is there anything I can get for you?"

"Not a thing. I'll see you at six o'clock." Fanny nodded.

Instead of going shopping, Fanny stopped at the first drugstore she came to and called Simon. When the machine came on, she left her name and said she'd call back later. She meandered through the drugstore looking at the array of cosmetics. She stifled a laugh when she recalled how Bess had snitched almost all of her cosmetics from her father's drugstore. It was strange how she remembered things from the past, pleasant things. Memories. So many of them. In the end, she settled for a paperback novel about murder and mayhem and went to the park to read it.

By the end of chapter two she'd figured out the murderer so she tossed the book into the trash barrel next to the bench. She concentrated on watching a group of plump pigeons squabble over a child's spilled popcorn. She sat for a very long time staring off into space. When a toddler's ball rolled against her shoe, she kicked it toward the little boy, who squealed his pleasure. She thought about her grandson, Jake. She wondered if he had a bright red ball. Sunny was partial to yellow and blue. She should know what color his ball was. She'd never heard him call her grandma. Her eyes started to burn. Guilty! Guilty! Guilty of being a lousy grandmother. She sat bolt upright on the wooden bench. What if Tyler tried to take the children from Sunny because of her condition? "Over my dead body," she seethed. She was certain it would happen unless he signed away his parental rights. *Don't think about that, Fanny. If it happens, you'll deal with it then. All the worrying in the world won't change things if they're meant to happen.*

Fanny looked at her watch. Time to head back to Babylon. In the lobby she stopped at the florist and bought two dozen yellow roses with assorted greenery. When she paid for them, she realized how stupid it was. Ash was going to the mountain and she was leaving. Who would enjoy the flowers? She was doing a lot of stupid things of late.

Ash was waiting for her, his hair still damp from the shower. She handed him the flowers. He sniffed them and smiled. "I don't think anyone ever gave me flowers before. Thanks, Fanny."

"What do you want to talk about, Ash?"

"Everything in the world. Fanny, look at me. Tell me what you see, and be honest."

"I see a tired, weary, bitter man."

"You're right. I'm also a man who's lost his edge. I can't do this anymore. I need to get out while I can still wheel my chair. I got the results from my tests yesterday. I didn't tell Sunny because she has enough on her plate right now. The doctors were kind, but truthful. I have two years, Fanny, three if I'm lucky. One of the more outspoken doctors said a year. I guess it's a crapshoot. There's nothing they can do for me, just like there's nothing they can do for Sunny. I bawled, Fanny. I just sat there and I goddamn bawled my head off.

Some cockamamie part of me really believed I could live forever."

Fanny blinked. She felt like someone had taken a sledgehammer to the middle of her stomach. "Ash, there are other doctors. They make new discoveries every day in the medical field. You can't give up. A positive attitude is half the battle."

"Fanny, I had the best of the best. Tests don't lie. To show you what a bastard I am, I made them run those tests three times because I refused to believe the results. My liver is almost gone, and so are my kidneys. I'm over the worst of the shock now so I can think clearly. Birch is leaving. I think we both knew that was going to happen. He hates this business just the way Sage hates it. Sunny loves it. Go figure."

"Ash, what are you trying to say?" Fanny felt naked with fear.

"I want to move to the mountain and leave this behind me. I want to know I'm leaving it in good hands—*your hands.* It's the only solution, Fanny. Sunny needs me. The truth is, I need her just as much. If you stop and think about the whole picture, it makes sense. You and Simon can handle this casino. Billie and Sage can handle your clothing business. You don't work at it anymore anyway."

"No, Ash, no, no, no. I hate this town. I hate this business."

"You hate it because of me. Be fair."

"Sell it, bank the money."

"Fanny, it's a gold mine. Only a fool would sell a gold mine."

"Hire people to run it. No, Ash, I can't do it. How can you ask me to give up my life? Simon hates this business, too. *NO!* Besides, he would never agree."

"It's for the family, Fanny. I'm going to die. You aren't doing it for me. Sunny is going to be incapacitated sooner than you think. You know what, it was her idea to ask you. She said . . . never mind. It's not important what she said."

"What did she say, Ash?"

"She said exactly what you just said. She said you would never give up your new life for any of us. She told me to ask you what Jake's middle name is? What is it, Fanny?"

"It's . . . it's . . . damn you, Ash, that child's middle name has nothing to do with this."

"It has everything to do with it, Fanny. How old was Jake when he started to walk? How old was he when he cut his first tooth? When did he get his first black eye? How come, bastard that I am, I know those things and you don't? Just for the record, those were questions Sunny asked first. I'm waiting for your answers, Fanny."

"I'm not going to let you throw a guilt trip on me, Ash."

"This is family, Fanny. When it's family, you pick up the slack. Isn't that what you always said? Where's all that family bullshit you doled out like cod liver oil? It *was* bullshit, wasn't it? Family is important when it's convenient for you. You got what you want so fuck the rest of us, right?"

"No, that's not right."

"Sure it is. Jesus Christ, we couldn't even find you for four days when Birch had his accident. You were off thinking. Thinking about this family and what was wrong with it. What the hell happened to motherhood, apple pie, and all that good stuff you used to jam down our throats?"

"I'm never going to forgive you for this, Ash."

"Like I give a good rat's ass about your forgiveness. When you're looking at what I'm looking at, it hardly seems important. Your blissful life doesn't seem too important to me either. Yeah, I have bushel baskets full of regrets. This is my one chance; hell, it's my only chance to make things right. I'm looking it right in the face, Fanny, and I'm not denying any of my misdeeds. My mother came to this state and made it what it is today. Babylon was built for my mother and father. It was my living monument to them. It's staying in this family, one way or the other. What that means to you is it's an either or answer."

"What's the or?"

"You don't want to know."

"Yes. I want to know."

Ash's voice was so low she had to strain to hear the words. "Sunny said she'd give the kids up to Tyler and come back here and run the casino. Before you jump down my throat, I told her it was out of the question. She would do it to show you up, Fanny. You committed the cardinal sin. You fucked with her kids. You know, Fanny, it's that motherhood thing. Lioness protecting her cubs. You should recognize the drill."

"I'd never have given up my children. Not under any circumstances. I would have cleaned toilets in dirty gas stations before I did that. Don't threaten me, Ash. No daughter of mine would do such a thing. Sunny loves those children. She's a wonderful mother."

"How would you know? Cut the bullshit, Fanny, this is me you're talking to. Yeah, Sunny loves the kids, but guess what. Tyler loves them, too, and he's going to fight for them at some point in time. Sunny is going to fight for what she wants just the way you're fighting for that wonderful new life you have. Surely you understand where she's coming from. That girl is never going to forgive you, Fanny, for not being there for her children. I know that hurts you right down to your soul. I see it in your face. Jesus Christ, Fanny, I didn't want to tell you that. You left me no choice. You're the last to know. You probably think I'm lying. Check it out, talk to the kids, with Bess, they'll tell you. Just don't tell Sunny I told you. The fact that you think I'm lying is pretty goddamn sad if you want my opinion.

"Fanny, I want you to know something. In my own way I loved you as much as I was capable of loving anyone. I'm sorry for what I put you through, sorry I couldn't love you the way you wanted to be loved. I'm sorry I wasn't a better husband and father. I guess when it comes right down to it, I'm sorry about everything."

"Ash, what's Jake's middle name?" Fanny whispered.

"Matthew. At first she was going to name him after Birch or Sage but changed her mind at the church. She didn't want to show favoritism. He walked when he was ten months. He cut his first tooth at seven months. He crawled backwards for a little while. Sunny was really concerned about that, but the doctor said it was okay. He's allergic to penicillin and he has this monster strawberry birthmark on his rump. He gave up his bottle at eleven months, said his first word at a year. He called me Pop Pop the day he turned one. I got such a kick out of that. He knows who you are because Sunny showed him pictures of you and talks about you to him. You should have seen his last birthday party, Fanny. We laughed ourselves silly over that kid. He has friends on the mountain. Chue's grandkids come over to play all the time. You wouldn't believe Christmas. I honest to God had fun."

"Ash, don't tell me any more."

"Why, Fanny? Aren't you the one who always said look it in the face and go on from there? Time's up, I gotta pick up Sunny. Stay as long as you like or leave if that's what you want to do."

"Aren't you coming back?"

"Nope."

"Ash, you can't do this!"

"Watch me."

"Simon won't agree to this. I don't know how to run this casino. I'm not saying I'm not going to do it . . . Ash, come back here."

"I bet you could turn this place into something spectacular without even trying. Just look what those flowers do for the table."

Fanny ran after the wheelchair. She dropped to her knees. "Ash, would she give those babies of hers up?"

Tears blurred Ash's eyes. "I'd try to stop her, Fanny. I don't know what she'll do after I'm gone."

"I hate your guts, Ash Thornton," Fanny screamed.

"I used to hate yours. I don't anymore. See you around, Fanny."

Fanny beat at the thick carpeting with her clenched fists until her hands were numb. Sobbing, she crawled on her hands and knees to the coffee table. She reached for the vase of roses and threw it at the double teakwood doors. "Do you hear me, Ash Thornton, I hate you? I hate you for doing this to me. All you do is take and take and take."

Exhausted, Fanny crawled up onto the deep sofa. She needed to call Simon. No, she needed to call Bess to verify Ash's cruel words. She dialed her friend's number and spoke haltingly. "Bess, I'm going to ask you a question. If you know the answer just say yes or no. When I hear your answer, I'm going to hang up. No, I'm not all right. I will probably never be all right again. In the scheme of things I don't suppose it matters very much. Did Sunny tell you and my children that she would never forgive me . . . for not being there for Jake?" Fanny sucked in her breath as she waited for Bess's response. "Your answer is yes?"

Fanny hung up the phone and drew a second deep breath.

Now it was time to call Simon.

11

Fanny stared at the ringing phone in her hand. She broke the connection as tears dripped down her cheeks. Her life was slipping away, and she was helpless to stop it. She picked up the phone again. She slapped the receiver back into the cradle. How in the world was she going to tell Simon what had just transpired with Ash?

Jackson Matthew Ford. A blue-eyed, blond cherub nicknamed little Jake. Fanny's thoughts whirled back in time to the holdup on the bus where a man named Jake had asked her to hold his money and then disappeared. Now there was a little Jake in her life. A grandson. Her daughter's firstborn child. How could she have been so stupid? She thought about the first three years when all the brown envelopes arrived at the ranch with huge scrawled letters across the front, PHOTOGRAPHS—DO NOT BEND. She remembered looking at them, remembered smiling at the infant's chubby cheeks and commenting to Simon that Jake looked like Tyler. Simon's cold-eyed stare forced her to shove the pictures in a drawer. She had all good intentions of framing them at some point in time. She never had. What was it Ash said? You're a piss-poor excuse for a mother and a bigger piss-poor excuse as a grandmother. Guilty as charged.

Fanny looked at the clock. She closed her eyes and envisioned Simon sitting on the front porch waiting with a bottle of wine in an ice bucket. He'd be sitting on the glider with a clear view of the road. The moment he saw her headlights, he'd run to the road and sweep her in his arms as she stepped from the car. It wasn't going to happen. At best it wasn't even a good dream. If anything it was a nightmare.

Fanny felt a surge of panic. Her mind screamed, *Run.* Don't let Ash do this to you. Too late; he'd already done it, and she was here, the living proof that once again Ash called the shots. She looked around, her face contorting in rage.

She moved then, upending the glass-topped coffee table. Stark alabaster figures sailed through the air, shattering the mirrored walls. She kicked and gouged at the leather furniture with a gold letter opener. Stuffing spilled everywhere. Pushing and shoving, she managed to topple the chrome shelving that held stereo equipment and a monster television set. When the glass remained intact on the television, she slammed a crystal lamp into the middle. Glass scattered everywhere. The portable bar on wheels with every liquor known to man along with crystal glasses skidded across the room to topple over in a pile of broken glass. The window treatments puffed and billowed as she yanked and ripped. The neon night outside the building glared at her.

Hate and despair drove her to the phone. She dialed from memory. "This is Fanny Logan. Turn the power off at Babylon. Do it NOW!" She yanked at the phone wire, the phone spiraling across the room to land in a pool of brandy.

Fanny squeezed her eyes shut. When she opened them a second later, she was standing in darkness. She made her way across the room before she crumpled to the floor, her outstretched hand grappling for the phone. She plucked at the receiver. There was no dial tone. She cried then because she didn't know what else to do.

What seemed like a long time later, Fanny wiped at her tears when she heard someone hammer on the double doors. Her head high, she smoothed back her hair and straightened her dress. Slipping and sliding in the broken glass, she made her way to the door. A circle of light slapped her in the face. She turned her head. "Yes, what can I do for you?"

"The power went off in the casino. Is Mr. Thornton here? He's needed on the floor."

"Mr. Thornton doesn't live here anymore," Fanny said.

The beam of the flashlight arched around the interior of the room. "Mrs. Thornton, did something happen here? Are you all right?"

"I guess you could say something happened. Do I look all right to you?"

"Yes, ma'am. What should I tell the staff? No one knows how to work the generators except Mr. Thornton."

"Is that so? You are of course referring to those three-million-dollar generators?"

"Yes, ma'am. What should we do?"

"Go home and go to bed. That's what I'm going to do. Don't disturb me again tonight." Fanny slammed the door shut in the man's face.

Fanny made her way to the bedroom, where she fell across the bed. She was asleep in the time it took her head to touch the pillow.

Fanny bolted from the bed when she heard sharp banging on the door. She was appalled at her reflection in the floor-length mirror. She'd slept in her clothes. What was worse, she *looked* like she'd slept in her clothes.

Fanny opened the door. Ash's heavy hitters. The second, third, and fourth string in the chain of command. "Yes?" She stood aside for the men to enter the apartment. She offered no explanations or apologies for the condition of the room.

"Mrs. Thornton, we need to speak with your . . . with Mr. Thornton," the second string said. The third and fourth string bobbed their heads in agreement.

"Mr. Thornton vacated the premises yesterday."

"Is there a way to reach him?" the second string queried.

"No."

"The power's off in the entire building. We're losing money, Mrs. Thornton. We're the only casino with a power loss. By any chance, did you turn the power off?"

"As a matter of fact I did. I was making a statement."

"A statement," the first, second, third, and fourth strings said in unison.

"Uh-huh. When I'm ready to make my coffee I'll turn the power back on. Is there anything else this morning?"

"Well . . . do you want housekeeping to, ah . . . ?"

"Not at this time. You can send a telephone repair man up here immediately. Have all the employees assembled in the ballroom at noon for a company meeting."

"Is Mr. Thornton coming back?" the fourth string asked.

"No. Good day, gentlemen."

Fanny finished showering and dressing just as her telephone was repaired. "It must have been some party," the man quipped as she signed her name to the work order.

"I was having a bad hair day," Fanny said.

"Uh-huh," the man said, backing out the door.

Fanny picked up the phone and dialed the power company. "This is Fanny Logan." She gave her password and said, "You can turn the power back on."

You need to call Simon now and explain why you're still here.

The phone in her hand started to ring. She waited till it grew silent before she picked up the receiver. "Bess, I know it's early, but could you come over to the penthouse and have coffee with me? I really need to talk to you. Fine. I'll be waiting."

Call Simon. By now he knows something is wrong. Call him.

The phone rang again. Fanny ignored it as she measured coffee into the wire basket. She chain-smoked until she heard the last plop-plop and the electric pot shut itself off.

The phone continued to ring. Fanny continued to ignore it. When she couldn't stand the continual jangling a moment longer, she took the receiver off the hook and disconnected the answering machine.

Now, if she could just remember where her purse was, she could make her second call. It was on the kitchen counter, right where she'd left it. Fanny rummaged until she found her address book. She flipped through the pages, memorized the number as she spieled it off to the operator.

The receiver was picked up in a faraway place by a sleepy voice. The sleepy voice became wide-awake the moment Fanny identified herself and apologized for the early-morning time difference. "I can be there by four o'clock your time, possibly sooner. Reschedule your meeting for five o'clock. With Bess, you, and me, we can handle anything. Take a deep breath and call Simon."

On the other side of the Pacific Ocean, Billie Coleman turned to Thad. "Fanny needs me, Thad."

He asked no questions. "Then we better get cracking so I'm first off the runway."

As Billie and Thad packed their bags, Bess Noble was ringing the doorbell at the penthouse apartment in Babylon Towers. She linked her arm with Fanny's as she pretended not to see the destruction all about her.

In the kitchen, Bess listened to her longtime friend until she stopped speaking, breathless with the effort. "And you haven't called Simon? Fanny, that's not like you. Regardless of what's going on in your life, you have to be fair to him. You can't know Simon won't agree to come here."

"There are some things in life that are a given, Bess, and this is one of those givens. Simon left this town when he was sixteen. He hates it with a passion. He told me once nothing in the world could make him live here. I think Simon is lost to me now. We've come to the end of our particular road, Bess. I know it in my heart. You know it too, so don't pretend with me. You and I always used to say we had choices and options. Mine all ran out yesterday."

"Fanny, I am so sorry. I know you don't want to hear this, but Ash is right about Sunny. As for Ash himself, he's doing what he has to do. It sounds like he's finally . . . What's that tired old cliché, seen the light?"

"And once again he's left it up to me to carry on. I'm tired, Bess, I can't keep doing this. What about my life? Somewhere, someplace, somehow, I must have earned some small measure of happiness. Is that all I get, a few lousy years? I could count the happy days on both hands during those years."

"I think you might be selling Simon short. He won't let you get away from him. He loves you too much. When you find people you can trust you can have them take over the casino."

"It's not that kind of business, Bess. Owner-operated means owner-operated. The Strip is full of sharks and barracudas. Right now the word is out, and they're gathering. The smart money is saying I can't do this and the dumb money . . . well, there isn't any dumb money. That's the bottom line. I want you to help me run this casino.

I called Billie, and she'll be here by four this afternoon. Which reminds me, I have to reschedule the meeting. Are you in, Bess? Do you have to talk to John first? It's going to be different from Sunny's Togs and Rainbow Babies."

"I'm in, Fanny. No, I do not have to talk to John, but I will. ST and RB run so smoothly it bothers me to take a paycheck. Now why don't you call Simon, and I'll start cleaning up the living room?"

"I don't want you cleaning up the living room. I need to live with that mess for a while so I don't ever forget the rage that attacked me last night. I never thought it was possible for me to . . . go berserk like that. Who knows, I may never clean it up."

Bess made a fresh pot of coffee while Fanny called downstairs to the office to reschedule the meeting.

"Sunny will never forgive me, will she, Bess?"

"At some point she will. A mother-daughter bond is very strong, Fanny. She's going through a lot right now. Time heals all wounds. We both know that."

"The scars never go away. Both of us know that, too. How could I have been so stupid? Do you know the middle names of your grandchildren?"

"It's not the same thing, Fanny."

"Don't try and make me feel better. Ash was right. All I was concerned about was my happiness. That's a laugh in itself. I had to work at pretending to be happy. Look what those years have gotten me. Yesterday I wanted to take a handful of Ash's pills and end it all, but I was too much of a coward. Ash is going to die. Sunny's prognosis isn't good, but she's handling it in true Sunny fashion. She's close to Ash now and he needs her as much as she needs him. I'm grateful for that. Birch is going away to . . . contemplate his life. Billie is so wrapped up in the business half the time she doesn't know what day it is. Sage is polite to me. I feel like a stranger in my own family."

"Think of it as temporary, Fanny. There's light at the end of the tunnel. You just haven't gotten far enough into the tunnel to see it."

"If I had one wish, do you know what it would be, Bess?"

"That Simon would pop up on the doorstep saying he's always wanted to live in a penthouse."

"Not even close. I don't even think Simon loves me. He plays a good game of pretend, but that's what it is, a pretend game. I feel so stupid. I'd wish Sunny would bring Jake here so I could get to know him. I think Ash loves that little guy more than he loved his own kids when they were little. He knows everything about him. He must have gone to Sunrise a lot. I never knew that. No one ever told me. Ash isn't the same anymore. It's not just the death sentence he's living under either. The change must have started when Jake was born. If only I could unring the bell."

"You can't, so stop torturing yourself. Go in the bedroom and call Simon. I'll make us some pancakes."

In the bedroom, Fanny kicked off her shoes before she snuggled between the periwinkle-colored sheets. Her hand trembled as she dialed the operator to place the call. She wasn't surprised when it was picked up on the first ring. "Simon, it's Fanny."

"Fanny! Thank God. Are you okay? Did you break down along the way? I've been chewing my nails here. I planned to give it one more hour and then I was going to start out to look for you. We need to get a phone for your car. Damn, I keep forgetting you're driving a rental. Why didn't you call, Fanny? I waited up all night for you. I didn't think it was possible to miss someone so much. Where are you? When will you get here?"

Fanny clenched her teeth. He *sounded* like the old Simon, the Simon she'd fallen in love with. Underneath, though, she could hear the anger.

"Simon. Oh, Simon . . . Ash is dying. He doesn't have long. A year, maybe a little longer. Ash puts his own spin on everything including his death. Sunny . . . oh, Simon, I've made such a mess of things because I let you dictate to me where my family is concerned. It's not all your fault, I went along with it. What I'm trying to say is, Ash dumped the casino on me. I had no other choice. I need to hear you tell me you understand."

"I can't do that because I don't understand. What in the world are you talking about? Ash wouldn't dump his casino on anybody. He thinks it's his. How do you know this isn't just another one of Ash's schemes?" Fanny shuddered at her husband's frosty voice.

"Give me some credit, Simon. I know."

"What are you trying to tell me, Fanny?"

"I'm trying . . . what I'm trying to say is . . . I can't come back to the ranch. If I do, I won't be able to leave. You had too much of a hold on me. I can't allow that to happen again. I have to stay here. I have to take over for Ash. He's doing what has to be done for Sunny. I have to respect that. If he doesn't have that much time left, I need to do what I can. Please tell me you understand. It's my family, Simon. I turned my back on them once. I'll never do it again."

"Fanny, you don't know the first thing about running a casino. Ash can hire qualified people. He's jerking your strings, and you're allowing it. I didn't sign on for this, Fanny. At the risk of repeating myself, your children aren't kids anymore."

"No, Simon, this time he is not jerking my strings. A family business cannot be run by outsiders. I didn't know anything about the clothing business in the beginning either. I can learn because I have to learn. Don't you see, I have to try and make it right for everyone?"

"Fanny, listen to me. Sell the damn casino. If you don't, it's going to destroy us. Jesus, you know how much I hate that business and that town."

"I can't do that either. I am so sorry. I think I always knew this was going to happen at some point. Is there anything I can say to make you want to come here and run the casino with me?"

"Not if you paid me my weight in gold."

Fanny's voice was a bare whisper. "I know. You always knew my family would come first. You tried to rob me of them, Simon. I'm having trouble dealing with that."

Simon's whisper matched her own. "Yes, I knew. We both gambled. Something both of us said we would never do. This is the result. What if you fail, Fanny? Then will you come crawling back to me?"

"That's an awful thing to say to me, Simon. I'll know I gave it my best shot. All any of us can do is our best. If I fail, it won't be for lack of trying. I can't turn my back on my family. I did it once when I married you. Do you realize, Simon, that I don't know my grandson? I never framed his pictures. I didn't hear my own daughter's pleas. Ash, of all people, knew those things. I didn't. I'm having a really hard time with that, Simon. Ash has stepped in and taken my place with Sunny. That alone is eating me alive. It's a good thing, so I can live with it. Right now they need each other. The only thing left for me to do is what I'm doing now. I wish it were different."

Simon's voice was so angry and choked, Fanny had trouble distinguishing the words. "I would do anything in the world for you. Except move to that hellhole. Inside of a week they'd have to lock me up."

"I know. That's why I'm not asking you to come here. I love you, Simon."

"Not enough to turn your back on that damn casino."

"The casino is only part of it. I cannot, I will not turn my back on my family."

"Ash isn't your family anymore."

"He's the father of my children and he's dying. This is tearing me up inside, Simon. We can talk it to death, but in the end we'll be back at our starting point. The day we left to come here you knew I wasn't happy with the way things were between us. We need to talk about us very soon. Will you send Daisy here? Her crate is in the garage."

"What am I supposed to do now? We had a life up until a month ago. Do you want a divorce? Are we separating? I need to know."

"I . . . I didn't think that far ahead, Simon. I'll do whatever you want. Perhaps in time things will change. I'm in no position right now to make promises."

"Aren't you coming back for your things?"

"I can't. If I see you, if I see the dogs and the ranch, I won't leave. I'll hunker in and be miserable. You'll find a way to keep me there. I can't allow that to happen. I have to begin over right here. I have such rage and anger inside me. Last night I smashed up this apartment and had the electric company turn off the power in the casino. Does that give you some idea of the state I'm in?"

"Fanny—"

"It is what it is. I love you, Simon." Fanny waited for Simon to repeat the words she'd just uttered.

"The way you say a part of you will always love Ash? That's not good enough for me, Fanny." What she heard next was the connection being broken. She knuckled her burning eyes.

Bess had said something about pancakes. Fanny climbed from the bed and straightened the sheets. Ash Thornton's credo; never look back. She needed to subscribe to that credo starting right now.

In the kitchen she sat down at the table. "Simon doesn't want to live here. He asked me if we were getting divorced."

"He just needs a little time, Fanny. When he starts to miss you so much he can't stand it, he'll show up. He needs you too much to walk away."

"He's not doing the walking, I am. You're wrong. Nothing in this world could make Simon come here to live. Absolutely nothing. He's going to send Daisy down by air. I'll have to pick her up at the airport."

"Eat, Fanny."

Fanny mashed the pancakes on her plate. "What do I do now, Bess?"

"You take it one day at a time. What's meant to be will be."

"We're home, Dad. Five bucks says Jake is here in"—Sunny looked at her watch—"forty-five seconds."

"That's a sucker bet," Ash said, engaging the lift device in the van. "However, I'll take it and say he gets here in thirty-nine seconds. Here he comes, chocolate ice-cream cone in hand, two fat kittens on his trail. Thirty-eight seconds! Fork it over, young lady."

Sunny fished in the pocket of her jeans and handed over a five-dollar bill.

"Here you go, sport. Tell Pop Pop where it goes."

"Jake's bank?" the little boy giggled.

"How much do you have in your bank?"

"A fortune."

"Attaboy. Climb on and we'll ride into the house." The little boy climbed onto Ash's lap, his chubby arms circling his grandfather's neck.

"Luv you, luv you, luv you," Jake said, smothering Ash's face with kisses.

"What about Mommy?"

"Luvs her, too."

"Man, you'd think we went away for two months instead of an hour at the grocery store. You kids never greeted me like this when I came home. Or, did you and I just can't remember?"

"Sometimes we did. Sometimes we didn't. Mom always waited to gauge your mood and then told us if it was okay. Most times it was. Go inside. I'll carry the groceries in."

"I can carry something. Just dump it in my lap."

"Dad, stop babying me. I can do it. I want to do it. I want to do everything I can while I can. Let's have some lemonade in the garden."

"Make that beer and it's a deal. God, I can't tell you what a relief it is since the elevator was installed. That was good thinking on your part to have it done while we were at Johns Hopkins. No mess, no bother."

"I did it as much for me as for you. Tyler and I had an unholy row about it. He said it was an asshole thing to do."

"Guess what? Tyler's an asshole," Ash said. "We shouldn't be talking like this in front of Jake."

"No, we shouldn't. It slipped out. He's heard worse when Tyler and I went at it. Come on, slumber bunny, time to take a nap. You need to tell me how your sister did while I was at the store with Pop Pop. Did she cry?"

"Lots and lots. Hers sleeping now."

"That's good. Run to the bathroom the way Daddy showed you. Lift the seat, okay?"

"Where's Daddy?"

"Daddy went away."

"Him come back?"

"Sometime. Pop Pop is here now. He's going to sleep in the room next to yours. Won't that be nice?"

"Uh-huh. Him eat eggs with me."

"You bet. Give me a kiss. Sleep tight."

"Don't let the bed bugs bite," the little boy giggled.

Sunny checked on the sleeping baby. How beautiful she was. *Please, God,* she prayed, *let me stay here long enough to see them both grow up.*

The garden was in full bloom, the colorful chaise longues vying for attention with the rainbow of flowers. Ash slipped from his chair to the thick padding and stretched out his legs. "Take a load off, kiddo, and let's talk. I say we start with Tyler and get that out of the way."

"I'm okay with it. I've had a whole year to get used to the idea that the marriage wasn't working. It's better we split up now than later. He's young. He has a wonderful career ahead of him. He needs a wife who can do that social thing. I can't do that. Sooner or later he'd cheat on me, and I'd be devastated. He can see the kids when he wants, he's promised to send support money. We'll alternate holidays, that kind of thing. He loves Jake. He's hardly had time to get to know Polly. If he starts to make demands, well, isn't that why there are so many lawyers? I don't think he'll mess with this family. Now that's out of the way what else do you want to talk about?"

"Your mother."

"How about something else? How about those test results you say you didn't get?"

Ash shrugged. "Let's talk about both things. Your mother first. She loves you very much. I know that for a fact. Can't you ease up a little?"

"What did I do wrong?"

"You didn't do anything wrong. You were polite, you kissed her hello, and you kissed her good-bye. You two used to be so close. How can you negate that?"

Sunny shrugged. "Mom had other things on her mind. I was so miserable I'd call her two or three times a day. One day she snapped at me over the phone. She said 'what do you want this time?' I didn't want anything, I just wanted to talk to her because I missed her. I was going to tell her that, too. I didn't call after that. She called once a month, you know, duty calls. I didn't want that. I made sure I was never around between one and three on the first Sunday of every month. It was the same with Sage, Birch, and Billie. They started doing the same thing I did. They weren't available. They let the machine take the message. You know what, Mom never even noticed. She made the call. We weren't there, our tough luck. This family has gone to hell."

"She's going to take over the casino. What do you have to say to that?"

"Whoopee," Sunny said snidely. "What did Uncle Simon have to say about it?"

"I don't imagine he likes it at all. He'll probably stay in California and Fanny will stay in town and they'll visit on weekends."

"That won't last. Mom is one of those touchy-feely people. She'll want him with her. I don't think she can do it, Dad. Do you want me to give her a hand? I could do mornings."

"I think she can handle it. Let's give her a chance. We can take the kids down in a few weeks. We could even do a picnic if you're up to it."

"No. That is not a good idea. It won't work, Dad. Sage, Billie, and Iris are coming up next weekend. Sage is going to barbecue if you can believe that."

"Are you inviting your mother?"

"No, and don't keep asking me to do things like that. She had her chance, and she blew it. I have one last thing to say, and then we aren't going to talk about Mom anymore. I heard Bess tell Billie that when she went to the ranch to see Mom, there were no pictures of any of us in the house. I sent dozens of pictures of Jake. Mom got married, moved away and that was the end of us. It didn't just sting a little. It stung a lot. So, what did your tests show?"

"Well, the good news is they said I have three pretty good years ahead and the bad news is the rest of the years are downhill. I look at it this way, three is better than zip. After that, who knows, maybe someone will come up with something that will work for my condition. Attitude is everything."

"Aren't you going to miss Babylon? You don't have to stay here with me."

"I want to. I love Jake. I want to watch him grow up. I want to be a part of his life, and I want to be around in case Tyler starts getting strange ideas. The noise, the crowds, the late hours, the drinking, the cigarette smoke, it started to get to me. We built it, got it off the ground, and it's taken off. They said it couldn't be done, but by God, we all pulled together and did it. Now, it's time for me to rest on my laurels. For the first time in my life I'm looking forward to doing absolutely nothing."

"There's plenty of nothing up here. What would you like for supper?"

"How about some good old pan gravy, pork chops, and those seasoned potatoes?"

"Sounds good to me. Mitzi made fresh bread today."

"Ah, soft butter, strawberry jam, and a good cup of coffee. Better than any dessert. And before we go to bed one of your peanut butter and banana sandwiches."

"Absolutely. Take a nap, Dad. Polly is due to wake up, and I don't want her waking Jake. I'll put your supper order in and see you later."

"I think I will take a nap."

The moment Sunny was out of sight, Ash squeezed his eyes shut. "I tried, Fanny. I'll keep at it. It's the least I can do for you," he muttered as he drifted into sleep.

12

"Listen," Fanny said, a desperate tone to her voice, "this isn't necessary. Why do I need this ritzy outfit and fancy hairdo? This is not who I am. I'm a simple person with simple wants and tastes. I feel like I'm playing dress-up."

"You *were* a simple person," Billie Coleman said. "The key word is were. Image is everything. I am so glad I had this dress with me. If you don't make any sudden movements, the pins will stay intact and you'll be fine. You could pass for a Wall Street banker in this outfit. First appearances are everything."

"Your hair and makeup are perfect. You march into that room like you're in control. We'll be right behind you," Bess said.

"And say what?" Fanny demanded.

"You say what we just discussed. You say things will remain as they are. Then you say, for now. You emphasize the words 'for now.' That alone will keep everyone on their toes. Remember, you are not stepping into Ash's shoes, you're stepping into Sallie Thornton's. That's how your staff, the casino owners on the Strip, as well as the media are going to view you. It's not a bad thing, Fanny. Sallie was a legend in her own time. Even if you don't think you can wear her shoes, pretend they fit. The way I see it, men don't like taking orders from a woman. That's going to be your biggest hurdle. You speak once, you speak softly, and you carry a big stick. If it worked for Teddy Roosevelt, it will work for you," Billie said.

"I don't answer any questions, especially where Ash is concerned," Fanny said. "I have that down. For now, it's business as usual. After the meeting we're bringing all the personnel files up here to go over them. Then, over the next few days, we'll conduct one-on-one meetings with all the key players."

Bess clapped her hands. "See. You got it. Practice that look where you stare right through a person. Power is the most powerful aphrodisiac in the world, and right now the word is out and everyone in this town is frightened out of their wits. Turning off the power last night was a stroke of genius. All the owners on the Strip are wondering why. The fact that you did it to your own casino has them all in a tizzy. They're just waiting for your next move. Tonight we have to decide that next move. You're the star of this meeting, Fanny. Bess and I are just observers. It's five minutes to five. Time to go downstairs. Before we go, Fanny, did you really tell those guys you turned the power back on so you could make coffee?"

"Yes. I imagine the word is out on the street about that little tidbit by now."

"Always keep 'em guessing," Billie said as she held the door open for Bess and Fanny.

"Remember now, Fanny, you aren't a Girl Scout leader. March in there like you own the place."

I can do this. I know I can do this. I will do this. I will do this because I have to do this. Fanny opened the door to the grand ballroom. She almost faltered at the sea of faces staring at her. She walked across the room and up the four steps to the bandstand. She held her hand up for silence and wondered why she bothered. If a pin dropped, she could have heard it.

"Ladies and gentlemen, thank you for coming. I'll make this as brief as possible. As of today I will be in control of this casino. You will take your orders from me and you will answer to me and no one else. If this is going to be a problem for any of you, you should leave now." Fanny waited several minutes to see if anyone was going to walk toward the door. "It's business as usual. *For now.* One last thing. Babylon business stays in Babylon. I don't think I need to spell out what that means to any of you. Oh, one other thing, always be aware that I have friends on the *other side of the street.* That's all, ladies and gentlemen. You may resume your duties."

When the door closed behind the employees, Bess did a jig and Billie clapped her hands. "You handled that just right. The other side of the street? I saw two people turn white when you said that."

"Let's have dinner in the private dining room. We'll work the floor and make our presence known afterward. I'm so nervous I need to sit down," Fanny said.

"Dinner's good," Bess said. Billie nodded.

Over potato-crusted salmon and a crisp garden salad that Fanny only picked at, she said, "I hoped . . . all day I was . . . I wanted to believe Simon would come. My brain knew he wouldn't, but some small part of me wanted to believe he would. How do I turn that part of my life off? What kind of person am I that I can do something like this? I need a goal, something to strive toward. Like . . . in two years, maybe three, I can go back to Simon and he'll be the way he was when we first got married. I don't know if I can handle two bad marriages. To brothers, no less. When Ash is . . . when . . . Long-distance marriages never work. If I have to stay here for the rest of my life, I'll go out of my mind. The words, *for now,* mean this is a temporary situation. This is a lifetime commitment, so who's fooling who here? I know in my heart Simon won't wait for me. I hate it. I just hate it."

"Fanny, give it a chance. Give Simon a chance, too. This is only day one. You could turn out to be so good at this business you might not want to give it up. A week from now, a month from now, Simon can have a change of heart. Sometimes the things you hate most in life are the very things you end up loving the most. It's strange but true. I wasn't going to bring this up, but this might be a good time to offer you a goal. This casino makes tons of money. Why not think about building one of those centers like they have in Texas for people with multiple sclerosis? Think about this, too. Maybe you could build a separate facility where a patient's children can come for periods of time. Think in terms of Sunny. Think about how much good you can do. It's what Sallie did, Fanny," Billie said.

Fanny's eyes glistened. "I don't want to be like Sallie. I just want to be me, Fanny Thornton. You're right, though, I could do that. I'll look into it." She lost some of the glazed look in her eyes at Billie's suggestion.

"Fanny, you *are* you. I didn't say you should turn into Sallie. Sallie did thousands of wonderful things for the people of this town. Her private life had nothing to do with her philanthropic goodness. Use the money from this casino to do good things. Maybe you won't hate it so much if you have worthy goals and you achieve them."

"I think Billie's right, Fanny. I'll pick John's brains and see what he says. You can set up a foundation. I think, and this is just a thought, but I'll bet my wedding ring Chue's sister Su Li will come back and oversee it for you. Oh, Fanny, it's a wonderful idea."

"It will take a fortune," Fanny said.

"It will take several fortunes. I'll see to it that the Colemans contribute half. We could make it a family foundation. We'll be helping Sunny and hundreds of people like her. I vote yes," Billie said.

"I don't have any money to give, but I can give my time. If my vote counts, then mine is yes, too. You need to cast your vote, Fanny," Bess said.

"Oh, yes. Yes, yes, yes. Maybe some good will come of this after all. Thank you both for coming here today. Let's eat our dessert and then work the floor for a while. After that, we'll go upstairs and brainstorm like we used to do in the old days."

"Hear, hear!" Billie said.

Across the street in a windowless room, men, impeccably clad, took their seats at a highly polished table. An elaborate centerpiece of fresh orchids sat in the middle of the table. To the left of the floral arrangement was a sterling silver coffee service. To the right, an identical sterling silver tray with crystal decanters containing one-of-a-kind cordials and old brandy. Crystal ashtrays and fresh packages of cigarettes were at each place setting.

The man at the head of the table, a Harvard graduate, opened the meeting simply by raising his hand for silence. His voice was cultured and resonant. "If my information is correct, The Emperor of Las Vegas is no longer with us. Do you see a problem, gentlemen?" The men shrugged as one. "How did it happen?" was the second question. Again, the men shrugged.

The man at the head of the table poured coffee. "The incident that occurred last night did not affect any of us. Business-wise, we made money. I understand that the explanation for the incident was that Mrs. Thornton was making a statement. I think we would all be wise to take that particular statement at face value. Mrs. Thornton is in total control of Babylon. I do not believe Mrs. Thornton has any desire to cross over to your side of the street.

"Mrs. Thornton has a sterling reputation, as did her mentor, Sallie Thornton. The Strip, this town, needs her. As long as your gentlemen stay on your side of the street she gives all of you respectability. The lady has class, power, and wealth. To my knowledge, that power and wealth have never been abused except once. All of you felt that abuse because some of you tried to cross the line and pull an unsavory business deal."

"A deal is a deal. We buckled under to a woman," a voice at the end of the table snarled.

"You conducted a business deal. Your tone of voice is not appreciated, nor will it be tolerated. You are not hoods, you're businessmen. You knew the ground rules when you hired me. Remember that."

"Mrs. Thornton is in the rag business. What does she know about the gambling business?" someone asked.

"I would imagine you'll find out very soon. Mrs. Thornton is a lady . . . of her word, as you all know. You might be wise to work behind the scenes to aid her endeavors if those endeavors turn out to pertain to something other than the gaming business."

"That would be aiding the enemy. Ash Thornton was the enemy."

The man at the head of the table sighed. "Ash Thornton was your competitor, not your enemy. All of you here need to recognize that the old days are gone forever. There's a new game in town called 'the legitimate way.' Are there any questions, gentlemen?"

"With The Emperor gone, what do we call Mrs. Thornton?"

"Mrs. Thornton sounds appropriate." The voice at the head of the table held a rich chuckle. A hint of a smile tugged at the corners of his mouth.

"If there are no questions, we're adjourned."

Marcus Reed stood to shake the hand of each man filing past him. His job here was done.

Fanny sat down at a small table in the Harem Lounge. She wished she could kick off her shoes and remove her hose so she could wiggle her toes. How in the world did Ash do this, night after night, week after week? She couldn't ever remember being this tired. She reached out to accept a glass of ginger ale from the bartender.

"It gets to you after a while, doesn't it?" a man at the next table said. Fanny watched as he unbuttoned the top button of his shirt and yanked at his tie.

He looked like a contented customer. She needed to smile and make polite conversation even though it was doubtful the man knew who she was. "It's these shoes. I'd give anything if I could take them off and wade in one of the pools."

The man smiled. "What's stopping you?" The tie was in his hands and then stuffed into his pocket. "I feel about ties the way you feel about your shoes."

"I think I'll just get lower heels. It was a lovely tie." *He was flirting with her.* Fanny felt her face grow warm. He was handsome, middle fifties, dark hair tinged with gray at the temples, classic features, winsome smile. *Winsome?* He was wearing a magnificent suit, custom-tailored. She knew a thing or two about fabric.

"I like the idea of wading in the pool better. I wonder if anyone has ever done that."

It was Fanny's turn to smile. "I rather doubt it. Did you win or lose tonight?"

"Actually, I broke even."

"That's not good for the house."

"Do you work here?"

"In a manner of speaking," Fanny said. She tried wiggling her toes inside her shoes. A corn was forming on her little toe, she could feel it start to burn. Three more hours to go. How *did* Ash do it?

"What does in a manner of speaking mean? Marcus Reed," he said, extending his hand.

"Fanny Thornton," Fanny said, reaching for his hand. When she didn't see any acknowledgment of her name, she said, "I more or less watch over things on the floor. It's an education in itself. I might enjoy it more if my feet didn't hurt so much."

"That does it." The man was off his chair in the blink of an eye.

In the time it took her heart to beat twice, Fanny found herself slung over the man's shoulder and whisked out of the Harem Lounge to the stunned surprise of the bartender. "One pool coming up."

"You need to put me down, Mr. Reed. People are staring and gawking at us. This is not funny. What if someone takes a picture. My rear end is in your face," Fanny said, her head bobbing up and down.

"So it is, now that you mention it. Here we are. As someone who once wanted to be an architect, I can appreciate the work and beauty of this pool. There you go, Fanny Thornton. Doesn't it feel good?" he said, standing her up inside the pool. "I'll hold your shoes until your feet cool off. Nylons dry in seconds according to my sisters."

"People are staring," Fanny hissed.

"Then let's give them something to *really* stare at." Marcus stepped into the pool. "Good lord, there's fish in here."

Fanny doubled over laughing. When she raised her head, Marcus splashed her. She splashed back. A crowd gathered, Billie and Bess in the front line. Fanny laughed harder at their startled faces. "I'm, ah . . . what I'm doing is . . ."

"Having fun," Marcus Reed laughed. "Well, as much as I'm enjoying this, I really have to leave. I have a plane to catch. It was nice meeting you, Mrs. Thornton."

"I'm sorry about your shoes and pants."

"Don't be. I haven't had this much fun in a long time."

Fanny watched Marcus walk away. She was suddenly aware of the people staring at her, of her friends Billie and Bess. It took her a second to realize she was seeing spots in front of her eyes. *Flash bulbs.*

"Did you have fun?" Bess asked.

"Actually, Bess, I did. My feet feel better, too. I don't think I've ever done anything quite so public before," Fanny said, stepping from the pool.

"I say we call it a night," Billie said.

Fanny picked up her shoes to follow her friends. She waved to the onlookers and grinned.

"Who *was* that man?" Bess asked in the elevator.

"He said his name was Marcus Reed. I met him in the Harem Lounge when I went in to rest my feet. He seemed like a real gentleman."

"Well, his three-hundred-dollar shoes and thousand-dollar suit are ruined. He didn't seem to mind," Billie said, a thoughtful look on her face.

"I have a feeling I'm going to be in the morning papers," Fanny said.

"Do you care?" Bess asked.

"Too late now," Fanny said. "They'll probably call me the Mermaid of Babylon or something equally silly. Ash will throw a fit."

"Life goes on," Billie said, the same thoughtful look still on her face.

"Okay, let's have some coffee while we go through the personnel files. Tomorrow is another long day."

Fanny snuggled beneath the flannel sheets. It dawned on her, just as she was drifting off to sleep, that she could get up out of bed and turn the air conditioning higher. She adjusted the thermostat and climbed back into bed just as the telephone rang. *Please, God, let it be Simon. Please.* But it was her ex-husband's voice on the other end of the phone.

"Ash, why are you calling me at quarter to four in the morning? You are the last person in the world I want to talk to right now. Furthermore, you said you were walking away and you didn't care what happened. You're calling to find out what happened, right?"

"Wrong, as usual. I just wanted to see how you were. I used to wind down about this time every night. It will get easier as time goes on. I think I really called to thank you. I don't suppose that means anything to you. How is Simon taking it?"

Fanny felt her throat constrict. "Simon won't be joining me here in these sumptuous surroundings which really aren't so sumptuous right now. I smashed up the place last night, Ash. Then I turned the power off."

"Way to go, Fanny."

"Tonight some guy from the Harem Lounge tossed me over his shoulder and stood me up in one of the pools because my feet hurt. Someone took pictures. I'll probably make the morning papers, so be advised."

"Did you have a good time?"

"Sure. My feet feel better, too. No one knows how to work the generators. Perhaps you should tell me how to start them."

"There's an On/Off switch. You turn On and *voilà*. You got light. I would have thought you could figure that out. When the generators are working, they only juice the first three floors."

"I didn't try. Your people made it sound mysterious. They said you were the only person who knew how they worked."

"I didn't want anyone messing around with them. One klutz, and three million bucks would have been shot to hell. Run that business about Simon by me again."

"I said he wants no part of this. He won't be joining me."

"So what's the big deal? You can go up there weekends or he can come down to Vegas. Constant togetherness in a marriage causes it to erode. I'm glad you made it through the first day."

"Oh, yeah. I even called a meeting. Do you want to know how it turned out?"

"No. Listen, I hear Polly whimpering. I want to get to her before Sunny wakes up. She had an elevator put in for the two of us. Is that something or what?"

"Yes. That's something. Take care of your granddaughter, Ash."

"She takes six ounces. You should hear her burp!"

"Good-bye, Ash." There was no response.

Fanny buried her head in the pillow and sobbed. "You're dying, and you're finally happy. How am I ever going to understand something like that? I don't wish you ill, Ash, truly I don't. Just take good care of Sunny and the kids. When you can't to do it anymore, I'll step in if she lets me."

Damn, she was wide-awake now.

Fanny picked her way through the debris in the living room on her way to the kitchen, where she brewed a pot of coffee.

What are you doing, Simon? Are you awake? Of course you are. I'm sitting here thinking of you and I know you're sitting on the glider thinking of me. If it wasn't so tragic, it would be funny. Change your mind, Simon. Maybe this won't be forever. If we love each other, we should be able to make it work. I cannot desert my family no matter how much I love you. I just can't. A man flirted with me tonight, Simon. I enjoyed his attention. Oh, Simon, what's going to happen to us?

Careful not to make any noise, Fanny made toast. She really didn't want or need the coffee. She was already one big jangling nerve.

Fanny leaned her head into the palm of her hand. She stared at the stark white refrigerator. She thought about her husband and her family. She wished she was young again, back in Shamrock, Pennsylvania, knowing what she knew now. Such a foolish thought. She thought about Sallie; she always thought about her mother-in-law when she reminisced. No matter how hard she tried, no matter what she did or didn't to do, Sallie's life paralleled her own.

Fanny's thoughts took her backward in time to the day her father-in-law had his stroke and Sallie went to Devin Rollins to break off their twenty-year-long affair. Devin had pleaded with Sallie to no avail. With his love lost to him he'd committed suicide that very evening. Sallie gave up her life to take care of Philip, and, in the end, her guilty, sick devotion to a man she didn't love had killed her. Now, Fanny thought, she was doing the exact same thing, following in Sallie's footsteps. She screamed her despair, banging her head on the glass-topped table.

Bess and Billie leaped from their beds to race to the kitchen. "What happened?" they asked in unison. They listened to Fanny babble incoherently, their eyes wide with disbelief.

"Don't you see, no matter what I do, no matter how hard I try, it always comes back to Sallie and me. It's almost as if she cloned me when I wasn't looking. I don't know how to break the chain. Just look at the similarities. I'm taking over for Ash, doing something I absolutely hate, because he's dying. Sallie gave up Devin to devote her life to Philip, out of guilt. We all know I'm giving up Simon for the same reason. It's never going to end. Never!"

Billie and Bess dropped to their knees. "It isn't the same thing, Fanny," Billie said gently.

"Oh, Fanny, please listen, Billie is right. Sallie wasn't divorced. You are. Sallie didn't remarry. You did. Sallie didn't have a daughter with a progressive disease. Devin committed suicide because he was a weak man. There is nothing about Ash that is weak. Ash has taken the horns of his bull and he's dealing with it the only way he knows how. All he asked of you was to take over his job. It's totally different, Fanny."

"This is a new time, a new place. You hate this business, Sallie loved it. That alone should tell you something. Sallie was locked into a situation of her own making. She wasn't smart enough to climb out of the trap. She gave up. We all loved her, but that doesn't make what she did right. You haven't given up on Simon. He has to be man enough to recognize the sacrifice you're making for your family, recognize that he loves you. If he chooses, and choose is the right word, Fanny, and does not accept it, then he isn't the man you thought he was. Do you agree, Bess?"

"One hundred percent," Bess said.

"How can a person exist twenty-four hours a day doing something he or she hates with a passion? It can't be emotionally healthy. What's going to become of me?"

"If you go into something with a negative attitude, everything you do will be negative. When things are at their worst, they have to get better. Jump into it, embrace it, and remember our goal. Think of this as opening-night jitters. Bess and I are here for you. I'm staying for a full month because my wonderful guy recognizes that I need a separate life. Bess is going to be right here with you all the time. If you falter, we'll pick you up. It's up to you to do the rest, and you can do it. Right now you're still smarting over Simon's attitude, and the way your marriage was the past two years. You've committed, but you haven't committed one hundred percent. When you do that, you don't look back. It will be whatever it's meant to be. Let's go back to bed now," Billie said.

Fanny allowed herself to be led back to bed. "What would I do without you two?"

"You'd do just fine. We're just moral support." Bess smiled. "Do you want us to tell you a story or sing you a bedtime song?"

"Only if it has a happy ending," Fanny said, punching at her pillow.

"No guarantees, Fanny," Billie said softly. She turned out the light and closed the door.

Fanny drifted into sleep. Her dreams weren't of her ex-husband or of her husband. They were of a dark-haired, dark-eyed man splashing water on her as goldfish tickled her feet.

In the room down the hall, Billie kicked off her slippers. "I don't see a happy ending to this chapter in Fanny's life. What do you see, Bess?" Billie's voice was so fretful-sounding, Bess punched at her pillow as though she was pummeling dough in preparation for making bread.

Bess nodded. "Who was that man in the pool? I saw the way he looked at Fanny. You wait and see, he's coming back. Fanny's vulnerable right now." She punched the pillow again, so hard that feathers sailed upward. "I would have thought Ash Thornton was a foam-rubber man."

Billie reached out for one of the feathers. "Maybe it's an omen of some kind. I believe in stuff like that. Do you, Bess? I can't sleep. I'm too wide-awake now."

"Me too. Billie, all that stuff we told Fanny before . . . did we lie? It's getting downright spooky. Fanny's life really does parallel Sallie Thornton's. Sometimes I think Sallie choreographed the whole thing and she's . . . up there saying, yes, no, this is wrong, this is right, do this, don't do that. Am I nuts?"

"Well, if you are, then I am too, because I feel the same way. What we have to do is convince Fanny it isn't so."

"That makes us traitors," Bess murmured.

"I prefer the word friends looking out for another friend. We need to get some sleep. Tomorrow, today really, isn't going to be much better than yesterday. Our first order of the day should be getting that living room cleaned up. Maybe Fanny will let us decorate this place. If I had free rein here, I could turn this penthouse into something Fanny would never want to leave. Maybe that's not good, though."

"For now, it's wonderful. Billie, who *was* that man? He was no ordinary customer, was he?"

Billie was quiet for so long, Bess repeated her question.

"I think he's Fanny's true destiny. If that sounds corny, I'm sorry. When I saw the way he looked at her I got goose bumps. Look at my arms, just talking about him gives me the chills. We need to go to sleep. Fanny's private life is not our business. I'm already spooked, so let's not talk about it anymore, okay?"

"Okay. He had a sense of humor. I like that in a man. Simon takes life too seriously. Ash doesn't take life seriously enough. In my opinion the Thornton men are misfits. I always said that."

Billie snorted. "It's in the genes. The two Coleman men I knew were misfits, too. It's Fanny's and my infusion of blood that made our kids the people they are. *Good night, Bess.*"

"Night, Billie."

Simon stroked Daisy's head as he rocked back and forth. "I'm going to miss you, little girl. Tootsie and Slick are going to miss you, too. All your gear is packed up," he said, a catch in his voice. He stared off into space as the little dog snuggled in his arms.

Off in the distance he heard the sound of a car. Simon's head jerked upright. His shoulders slumped when he saw the military style jeep being driven by the mailman.

"Special Delivery, Mr. Thornton. You have to sign for it or I would have stuck it in the box at the end of the road."

"Thanks, Clyde," Simon said as he signed his name with a flourish.

"Looks like another nice day. How's Mrs. Thornton?"

"Fine, Clyde." *Go already so I can see if this is from Fanny. Please, let it be from Fanny.* Simon tortured himself for another five minutes before he looked down at the address on the heavy manila envelope.

It was addressed to Mr. and Mrs. Simon Thornton. The sender's name stood out starkly in heavy black lettering. THE APEX IN-VESTIGATIVE AGENCY.

Simon tossed the envelope on the floor of the porch. Like he really wanted to know more about his weird family. Colemans, Thorntons, they were all the same. Finding his mother's brother Josh didn't seem important in the scheme of things. Let Fanny deal with it.

Things seemed to be coming full circle these days. Fanny had at long last found her mother. It hadn't made her any happier. If anything, it had made her more unhappy, because she'd been denied the magical moment she'd always dreamed of. Ash and his decision to leave Las Vegas and turn over the casino to Fanny was something he had always known would happen. And now this envelope. More family. More family meant more troubles, more unhappiness.

Simon leaned over to pick up the envelope. He put it in the dog crate. "Time to go, Daisy. Fanny's waiting for you."

Simon loaded the kennel and a taped box full of Daisy's toys, blanket, and leashes in the back of the heavy-duty utility truck, then walked inside the house to call his wife. He wasn't surprised when the answering machine clicked on. He left his name, the flight number, and the time of Daisy's arrival. He paused a moment, wondering if he should say something else. He decided there was nothing to add and hung up the phone.

"Let's go, Daisy."

13

Fanny slipped onto a thickly padded barstool in the Harem Lounge. Billie and Bess joined her five minutes later. "I won two hundred dollars," Bess said, sitting down next to Fanny.

"And I lost fifty dollars," Billie lamented.

"Tea, ladies?" the bartender queried. The women nodded.

"How do your feet feel, Fanny?" Bess asked.

"They're numb, but the lower heels help. Wow! Would you look at that? I wonder who the lucky recipient is?" Fanny said as three uniformed young men walked past the bar carrying vases of yellow roses.

"Somebody must have won big tonight and they're paying off their good-luck charm. Probably one of the showgirls kissed the dice or something equally stupid," Billie said.

The women watched as the uniforms turned about and reentered the Harem Lounge. "Mrs. Thornton, these are for you," one of the young men said, setting the flowers down on the teakwood bar.

"For me! Are you sure?"

Billie unobtrusively looked at the watch on her wrist and gave a slight nod to Bess as Fanny removed the small card from the holder nestled in one of the arrangements.

"Can you imagine Simon doing something so sweet? He knows I adore yellow roses. There must be six dozen of them. On the other hand, maybe they're from Ash, you know, that good-luck thing. Should we make a bet? I think they're from Simon. He left a message you know. I'm just so glad he sent Daisy. That shows he's thinking about me. Billie, who do you think sent them?"

"Simon or the kids."

"Bess?"

"I agree with Billie. Will you open the card already before we die of curiosity?"

Fanny ripped at the card. *Please let them be from Simon. Please, please, please.* Fanny stared at the card. Her voice was flat when she said, "We're all wrong. The flowers are from Marcus Reed. The man who put me in the pool last night."

"Is there a message?" Bess asked.

"Yes. It says, 'Thank you for the most enjoyable thirty minutes of my life.' "

Billie's voice was almost as flat as Fanny's when she said, "Isn't this about the same time as it was last evening when you went *wading?*"

Fanny looked at the clock over the bar. "I think so. What should I do with them?"

"What do you want to do with them?" Billie asked.

"If they were from Simon, I'd sit here and stare at them for the rest of the night. However, since they aren't from Simon I guess I'll just leave them here. The bartender can put them on the tables. They're gorgeous, aren't they?"

"Magnificent. Costly, too. That guy must have some bucks," Bess said.

"I'm flattered," Fanny said. "Things seem to be slowing down. Ash always said the casino's busiest time was around midnight. Do you suppose something fantastic is going on at one of the other casinos?"

"You would have heard if there was. Each casino has its spies. Sometime, you just have an off night."

"I had an idea a little while ago," Fanny whispered. "Do you remember when I gave you the tour and we opened that small empty suite next to the Spa Shop? Think about this, ladies. We decorate it to fit our theme and hire a seer. Fortune-teller, whatever you call those people. We might even be able to hire a *real* psychic. We'll give her a mystical-sounding name of some sort. It could be a lot of fun. Women absolutely love that kind of thing. I always read my horoscope, don't you? Tarot card readings and individual astrology charts go for hundreds of dollars. We could try to locate one of those hands-on people who touches something of yours, closes her eyes, and tells you about your life. It would be a tremendous draw and perfectly in keeping with the theme of Babylon. Billie, you could design us some razzle-dazzle outfits to fit the mood. What do you think?"

"Mega advertising," Bess said. "Reservations only, to begin with, because she's booked three months in advance which means you pay her while she does nothing until you generate enough interest. When you have to wait or can't get something, you want it all the more. It can't be shoddy. It has to be a real class act. When it comes right down to it, it is an act," Bess said.

"I just love harem pants, veils, beads, and bangles. My mother always said I was a gypsy in my other life. I'll make you an outfit that will blow your socks off," Billie promised. There was such enthusiasm in Billie's voice, Fanny laughed.

"We're cookin', ladies. Whoever said this was a man's business was wrong."

"My ex-husband said that, Bess. Three more hours and we can call it a night. I want to go upstairs to check on Daisy. I'll be right back."

Fanny's jaw dropped when she stepped from the elevator. Shoe boxes, one on top of the other, were piled every which way outside her door. She knew immediately who they were from. She struggled to count the boxes and finally gave up. She wondered what kind of taste *he* had and how *he* knew her shoe size. Charles Jourdan. *He* must have looked inside her shoes when *he* was holding them for her. Fanny opened several boxes and nodded approvingly. She couldn't accept these shoes. The question was, where and how was she to return them?

Daisy ran to meet her the moment she opened the door. She fondled the little dog as she pressed the play button to hear her messages. Her eyebrows shot upward when she heard Marcus Reed's voice. There was no hi, no hello, no this is Marcus Reed. "I'm just calling to tell you my sister tells me, and she claims to know everything, that if you soak your feet in Epsom salts and liquid peppermint, your feet will heal and feel wonderful. Both ingredients can be purchased at any drugstore. I'd like us to have dinner the next time I'm in Las Vegas. Lunch is good and so is breakfast if your schedule is tight. Good night, Fanny Thornton."

Fanny sat down with a thump, Daisy cradled in her arms. "Didn't he see my wedding ring? He didn't seem like the kind of man who would hit on a married woman. I did notice that he wasn't wearing a ring. Women notice things like that, Daisy. What am I going to do with those shoes? The flowers were a nice gesture. The shoes are something else." Daisy yawned. "Guess I woke you, huh? I'll take you for a long walk tomorrow and find some grass for you. It's a different kind of life here."

Fanny stared at the answering machine. She could call Simon and thank him for sending Daisy. She placed the call and held her breath while she waited for Simon to pick up the phone. "Simon, it's Fanny. Thanks for sending Daisy. I just came upstairs to check on her. It's late, I thought you might be sleeping."

"No. I was sitting on the front porch. I saw the paper today, Fanny."

Fanny sucked in her breath. She hadn't imagined that she would make news in a small California paper. "It was one of those things that just happened. My feet were burning and I could feel a corn starting to form on my little toe."

"You looked like you were having a good time. Who was the man?"

"Somebody in the casino. He left right afterward. I heard him say he had to catch a plane."

"I guess you're starting to like the bright lights and the noise."

"No. I came up with an idea tonight, though." She told him about her plans for the empty suite next to the Spa Shop. When Simon made no comment, Fanny babbled on, not wanting to hang up. "Billie is here for a month and so is Bess. Billie has agreed to decorate

Ash's apartment so I feel comfortable living here. Simon, can you see your way clear to coming here for a long weekend?"

"I can't, Fanny. I'll say good night now."

"Good night," Fanny whispered to the dial tone ringing in her ears. Tears rolled down her cheeks.

Fanny returned to the casino floor in time to hear excited squeals, ringing bells, and shrill whistles. Bess motioned to her. "A grandmother from Edison, New Jersey, just won the hundred-thousand-dollar jackpot on the dollar machine. Here comes the photographer and the floor manager with the IRS forms. Remember how excited we were the night Sallie let us each win a thousand dollars?"

"I remember. I called Simon and he saw today's paper. He cut me off and said good-night. There was a message on the machine from Mr. Reed and fifty boxes of shoes outside my door."

"Oh my God!"

"That's pretty much what I said myself. I can't even return the shoes because I don't know where Mr. Reed lives."

Fanny hugged the grandmother and posed for a photograph before she handed over the check to the speechless blond-haired lady. "If you don't mind me asking, Mrs. O'Leary, what do you plan to do with your winnings? Readers always want to know things like that."

"Call me Tootsie, Mrs. Thornton. Help my children, save some, maybe Daniel and I will take a vacation. I might buy a new lawn mower for Danny."

"What will you get for yourself?"

"I might buy some books. I love to read. I can't believe this. I've been here a whole week and haven't won a thing. My daughter Mary is going to be so surprised."

"Enjoy it, Tootsie. And come back and see us again."

"I will. I absolutely will, and if you ever come to Edison, New Jersey, stop and see us. We're in the phone book."

"I'll be sure to do that."

Fanny turned to Billie. "I think we can call it a night."

"And not a minute too soon," Bess said.

Fanny yawned, her eyes on the calendar. She'd give anything for twelve uninterrupted hours of sleep. Working the floor at night, sleeping for three or four hours in the early dawn, then working in the office for another four or five hours, snatching a catnap when she could, didn't make for an alert individual.

"A penny for your thoughts, Fanny," Bess said. "If it's any consolation to you, I feel as tired as you look."

"I forget what fresh air is. We've been here four months, Bess. Billie's been gone a month and Thanksgiving is only four days away."

"We've made progress though," Bess said. "We've managed to weed out all the deadbeats Ash had on his payroll, we've hired new people, we stopped the skimming, changed suppliers who were giving the deadbeats kickbacks. On top of all that we work the floor at night and Madam Sarika has turned into a class act. If you really want to take a bow, you're entitled. The Foundation is up and running. Billie's made her family's contribution and Madam Sarika's money is flowing into the account. We done real good, Mrs. Thornton."

"I haven't heard from Simon. Ash never calls. I was hoping Sunny would invite me for Thanksgiving. I hoped against hope that Simon would do the same thing. I called Sage this morning and he let it slip that he, Iris, and Billie are going to Sunrise. They were invited. Do you have any idea how terrible I feel, Bess?"

"Have you called Sunrise?"

"Of course. Several times a week. Sunny says hello, says she's fine, says the children are fine, her dad is fine, then she hands the phone to Ash, who basically tells me to stop calling because things are under control. He doesn't want to hear one word about this casino. My daughter and my ex-husband are living in their own world, and it does not include me. Now, what would you do if you were me?"

"I'd stop calling. Fanny, you're killing yourself and for what? You don't have to prove anything to anyone. You can't be all things to all people. My daughter is cooking Thanksgiving dinner and we'd love to have you join us. I know Billie invited you to Washington. That's two offers."

"I appreciate it, Bess. I'm still hoping Simon will call."

"Fanny, it's been four months. It's time to get your ducks in a row. Stop calling him and leaving messages on his machine. You must have left five hundred by now, and not one was returned. What does that tell you?"

"Hope springs eternal. Maybe I'll drive to the ranch over Thanksgiving. I could cook a turkey, fix all the trimmings, and . . ."

"And if he isn't there?"

"I'll call and leave a message first. If Simon doesn't want me to make the trip, he'll call back and tell me. This silence is so unlike

Simon. He's carrying this beyond stubborn. What he's doing is punishing me. He's done it before when I did something he considered stepping out of line."

"I would have blown up three months ago. Men do not have an understanding bone in their bodies. When John starts to act like that I put him in his place right away. He usually thanks me, saying he didn't think of it that way, whatever that way is. It works for us."

"Simon has a point."

"Which is?" Bess said.

"Those first few weeks when we did speak, he didn't understand how I could be doing something like this for my family when that same family turned their backs on me. I ask myself the same question every day. He doesn't understand that I have to earn back Sunny's respect and love."

"Excuse my language, Fanny, but that's bullshit."

"No, it isn't. I wasn't there for her. She doesn't want me anywhere near her or her children. I haven't told anyone in the family about the medical rehab center we're going to build. They aren't interested in anything I do. They'll view it as a ploy to get back into their lives."

"Oh, Fanny, you don't know that."

"Yes, Bess, I do know that. I'm okay with it. Each day it gets a little easier. The anger is starting to dissipate. Simon is a different story. I could make a life for us here if he would agree. I'm more than willing to give us another chance. Why is it women bend where men are concerned and men trench in?"

"It's the way it is. I hope you weren't expecting magical insight."

Fanny's voice was weary yet stubborn. "If Simon truly loved me, we could work something out. He's unwilling even to talk to me. That, Bess, tells me more than I want to know."

"Time will take care of everything. One day at a time. Look on the bright side, Fanny. Every day you get a dozen yellow roses. Four months is a long time for a person to send roses to someone he only met for thirty minutes. It's so mysterious."

"There's nothing mysterious about it at all. Mr. Reed left a standing order at the florist. He probably forgot all about me. As you said, four months is a long time."

"What did you do with the shoes?"

Fanny snorted. "I've been wearing them." Bess laughed.

"It's kind of quiet this afternoon. Go upstairs, get Daisy, and we'll go for a long walk. We'll get an ice cream on the way back. Both of us need some fresh air."

"That sounds like a marvelous idea. I'll meet you by the service elevator."

Fanny took a moment to savor what Bess called her "new digs." With Daisy in her arms, she walked around the spacious, newly decorated apartment. The chrome, glass, mirrors, marble, and leather furniture were all gone. In their place were cream-colored walls, ankle-hugging wheat-colored carpeting, matching draperies, and soft lighting. Low, deep, comfortable sofas in various shades of brown and beige with matching chairs welcomed her. Green plants dotted the corners next to well-stocked bookshelves. The cream-colored walls hosted vibrant watercolors signed by local artists. The electric fireplace was smoky black flanked by two enormous red chairs—duplicates of the chairs in her old studio at Sunrise. "My personal gift to you," Billie had said. "One for you, one for Daisy." A luscious jade plant and small Tiffany lamp sat in the middle of the table that separated the two chairs. All the comforts of home. "It's gender neutral," Billie had said. What that meant to Fanny was if Simon ever changed his mind, he wouldn't object to the decor. Her bedroom and the guest rooms were in various shades of green and beige.

The kitchen that had once been sterile white with touches of black was now homey and fragrant. The new appliances were almond-colored. The glass-and-chrome table and chairs had been replaced with antique oak, the chairs covered with red-and-white-checkered cushions. The pristine white cabinets had been resurfaced and now sported a rich oak veneer. Green plants in apple red crockery stood on the counter and in the center of the oak table. Braided, colorful rugs replaced the cold black-and-white marble floor. A small metal dish with orange peels and cinnamon sticks warmed over the pilot light, sending off a delicious aroma. The kitchen always smelled like she'd just baked an apple pie.

Fanny reached for Daisy's leash. The little dog danced and yipped as she tried to snare the leash to hurry Fanny along.

As she was locking the door behind her, Fanny heard the phone ring. She fumbled inside her pocket for the key. No one called her during the day. Maybe it was Simon or Sunny. The moment she opened the door, the phone stopped ringing. In dismay she listened to Marcus Reed's voice on her answering machine. A chill raced up both her arms. Her eyes wide, Fanny listened to the mesmerizing voice.

"Mrs. Thornton, this is Marcus Reed. Again, I hope I've dialed the right number. I checked with information and was told there were three listings for Thornton. I've left messages on the other two numbers since I wasn't sure which number was yours. I do hope that won't cause a problem. I've been on the other side of the world these past few months. I'll be coming to Las Vegas in the next few days. I'd like to take you to breakfast, lunch, or dinner if you're free. Since it is a holiday weekend, I'll understand if you aren't available. Family comes first. I'm sorry I missed you."

Fanny pressed the save message and didn't know why.

"Something wonderful must have happened while you were up there. I see a very noticeable sparkle in your eye. Did Simon call? Did you call him, or did the kids call about Thanksgiving?" Bess asked.

"No to everything. Mr. Reed left a message. He said he's been leaving messages at two other numbers. I would imagine those numbers are Sage's line and Billie's. Plus Ash. I wish he wouldn't do that. He never leaves a number so I can't return his call to tell him to stop. He has to know I'm married," Fanny said, wiggling her wedding ring finger.

"Maybe he checked you out. Men do that, you know. Who knows what was said. People here in the casino probably wonder where your husband is. You're working seven days a week and there's no sign of Simon. Ash is gone. You've never offered up any kind of explanation, so that means people can put their own spin on whatever story they feel like telling. Maybe he doesn't even know about Simon. Maybe he thinks you're divorced from Ash, which is true. You have to admit marrying your ex-husband's brother isn't really the norm. So, what did he want?"

"To have breakfast, lunch, or dinner. He's rather persistent, don't you think?"

"I'm not exactly the right person to ask. I'd say the man is interested in you."

"Well, that's just too bad. I'm married. At least I think I am. You know, Bess, it only takes a few seconds to make a phone call. I need to do something where Simon is concerned. The anger I'm starting to feel scares me."

"Fanny, why don't you take the rest of the day off and drive up to Sunrise. Sunny is the one you need to talk to. Ash, too, for that matter."

"Not today. If I'm going to do that, I have to work myself into it. I might call Ash later to . . . to talk. I probably shouldn't even bother since he brushes me right off, just the way Sunny does. Let's just enjoy our walk and talk about something else."

"You're the boss," Bess said as she fell into step alongside Fanny and Daisy.

Fanny kicked off her shoes as she flopped down in one of the big red chairs. Would she ever get accustomed to ending her day at three-thirty in the morning? She was too wired to go to bed, there wasn't anyone to call because no one else kept the kind of hours she did. She wasn't hungry, and she wasn't thirsty. There was nothing to watch on television, and her ears were too sensitive at this time of night to listen to music after listening to the sounds of the slots on the floor all evening long. She stared at her feet and then at the shoes she'd worn all evening. Shoes from Marcus Reed.

Who was Marcus Reed? Where did he live? What did he do for a living? She had to admit the man had managed to pique her curiosity. The big question was, what should she do, if anything, when he came to town? Her conscience took over. *What do you want to do, Fanny? I'll tell you what I want. I want my husband, and if I can't have my husband, I want . . . I need . . . What's wrong with breakfast, lunch, or dinner? Nothing. Nothing at all. So what if the man sends me flowers and shoes. So what! My husband should be sending me flowers and shoes. My husband should be calling me. My family should pretend they care if I'm alive or dead. No one is interested in me. This man is.*

Fanny howled her unhappiness into Daisy's soft fur. The little dog whimpered as she snuggled deeper into the crook of Fanny's arm.

Fanny reached for the phone. Ash would be awake. Ash never slept. She dialed the number in Sunrise and wasn't surprised when he picked up after the first ring. There was no greeting. "Fanny, what the hell are you doing calling here at this time of night? You're going to wake the kids. It's a good thing I was awake. What's wrong? Not that I care. I was going to call you later, after breakfast."

"Now that sounds like the Ash I know. I want to know two things. Have you heard from Birch since he went away? The second thing I want to know is why wasn't I invited to Sunrise for Thanksgiving?"

"No, I haven't heard from Birch. I got a postcard from somewhere in England. I had nothing to do with the guest list for Thanksgiving. I don't blame you for being upset. I imagine you'll be more upset when Christmas rolls around. I want you to know I tried to talk some sense into Sunny. She turned a deaf ear. She said she didn't need you taking over her kitchen and her dinner. She said she could mess it up all by herself."

"Whose kitchen?" Fanny's voice was sharper than she intended.

"Look, I know how you feel. Kids can be ungrateful little snots sometimes just the way ex-husbands can be. She's not doing real good, Fanny. I'd ask you to come up, but that would just throw her into a tizzy. She gets these spells when she gets excited and then she's drained for a few days. It's a damn good thing I'm here, I can tell you that."

"I'm grateful that you are there, Ash. I want you to believe that."

"Fanny, she doesn't even want me to bring up your name. She smacked Jake the other day because he wanted to know where Grandma Fanny was. I was telling him about the family earlier and I kind of made a story out of it and the little guy remembered. Don't you have anywhere to go for Thanksgiving?"

"Of course I have somewhere to go. I've had many invitations. I think it's pretty terrible of my own daughter not to invite me for dinner."

"Iris was upset. Everyone's upset. Where's Simon?"

"Everyone's upset but not so upset that they won't attend. You know what, Ash, I'm starting to get that hard-edged shell you used to have. I don't care anymore. All of you have stuck the knife in me so many times my heart is full of holes. As to Simon, I don't know where he is. He doesn't write, and he doesn't call. You ruined my marriage, Ash."

"If I could do that, then it must not have been worth very much. I'm sorry you feel that way. Is there anything I can do?"

"Yes, yes, yes. Sell this damn casino and let me get my life back."

"Anything but that, Fanny. Look, when I'm dead you can do what you want. Until that happens, it's business as usual. I'll call Simon and talk to him."

"I don't want you to do that, Ash. Don't interfere. I'll handle it. How are you feeling?"

"I have good days and I have bad days. I'm outside so much of the time I can actually sleep a few hours at a time. I have to tell you, Sunny can't cook worth a damn. I'm doing the turkey for . . . sorry, I didn't mean to bring that up."

"Ash, if I tell you something will you keep it to yourself?"

"Sure."

"Some guy sent me fifty pairs of shoes. It's that man who put me in the pool that first night. He sends a dozen roses every night. I don't know what to do about it."

"No shit! You mean you don't know what to do about Simon or the guy?" Not bothering to wait for a response, Ash babbled on. "Simon is as much of a bastard in his own way as I am in mine. You just never wanted to see it. Simon is not the knight in shining armor you thought he was. If he was all things to you as you believed, then where is he? He won't bend, Fanny. You need to know that. I hope you aren't the type to buckle under. If you do, I think I'd lose all respect for you. Play hardball with Simon. One way or another Simon always got his way. In everything, Fanny."

"That's what Simon always said about you."

"There you go. It's up to you who you choose to believe. What else can I do for you?"

"Do you know if Sage heard from Birch?"

"He got the same card we all did. Fanny, do you know Iris is pregnant?"

"Oh, Ash, no, I didn't know." Fanny started to cry.

"We just found out yesterday. I'm sure they'll tell you today. Iris adores you. Sage is walking on a cloud, or so Iris said. I think it's kind of wonderful. Call her up, Fanny, and invite her to lunch. I think she'd like that."

Fanny dabbed at her eyes. "I can't do that, Ash."

"No, I guess you can't. So, what's that guy's name?"

"Marcus Reed."

"Never heard of him. Dangle him under Simon's nose and see if he reacts."

"Ash, I'm not interested in the man."

"Sure you are. If you weren't interested, you wouldn't have brought up his name in the first place. He's intriguing you. Women love that. I am an authority on that subject as you well know. I bet the roses are yellow or pink. Not red, right?"

"What's that supposed to mean?"

"He's setting the scene for a seduction. Same thing as the spider and the web. Don't say I didn't warn you. I played that game hundreds of times."

"You really had to tell me that, didn't you?"

"I care about you, Fanny. I don't want to see some guy sucker my ex-wife. How's that make me look?"

"Like the ass you are," Fanny said. "Why were you going to call me?"

"I want you to go to Atlantic City and buy some property. I have a map and the lots are marked. Pay whatever you have to. You need to do it right away. Atlantic City is going to turn into a mini Vegas. We'll get your brothers to build Babylon II. Swear you won't drag your feet on this. I want it for the grandchildren. I want your promise, Fanny. One for Mom and Dad and one for the kids. It makes sense, Fanny. Before you know it they'll be all grown-up. Will you tell them I did it for them?"

Fanny's head buzzed. She knew there was no point in arguing. "What does pay whatever it takes mean, Ash?"

"Just buy it, Fanny. We'll worry about building it later. Right now boardwalk land is all that's important. Can you leave in a few days?"

"Do you want me to stop at the moon along the way? What is it about you that you can get me to do these things?"

"My irresistible charm. You'll do it then?"

"I'll do it. There's no money to build a casino though."

"There will be at the right time. I feel it in my gut, Fanny. When we're dead and gone, Jake will take over. That's a hell of a legacy, don't you think?"

"You know what, Ash, you're nuts. I'm nuts, too, because I'll be doing it. I'm hanging up now because you're getting on my nerves."

"I love you, Fanny."

In spite of herself, Fanny smiled as she hung up the phone. One more cockamamie scheme to deal with. And she would deal with it. She'd given her promise.

Fanny's clenched fists pummeled the arms of the red chair the moment she hung up the phone.

Alone and weary, Fanny finally slept, Daisy nestled at her side.

14

Fanny eyed the plump turkey sitting on her kitchen counter. It was years since she'd prepared a holiday dinner. She'd spent hours in the supermarket picking just the right yams, just the right cranberries, just the right turnip. And, for what? For whom was more like it. "Me and you, Daisy," Fanny muttered.

All day the phone on the kitchen wall beckoned. She'd lost count of the times she'd almost picked up the phone to call Simon. Instead she went back to unpacking her groceries and cleaning the oven in preparation for roasting the turkey. Daisy sat on one of the kitchen chairs, her eyes following Fanny. She yipped softly. "Okay, I'm going to call him. This is the last time, though," Fanny said as she dialed the number at the ranch, Ash's assessment of Simon ringing in her ears. *It's up to you who you choose to believe.* When Simon's voice came over the wire, Fanny's heart started to flutter. "It's Fanny, Simon. How are you? Simon, why haven't you answered any of my calls?"

"Fanny, there's nothing to say. You stated your position, and I stated mine."

Fanny bit down on her lower lip. Her back stiffened as she eyed the turkey. "This is my last phone call to you, Simon. I want to be clear about this. It's almost Thanksgiving. We all have so much to be thankful for. Especially you and me. Can we meet at some halfway point and share dinner? I was going to make a dinner for Daisy and me, but I'll forgo it if you can see your way clear to meet me. I won't beg you, Simon."

Simon's voice was so cold and bitter when he responded that Fanny flinched. He might just as well have slapped her in the face. "Are you saying you turned your back on our marriage for your wonderful family who now won't be joining you or inviting you for dinner?"

I will not cry. I absolutely will not cry. "Where do we go from here, Simon?" Fanny asked, her voice chilly.

"You tell me, Fanny."

"No, Simon, it doesn't work that way for me. Both of us need to agree on a decision. We might as well do it now, so we can get on with it." *It's up to you who you choose to believe. Simon's a bastard in his own way just the way I am. Simon always gets what he wants one way or the other.* "Are we just going to let it all fade away, Simon?"

Fanny heard his indrawn breath. "Unless you come back to the ranch, I don't see any other way for us to go."

"Even though the last two years weren't happy for me? You're giving me an ultimatum, Simon. I would never do that to you. Why are you taking such a stiff-necked position? Ultimatums mean one person will be happy and the other person will be miserable. Why can't we work this out? I'm willing to try. I'm willing to bend. Why are you refusing to understand what my family means to me? I never saw this stubbornness in you, Simon. How could I have been so blind? I know marriage is never easy unless both parties agree together on issues. You work it out, you learn from each other and you go on. You won't even meet me halfway. Ash was right, you're just as big a bastard in your own way as he is in his. My last words to you, Simon, are, you know where I am, you know my phone number. I won't be calling you again. Have a nice Thanksgiving."

Fanny fixed her gaze on Daisy. "It hurts too damn bad to cry. You know what, Daisy? You are my most precious possession. You're always there for me, you love unconditionally, and you're loyal. You'd never, ever desert me, nor would I desert you. That's what love is all about. Why do I understand that, and Simon doesn't? It's over," Fanny said. "Love stinks." She banged her fist down on the oak table. Pain richocheted up her arm as she yelped in frustration.

Fanny continued to talk to the little dog, who appeared to be listening intently. "This is how I see it. I have given myself a two-day holiday. That means I am not going anywhere near the casino floor or office. I'm going to cook, I'm going to watch television, I'm going to take naps, and I'm going to drink wine. In between all of that I'm going to take you for long walks. When it's time to eat, we're going to stuff ourselves because someone said that's what you're supposed to do on Thanksgiving. You and I will break the wishbone after dinner. Come here, Daisy."

Fanny cuddled with the little dog, who tried vainly to lick at the tears dribbling down her cheeks. Despair, unlike anything she'd ever experienced, flooded through her. "All those magazine writers, they're wrong, Daisy. It's not true that you have to be vulnerable before you can fall in love. To fall in love you have to have the hide of a buffalo."

Thanksgiving morning Fanny woke slowly. She felt Daisy inch up closer to her chest from her position at the foot of the bed. Fanny stroked her silky head as she stared at the ceiling. Two marriages down the drain. To brothers, no less. Yesterday she'd cried her tears. Today was a new day, and it was Thanksgiving. Time to get up and prepare the turkey. Time to get on with the day.

Yesterday was gone.

"Time to go out, Daisy. Get your leash and we'll do a quick scoot down the service elevator and out to the back driveway. Maybe we'll do the long walk after breakfast."

Fanny was back in the apartment and in the shower twenty minutes later. She dressed in jeans, an oversize sweatshirt that said WEST CHESTER and once belonged to either Birch or Sage. She stuffed her bare feet into ratty-looking sneakers with a hole in the big toe. She pulled her hair back into a ponytail with a rubber band, dusted her hands together, and marched out to the kitchen, stopping to turn on the stereo on the way. Soft music flooded the apartment.

Fanny prepared scrambled eggs for herself and fed Daisy as she contemplated the menu for her solitary dinner. The turkey was large enough to feed her entire family with leftovers for at least three days. She would be eating it for at least a month. She must have been out of her mind when she was shopping. She had too many yams, too many marshmallows, too many cranberries, and just the right amount of wine—three exquisite bottles of the best the French had to offer. She'd baked a pumpkin pie, a mince pie, and an apple pie along with some apple dumplings the day before. The aroma was still in the kitchen.

Fanny thought about other times then, other holidays when her family all gathered together. She'd been happy then, her children had been happy. Now, all that was gone. Now she was alone with only a dog for company. "I couldn't ask for more, Daisy," Fanny said, fondling the little dog's ears. "If this is all I'm going to get, we'll make the most of it."

Fanny worked diligently, doing all the things necessary to preparing a holiday dinner. She used her finest linen tablecloth, her china, her sterling, and her crystal. Daisy's place was set on the floor next to her chair on a lace-edged linen place mat. Her bowl was Bavarian crystal, her napkin linen as was Fanny's own. Daisy liked to clean her whiskers after eating.

Candles in silver holders graced each end of the table. The daily delivery of yellow roses sat in the center of the table, festive but lonely-looking. When the candles were burning, when the table was filled with platters and bowls, it wouldn't look so forlorn.

"I used to like to cook," Fanny muttered. "This is a chore." The moment she slid the heavy bird into the oven, Fanny uncorked the first bottle of wine. She poured a generous amount into a crystal flute and sipped appreciatively. She read the paper, smoked, and sipped.

By two o'clock, when she checked on the turkey to baste it, she had consumed one whole bottle of the exquisite wine. She carried the second bottle into the living room and turned on the television.

When the movie ended at four o'clock Fanny decided to check on the turkey, whose instructions said would cook itself. "Good thing," she mumbled as she tried to focus on the browning bird. "I think it's okay." She placed the second empty bottle next to the first one. "We're having a good time, aren't we, Daisy?" Daisy yipped, either in approval or denial. Fanny wasn't sure.

The phone rang as she was tottering back to the living room, the third bottle clutched to her breast. She debated whether she should answer it or not. "You gotta do what you gotta do."

"Hello."

"Fanny, it's Ash. I'm calling to wish you a happy Thanksgiving."

Fanny heard laughter and Jake's voice on the other end of the line. "Isn't that above and beyond the call of duty, Ash? I wasn't going to call you, so why should you call me? Personally I couldn't care less what you're doing there with *my* family."

"You sound funny. Have you been crying?"

Fanny's eyebrows shot upward. "Absolutely not! You aren't worth crying over, and neither is that brother of yours. So there, Ash."

"Fanny, are you drinking?"

"So what if I am. I'm cooking. So there again."

"I see."

"I see, I see. You don't see at all, Ash. You're too stupid to see just like your brother is too stupid to see. So there again and again."

"How much have you had to drink?"

"Is it important for you to know that?"

"Fanny, turn off the stove and lie down. Take a nap. Will you do that?"

"No. Why should I? I'm sick and tired of doing what you want me to do. The answer is no."

"Then I'll have to call Neal to shut off your stove. You sound sloshed."

"Well, you should know. I won't let him in. I changed the locks. Go away, Ash. Go back to my family and pretend everything is fine. I don't want to talk to you anymore. I don't want to talk to Simon either. So there."

"What happened, Fanny? Tell me, maybe I can help."

"Help! You want to *help*? You ruined my life, and now you want to help me! Drop dead, get out of my life! Wait, wait, I'm sorry. I didn't mean that."

"I know you didn't."

"You were right, Ash," Fanny hiccuped.

"About what?"

"About Simon is what. You said he was a bastard just like you are. He won't listen. He won't bend. Life is full of comp-ro-mises," Fanny said, enunciating the word for Ash's benefit. "I'm damn sick and tired of doing all the comp-ro-mis-ing. So there."

"Fanny, I'm coming down there. I'm going to leave right now."

"You better not. If you come here, I'll tell Daisy to bite you. She will, you know, because she loves me."

"Will you turn the oven off and will you stop drinking?"

"I'll turn the oven off, but I still have some wine left. This is the last time I'm going to do what you tell me. I hate your guts, Ash Thornton."

"Everyone in the world hates my guts. I'm going to hold on while you turn off the stove. After you do that, come back to the phone."

"I'm not stupid, Ash. Did you hear me? I hate your guts."

Fanny trotted out to the kitchen, opened the oven door, stared at the turkey for a few seconds before she turned off the oven. "I hate Simon's guts, too."

"Did you hear that, Ash, I hate Simon's guts, too? So there."

"I'll make it right, Fanny. I'll call Simon. He might listen to me."

"You're *toooooo* late. He gave me an . . . ultimatum. Go away, Ash. I don't want to talk to you anymore. You make me crazy. Did I tell you I hate your guts?"

"Numerous times. I wish you were here, Fanny, I really do. This little reunion is fizzling. No one is comfortable. I mean it, Fanny, I wish you were here."

"I wish I was too. Good-bye, Ash."

Fanny stared at the hole in her sneaker. She wiggled her big toe until it worked through the worn canvas. "Did ya see that, Daisy? I can accomplish whatever I set my mind to." She looked around for her wineglass. *Damn, I must have left it in the kitchen.* She swigged from the bottle.

The doorbell rang.

"Shit!" Ash must have called Neal to come up and turn off the stove. "Go away!" she bellowed. The bell rang again. Daisy barked and wouldn't stop.

"All right, all right!"

Fanny opened the door with a wide flourish, waving the wine bottle as she did so.

"Mrs. Thornton."

"Yep, that's me, two times. Soon to be ex for the second time. And you are . . . the shoemaker . . . the shoe man . . . the man with the shoes . . . Roses. They're on the table. I guess you came to see for yourself. Or did you come to see if I turned off the oven? Who cares? Do you want your shoes back? Look!" Fanny said, wiggling her foot with her toe sticking out of the sneaker. "It was hard to do that, but I did it." She took a long pull from the wine bottle as she stood aside for Marcus Reed to enter the apartment.

"Did I invite you for dinner?"

Marcus smiled. "No, I invited you."

"Oh. Ash made me turn the oven off. Dinner's going to be late. Maybe there won't be any dinner. Daisy is hungry."

"I'm a very good cook. Do you want me to finish your dinner for you?"

"Why would you want to do that?" Fanny asked suspiciously.

"Because you're in no shape to do it. There are a lot of starving people in the world, and it's a shame to waste food."

"You're absolutely right," Fanny said smartly.

"If I make some coffee, will you drink it?"

"I love coffee. I drink coffee all day. I hate Ash's guts. I hate Simon's, too."

"Tomorrow you'll feel different."

"Oh no I won't. What are you doing here? Do you know I'm married?"

"I know now. Are you happily married? Marriage is a wonderful institution."

"Yes. No. I don't think so. You have to turn the oven on to make it work. It was almost done when Ash made me turn it off. I used to like to cook. I hate cooking. I hate everything."

"That's not good, Mrs. Thornton."

"Why not? You can call me Fanny. I wear those shoes all the time. That was very clever of you. Did you see what I did with the roses and the wine bottles?"

"Yes, I did. You have to put water in the bottles or the bloom will die."

"That's sad. I don't like it when things and people die. Do you?"

"Of course not. Why are you alone today, Fanny? Don't you have a family?"

"I have a family all right. They didn't invite me. Do you believe that? I love them all so much. I was a good mother. I know I was. I never had a mother, so I made sure I was the best mother I could be. I make one mistake and . . . it's none of your business, Mr. Reed."

"That's true. It isn't."

Fanny did her best to focus on the man standing in her kitchen. "Sallie would never have let it get this far. I'm like Sallie sometimes. For a long time I wanted her to be perfect. She wasn't. I'm not either. That's a perfect-looking turkey. Do you think this coffee will make me sick? I only got drunk once in my life. Me and Sallie."

Marcus Reed chuckled. "What was the question again?"

"I don't know. Can't you remember?"

"No. Did you make these pies?"

"Every last one," Fanny said proudly.

"I think things are under control. What time would you and Miss Daisy like to dine?"

Fanny tossed her hands in the air. "Are you joining us?"

"If you would like me to, then I'd be honored."

"What should we do now?" Fanny asked.

"I think you should take a nap. I'll watch the football game and the turkey."

"That doesn't . . . seem . . . proper. I hardly know you," Fanny sniffed.

"Isn't that strange? I feel like I've known you forever."

Fanny could feel the bile swishing around in her stomach. "You shouldn't be around me. My family doesn't like anyone I . . . never mind. It isn't important."

"Would you like to talk about it, Fanny? I'm a good listener."

"No. Everyone says that, then they judge you. No thanks. I think I will take a nap. Do you promise to watch the turkey?"

"I promise," Marcus said solemnly.

Fanny's voice turned crafty. "Why should I believe you?"

"Because I'm a man of my word."

"Oh. You have lovely taste in shoes, Marcus. Will you call me when dinner is ready?"

"Absolutely. Do you want me to answer the phone if it rings and if so, what should I say?"

Fanny teetered over to where Marcus stood. "Do you want to hear something sad, Marcus? No one calls me anymore. I do all the calling. All my life I tried to live by the Golden Rule. I always put everyone else first. Myself last. This is what it got me. I live with a little dog. I have two friends. That's it. That's the story of my life. It's sad, isn't it?"

Marcus smiled. "Yes. But things will change. When things look the darkest, a light suddenly appears."

"I think you're wrong."

"Why don't we talk about it after you've had a nap?"

"If anyone calls and their names are Ash or Simon tell them . . . tell them—"

"Yes?"

"Tell them to go to hell."

"Yes, ma'am, I can do that." Marcus turned to hide his smile.

"I love these sneakers."

Marcus threw back his head and roared with laughter. Fanny sniffed as she tottered down the hall to her bedroom, Daisy behind her. Inside her bedroom, she locked the door. She looked across the room to where the bed was. It was much too far. "Get me a pillow, Daisy." A moment later she was sound asleep.

"Simon, Ash here. I called to wish you a happy Thanksgiving and to ask you what in the goddamn hell you're doing to Fanny. She's spending Thanksgiving alone with her dog. Even I have to admit that's pretty sad. I talked to her today, and she told me you gave her an ultimatum. You don't ever give Fanny an ultimatum. Are you just going to write her off because she won't do what you want when you want it done? That's how you train a dog, not a wife."

"Mind your own business, Ash. This is all your doing, you and that fucking casino. If it wasn't for you, Fanny would be here with me now."

"I didn't twist her arm, Simon. Fanny has loyalty, something you and I don't have. Yes, I traded on that loyalty. Let me tell you, she's doing a hell of a job."

"For what? So you can die happy?"

"That's a low blow, even from you. I like to think it's my legacy. I wanted Mom to be proud of me the way you wanted Pop to be proud of you. Don't give me that shit that you saw a shrink and came to terms with things. You didn't any more than I did. Face it, Simon, we're both misfits, you in your way and me in mine. The only difference between us is you wore a three-piece suit. At least I look it in the face and admit to my screwups. Fanny told me she loved you so much she ached. That's a hell of a testimonial, little brother. I personally don't give a shit what you do. What I do give a shit about is Fanny's happiness. She deserves better. I know she's going to sell the casino when I'm gone. You must know it, too. Couldn't you have given her the year? Even two if I make it that long. Oh, no, that interfered with that new life of yours. You blew it. That fucking silence of yours, that withdrawal you use as a weapon won't play with Fanny. One last thing, don't come to my funeral. I'm leaving instructions with the kids if you show up they're to boot your ass all the way down the mountain. In other words, Simon, kiss my ass. It's beyond me what Fanny ever saw in you. Enjoy the rest of the day."

Okay, Fanny, that's all I can do. The rest is up to him.

"I guess my dinner was a bit of a disaster," Sunny said.

"It wasn't that bad," Iris said generously.

"Mom always made a great Thanksgiving turkey," Billie said. "Remember how we'd eat off the leftovers for days and days? The stuffing was almost better than the turkey. You should have invited her, Sunny."

"No, I shouldn't have. Why didn't you cook dinner and invite her? Or you, Iris?"

"I was going to, but you invited us first. Sage and I thought you were inviting your mother. It was a slap in the face, Sunny. Does anyone know where Fanny was having dinner today?"

"She was home by herself," Ash said. "She told me she was cooking dinner for her and Daisy. She said she had invitations but elected to stay home."

"Oh my God," Billie said. "Mom was always the first one to invite people so they wouldn't be alone on Thanksgiving. Grandma Sallie used to do the same thing."

"So now it's all my fault," Sunny cried.

"Since it was your dinner and your invitation list, I'd say so. What kind of family dinner did you expect with Birch and Mom missing from the table?" Sage grated.

"This was supposed to be a family dinner where everyone smiles and gets along. At least I tried."

"You aren't Mom, so don't try and pretend you are. Mom is what holidays are all about. Don't even think about asking me for Christmas," Billie said as she started to clear the table.

"Me either," Sage said. "Iris and I are going to her sister's house."

"So go," Sunny yelled as she stumbled from the table.

Ash stared at his son and daughter. "This isn't good for her."

"She's stupid. Did she really think this was going to be a fun day?" Sage growled.

"Yes, she did."

"Guess she was wrong. You know what, I feel like shit," Sage said.

"Me too," Billie said. "I was hoping Birch would call. I guess he won't since it's later in England if he's still there. Maybe he called Mom. Birch was always good about the holidays. I'm going to help with the dishes, and I'm leaving."

"I'll help," Iris said.

"Don't bother. Dad and I will clear up. Jake likes to carry in the plates. If you have someplace to go, feel free to leave. I'm sorry this wasn't what you all expected."

"You need to get those marbles out of your head and grow up. This is the real world we're walking around in," Sage said.

"That's enough, Sage," Ash said, reaching for his arm.

"Now why did I know you were going to say that? It might be a good idea to get Sunny some counseling or a shrink. Get her something, for God's sake, before she goes off the deep end. My advice is to stop babying her." Sage turned on his heel, scooped Jake onto his shoulder pretending to be a horse shouting, "Giddy-up, pardner." The little boy squealed in delight.

"You're leaving?" Sunny said, her face full of outrage.

"Under the circumstances . . ." Iris said.

"I thought we'd play some cards or something."

Sage set Jake on his father's lap. "No, we're leaving. Maybe we'll stop and see Mom and wish her a happy Thanksgiving."

"That's an idea," Billie said, shrugging into her coat.

"I think that's a good idea. I want to tell her about the baby," Iris beamed.

"Say hello for me," Ash said.

"Little shits," Sunny said when the door closed behind her guests.

"Little shits," Jake mimed her.

Ash flinched at the sound of the slap the little boy took to his bottom. He reached for him and held him close. "Sunny, if you strike this child again, I will personally call Tyler and tell him you're being abusive. Do we understand each other?"

Sunny fled the room as Ash crooned to the little boy, stroking his head. "It's okay, it's okay, Jake. Let's take a ride in the elevator and guess who gets to push the button. But first we have to check on Polly."

"Hers sleeping."

"I know. We're going to check to see if she's sucking her thumb."

"I loves you, Pop Pop."

"I love you too, Jake." *Now I know what Fanny means when she says she loves so much it hurts. Now I know. Now, when it's too late.*

Marcus Reed wandered around the comfortable living room. He stopped to look at family pictures, touching a knickknack, leafed through a book. This place might be an apartment but it was a home in every sense of the word. He tried on Fanny's reading glasses and winced. They smelled powdery.

He wandered back to the kitchen. He sniffed appreciatively. If he ever got this dinner on the table, it would be a miracle. The clock said 7:10. He was trying to decide if he should wake his hostess when the phone rang. He picked it up after the second ring.

"I'd like to speak to Fanny."

"Fanny isn't available at the moment. Would you care to leave a message?"

"Who is this?"

"Who are you?"

"This is Simon Thornton, and I asked you who you were."

"I'm Marcus Reed, a friend of Fanny's. If you care to hold on, I'll wake her."

"You'll wake her. Why is she sleeping? It's only seven o'clock."

"Earlier, Fanny wasn't feeling all that well. Please, hold on."

Marcus walked down the hall to Fanny's room. He assumed it was her room because the other bedroom doors stood open. He rapped sharply. "Fanny, you have a telephone call. It's Simon Thornton." When there was no response he rapped again, this time louder. Daisy barked furiously. "Fanny, can you hear me? You have a telephone call."

"Yes. Yes, thank you. I'll take it in here."

Marcus walked back to the kitchen. As much as he wanted to hear the conversation, he replaced the receiver in the cradle. He turned knobs on the stove. Dinner was finally under way. He sat down at the table with a cup of coffee to wait for his hostess.

Fanny picked up the phone, her tongue thick in her mouth. "What is it, Simon?"

"I thought I might drive down to Vegas tonight."

"Thanksgiving is over, Simon."

"I guess we need to talk."

"No, I don't think we do. I have a job to do here, Simon, and I cannot leave. You rejected all my overtures these past four months. Now all of a sudden you want to grace me with your presence. I don't think so."

"Who answered the phone? He said you weren't feeling well."

"Actually, Simon, that was a polite way of saying I was drunk and sleeping it off. Mr. Reed is a . . . friend of mine. He stopped by to finish cooking dinner for me and Daisy because I was too drunk to do it. Is there anything else you want to know?"

"Now you're telling me you don't want me to come there after begging me for four months."

"I don't take kindly to ultimatums. Look, I think we both need to cool down a little. We'll talk another time."

"When?"

"When? When I decide, Simon. You've managed to keep me on a string for four months. Don't expect me to rush to any quick decisions. I'm going to hang up now."

"Maybe you shouldn't bother calling me at all."

"Maybe I shouldn't."

"Ash said you would do this."

"What does Ash have to do with this?"

"He called me today and told me off. He also told me not to attend his funeral."

"Well guess what, Simon, Ash told me a lot of things about you, too. I'm thinking about those things right now, and the more I think about them, the more I'm starting to believe them. Good-bye, Simon." Fanny broke the connection. She waited a moment before she picked up the phone again. When she heard the dial tone, she stuffed the receiver under her pillow.

Fanny stared at herself in the bathroom mirror. Holy Mother of God! Who was this person staring at her? She clenched her teeth until she realized she had to pry them apart in order to brush. She gargled, washed her face, slapped on some powder, and brushed her hair.

She was halfway down the hallway when the doorbell rang. Thinking it was Bess, she didn't bother to hurry, since each step she took thumped its way to her head. When she entered the living room, she saw Marcus Reed open the front door.

Fanny shrank back against the wall.

She almost fainted when Marcus came up to her and said, "Your children are here. Look, I don't know what's going on. You look as miserable as they do. If I may make a suggestion, invite them to dinner. Don't make apologies, and smile even if it kills you. Can you do that, Fanny?"

"Yes. Yes, I can do that. Thank you. Thank you very much."

"Okay, stiffen those legs and forget the headache hammering behind your eyes. You have lovely eyes you know. Your children are lucky to have someone like you. Sometimes young people don't see what's right under their noses. Just be their mother and everything will be fine. Trust me, okay?"

"Okay."

15

Fanny did her best to turn an awkward situation into one of comfort. She managed to smile, to hug her children and say kind things while the sledgehammer inside her head pounded away at her temples. "Marcus, I'd like you to meet my daughter Billie, my daughter-in-law Iris, and my son Sage. This is Marcus Reed. Of course you all know Daisy. Please, come in and tell me what you think of my . . . new digs."

"It's hard to believe," Billie said, her face registering awe. "Did Aunt Billie do it?" Fanny nodded.

"Would anyone like a drink?"

"I'd like a beer," Sage said. He tried not to stare at the tall, handsome man who seemed so at ease in his mother's apartment.

"Nothing for me," Iris said.

"Coke," Billie said.

"Entertain your children, Fanny. I'll get the drinks." Fanny nodded, amused at the curiosity in her children's eyes.

"Would you like to stay for dinner?"

"I sure would," Billie said. "I was hoping for leftovers. A full dinner sounds wonderful. Aren't you eating rather late?"

Fanny was about to confess to her afternoon folly when Marcus returned and said smoothly, "I'm afraid it's my fault. My plane was late getting in."

"They're staying for dinner, Marcus."

"That's wonderful. Now you won't have to eat turkey for the next thirty days. You visit, Fanny, and I'll get the food on the table. I hope you all brought your appetites."

Not wanting a lapse in the conversation, Fanny said, "Did any of you hear from Birch?"

"Tomorrow he'll realize it's Thanksgiving and he'll call. He's fine, Mom, trust me on this. Birch just needs to get things in perspective. Near-death experiences affect people differently. He'll be home before you know it. Mom, Iris and I have something to tell you. We stopped by twice yesterday, but you were out. It's not the kind of thing you announce on the phone, and we didn't want to leave a note. Iris is pregnant."

"Oh, Sage, how wonderful!" Fanny said, pretending not to know the good news. "Iris, you must be so happy. Will you allow me to make the layette?"

"Of course. I got some experience today holding Polly. She's a very good baby. Would you like to see a picture of her? We took some Polaroids today."

"Yes, yes I would." Fanny's eyes burned as she stared at the pictures of her grandchildren. "They're beautiful. I'm sure every grandmother says that."

"Jake is a piece of work. He's all boy. He's got Dad wrapped. Dad says Jake gets out of bed at night and sleeps with him. I don't know how long that will last because Jake wets the bed. Dad thought it was funny." Fanny smiled.

Fanny handed back the pictures.

"If you like, you can keep them," Iris said.

"Thank you. Yes, I would like that very much."

"You could go up there, Mom. You might want to think about it before Sunny gets it into her head to put those gates back up. She mumbled something about it today."

"I can't do that. Where I'm concerned, it's by invitation only. I understand her feelings, and I have to respect them. Sunny will do what she feels she has to do. Is she all right?"

"Hell, no, she's not all right. I don't want to talk about Sunny, Mom. How's Uncle Simon?" Sage asked.

"I'm afraid I can't answer that, Sage. I haven't seen him in four months. He did call today though. Just a little while ago, as a matter of fact."

"Dinner's ready," Marcus said from the dining-room doorway.

He looks like he belongs here. Evidently her children were of the same opinion.

"God, real food," Sage said, folding his hands. He said grace, his eyes on the turkey.

"I'd say we made a serious dent in this bird," Marcus said an hour later, pushing back his chair. "Would anyone like food to go? I saw some aluminum trays that would be perfect for one more complete meal for each of you."

"I'm your man," Sage said.

"I'm your girl," Billie smiled.

"I'm eating for two now, so fill my tray," Iris said.

"You ladies sit here and Mr. Reed and I will clear up," Sage said. "I'll wash. You dry. This is Mom's good stuff, so be careful. It all belonged to my grandmother Sallie."

"I'll keep that in mind," Marcus said. Fanny noticed the twinkle in his eyes. For some reason she felt flustered

"Who *is* he, Mom?" Billie asked.

"A friend. A friend who got me through a very bad day."

"Mom, we didn't know for certain that you weren't invited until we got to Sunrise. It was awful. I couldn't wait to leave. Sage and Iris felt the same way."

"Sunny's going through a bad time. You need to be tolerant."

"Mom, it has nothing to do with her condition. It's that thing with you and her. She *will* put the gates up."

"Then she puts the gates up. It won't be the end of the world."

"How is the casino business?" Iris asked. "Later on I'll think about making an appointment with Madam Sarika to tell me if I'm going to have a boy or a girl."

"You don't *really* want to know, do you, honey? That's one of the best things about giving birth, the surprise at the end. At least I always thought so. You're married to a twin so there's a good possibility you might have twins."

"I would love to have twins," Iris gushed. "I'd like to have a little boy that looks like Sage and a little girl that looks like me."

Fanny smiled. "Will you go back to work?"

Iris shrugged.

"Ah, December, the most wonderful time of the year. I have to start thinking about decorations for the casino. I have meetings scheduled all week with decorators who specialize in such things. I didn't even know there were companies like that. Running this casino is an education in itself."

"Mom, do you remember that play village I made when I was ten or so?" Billie asked. Fanny nodded. "What if we shut down Rainbow Babies and Sunny's Togs for a week and make one like it, life-size. We could set it up outside in the hanging gardens. Chue can take the plants out, store them, and after New Year's he can replant them. Sage is great with a hammer and nails."

"I can sew," Iris said. "I can do the elves. Children will love it. Since I'm on a leave of absence I have a lot of free time and I would love to work on this."

"We could have it ready for the first of December," Billie said.

"Honey, that's only a week away."

"We can do it, Mom. We need a Christmas tree, a really big one like they have in New York."

"I went to school with a girl whose father owns a Christmas tree farm in Oregon. I'll call her when we get home. Oh, this is so exciting! I just love this family. You're all so interesting," Iris trilled.

Fanny laughed.

"We need to get on our sticks. Sage!" Billie bellowed. "Let's go. We have business to take care of. *NOW!*"

Sage and Marcus came on the run.

Fanny watched Marcus's face as her children started talking all at once. His head bobbed from side to side as Billie and Iris chattered like runaway trains.

"Are you honest to God saying I finally get to use my carpentry skills after all these years? Yahoo!" Sage boomed. "One week is cutting it pretty close. We can do it. Jesus, I wish Birch was here. He'd get a kick out of this. Marcus, do you know anything about carpentry?"

"I worked summers in construction to put myself through college. Are you requesting my help?"

"Well, hell yes. Do you think you can handle it?"

"Sage . . . Marcus . . . where are your manners, Sage?"

"At the table, Mom. You always said to leave them there. Where are we going to do this?"

"How about calling Red Ruby and asking her if we can do it at the ranch. She's got all those barns and stuff. It won't interfere with her . . . ah, business."

"Are you referring to the famous"—Marcus cleared his throat—"establishment?"

"Yeah, that's the one." Sage grinned. "My grandmother set her up out there. She always gives us a Christmas present. She was in love with my grandfather."

"Sage! How do you know that?" Fanny demanded.

"She told me. She loved Grandma Sallie, so she never, ah, you know."

"Good Lord," Fanny muttered.

"It's settled then. Mom's going to take care of the inside, with those companies she's meeting with, and we're going to do the outside. Are you helping, Mr. Reed?" Billie asked.

"What time should I report for work?" Marcus asked smartly as he slapped the dish towel over his shoulder. "I'm afraid I didn't bring the proper attire with me."

Fanny grew light-headed when Marcus winked at her.

"We can outfit you right now, right here. I'll call downstairs and have them send up some stuff. Is that okay with you?"

Marcus shrugged.

"Mom, there's no dial tone."

"Oh. The receiver's under the pillow in my room."

"I'll put it back on the hook," Iris said.

"I don't suppose you want to tell us why the receiver is under your pillow," Sage said.

"That's right. I don't. Marcus, you don't have to do this."

"I would like to do it. I can take care of my business in the evening. Most of it is entertaining anyway."

"I'm afraid not. This project will be around the clock. You can back out now if you want to," Sage said.

"I'm a man of my word. It won't be a problem. The more I think about it, the more the idea appeals to me."

"Okay, we're out of here. I'll pick you up by the front door at six-thirty. Are you staying here?"

"No. I'll be ready."

"Night, Mom, the dinner was swell."

"Don't forget your leftovers," Fanny said, hugging her children.

When the door closed behind her children, Fanny stared helplessly at Marcus. "I don't know what to say. They really did put you on the spot. How do I thank you for all you did today?"

"I enjoyed every minute of it. How do you feel?"

"I have a monster headache."

Marcus handed Fanny the dish towel. He shrugged into his jacket, straightened his tie just as the doorbell rang. Fanny smiled as he inspected his new working attire, right down to the yellowish brown boots.

"I'll say good night. I would say thank you for inviting me, but then I invited myself. It was a wonderful day. You have very nice children, Fanny. I think I envy you."

"What you see isn't always the way things are, Marcus." Her voice was so sad Marcus stared at her longer than he intended. He nodded to show he understood.

"If your children give me a dinner hour, would you join me?"

Fanny laughed. "Forget the dinner hour. When they get immersed in a project, they gobble donuts on the run. I'll bring out some food around six o'clock. We can have a picnic. You realize you aren't getting paid for this, don't you?" She could hear Marcus laughing all the way to the elevator.

For the first time in months, Fanny looked forward to waking in the morning. She hurried through her duties in the office, tidied the apartment, cooked, and made two trips a day to Red Ruby's with baskets laden with food. She knew she was in the way, but she didn't care. She loved watching her children create things, loved watching Marcus Reed's rippling muscles as he worked alongside her son.

On the third day, Marcus groaned when he saw Fanny approach with the heavy basket. "If it's turkey again, I quit."

"It's not turkey. It's pastrami on rye with real deli pickles and lots of mustard."

"In that case, I'll stay. Sage and I were just talking about opening our own construction business. He only banged his thumb thirty times."

"I don't think either one of you should quit your day jobs." Fanny laughed.

"I'm of the same opinion. I never would have believed this if I wasn't right here on the scene. That little-bitty matchstick thing stuck on a piece of cardboard is now something to take notice of. I'm anxious to see what it looks like when it gets painted with all the Christmas colors. You must be very proud of your daughter, Fanny. I was married once but never had children. I suppose it was a good thing because the marriage didn't last."

"I'm sorry. When all else fails, when things don't go right, you can always count on family to get over the trouble spots. It isn't always a constant in one's life, but it should be."

"Where will you be this Christmas, Fanny?"

"At the casino. Would you like to join us? Don't feel you have to, just to be polite. It will probably be just me and Daisy. The kids might stop by. I can't be sure about anything these days."

"I can't think of anything I'd like more. Of course. Do you do the tree, sing carols, drink eggnog, open gifts?"

"The whole nine yards. We do it Christmas Eve. We have a big as in very big dinner first. Sallie always did it that way. It was wonderful. She invited everyone she thought might be alone. Sallie was the kindest, gentlest, most wonderful person I've ever met. I don't think she was ever truly happy. Are you happy, Marcus?"

"Define the word happy, Fanny. This is a tremendous sandwich."

"Well, it's a wonderful feeling. You can't wait to get up in the morning and you hate going to sleep at night. It's that contented feeling that all is right with your world. It's caring about people who care about you. The sun is brighter, the stars shinier, that kind of thing."

"Then I guess I'm sort of happy. I like crunchy apples. I'd like to stay and talk, Fanny, but your son cracks a mean whip. He doesn't much care for cigarette breaks either. He puffs as he works. Thanks for lunch."

"Isn't it great, Mom? The tree's coming late this afternoon. The delivery people are going to set it up. Mom, would it be impossible to shut down Babylon so we can do all this without interruption? I know we'll lose money, but this stuff is going to bring in people by the drove. How long did the company you hired say their work will take?"

"A day and a half. Sure, we can close down. I'm the boss, remember."

"We have to cover the front doors and windows. We want this to be an in-your-face, blow-your-socks-off opening. By the way, what's it costing for the casino?"

"You don't want to know. We'll recoup. I'll have Neal put up signs, and we'll announce it hourly over the loudspeaker. I have to get back."

"He's got a nice tush. For a man his age. Did you notice, Mom?"

"No, I did not notice." Flustered at her daughter's comment, Fanny packed up her picnic basket.

"C'mon, Mom, he's a groovy-looking guy. For his age. He's nice.

I like him. Sage does, too. The truth is, he's a better carpenter than Sage is. They're both having the time of their lives. I think you are, too; but you won't admit it. He's nothing like Dad or Uncle Simon."

Fanny changed the subject. "How's that twenty-foot-high Santa coming?"

"I'm doing the beard this afternoon. It's one silky strand at a time, and it takes time. The ladder isn't all that steady. The guys are making me a scaffold. I stitch as I go along. Where are we going to store this stuff after Christmas?"

"Right here in Red's barns. The bigger question is, how are you going to transport this to Babylon?"

"In eighteen wheelers. It's all taken care of, Mom."

"All right. Don't fall off the ladder, Billie. I'll see you this evening."

Fanny turned to risk a quick glance in Marcus Reed's direction. There was something about a man in jeans and hard hat. Billie was right. He did have a nice tush. For someone his age.

Back at the casino, Fanny tracked down Ash's business manager and Security chief. She hated going toe to toe with people when they wore the stubborn look Neal was wearing. "It is good business, Neal. We aren't going to fold because we close our doors for two days. I'm not asking you. I'm *telling* you what we're going to do. Post notices at all the entrances and announce it hourly. We'll be open for business Saturday evening at six o'clock. I would suggest you hire extra security. The media will be here in full force. Starting tonight on the six o'clock news, ads will begin to air. They'll run until Saturday. Full-page ads will be in the papers starting tomorrow. Your staff won't be able to handle the crush of people so you should bring in all your people who are off for the weekend. Santa arrives promptly at seven. Do whatever you have to do so there are no glitches. I want this to run smoothly. Oh, one other thing. Mr. Thornton will be in attendance. Ah, I rather thought that would get your attention."

Fanny beelined to her office and immediately dialed the number at Sunrise. Ash answered, laughter in his voice. "It's Fanny, Ash. Is everything okay?"

"Yep. Jake is tickling my feet. What's up, Fanny?"

Fanny told him. "I'd like you to come, Ash. I'd like it even more if you'd bring Jake. Polly's too young. Will you do it? I think I just want to hear you say you're proud of me. The kids are really doing a job on this. It's going to be the most wonderful fairyland. I'm sure

Jake knows about the North Pole, Santa, and the elves. You read him stories, don't you?"

"I can come of course. I'm not sure if Sunny will allow me to take Jake though."

"Ash, Sunny is invited. I wasn't excluding her. Do your best, okay? The kids did everything with Jake in mind. You are absolutely going to be blown away. The kids stopped by on Thanksgiving. Did you tell them to do that? If you did, then I need to thank you."

"It was their own idea. It was miserable when they were here. There's some problems here, but we can talk about them when I come down. I need your clear head on some stuff."

"I'll be here, Ash."

Ash sat for a long time, his thoughts whirling chaotically. He eyed the little boy sleeping on the sofa. His features softened and he smiled. They were going fishing later. Chue had a small natural pond he stocked with plastic goldfish for his grandchildren along with a basket of ten-cent prizes in case one of the children was lucky enough to snare one of the plastic fish. Regardless, they always came home with a prize and a fortune cookie.

Ash steered his way to the closed-in garden room, where Sunny reclined in the last patch of afternoon sun. "How's it going?" he asked.

"Hi. I was sitting here thinking about Tyler. He called earlier and wanted to know if he could take Jake to New York the day after Christmas. He said he'd take him ice-skating and do some father-son things. I didn't say yes and I didn't say no. I wanted to talk to you first. It's just for two days. Jake would like going on a plane."

"By himself!" Ash said, horror written all over his face. "He's only three, Sunny. If someone was to take him, it would be different. I don't think it's a good idea, but it's your decision."

"I always make the wrong decisions. That's why I wanted to talk to you. Jake does miss Tyler. He didn't even ask about Polly. I did send a picture of her that we took on Thanksgiving. He didn't mention it at all. He also said he's dating someone. 'Seeing someone' is the way he put it. I thought that would bother me, but it doesn't. I wonder why that is. Is Jake still sleeping?"

"On the sofa. He climbed up, and he was asleep as soon as his head touched the pillow. This is just a little catnap. He's too excited about going fishing."

"That's so silly, fishing for plastic fish."

Ash bristled. "He loves doing it. I'd like to take him down the mountain on Saturday if you have no objections. Santa is coming to Babylon and it's going to be decorated. A monster tree came in from Oregon, and they're going to turn on the lights. Why don't you come with us?"

"Are you going to see Mom?"

"I imagine so if she's around." Ash wondered if his vague, bland attitude was working. "I thought it would be a good time to pick up my old train set, so we can put it around the tree. It's the only toy I saved from my childhood. I think Simon still has his. The engine belches smoke, there's a real whistle, and the cars have little people in them. Jake will love it. I think you should come with us, though."

"No. I'll stay here. If you take Jake, that will give me time to wrap some of his Christmas presents. He's so curious and already he's poking in the closets."

"Would you object if we stayed overnight? I don't like driving at night with Jake in the car."

"Are you going to stay at Mom's?"

"I could get a room. It would be better if we stayed with your mother."

"No, it wouldn't. If you promise me you'll stay in the hotel, it's okay. Staying with Mom is not okay."

"You're carrying this too far, Sunny."

"You're entitled to your opinion, Dad. I want your word. Jake will tell at some point if you stay with Mom. Please don't make him lie to me."

"All right, Sunny. We'll take a room. Are you sure you don't want to come with us?"

"I'm sure. I think I'll call the people who installed those awful gates for Mom and have them put up again."

"Sunny, for God's sake, why? Your mother doesn't come here. No one comes here unless you invite them, and if you keep on the way you're going, even invited guests won't come. This is your mother's house. It isn't yours. Please remember that. She could put you out tomorrow if she wanted to, and it would be perfectly legal."

"She would never do that," Sunny blustered.

"Don't be so sure. Fanny is a constant surprise. Just when I think I have her down pat, she throws a curve. It's my personal opinion that you've pushed her as far as she will allow. It won't be pleasant if she decides to push back. Leave the gates alone. They don't belong to you."

"I can move back to town," Sunny continued to bluster.

"Yes, you could. The question is, would you and the children be happy there. For the record, I have no intention of moving. I was born here, and I plan to die here." At Sunny's stricken look he added hastily, "At some point in the far future. Sunny, don't you have any friends? We've been here more than four months and no one comes up, no one calls."

"I did. They have lives of their own with families. Two of my best friends moved away. We write once in a while. It's okay. You see how busy I am. Jake and Polly take a lot of time. I'm not devastated about Tyler. It's what it is. Maybe someday things will change."

"They aren't going to change unless you open your mind and heart."

His training pants around his knees, fishing pole over his shoulder, Jake entered the garden room. "Time to fish, Pop Pop."

"Oh, Jake, you peed on your socks. Run in your room and bring me a clean pair. Tell me if Polly is awake."

Jake returned with his socks. "Hers awake. Hers playing with her toes. Mitzi said . . ."

"What did Mitzi say?"

"Hers giving her her bottle."

"Okay. Go with Pop Pop and catch me a big fish."

Sunny watched her father and son until they rounded the bend that would take them to Chue's house. What would she do when her father was no longer here? What would she do if Tyler took the kids? She knuckled her eyes as she shuffled back to the house.

"I've never seen anything so magnificent in my life," Fanny said breathlessly as she walked around Babylon. In every corner, in every aisle, golden Christmas trees complete with gaily wrapped packages graced the casino. Overhead, red velvet swags with golden angels carrying golden trumpets moved in the air from the ventilation system. Bouquets of holly and mistletoe tied with red velvet ribbons could be seen everywhere. Exquisite miniature sleighs, Santas, and elves hung from the tinsel-wrapped chandeliers. Red-and-green signs, their arrows pointing in the direction of the hanging gardens, were in every aisle and by all the exit signs. In the central entrance, a wire arrangement in the shape of a Christmas tree was transformed into a thirty-foot-high poinsettia. Empty boxes wrapped in gold and silver with large red velvet bows sat at the base. In the middle of the casino, above the wide center aisle, suspended from wires, was a real sleigh, with a life-size stuffed Santa, complete with a sack of presents, a small evergreen nestled in the sleigh, and eight prancing reindeer. Every five minutes the Santa offered up a roughish wink and a jolly, Ho-Ho-Ho. Fanny clapped her hands in glee.

Her children and Marcus Reed behind her, Fanny followed one of the red arrows leading to the hanging gardens, where all she could do was stare in amazement. The North Pole complete with swirling snow. "It isn't really snow," Sage whispered.

"I know," Fanny whispered in return. "It's wonderful. You actually built an entire village. Where did the mechanical elves come from?"

"Santa," Marcus quipped. "How do you like Santa's workshop?"

"It isn't a real fire in the fireplace, Mom," Sage whispered.

"I know. It takes my breath away. It's so real. The buckets of paint look real too."

"They're colored pudding with preservatives added. We have to change it once a week," Billie volunteered.

"You actually created an entire village as well as Santa's workshop. I feel like I'm peeking into the magical man's private world. That scroll must be a mile long. Every little boy and girl's Christmas list. And the barn with the reindeer. Oh, my, there's Rudolph. Jake is going to love this. What's in all those baskets?"

Everyone laughed. "Reindeer treats. They're giveaways. Jake asked me what he could leave for Santa's reindeer. They're little bags filled with hay and glitter and tied with a red ribbon. A small instruction slip says, 'Leave outside the front door.' I hired some kids from the university and they made up ten thousand packets."

"It's mind-boggling is what it is. When does the giant Santa go up?" Fanny asked.

"As we speak. I had to polyurethane him. I wanted to make sure he dried. He's under the canopy with his own twenty-four-hour guard. Okay, time to shower and be on hand when the door opens. See you guys later," Billie said with a wave of her hand.

"We're off, too," Iris and Birch said in unison. "See you later."

Marcus Reed held out his hand. "I don't think I ever worked so hard for zero pay. I also didn't think it was possible to enjoy myself as much as I did. I want to thank you, Fanny, for allowing me to be a part of this. I'll say my good-bye now, too."

"You're leaving! You aren't staying for the opening?"

"Business calls. I hate crowds. I hope tonight is everything you want it to be."

Fanny watched Marcus walk away. Suddenly everything seemed off-color and out of focus. The urge to run after him, to ask him to stay, was so strong, Fanny forced herself to dig her heels into the soft artificial snow.

"I'm alone again."

"Did you say something, Mrs. Thornton?" Neal asked

"No. I guess I was thinking out loud. Tell me, what do you think?"

"I never would have believed it. When you said decorate I thought you meant a wreath, a tree, and some red bows. I've never seen anything like this. I think your assessment was on target. We'll recoup our money. Do you mind me asking who that man was in the red plaid shirt?"

"Mr. Reed. He helped build this stuff. Do you know him?"

"No. I think I've seen him somewhere, though, or else he reminds me of someone. It will come to me at some point. You only have ninety minutes, Mrs. Thornton, before the doors open."

"I guess I better hurry then."

Fanny pressed the play button on her answering machine. Ash's voice pealed into the room. "Fanny, I have the okay to bring Jake down. We'll be there for Santa's arrival. I'll book a room. The kid is so excited he's going to make himself sick. He's bringing you a present, so act like you've been waiting all your life for it, okay. We'll see you in a couple of hours."

Fanny sat down on the floor and tussled with Daisy. "Wait till you see who's coming to see us. Actually, we'll be going to see him. I think you might like him since he's a little person. Ah, that's it, give me kisses." Fanny rolled over and over, Daisy yipping and yapping as she tried to snuggle against Fanny. "Okay, okay, you win, two cookies. Roll the can over here." Fanny fumbled with the lid as the phone rang. She burst out laughing when Daisy knocked the can out of her hand, cookies scattering everywhere. "Hello," she gasped.

"Fanny, it's Simon."

The laughter died in Fanny's throat. Her voice went flat. "Hello, Simon."

"I thought I'd drive down tomorrow."

"Why?"

"Why? To see you."

"Why?"

"We need to talk."

"Don't you mean you need to talk, Simon? I said everything I had to say."

"Are you saying you don't want me to come?"

"You can do whatever you please, Simon. I'm a person, Simon, with feelings, with needs. I'm not a possession you can pull out on a whim and then store away again. This weekend is the opening of the Christmas season for us. I won't have any time to spend with you. Ash is bringing Jake down."

"Let me make sure I understand what you're saying. You are too busy to see me and talk to me but you have time to spend with Ash and Jake."

"That's about it, Simon. Ash will be taking care of Jake. I just get to see him. That little boy is very important to me."

"When will you have time? Do I need an appointment?"

"Sometime after the first of the year. Do you realize, Simon, you did the same thing to me your brother did? I will not tolerate that."

"What about Christmas?"

"What about it?"

"Do you want me to come for Christmas?"

Did she? "No, Simon, I do not. I'm sorry to cut you short, but I have to get dressed and be downstairs when the doors open. Have a nice evening."

"Fanny, I'm sorry."

"Sorry is just a word. I've heard it so much in my life it doesn't mean anything. Good-bye, Simon."

Fanny scooped Daisy up into her arms. "Four months ago I thought I was going to die if Simon didn't call me. I thought I couldn't live without him. Guess what, I did . . . I am. Whatever. What's even more amazing is I'm starting to like what I'm doing. Okay, go finish those cookies while I get ready."

What was it Sallie used to say when something was after the fact? Too much, too little, too late.

The story of my life, Fanny thought as she stepped into the shower.

16

~

Simon Thornton knew his eyes were as wild-looking as he felt. For one crazy moment he debated putting his booted foot through the television screen. He looked around the oversize cabin he and Fanny had called home for three years. Everything he was seeing shrieked Fanny, Fanny, Fanny.

In his gut he knew she was never coming back. In Fanny's eyes he'd done the ultimate, the most unforgivable thing possible; he'd ignored her. He'd given her an ultimatum. *You're doing to me what Ash did, and I will not tolerate it.* He wasn't Ash. Hell, he hated his brother's guts. Whatever Ash did Simon always made sure he did just the opposite. Where in the hell did Fanny get off saying something like that?

Four months of silence. On his part. He regretted that silence now. If he'd just given a little, bent a little—

Simon threw more clothes in his bag. If he put the pedal to the metal he could make John Wayne Airport and be in Vegas before midnight. His shoulders tensed when he heard the snap of the locks on his suitcase. The sound was an ending sound, if there was such a thing. Perhaps, he thought, the word he was looking for was terminal. Suddenly he felt sick to his stomach.

Simon carried his bag down to the kitchen. He looked around. In the beginning the kitchen had been his and Fanny's sanctuary. They'd sit for hours at the old scarred table, talking, drinking coffee or tea, the dogs at their feet. The kitchen had always sparkled. Now it was dreary and grimy. The braided rugs in front of the stove and sink were dirty and stained. The green plants were limp and yellowish-looking. Piles of dirty dishes were everywhere. The copper-bottomed pots hanging from hooks on the rafters had lost their luster. The stove was full of grease and dirty fry pans. The magnets Fanny collected for the refrigerator had shifted to the bottom because he constantly slammed the door. He knew there were bugs in the sink and ants on the floor. He didn't care. He didn't much care about anything these days.

He pressed the intercom and spoke to his kennel manager. "I'll be gone for a few days. Take care of Tootsie and Slick till I get back. If you know of anyone who does housecleaning, will you call them to clean up after me. Pay them out of petty cash. The key to the back door is under the mat. I'll see you when I get back."

Simon looked at his watch. By midnight he'd be face-to-face with Fanny.

Fanny slipped into her red velvet gown. She smiled when she stroked the faux ermine trim. She'd made the dress herself, and one for Bess, just this week. She grinned when she settled the furry white cap with the red tassel onto her head. She couldn't remember the last time she was this excited. Was her excitement due to Ash's arrival with little Jake, the anticipation of seeing the crowd's reaction to the holiday decorations, or was her elation due to a man named Marcus Reed? All of the above.

Whatever it was, it was heady indeed. Something tugged at her memory, something she meant to do. It concerned Ash, but what was it? Ah, Daisy's kennel. She wanted Ash to take it back to Sunrise so she could use the space to line up all her shoe boxes. Fifty pairs of shoes, as she'd found out, took up a lot of room. Well, she might as well drag it out now and put it by the front door so she didn't forget again.

Daisy sniffed and barked as Fanny dragged the huge crate to the foyer. "Take out everything, Daisy. You aren't going anywhere, so relax."

The little dog pawed at the small quilt and a stuffed toy that had been left behind. "What's that?" Fanny asked as she bent down to pick up a manila envelope. She stared at the return address, at hers and Simon's name and then at the date. The thick package was four months old. "Damn you, Simon, you could have told me you put this in the kennel," she muttered. She didn't have time to look at it now. She'd do it later when she was in bed. Five minutes to go.

The private penthouse elevator whisked Fanny to the lobby. "It's wonderful!" she shouted as she looked around at her employees. All the girls wore short skating-style red velvet outfits and caps trimmed in the same faux ermine as her own gown. The men wore red velvet Santa suits and shiny black boots.

"Bess! You look gorgeous."

"Then it must be true. John said the same thing. You look beautiful, Fanny. The outfit is very becoming. My thick waist doesn't do this gown justice the way your twenty-six-inch waist does. Remember now, get under the sleigh, and when the doors open you yell, Merry Christmas!"

"Bess, that's pretty corny."

"Your patrons expect it. One minute to go!"

"Open the doors, Neal!"

The police and security guards held their arms out to allow the first four guests through the front doors; Ash in his wheelchair, Jake on his lap. Billie Coleman Kingsley was on his right, Thad on his left.

Fanny ran to the front of the casino. She kissed Ash's cheek, hugged Jake, whose eyes were so wide they almost popped from his head. "Thank you for coming," she said to Billie and Thad.

"We wouldn't have missed this for the world. You made the news in Washington, D.C. It was one of those television channels that gives a little synopsis of what's going on around the country. Thad gassed up his plane the minute we saw it, and here we are."

"We have to get out of the way."

"Fanny, I don't know what to say," Ash said.

"Don't say anything until you see the village. Take Jake to the hanging gardens, and I'll join you as soon as we fill up."

"The Strip's empty, Fanny. I think everyone in the world is outside. I think there are more people here than we had for the grand opening. This is your grandma Fanny, Jake."

Jake stared at the red gown, his little hand reaching out to touch the fur. "You get me Santy Claus hat, Pop Pop?"

Fanny removed her hat in the blink of an eye. She handed it to Ash, her eyes filling with tears. "He's so beautiful, Ash."

"Yeah, I know," Ash said gruffly as he settled the white fur cap on his grandson's head. "It's a red snowball, sport." The little boy giggled as he tickled his grandfather under the nose with the red snowball.

"We'll see you later, Granny," Ash laughed. "We're in room 2311. He had two naps, so he can probably hold out till midnight. You might want to tuck him in."

"Oh, Ash, yes I would. Let's meet at the entrance to the village say around ten-thirty and see how he's holding up. I sent some presents up to the room earlier. Big red bows and all that. Our kids used to like the paper and bows better than the presents. The empty boxes, too. They used to play with empty boxes by the hour."

Ash stared at Fanny, his face blank. "I never knew that, Fanny."

"I know, Ash. It's all right. It wasn't something important. It was a memory. You better get to the village before the crowds become too dense. Besides, I think that little guy is about to explode. Get his picture taken with the Santa. Be sure to get one for me."

"Okay. You ready, sport? There's a big guy in there in a red suit who is just waiting to ask you what you want for Christmas. You got your list ready?"

Jake fished in his pocket and pulled out a piece of paper. He waved it triumphantly in Ash's face.

"It's almost like a miracle, isn't it, Fanny?" Billie whispered.

"That's strange, Billie, I was thinking the same thing. That man is not the man I was married to. I like the man I was just talking to. Am I crazy?"

"Not at all. I'm glad for you and for Ash. You had so much bitterness for so long. Jake looks like one of the cherubs on a Christmas card."

"Ash said I can go up to their room and tuck him in later."

"I hope this visit is everything you want it to be. I don't suppose Simon is coming, is he?"

"That's right up there with the Pope coming to Vegas, Billy. He did call earlier, and it wasn't a nice conversation. I'm not discounting the fact that he made an overture, but he made it in anger. I could hear it in his voice. I don't feel the same way about Simon anymore, Billie. I want to, but something in me died. It's the same feeling I had when Ash and I split up. Simon asked me if I wanted him to come for Christmas, and I said no. I said no because I'm sick and tired of stress and strain. That's what holidays are, you know. I refuse to put myself through that ever again. Daisy and I can manage just fine. I think I'll get her a playmate."

"I hear something in your voice, Fanny, and there's a strange look in your eyes. I want a full accounting."

"Later, when things quiet down, okay?"

"Okay. Now I better find Thad. He's got money from his colleagues, a dollar each, to play. Big spenders. I wish they'd be that frugal with our tax dollars."

Fanny laughed as her eyes searched the crowd. It wasn't until a long time later that she realized she was looking for Marcus Reed. The realization made her warm all over.

The room looked the same. The men seated around the huge table looked the same. The sterling service was the same. The orchid flower arrangement had been replaced with festive greenery and poinsettias in deference to the approaching holidays.

"The Emperor is back."

"Just to visit. He brought his grandson with him."

"Our customers deserted us. Everyone is outside, waiting to get into Babylon. Who the hell thought Christmas decorations were important. Women!"

"Babylon is one of the seven wonders of the world. The Christmas decor is worthy of the establishment. It's time you all gave some serious thought to hiring a few women. Women have ideas. Women know what other women want. Most women are mothers and, consequently, anything geared toward children will hold a great deal of appeal. Women do not, I repeat, do not want to see tough-looking men in dark suits, cigars, and smelly rooms. They want flowers, bright colors, and an air of gentility. I told you repeatedly your old ways no longer work. Tell me, how many of you here made your way across the street this evening? A show of hands will do nicely." Every hand in the room went up. "Since money is no object, what seems to be your problem?"

"Who can compete with the Thornton name?"

The man at the head of the table shrugged. "You asked me to assess the situation and to come up with a remedy. What do you do when you have an out-of-control fire?"

"Fire, shmire, what the hell does a fire have to do with the gambling business?"

"You dig a trench. Then you build a second fire so they slap at each other, at which time both fires are extinguished."

"You want us to burn down Babylon!" someone asked in amazement.

"NO." The single word was a thunderbolt of sound. "Does the word copycat mean anything to any of you?"

"You want we should make our establishments look like Babylon? *They* won't agree to that."

"All of you here told me money was no object. Are you saying you lied to me?"

"No. We aren't saying that at all."

"If you don't wish to fight fire with fire, then you will have to come up with some other remedy. Short of torching the building."

"We'll offer to buy her out. Things happen all the time."

"Those things will come back to haunt you. How many times do I have to tell you, your old ways no longer work?"

"Women don't know anything about operating a business. She'll run it into the ground in a year. We'll pick up the pieces."

"Let me show you gentlemen something," the man at the head of the table said. "These are P & L sheets for Mrs. Thornton's two companies, Sunny's Togs and Rainbow Babies. It's not important how they came to be in my possession. Look at them carefully and tell me this lady doesn't know what she's doing. All you have to do is look to your own businesses and then look across the street."

"She's stealing our business."

"*NO.* Mrs. Thornton is *generating* business by using her head. A detailed report of my findings will be in your superior's hands by the close of business tomorrow. Good-bye, gentlemen, and good luck."

"That's it! We paid you a million dollars for *this!*" someone shouted.

"You paid me a million dollars to show you what you were doing wrong. I showed you. I still contend Mrs. Thornton is no threat to any of you. She's running her business the only way she knows how, successfully. She has no interest in this side of the street. My original opinion stands: Mrs. Thornton affords you respectability."

"What's she building out there in the desert?" someone sneered.

"A state-of-the-art medical and rehabilitation facility for her daughter and others like her who suffer from muscle and nerve diseases. At our last meeting I suggested you might want to anonymously donate some monies to such a worthy cause. I'm sure Mrs. Thornton will be astute enough to figure out where the money came from and give credit where credit is due. Good day, gentlemen."

"How can we reach you if things change?"

"Your employers know how to reach me. Have a nice holiday."

It was almost midnight when Marcus Reed crossed the street to Babylon. He walked up to the plate glass window and stared inside. He felt like he was a kid again with his nose pressed close to the bakery window. His eyes searched the crowds and then he saw her. She was smiling at someone and talking animatedly. "Well-done, Fanny," he whispered, before he walked away.

Fanny turned when she felt someone was staring at her. Her gaze swept the room and then moved to the front of the casino. Her heart lurched when she thought she saw Marcus Reed. It must have been a trick of the lighting. She moved off toward the elevators. She crossed her fingers, hoping Jake was still up.

"Fanny. Jake and I have been waiting. He's so full of piss and vine-

gar he's never going to go to sleep. He loves those toys you bought
him."

"Ash, if you want to go downstairs, I can stay with Jake."

"Tomorrow is soon enough. I realized I don't miss this place at
all. You did real good, Fanny. I'm proud of you."

"Really, Ash. Did Jake love it?"

"Do birds fly? The kid ate it up. He asked more questions. He ate
so much junk he's got to be high on sugar. Sunny would take a fit if
she knew. He never gets candy, and once in a while she gives him a
cherry Popsicle. She pumps him full of all kinds of vitamins and
stuff."

Fanny nodded. "Hi, Jake."

"Hi."

"Did you have a good time tonight?"

"Yep. Santy Claus give me this."

"A net. What's it for?"

"Fishing. Where's the present, Pop Pop?"

"Right here."

The little boy ran over to his grandfather, reached for the present
and handed it over shyly. "Is for you."

"For me?"

"Merry . . . merry . . ."

"Christmas," Ash said.

"Yep, Christmas."

Fanny unwrapped the small gift that had more cellophane tape
than paper on it. "Oh, my goodness, a plastic goldfish."

"Me and Pop Pop caught it. Is a present."

"And a lovely one it is. Thank you very much."

"Do you want to play?"

"Sure." Fanny kicked off her shoes and hiked up her gown before she sat down cross-legged on the floor. "Let's build a castle
with the blocks. You'll be the prince and Pop Pop will be the king.
Polly will be a princess."

"What's Mommy?"

"Mommy's the queen."

"What's you?"

Fanny's throat closed tight. She struggled to swallow. Her eyes
implored Ash.

"Who do you think she is, Jake?"

"Santy Claus's mommy."

Fanny started to giggle. "Okay, that's who I am."

At one o'clock Fanny called a halt to the castle building. "I think it's time to brush your teeth and get ready for bed."

"No."

"No? Are you telling Santy Claus's mommy no? Tsk tsk," Fanny said, clucking her tongue.

"C'mon, sport, let's hop to it. I want to see if there's any fairy dust on those back teeth."

"Okay, Pop Pop. I got it all out the last time."

"Yeah, I know, but it grows back really quick. Stand on the stool and do a really good job."

"Fairy dust! Ash, you never cease to amaze me. He's wonderful. I can see why this place lost its hold on you."

"It works every time. The kid is just dying for me to find some in his teeth. He makes me laugh like hell."

"I guess you're good for each other. Is Sunny doing okay?"

"It depends on what you mean by okay. In my opinion she's doing lousy. She does her exercises, she eats right, she sleeps a lot, and her patience is at the low end of the scale. Tyler wants to take Jake to New York. She's considering it. He told her he was dating someone. She seems okay with it."

Jake returned to the living room half-dressed, his mouth open for inspection. "I think you got it all, Jake."

"Goody. Wanna see?" he said to Fanny, opening wide.

Fanny plucked a sparkling sequin from the cuff of her sleeve. "Oops, looks like you missed one. Hold still. There, I got it."

"Wow! Did you see that, Pop Pop?"

"Boy are you lucky Grandma Fanny found that last little bit of fairy dust. Next time try to remember to brush harder." The little boy nodded solemnly as he hopped up on the couch. He curled into Fanny's arms.

"Tell me a story."

"All right. Once upon a time there was a . . ."

"Out like a light. That's usually how far I get. Then he wakes up around three or four and wants to know what comes next."

"I envy you, Ash," Fanny said softly.

"Don't ever envy me, Fanny."

"You know what I mean. What did you want to talk to me about?"

"Sunny's been hitting Jake. I don't mean a tap on his tush either. She gives him some pretty heavy-handed wallops. I told her if she did it again, I was going to call Tyler. I've suggested everything under the sun. She closes her ears. Her big thing right now is putting those gates back up. She thinks if she does that, it will keep you out. What she's trying to do is lock herself in. Or maybe she wants you to drive up and smash through them the way she did. Aside from that we have some good days. We watch television together sometimes. We cook together. We usually take a walk every day. Like I said, she sleeps a lot. Jake is with me all the time."

"And Polly?"

"Mitzi takes care of her. She's a good baby. There are days when Sunny doesn't see her at all. It's almost like she's forgotten she has a baby."

"Ash, I'm building a facility for her, and others like her, out in the desert. It's like the one you described to me in Texas. Billie Coleman is funding half of it. It's so high-tech it spooks me. We're building an adjacent building for families, so when they come to visit they can stay close, and those patients with children won't feel so separated from their families. It's going to be wonderful. I think, Ash, when it's completed, you might want to talk Sunny into going in for a while. We'll have the best doctors, the best therapists, and round-the-clock care."

"You're really doing it for Sunny, aren't you?"

Fanny nodded.

"I hope she appreciates it."

"That part doesn't matter. Getting her help is what counts. It will be up to you, Ash. I can build it, but I can't make her want to go. If you think I should go to Sunrise and smash through the gates, if she puts them up, and let her get in my face, you know I'll do it. But, if it doesn't resolve anything, what's the point? I apologized, I admitted I was wrong. Now, all I can do is give her the space she says she wants and hope she can work through it. Damn it, I never said I was perfect. I never pretended to be perfect."

"I know, I know. Listen, tomorrow is another day. I'm tired of beating at this particular horse. Let's call it a night."

"I'll stay a little while. He feels so warm and cuddly. I'll try not to wake you when I leave."

"Stay all night, be my guest," Ash said wearily.

Fanny closed her eyes. She was asleep in five minutes.

Ash undressed and lurched onto the bed, his face grimacing in pain. He stared at his ex-wife and grandson for a long time. He picked up the phone and called the desk. "Myrna, this is Ash Thornton. Yes, I'm glad to be back. How's your family? That's wonderful.

Listen, do me a favor. Don't put any calls through. I have my grandson with me, and I don't want to be disturbed. If the president calls, tell him he has to wait till tomorrow at noon. You got that, Myrna? Thanks, sweetie."

Ash continued to watch Fanny and his grandson. When his eyes started to burn, he turned off the light. He, too, was asleep within minutes.

Simon rode the elevator to the penthouse. He rang the bell again and again. All he could hear inside was Daisy's sharp barking. He let his bag thump to the floor. He was more than annoyed that he didn't have a key to the apartment.

His shoulders stiff, his eyes cold, Simon rode the elevator back to the lobby. He headed for the registration desk. He worked a smile he didn't feel onto his face. "I'm Simon Thornton. Can you tell me if my brother is registered in the hotel?"

"Yes, sir, he is."

"Would you ring his room please?"

"I'm sorry, sir, I can't do that. Mr. Thornton left instructions that he wasn't to be disturbed."

The smile left Simon's face. "I'm his brother for God's sake."

"I'm sorry, sir."

"All right. Give me the key to the penthouse."

"I beg your pardon!"

"Fanny Thornton is my wife. She lives in the penthouse. I've come to visit. Will you give me the key?"

"Sir, if you want a key, you'll have to get it from Mrs. Thornton. We do not give out keys to guests' rooms, much less the owner's apartment. There are privacy laws, Mr. Thornton."

"Have you seen my brother or my wife recently?"

"Mrs. Thornton was on the floor all evening. I saw her from time to time. I personally did not see your brother, but I did speak to him."

"I'd like a room, please."

"I'm sorry, sir, we're sold out."

Simon expressed his disgust with a four-letter word. He marched across the lobby to the casino, his eyes seeking and searching. When he saw Bess, he shouldered his way through the crowds, shouting her name.

"Simon! How nice to see you. So, what do you think?" she asked, waving her hands around.

"Very colorful. Where's Fanny?"

"I have no idea. It's been so busy all night, we kind of lost track of each other. Billie and Thad were over by the first row of slots a few minutes ago. She might know. Did Fanny know you were coming?"

"No. I wanted to surprise her."

"I see anger written all over you, Simon. That can't be good for either one of you."

"Have you seen Ash?"

"The last time I saw him was the last time I saw Fanny. Ash brought Jake down from the mountain today."

"Do you know what room he's in?"

"Simon, how would I know that?"

"Jesus Christ! Do you have a key to the penthouse?"

"I don't believe you're asking me that. I do not have a key. If I did have one, I wouldn't give it to you. You should have called ahead. You're very selfish, Simon. Walk around, maybe you'll spot Fanny. She usually stays until around three. Check with Billie and Thad. I'm off. It was nice seeing you again, Simon."

Simon headed for the bar. Bartenders had their fingers on the pulse of everything. He fought his way through the throngs and ordered a scotch and soda. Any idea of talking to the bartender was out of the question. The decibel level in the bar was so high he was surprised the glasses weren't shattering.

He paid for his drink and headed for the bank of elevators. Maybe he could pick the lock on the penthouse. He sure as hell wasn't going to stand around in a bar all damn night.

Simon rang the bell four times before he pulled out the pen knife that was guaranteed to help him survive in the wilderness for a full year. Fanny had given it to him last Christmas as a joke. He picked at the miniature attachments that weren't really all that little. He picked, prodded, and gouged. In the movies a credit card always worked. He tried his. The door held fast. Daisy barked furiously. Simon stared at the door. The he-men in the movies used their shoulders. His eyes almost bugged out of his head as pain shot up his neck and then down his arm.

Simon wasn't about to give up. "Get away from the door, Daisy." He backed up, then ran, his booted foot straight in front of him. The door broke from the jamb. He used his good shoulder to push it in. Daisy cowered against one of the red chairs. Simon ignored the little dog as he stomped his way through the penthouse. He walked back to the door and picked up his bag. The door hung drunkenly on its hinges He carried his bag into the bedroom where he threw it on the bed, then went back to the living room, eyed the two red chairs and the small bar against the wall. He poured himself a drink, gulped at it, then poured a double. He looked at his watch. Three o'-clock.

The scotch bottle was almost empty at five o'clock. Simon drained it. At six he opened a second bottle. At six-ten he raised his bleary eyes to see Fanny towering over him, her gown wrinkled and mussed, the ermine trim hanging askew from the neckline.

"It's about time you showed up. Where the hell have you been? I've been waiting all goddamn night."

"You broke down my door."

"I didn't have a key."

"The reason you don't have a key is because you don't live here. I want you to leave. Where's Daisy?"

"Hiding under the bed. I tried to get her to come out, but she wouldn't listen to me. I asked you a question, where were you?"

"That's none of your business. I want you to leave, Simon."

"I'm not going anywhere until we talk. I can't leave. There aren't any rooms."

"Then go across the street. When you sober up I'll talk to you. Not one minute before. Where are your things?"

"I'm staying here with you. I'm your husband. Where were you, Fanny? You were with Ash, weren't you?"

Fanny walked into the bedroom. She yanked at the bag on the bed and carried it to the front door, where she pitched it into the hall. She didn't know the man sitting in her living room.

"I haven't seen or heard from you in four months. To me, Simon, that takes away any of your rights to question me. Please leave."

"Look at you!" Simon sneered. "You were shacking up with Ash. It's written all over your face. Come here, Fanny."

"If you believe that, then why do you even want me near you? Why are you in my apartment?" Fanny picked up the house phone on the wall at the side of the door. She pressed nine for Security. "Neal, I know it's early, but could you send someone up here to re-pair my door and two guards to escort an unwelcome visitor down-stairs."

"All right, all right, I'm going. I always knew you weren't over Ash. It was always Ash. I was a poor second rebound choice. Go to Ash, see if I care. I'm out of here, and I'll file for divorce first thing Monday morning."

Fanny sat down, her head dropping into her hands. "That's not true. I loved you so much, Simon. You made my world right side up. I gave all of my heart to you. I'm too tired to fight. I don't want us to say things we'll regret later on."

"They've already been said."

"By you, Simon, not by me." Fanny's voice was weary, choked with tears. She fled to the bathroom just as the head of Security arrived.

"Mrs. Thornton, are you all right?"

"I'm fine. Show the gentleman the door and don't admit him to the casino again unless I give the order to do so."

"I want to see Ash. Where is he, Fanny? I'll go, and I won't come back, but I want to see Ash before I go."

"Neal, take him to Ash's room. He's awake. Make sure you wait, though, and escort Mr. Thornton to the door."

Fanny walked over to her husband. "You have no idea, Simon, how sorry I am that this incident is taking place. I never wanted this for either of us. I understand that you will do whatever you have to do." She stood on her toes to kiss his cheek. Simon raised his arm to backhand her, but Neal was too quick. The two burly security guards each cupped one of Simon's elbows and escorted him to the elevator. Simon kicked at his bag as the guards dragged him forward.

In the bedroom, Fanny slammed the door and locked it. She raced over to the bed and dropped to her knees. "It's okay, Daisy, you can come out now. Come here, sweet love." Fanny held the little dog until she stopped shaking.

"That man is just someone we used to know, Daisy. I told you. It's just me and you. Why did I ever think it could be different?"

17

〜

Showered, shaved, and dressed for the day, Ash yelled, "Come in," when he heard the sharp rap on the door. Thinking it was Fanny, he whispered in Jake's ear. His stomach muscles started to tighten when he saw his brother's stormy face.

"Up and about early, aren't you, Simon?"

"Unlike you, I haven't been to bed."

Ash correctly interpreted his brother's dark features. He motioned for Neal to wait outside. "You look like this might lead to something so let me get Jake out of here." Simon nodded curtly.

Ash rang Housekeeping. "Mrs. Gonzales, I'd like you to do me a favor. Could you come up to 2311 and take my grandson out for breakfast? He's ready now. I'll have Neal bring him down. Yes, I miss being here. I'll stop by and see all of you before I leave."

Ash bellowed for Neal and explained the situation. He knew his own eyes were as wary as Neal's when he escorted the little boy from the room.

"Did somebody steal your lollipop, Simon?"

"Cut the crap, Ash, this isn't a social call."

"What the hell is it? If you think I'm going to discuss Fanny with you, you're wrong. Whatever is going on between the two of you stays with the two of you. Don't involve me."

"That's pretty hard to do, Ash, since your face is in everything that goes on between Fanny and me."

"That's because you make it that way. I have a lot on my plate, and I'm trying to deal with it the best way I can. Walk away from here, Simon, and let things be."

Simon advanced, one step, then another step, his fists clenched at his sides, until his knees touched Ash's knees. Ash saw his brother's arm pull back, saw the clenched fist but was powerless to move his chair. He took the full blow to his left eye and cheekbone. He felt the skin rip as the chair moved with the force of the blow. He catapulted out of the chair to land facedown on the sofa.

Ash feel his eye swelling. "I guess you felt you had to do that," he managed to say as he struggled to his knees. Simon's fist shot out a second time. Ash landed backwards, blood spurting from his mouth. He wiped at the trickling blood with his shirtsleeve, his good eye focused on his brother. He made no move to get up. "Who are you going to blame this on, Simon? What the hell do you want? I don't have anything left for you to take. You have an insidious, black, ugly mind, Simon. You're a sneak, you work behind the scenes with that wide-open innocent smile. Pop and I saw through you early on. He tried to tell Mom what a Jekyll and Hyde you were, but she wouldn't listen. You knew how to play the game to get what you wanted. It's so fucking sick it scares the shit out of me. You need help, Simon. You needed help from the time you were five years old."

"You're crazy. You were the one who drove Mom out of her mind."

"Because I was stupid. I refused to believe a mother could or would turn her back on one son to the exclusion of the other. I was a kid, I didn't know how to make her understand what you were. Pop took over to protect me from you. You know, Simon, I don't have much to do these days but think. I started writing stuff down, and then I saw the pattern. You were never happy unless you got what I had. You just waited until the time was right, then you'd strike like a snake. You always had to be first, the best. You even managed to snare someone else's identity just to beat me. It must have really galled your ass that I made Ace. You couldn't steal that from me though, could you? You switched gears then, you went off, supposedly to make it on your own. It wasn't your own, though. Pop told me Mom gave you a bundle with no strings. Self-made, my ass," Ash sneered.

"What the hell are *you?*" Simon sneered in return, his face ugly with his rage.

"For a long time I was the biggest fuck-up going. I never denied it. Nor did I ever hide it. I took my lumps and did the same thing all over again. I thought I was entitled. I used to watch, and yes, I even marveled at how easy it was for you to just take. So I started doing the same thing. You were a hell of a teacher, Simon. It's no excuse. It's the way it was."

"You're full of shit, Ash. You're the taker. You've never given anything in your life to anyone."

"You're right about that. It's funny how we never see our faults until it's too late. Get out of here, Simon. You make me sick just looking at you."

"I'll go when I'm fucking ready to go and not one minute before. I'm going to smash that face of yours until there's nothing left."

"Cut to the chase, Simon. It's Fanny and Babylon that's sticking in your craw. Babylon is mine, and there was no way for you to get it. When Fanny's family stepped in to finish up things, you were wild. For the second time you couldn't steal my thunder. Babylon was my red lollipop. Remember, Simon, when Mom was handing out those suckers you always threw a fit if I got the red one. Then Mom would take it back and give it to you and give me a yellow one. I hate lemon. I had to pretend to love lemon and we both know what you did then. You wanted lemon. It's Fanny, too. You waited and waited, until just the right moment, then you stepped in. Compared to me you really were the White Knight. Fanny fell for it. Mom pimped for you. She set it all up, and you walked right into it. You don't have one ounce of guts."

"Shut your lying mouth, Ash."

"We aren't kids anymore, Simon. I don't have to take your crap. I can say whatever I damn well please and it pleases me to say Fanny has finally seen you for who you are. You know what, she's doing a hell of a job here. Believe it or not, this is where she belongs. She's starting to see it, too. You saw it right away. That's why you did that silence thing you're so good at. You couldn't come here because this is mine. You want it so damn bad you can taste it. Why don't you just admit it? Even when I die, Simon, it can never be yours. Fanny will see to that. There's a bond between Fanny and me that you can never break no matter what you do. You tried. There's that one part of Fanny that will always belong to me. I don't deserve it, but that's the way it is." Ash struggled to his knees. His head high, his shoulders back he looked his brother in the eye. "Take your best shot, you asshole."

"She was here all night, wasn't she? I didn't know you could still get it up. Guess she'll take it any which way she can. She's still my wife."

Ash tottered forward, his hand grappling with the arm of the wheelchair. "I don't care what you say about me, but you leave Fanny out of this. Fanny slept on the couch with Jake all night. Just to keep the record straight, I can still get it up. Now get your fucking ass out of my building and don't ever let me see you again in this lifetime."

Ash brought the wheelchair around so he could lever himself into it but Simon's fists shot forward in a one-two shot that left Ash crumpled on the floor. He managed to let out one bull roar before he lost consciousness.

The door burst open as Neal arrived, two security guards and Fanny in their wake.

"My God, Simon, what did you do?" Fanny dropped to her knees at Ash's side just as he started to come around. "Call an ambulance."

"I don't need an ambulance, Fanny. It's okay. I'll be okay if my teeth don't fall out. Get him out of here, Neal."

Ash struggled to get into his chair. Fanny cringed at Ash's bloody, swollen face. Secure in the knowledge that Simon was in the firm grip of the two security guards, she started to pummel her husband with her fists. "God in heaven, what kind of man are you? How could you hit your own brother like this? How could you beat a man in a wheelchair? Who are you, Simon? More to the point, *what* are you?"

"He's my brother, Fanny, and he's your husband. Let it go and be damned glad this happened now, while I'm still around."

Ash waved the men out the door. "Fix me up, Fanny, before Mrs. Gonzales brings Jake back. How bad is it?"

Fanny dithered. "Don't you know? You were on the receiving end of things. I have to go upstairs to get my first-aid box. I'll be right back. You should see a doctor, Ash."

"I've seen enough doctors to last me a lifetime. Hey, I'm the guy who has a pill for everything, remember? Hurry up. I don't want Jake seeing me like this."

Fanny was back in five minutes. She talked as she wiped and swabbed. "You can't hide this from Jake. Your left eye looks like an open peanut butter and jelly sandwich. Your jaw is swelling, and you look lopsided. Are your teeth loose? Ash, what happened. Did you provoke Simon?"

Ash tried for a smile. He didn't succeed. "Simon is not a happy person these days. I don't know if Simon was ever happy. He has demons. Maybe we should talk later on in the day, Fanny, when Jake is napping. I need a little time to rebound. Do you have any makeup you can plaster on the worst of my bruises? Ditch this shirt. It's all bloody."

"I don't think it will help, Ash. I'll get you an ice bag. You could have a concussion. Ash, who was that person?"

"Fanny, look at me. That person is someone you used to know. He's someone I've known all my life. I have an idea of how you must feel and I want you to know I'm truly sorry. I want to thank you for being the one constant in my life. Now, you would do me the biggest favor if you would take Jake for the day."

"Ash, truly? Are you sure it's all right? What about Sunny? How will you explain it to her?"

"I'll tell her the truth. I'm on a truth kick these days. You know what, Fanny, when you tell the truth it's okay, everyone deals with it and goes on from there. Only a fool denies the truth. If we're lucky, Simon will admit to his truths and go on from there. At least I hope so. Here comes the kid, so don't say anything."

Jake ran to Ash, skidding to a stop in front of his chair. "You look funny, Pop Pop."

"Boo!" Ash said. The little boy giggled. "Grandma Fanny is going to take you out today. Get your sweater and I want a promise from you."

"Whazat, whatzat?"

"Promise me you'll have a good time."

"Promise, promise, promise."

Jake's hand in hers, her face radiant, Fanny turned at the door. "Can I get you anything before we leave?"

"Have them send up some coffee and a bottle of brandy."

"How about some blueberry pancakes and sausage?"

"That too. Don't worry about me, Fanny. I'm okay."

"Keep the ice pack on, twenty minutes on, twenty minutes off."

"Yes, Mother," Ash drawled. It brought the required smile to Fanny's face.

When the door closed behind Fanny, Ash wheeled himself to the couch. He eased himself onto it gingerly. His body started to tremble as tears burned his eyes. "How come you never saw it, Mom? Why wasn't I good enough for you to love? If there was a way for me to help Simon, I would. I don't know how. I didn't put up a fight. I let him beat the hell out of me because I thought . . . hell, I don't know what I thought. I wish you had told me just once that you loved me. Maybe if you'd done that I wouldn't be in this position now, and neither would Simon.

"Guess that's enough for now. We'll be seeing each other soon enough and when that day comes, I want some answers."

"What would you like to do, Jake?"

The little boy trotted alongside Fanny, his chubby legs pumping in his hurry to get outside the door. "Feed birds. Buy peanuts. Eat ice cream."

"I think we can do all those things. Do you know how to skip to My Lou?"

"Uh-huh. Watch me."

"Wonderful!" Together, grandmother and grandson skipped down the street with onlookers smiling their approval. *I need to do this because I want to do it. I don't want to think about what transpired earlier. I want to enjoy every single minute that I can with this little boy.*

It was three o'clock when Fanny led her weary grandchild back to Babylon. In one hand he held a red balloon and in the other a stuffed panda bear. His chin was streaked with chocolate ice cream, his hands sticky. He wore a happy smile as he tried valiantly to keep his eyes open.

"You're lookin' good, sport," Ash said, his swollen lips barely moving. "Are you ready for a nap?"

Jake nodded.

Fanny smiled. "I'll clean him up. We used up all my tissues with the first half of the ice-cream cone. I think I'd like some coffee, Ash. Would you mind calling Room Service?"

Fanny joined Ash just as the coffee arrived. "It's been a day, Ash. I probably would have gone out of my mind if you hadn't asked me to take Jake out. I wish . . . oh, God, I wish so many things. I know it's difficult for you to talk and even painful, but you have to tell me what happened. I need to know. I need to understand. I thought I had a good marriage with a good man. At least for the first year. Was I blind, Ash? What was I supposed to see that I didn't see? I don't know what I'm supposed to feel. Talk to me, Ash, I need to make sense of all of this."

Ash talked. Fanny listened. Then both were silent for a long time.

"Wouldn't it be nice, Ash, if we could turn the clocks backward in time? I know the time I would pick. You go first."

"I think I must have been four or almost four. Simon was trailing me in the yard and I fell and skinned my knee. It started to bleed and I was yelling at the top of my lungs. Simon stumbled and got his suit dirty. Mom picked him up to take him into the house to change his clothes. She didn't even look at my knee. I sat there and cried like a baby. I kept saying, look at my leg, fix my leg. I guess I either whispered the words or was just thinking them to myself. I wish I'd screamed the words so she would have noticed me. I wish that. You know what, you play the hand you're dealt. That's the bottom line."

Fanny's eyes smarted. "I don't have a particular time in mind. What should I do, Ash?"

"Don't do anything, Fanny. Simon will file for divorce. You'll be served papers, and then you'll be a free agent. I'm really sorry. If there's one person in the world who should be married, it's you."

Fanny smiled. "That was the old Fanny. This new Fanny is someone who . . . oh, never mind."

"Is your heart shattered? Are you wounded to your soul by all of this?" Ash queried.

"Strangely enough, no. I almost bolted that first month. I was one miserable human being. Like you, Ash, I had a lot of time to think. Twice divorced. That's not good."

"Sez who?"

"Sez me. Sunny will have a field day. How do you plan to explain your condition to her when you get back?"

"I hadn't thought that far ahead. I'll be leaving in the morning. Would you mind driving me up, Fanny? Bess or Neal can follow behind and bring you back. I'd chance it if it was just me, but Jake changes things. Wanna have dinner tonight?"

"Yes and yes. You should come up and see what I did with your place. You'll hate it."

"Okay, but I have to call downstairs to get someone to come up and sit here while Jake is asleep. You go ahead and I'll be up in a few minutes."

While she waited for Ash, Fanny washed her face and brushed her hair. She stared at herself in the mirror. "I look like I'm seventy years old," she muttered to her reflection. She turned around so she wouldn't have to view her reflection and sat down on the edge of the tub. She thought about all the things Ash had said. She wasn't sure why, but she believed him implicitly. She couldn't help but wonder why her heart wasn't shattered, why she wasn't wounded to her soul. At what point had she fallen out of love with her husband? "Maybe I'll never know," she muttered.

"You here?" Ash shouted.

"Coming. So, what do you think?"

"Jesus, Fanny, this place looks like a hunting cabin in the mountains. This is supposed to be glass and chrome, black and white. Modern . . ."

"Shitful." Fanny giggled. "You know me. I'm a nester. I had to redo it because I smashed all your stuff. It felt great. Come on, I'll show you the rest of the place. By the way, don't let me forget to take Daisy's kennel tomorrow. When you go back down you can take Daisy for Jake to play with if you want. She loves little kids."

"I suppose you got rid of all my black and white towels, huh?" Ash said opening the closet door. "For God's sake, Fanny, do you have some kind of shoe fetish? You never had this many shoes in your life."

Fanny leaned against the wall, her arms crossed over her chest. "You know that guy I told you about, the one who put me in the pool? Well, he sent them to me. He's got good taste in shoes, I can tell you that. He sends me a dozen yellow roses every single day."

"No shit!"

Fanny started to laugh and couldn't stop. "You should see your-self, Ash. I know you want to raise your eyebrows but . . ."

"Don't make me laugh, Fanny, it hurts too bad."

Fanny slid to the floor, still laughing. "I think he has the hots for me," she managed to gasp.

"Yeah?"

"Yeah. He came here on Thanksgiving, and I was drunk as a skunk. He's the one who finally cooked dinner for the kids when they showed up. He even did the dishes."

"Snatch that sucker right up, Fanny."

"Nah. You know what I think my problem is, Ash? I think I'm a one-man woman."

"Don't say that to me, Fanny."

"Okay. Forget I said it."

"You know what I mean."

"Yeah, I know, Ash."

"You know what I want to do, Fanny? I want to sit in one of those red chairs. By the way, where is Daisy?"

"At the groomers getting gussied up for Jake. She's getting her nails cut and her coat trimmed. She loves the blow dryer."

"I'd love it too if somebody blew warm air all over my body."

"Really," Fanny drawled.

"Yeah, really."

"I'm fresh out of warm air." Fanny giggled.

"Now how did I know you were going to say that?"

"That doesn't mean I won't have some later . . . say maybe around midnight when I take my break."

"Wait a minute here. Are you saying what I think you're saying?"

"What do you think I'm saying?"

"That you and me . . . me and you . . . like . . . you know . . . when we had our good times?"

"Uh-huh."

"What are the conditions?" Ash asked, his tongue thick in his mouth.

"No conditions. No strings."

"I'd be a fool to turn that down."

"I'd say so."

"You sound pretty sure of yourself," Ash said. Fanny loved the uncomfortable look on his face. "Is this going to be a performance kind of thing?"

"Whatever you want it to be. I think, Ash, I can sizzle the socks right off your feet. You think about that, okay? You have to put a towel over your head though; otherwise, I'll laugh and it won't be good."

"Jesus, Fanny, what kind of talk is that?"

Fanny giggled. "Do you remember how you used to want me to talk dirty to you? Well, guess what, I learned a *whole* new language."

"Goddamn it, Fanny," Ash blustered.

"Your face is red, Ash. I think Daisy's home."

"Thank God," Ash muttered. He needed time to think about this conversation.

Fanny laughed as she sashayed her way to the front door, her buttocks jiggling.

Daisy raced into the room and leaped onto Ash's lap, licking his face and neck and woofing softly.

"You can take her down with you if you want. You won't let Jake squeeze her or anything like that, will you?"

"He's good with animals. He's a gentle little boy, Fanny."

"Okay. Call me when you want me to pick her up. What time do you want to have dinner?"

"How does eight sound?"

"It sounds good."

"The place looks homey, Fanny. You're comfortable here, aren't you?"

"Yes and no. I miss the yard and the flowers. When that happens I go down to the hanging gardens and walk around. It's okay for now."

"And later?"

"We'll deal with later when later comes. We can have dinner here in the penthouse if you're uncomfortable with people seeing you. Or we could do the private dining room. You decide and let me know when I pick Daisy up. Ash Thornton, you're afraid of me, aren't you?"

"Where'd you get a cockamamie idea like that?" Ash said, his face reddening again.

"I just have to look at you to know." A devil perched itself on Fanny's shoulder. "I'll go easy on you."

"That'll be the day," Ash snorted, his neck as red as his face.

"Uh-huh," Fanny grinned.

The intercom in the foyer buzzed. Fanny raced from the bathroom, spritzing perfume as she went along. "Yes?"

"Mrs. Thornton, we have a delivery for you."

"Send it up, Martin."

Fanny's jaw dropped minutes later when a parade of young men carrying poinsettias marched into the room. "Good lord, how many are there?" she gasped.

"One hundred. They were sent in their own delivery truck from San Diego. They have a large poinsettia farm there," one of the young men said.

"Is there a card or message?"

"Not that I know of, Mrs. Thornton. I signed for them. It sure looks like Christmas."

"Yes, it does. Who in the world is going to water them?"

"Call down to the florist. I'm sure they'll be glad to oblige."

"Hey, anybody home?" Bess called out from the doorway. "Oohhh, are they from you know who? I like his style. I love multiples of anything. John's romantic leanings are one rose, one donut, one of whatever. Although, sometimes less is more if you know what I mean. I heard some stories on the floor. Want to talk about it?"

"I'm so sorry, Fanny. Are you okay with all of this?" Bess asked when Fanny wound down. "You look kind of peculiar."

"That's because I propositioned my ex-husband. For the first time in his life he was flabbergasted. I can't believe I did it. I don't even know why I did it. It seemed like the thing to do at the moment."

"The question is, are you going to follow through?"

"What would you do if you were in my place?"

"Oh, sweetie, I'd go for it. All the way. This is a whole new ball game, and the playing field is yours. It is what it is."

"I'm actually tingling at the thought. Just at the thought. I must be out of my mind. Stop and think about it, Bess. I'm divorced from Ash, I married his brother who turns out to be some . . . someone I didn't know . . . and I'm just walking away from that person and hitting on my ex. What does that make me?"

"Horny?"

"It's been a while." Fanny grinned.

"Probably longer for Ash." Bess's face was so blank, Fanny poked her on the arm. She burst into laughter.

"He's worried. He used the word performance. I don't think he ever used that word in his entire life, much less thought about it. He's thinking about it now though."

"Marcus Reed?"

"A friend. For now."

"Later?"

"I try not to think about later. I've been hearing that question too much of late. Sallie told me once that later never comes." Fanny paused. "Do you believe that, Bess?"

"Yes. When later comes it's the here and now. You never really get to later if you know what I mean."

"I want to feel something where Simon is concerned. A sense of loss. Grief, something. I shouldn't be feeling anger and relief."

"Why not?" Bess asked. "They're both honest emotions. You always say it is what it is. One day at a time."

"I loved him, Bess. I never saw what Ash saw. There were little things at times that didn't compute, but I negated them. Then there were bigger things I pretended not to see. It was easier that way. It all died in me when he refused to understand my feelings where Sunny and Jake were concerned, but even then I didn't see what I'd been blind to. Listen, let's talk about something else. Can you follow me in your car to Sunrise tomorrow? Ash is nervous about driving with Jake after . . . the beating Simon gave him."

"Sunny?"

Fanny shook her head. "I won't even go in. We'll just drop them off and turn around and come back. She'll understand my presence on the mountain when she sees her father."

"Maybe the holidays . . ."

Fanny shook her head. "No one has heard from Birch. I'm hoping he comes home or calls. I keep getting this sick feeling in my stomach when I think about my children. I want so badly for things to go right for them, but I realize I can't live their lives for them. We learn from our mistakes. Strange coming from me, eh?"

Bess hugged her friend. "C'mon, it's time to go downstairs and do what you do best, charm the customers."

"That's what Sallie used to do."

"You aren't Sallie. You don't sing. You socialize. Remember that lady from Edison, New Jersey? I rest my case."

"Ash, is it my imagination or are you just picking at your food? You love prime rib, and this is done to perfection. The baked potato has everything you like, cheese, butter, sour cream, chives, bacon bits."

"It's hard to chew, Fanny. It's even harder to open my mouth to get the food in."

"Ash, I'm sorry. I didn't think. Would you like some coffee or a milkshake?"

"No thanks. Fanny . . ."

"You're having second thoughts about . . . later?" It was a question more than a statement.

"If you were in my place, wouldn't you?"

"I don't think so. Are you trying to let me down easy?"

"Of course not. Why would you say something like that, Fanny?"

"You seem so jittery. It has been a long time for us."

"I have a good memory."

"So do I, Ash. Let's do this. Have Mrs. Gonzales baby-sit in your suite. I'll leave the door of the penthouse open. Go up and wait for me. We can have a drink and talk or we can . . . do other things. And, Ash, take the word performance out of your vocabulary. Think in terms of an old shoe and an old sock."

"Jesus, Fanny, that's not very romantic."

Fanny laughed. "Here sits a man who has been called a legend in his own time, a man whose sexual prowess is legendary. And then there's me, the ex-wife who never quite had it all together where you were concerned, intimidating you. Gotta go, Ash, duty calls. If you change your mind, leave a note on my door."

"You're enjoying this, aren't you, Fanny?"

"Uh-huh." Fanny tweaked Ash's ear. She laughed when she heard him groan.

She was still laughing when she walked out onto the casino floor.

Heading straight for her was Marcus Reed.

18

Fanny felt a head rush. Her step faltered. "Marcus!"

"Good evening, Fanny. You look lovely. Was your opening last night everything you wanted it to be?"

"And more. My grandson loved everything. He fell asleep on his feet twice. Did I misunderstand you? I thought you said you were leaving?"

"I was supposed to, but there were some loose ends to tie up. I did manage to get close to the front windows. I'm not much for crowds, so I contented myself by pressing my nose to the glass and staring. I'm glad things worked out. You can't buy the kind of media coverage you received last night. It will continue for the rest of the month."

"You worked like a Trojan, Marcus. It's a shame you didn't get your share of billing."

Marcus shrugged. "That's not important to me. I did it because I wanted to do it. I was wondering if you'd like to have a drink with me."

"I'd love to have a drink with you. Your poinsettias arrived a little while ago. My goodness, Marcus, they must have cost a fortune. You shouldn't do things like that."

"Why?"

"Why . . . because it's so extravagant."

"Do they make your apartment festive? Do you like the colors? Does it make everything very Christmasy?"

Fanny laughed. "Yes. Yes. Yes. I adore the holidays. Everyone seems so real at this time of the year. They're kinder, nicer, that kind of thing. Are you fond of the holidays?"

"Very much so."

"How long are you staying, Marcus?"

"Another hour or so. I wanted to say good-bye. I left rather abruptly the other day. If your invitation is still open, I'll be back for Christmas."

"Of course. I'll just have coffee. I have a long night ahead of me. My friend Billie and her husband are here, and I want to spend some time with them before they leave tomorrow."

"Coffee it is. Fanny, there's a rumor on the street. I heard it this afternoon. Are you aware of it?"

"If it's what I think it is, yes. I try never to discuss my family with . . . other people. I don't mean to offend you."

"Not at all. Is Mr. Thornton all right?"

"The elder Mr. Thornton is . . . okay. The younger Mr. Thornton . . . the best answer I can give you is I don't know. Where are you headed this time, Marcus?"

"Back to Chicago."

"What do you do, Marcus? You never said."

"In some circles I'm referred to as a hired gun. In other circles they call me an advance man or a troubleshooter. My services are for hire.

People call on me when things go wrong with their businesses. I assess the situation, make suggestions, offer remedies that I feel will work. It's interesting, but I never know where I'll be from one day to the next. It doesn't make for a very stable lifestyle. I get tired of hotel rooms, living out of suitcases and eating in restaurants. Sometimes I wake up in the middle of the night craving a peanut butter and jelly sandwich with a tall glass of cold milk. Sometimes I yearn to cook a hot dog and load it with everything. One of these days I might retire and do all those things."

Fanny smiled. "Somehow I can't see you in slippers reading the evening paper while a dog poops on the carpet. You are so . . . bankerish. Is there such a word?"

Marcus threw his head back and laughed till tears gathered in his eyes. "You could be right. You've given me food for thought. Tell me, have you heard from your son?"

"No. I'm hoping he calls or writes soon. If we're lucky, he might come home for Christmas. The boys always loved the holidays. I say a prayer every night."

"How are the rest of your children?"

"If you mean Sunny, I can't answer that. I hope she's well. Sage and Billie are fine."

"And how are you, Fanny? I'm asking because I am genuinely concerned about you. You can't be all things to all people. You need to be your own person."

"I tried that, Marcus. I wasn't very successful. Sometimes I don't think there is a Fanny Thornton. I'm somebody's mother, somebody's ex-wife, somebody's wife, somebody's friend. My husband is divorcing me. That makes two bad marriages. It doesn't say much for me. I have to think about that."

"That's where you're wrong, Fanny. Maybe it wasn't you, maybe it was the two men you were married to. Don't be so quick to shoulder all the blame, and don't listen to other people when they feel compelled to blame you. Until they walk in your shoes, they have no right to pass judgment."

"Thank you for saying that, Marcus. Life is never easy, is it?"

"Life finds a way of interfering in everyone's life. That's why it's called life, I guess. We are philosophical this evening. Whatever it is that's troubling you, Fanny, will pass. Time is a wondrous healer in all things."

"I'll remember that."

"I enjoyed the coffee, Fanny, and your company." Marcus smiled as he brought Fanny's hand to his lips. She flushed. "Fanny, are you going to have a Christmas tree?"

"Of course."

"A real one or a plastic one?"

"Bite your tongue. Real of course."

"Would you be amenable to going with me to the mountains to pick one out? I haven't done that in years. My childhood must be catching up with me. I could come early unless you want to decorate ahead of time."

"I'd like that. Let's say the day before Christmas Eve."

"It's a date."

Fanny felt flustered. "Do you mean it's the date, meaning the day on the calendar, or it's a date as in . . . date?"

"Both."

"Oh. I haven't had a date in years," Fanny confessed.

"Me either. I'm sure there's a book on it somewhere."

"I'm sure."

"Good-bye, Fanny."

"Good-bye, Marcus. Have a safe trip."

"Tell me, how much did you win?" Fanny asked, a lilt in her voice.

"Two bucks," Thad said. "Billie won eighty dollars about an hour ago, and she has five dollars left."

"I love it when a customer loses money. It's going to be a long month. We're jammed to capacity. The hotel is booked solid through January 3. We're taking in a record amount of money."

"Fanny, what's wrong? Don't tell me nothing. I know you too well, and I can see that all is not right with your world." Billie's voice was gentle as she led Fanny away from the crowds.

"Here, Thad, play my last five dollars, and if you lose it, we're going home."

Fanny rattled off the day's happenings. "How is it possible I didn't see, didn't hear, didn't know or even suspect, Billie? I blocked it out, didn't I?"

"You were in love in the beginning. Yes, Fanny, you blocked it out. You didn't want to believe what was going on. How much longer do you think you would have let things go on before you woke up and did something?"

"I think I had already made my decision on our anniversary. Yes,

I loved Simon, but that sick love, and it was sick love, cost me my daughter. I've had it with love and marriage. I'm going to grow old by myself."

"Fanny, you said you had one good year. Some people never even get that. It happened, it didn't work and you don't look back."

"I feel like such a fool."

"We've all been down that road. I don't know a single woman who hasn't felt that way at one time in her life. It's behind you. Are you sure Ash is okay?"

"He said he was. He looks awful. He's concerned about Jake. I'll be driving them home in the morning. When are you leaving?"

"Around noon. We could delay takeoff and have lunch. That's so I can brag about my wonderful Japanese-American grandson."

"Okay, sounds good to me."

"Didn't you leave something out of our conversation, Fanny?"

"You mean Marcus?"

"Yes, Marcus."

"I don't know how to talk about him. I know that must sound strange to you. He's a very nice person. He sent me a hundred poinsettias earlier. He does everything in such high numbers. I think he overwhelms me. He's a friend."

"Relationships are always best when they start out with friendships. Thad and I are the living proof. I didn't know love could be like this. It's what I wish for you, my friend."

"I think, Billie, my life is destined to turn out like Sallie's. Don't pooh-pooh this away. I'll live with that, too. I'm tired of fighting the tide. If something is meant to happen, it's going to happen. Ahhh, see that crowd! I think your husband just won one of our jackpots!"

"Are you kidding? Where! Do you do those bells and whistles every time someone wins?"

"Yep. That's to give the other customers hope that they, too, can win. Let's see how much he took the house for."

"Five thousand dollars!" Thad said hoarsely.

"Darling, that's wonderful! Now you can buy me a present from one of these exquisite shops."

Fanny posed for the obligatory pictures before she walked away to meet Bess.

"Fanny, wait a minute. I need to ask you something. I must be getting senile because each time I see you, it's on my mind, then I lose my train of thought. I want to close the books, and we never did reconcile that money Ash paid out once a month under cash. Five thousand a month is sixty thousand a year. That's a large sum of money. What should I charge it against? Did you ever ask him?"

"No, I never asked him. I will tonight."

"He's still writing the checks."

"Still?"

"Yes. He doesn't fill out the memo part. The signature on the back is just a scrawl. I suppose I could call the bank, but I didn't want to do that without talking to you first."

"I'm seeing Ash later, and I'll ask him. He shouldn't be writing checks on the business account. We'll talk about it in the morning. I'm off at twelve."

"Why don't you go up now? I can handle things down here. Jake might still be awake, and you can tuck him in."

"I just love that little boy. He reminds me so much of Birch and Sage when they were little. He asks a million questions and expects an answer. If the answer isn't something he likes, he asks again and expects a different response. Ash is so good with him, and Jake adores him. Okay, Bess, it's all yours."

Fanny stepped from the elevator, her eyes squeezed shut. She opened them expecting to see a note stuck to her door. Her breath exploded in a loud sigh when she saw that her door was bare. "This is good."

The blaze of red that greeted her made her blink. She really needed to disperse the plants, position them better so they weren't such an eye-blinder. She shed the red velvet gown and pulled on a silky hostess gown. Her high heels were replaced with feathery slippers that matched the gown. The word assignation rippled through her mind. She smiled.

It took her all of thirty minutes to arrange the poinsettias in every room of the penthouse. "Gorgeous! Absolutely gorgeous," she trilled. She looked at her watch; 11:15. Time to sit down and go through the contents of the manila folder. She read the nine-page report slowly as she tried to digest the contents. Now, after all these years, the agency had finally located Josh Coleman, Sallie's older brother.

Fanny read and reread the report. Josh was a widower with three children, two daughters and a son. He had three grandchildren, a boy and two girls. He lived on a five-hundred-acre farm in Mc Lean, Virginia, and raised Thoroughbred horses. The report said he was seventy-nine years old and in robust health. The summary at the end of the report read: Subject appears to be an upstanding citizen. His colleagues and friends have honored him many times for his contributions to the equestrian world. The Coleman farm is prime real estate. Subject's bank balance is not robust. His children are hardworking, upstanding citizens. Grandchildren are also hardworking. One grandchild (a boy) is mentally retarded. The elder Mr. Coleman is said to be devastated that the Coleman name is lost to the family. End of report. Attached to the last page was the bill for the agency's services.

Tomorrow morning she would make a copy of the report and give it to Billie to take back to Washington. Why was it that sometimes the important things in life only came to light when it was too late? Sallie would have given up her entire fortune to find this brother.

Fanny looked at her watch. Ten minutes to twelve. Almost the witching hour. She felt her heart take on an extra beat when the doorbell rang five minutes later. She swore her blood was singing in her veins as she ran to the door. She took a deep breath and thrust it open.

"Daisy's sleeping with Jake. Is that okay?"

"Sure." *He's nervous and jittery.* "Would you like a drink, Ash?"

"Well sure. Scotch on the rocks. Make it a double."

Fanny's eyebrows shot upward. Her smile was lazy when she walked over to the bar. *He's afraid of me. He needs the scotch to go through with this.*

"I'm not wearing anything under this gown, Ash. It looks to me like you're . . . *bundled* up. How long do you think it will take you to get out of all those clothes?"

"For God's sake, Fanny, I just got here. I need to finish my drink." Scotch dribbled down Ash's chin. Fanny tried not to smile.

"Why don't I help you so we can move things right along here."

"You're taking all the . . . fun out of this," Ash sputtered.

"Do you want me to start talking dirty to you now or as you undress?" Fanny leaned over his chair and whispered in his ear. She felt the hot flush that stained his neck and his ears.

"Where'd you learn . . . stuff like that?" Ash sputtered.

"Just you never mind where I learned it," Fanny drawled. She whispered in his ear again. She swiveled his chair until he was facing the couch. With both hands on his shoulders she propelled him forward. He landed in an undignified heap.

"I'm waiting," Fanny singsonged.

"Stop rushing me."

"Are you sure you can get it up, Ash? I'm going to be really upset if you're leading me on."

"It's up! It's up!" Ash squawked.

"But is it *hard?*"

"Like a steel rod."

"You always used to say that and you lied. I wanna see."

"You'll see it when I'm ready to show it to you."

"You never used to be afraid to show it to me. You used to want me to take *pictures!*"

"I'm not afraid!"

"Then why are you undressing under the afghan?"

"Because it's goddamn cold in here."

"It's 72° in here. That's warm. Very warm. Your face is flushed, the part that isn't black-and-blue." Fanny slithered around the back of the couch and leaned over. "For starters this is how it's going to be . . . are you listening, Ash?" She whispered in his ear.

"You can't possibly do *that.*"

"Really."

"Yeah, really."

"When you're ready, you whistle, okay?" Fanny said sitting down across from the couch. She fired up a cigarette and blew a perfect smoke ring. "Is it going down or staying up?"

"What do you think? How long is it going to take you to get out of that get-up?"

"Blink."

She was on top of him as the afghan flew across the room. "Are you in the spirit of things now?"

"You said something about sizzling my socks off."

"You want sizzle or you want a burn?" Fanny hissed in his ear, her hands everywhere.

"Burn me, baby, burn me."

"First we have to build the fire."

"You need to stoke a fire.

"No, no, that's stroke. Just do it. Ahhh."

"You let me know when you're on fire, sweetie," Fanny said.

"Now! I'm on fire now! This is good. This is *really* good. Ohhh, yeah, yeah, I'm blazing."

"Are you an inferno yet?"

"Almost, oh, yeah. More kindling. Stoke that fire, baby. Do it, do it, do it!"

"Am I dead?" Ash asked, a long time later.

"Probably not, but you look it."

"Where the hell did you learn *stuff* like that? What'd you do, take a seminar or something?"

"Or something," Fanny said. "Aren't you supposed to say, was it as good for you as it was for me?"

"I don't have to ask, I know. Where'd you learn that . . . you know *that?*"

"I don't kiss and tell." Fanny grinned.

"Do you know any other? You know . . . different . . . ah things?"

"Why do you want to know?" Fanny drawled.

"I just want to know. In case . . ."

"In case what?"

"Just in case. That's my answer."

"Nah. That was my best shot," Fanny laughed.

"It was a hell of a shot."

Fanny laughed again. "I thought so. I couldn't do it again if my life depended on it."

"Me either."

"You up for a fried egg sandwich?"

"Hell yes. You got any stray duds I can wear? It's a real struggle to get dressed."

"I still have my old flannel robe."

"It'll do."

"I'll meet you in the kitchen. Do you want a beer or hot cocoa?"

"Hot cocoa. It's almost like old times, isn't it, Fanny?"

"Almost."

Over sandwiches and cocoa, Fanny and Ash talked nonstop. She showed him the report on Josh Coleman.

"You should take Billie and go see the family. Mom would want you to do that. Take pictures, do that whole thing. More family. It's kind of wonderful if you stop and think about it."

"Ash, Bess brought something to my attention tonight. I've been meaning to ask you about it for a long time and like Bess, I keep forgetting. Who do you write a check to every month for five thousand dollars? We need to know what to charge it against, and if you're going to keep on doing it, maybe we should set up another account."

When Ash didn't respond, Fanny asked the question again. "Ash, did you hear me?"

"Fanny, please don't ask me that. Let it be, okay?"

"I can't do that, Ash, and you know why I can't do it. Is it your supplier? Who? Why can't you tell me? I won't tell anyone if it's a secret. You know you can trust me."

"I know that, Fanny. I don't want to hurt you. I don't want to talk about it. Some things are better left alone."

"Now you have me more curious than ever. I want to know, Ash."

"It's for my son."

"Your *what?*"

"You heard me. My son."

"How did that happen? *When* did it happen?"

"In the usual way. I unzipped my pants and she took off her underwear. It never should have happened, but it did, and Jeff is the result. He's finishing up his master's. In May my obligation will be over."

Stunned, Fanny could only stare at Ash as she tried to comprehend what he'd just said. When she did manage to find her tongue she said, "It's not the obligation, it's the act. That means you . . . you fathered a child to someone else while we were married."

"That's what it means, Fanny. I could say I'm sorry from now till the end of time, and it won't change a thing. I didn't tell you because I didn't want to hurt you. I took the responsibility. It was a one-night stand. She was a nice girl, and I took advantage of her. That's it. You and I are the only ones who know. Scratch that, I told Simon in a weak moment. I thought about telling the kids a few times, but our relationship was rocky at best. I provided everything I could for him and his mother. He's not in my will. However, I set up a trust fund some years ago. He won't want for anything. He knows the score. He calls me sir. Some things are better left alone."

"I wish you had told me, Ash. Did you ever spend time with him? Were you ever a father to him?"

"No. His mother wanted it that way. I never forgot his birthday or Christmas."

"Do they . . . did you tell . . . ?"

"No. I'm not someone in their daily lives. I'm a check once a month. Maybe it's a blessing that things worked out the way they did. I was never husband or father material."

"Ash, what about later?"

"Are you asking me if either one of them will make a claim once I'm gone?"

"Yes, that's what I'm asking."

"Everything was taken care of legally. If either the boy or his mother decided to renege on the arrangement, it would be tied up in the courts forever. The trust fund would revert to my estate. They aren't greedy people, Fanny. They're the kind of people you would like. Jeff's mother bakes cookies. She gardens and sews. She works part-time in a gift store. Jeff is bookish, an honor student. I bought him a car for his twentieth birthday. He's a greedy kid. Selfish too. I bought them a little two-bedroom bungalow with a nice backyard. They keep the property up. It's neat as a pin. It's me that's the louse."

"I think I'm in shock. Should I know their names in case?"

"Only if you feel you want to do or say something at some point in time. My lawyers will handle it all. Her name is Margaret Lassiter. They didn't take my name. The lawyers wanted it that way. I took care of it, Fanny."

"What if the kids . . ."

"If that happens, you tell them what I told you."

"Ash, it doesn't seem right."

"It is what it is. For whatever it's worth, Fanny, I am sorry."

"You know what, Ash? I believe you. In my wildest dreams I never thought something like tonight could happen. It almost seems like a dream."

"Some dream, huh?"

Fanny nodded.

"Time to go downstairs and my other responsibility. What time do you want to leave in the morning? By the way, I'm going to Atlantic City day after tomorrow."

"Around nine if that's okay with you. That's good, Fanny. Make the best deal you can. I had a good time tonight, Fanny. I guess there aren't going to be any encores, huh?"

"Nope."

"You sure you didn't take some kind of seminar or go to one of those sex classes?"

"What do you think, Ash?"

"I think I'm getting out of here is what I think. See you in the morning."

Fanny leaned against the door staring at nothing for a long time. She felt like she'd been kicked in the gut. Strangely enough, her stomach had taken the blow and was fine now. Was she numb, dumb, *and* stupid? Why wasn't Ash's declaration bothering her? *Because I've moved beyond all that.* Ash said he'd taken care of it, and she believed him. Ash's son had nothing to do with her or her family. She had to believe that, too.

Just another day in the life of Fanny Thornton.

On the ride up the mountain, Fanny and Ash deferred to Jake and his chattering.

"How bad do you think I look, Fanny? If you were Sunny, would you be upset?"

"Some of the swelling has gone down, but you have more purple and yellow in your face. You probably should have gotten some stitches over your cheekbone. It's an ugly gash."

"It's healing. What's a scar in the scheme of things? What should I tell Sunny?"

"Would the truth upset her?"

Ash shrugged. "It's a day-to-day thing with Sunny. What might be okay yesterday won't be okay today. I'll wing it."

"We go fishing, Pop Pop?"

"Sure. How many fish are you going to catch today?"

"Six."

"Are you going to tell Mommy you had a good time?"

Jake's head bobbed up and down.

"Where's the present you bought for Mommy? Do you have it in your bag?" Fanny asked.

"What did he buy?" Ash whispered.

"Two boxes of crayons and two coloring books. He wrapped them himself. He used three rolls of tape." Ash roared with laughter.

"Ash, listen to me. I think maybe it was a mistake to bring the toys I bought him. Sunny might not like it. Why don't you say you bought them?"

"We brought them with us because you spent a great deal of time and effort trying to find something Jake would like. He loves everything. You are his grandmother."

"In name only, Ash."

"I'm trying to change that."

"Don't jeopardize your relationship with Sunny over me, Ash. Promise me."

"Okay. Hey, sport, we're home. Toot the horn, Fanny."

"Ash, no. Let me get out and into Bess's car. You can toot the horn while we're turning around. I don't want a problem."

"Bullshit!" Ash leaned over and gave the horn two sharp blasts.

"Do it again, Pop Pop."

Ash obliged. Sunny appeared in the driveway. Fanny scrambled out of the seat so that Ash could maneuver his wheelchair onto the lift. She waited until he was on the ground and in control of his wheelchair before she climbed out. She reached for Jake and set him on the ground. "I'll see you guys. Have a nice holiday. Hello, Sunny."

Sunny ignored her. She had eyes only for her father. "What happened to you?"

Ash drew in his breath. "Simon and I got into it. He didn't look so hot when he walked away."

"Did you fight over Mom?"

"No. We fought a battle that's been raging all our lives."

As Sunny struggled to make sense of the words, Jake was straining and tugging to get his new toys out of the van. "Here's a present, Mommy. I wrapped it. Is it pretty?"

"Where did you get the money, Jake? Who bought you all that stuff?"

"Her did," Jake said, pointing to Fanny.

Fanny wished the earth would open up and swallow her whole.

"Give them back. Give her this, too," Sunny said throwing her gift in Fanny's direction. Jake started to wail.

"What did I tell you when you left?"

"For God's sake, Sunny, he's only three," Ash said. "Do you think he remembers that mile-long list of instructions? Hell, I can't remember it."

Sunny reached for her son. He howled. "Want to go fishing with Pop Pop."

"No fishing." Sunny grabbed Jake by the ear and started to drag him up the driveway to the house.

Fanny was a whirlwind of movement. She had the little boy in her arms. She was eyeball-to-eyeball with her daughter. "Our problem has nothing to do with this little boy. I want you to remember that. If you forget it again, you will answer to me. Do you understand me, Sunny?"

Sunny's face turned ugly. "You didn't want him before. Now, when you have nothing else, he's suddenly good enough for you. Wrong. Stay away from my son. Do you understand *me*, Mrs. Thornton? Don't think you can come up here and threaten me."

"I wasn't threatening you, Sunny. I made a promise to you. You know me. I'm a woman of my word. Remember that.

"Ash, I'm leaving now. This can't be good for you. I wish there was something I could do. Take care of them. Call me if there's anything I can do."

"Don't worry about us, Fanny. Tyler is my ace in the hole if things get bad. Go home and water all those plants."

Fanny bent over and kissed her husband full on the mouth. "That's so you won't forget last night."

Ash laughed.

Sunny stared at her laughing parents through the kitchen window. She almost fainted with the rage rushing through her.

Fanny waved from the car window. "Hurry, Bess, I have to get away from here."

She cried all the way down the mountain.

Fanny sat in the rental car as she contemplated the map that would take her to Cape May. Why was she doing this? Because Ash asked her to do it, and she could deny him nothing even when she didn't fully understand what it was she was doing. If she was lucky, she might be able to wind things down and take an evening plane out of Philadelphia and be home by midnight.

Ash had made it easy for her. The lots were clearly marked and the owner's name, address, and phone number had been penciled in the margin of the map. Ash had told her to go to the owner's home instead of calling. "When people are selling they want to see a face, not some fancy lawyer with a briefcase. Briefcases mean someone is going to get skinned. Just carry your purse and a couple of checks."

It was eleven o'clock when Fanny rang the doorbell of an old, dilapidated, paint-peeling three-story house in Cape May. She was chilled to the bone as she stood on the porch of the old house. She turned the crank on the doorbell and waited, the gusty wind slapping at her back. How barren it looked with the arthritic trees bending and swaying. Fanny shivered inside her warm coat. The door creaked open. "Mr. Scott, I'm Fanny Thornton. I'd like to talk to you if you have the time. May I come in?"

He was old, wizened, the woman behind him just as old and just as wizened. "Do we know you?"

"No. I'm from Nevada. I'm interested in buying some property you own. I believe you spoke to my husband several times."

"Everybody wants my property. They don't want to pay for it though," the old man cackled. "Ain't that right, Mother?"

"That's right. We want millions of dollars."

"Okay," Fanny said, sitting down on a chair full of cat hairs.

"We have conditions."

"What are they?" Fanny said as she did her best to breathe through her mouth. Cats, all shapes and sizes, scurried around her feet. There didn't seem to be a litter box anywhere.

"We want to sell this house, too. It's a package deal. Mother wants to move to Miami."

"All right," Fanny said.

"You'll buy this house, too!"

"I have a large family, Mr. Scott. These are the two lots I want, they're marked in red on the map."

"Got three lots for sale. Want to sell the whole kit and caboodle."

"All right. I'll take all three lots and this house. How much?"

"How much, Mother?"

"Ten million dollars," the old lady said smartly.

"Six," Fanny said.

"Nine," the old man countered. "Whatcha goin' to do with the property?"

"Eight and it's my last offer. My husband wants the property for our grandchildren's futures."

"That sounds all right, doesn't it, Mother?" The old lady nodded. "We'll take your offer." He turned to his wife. "She don't look like one of them gangsters, does she, Mother?" he asked.

"She sure don't, Dad."

The old man held out a gnarled, dry, wrinkled hand. Fanny offered up a gentle handshake. "We had everything sur-veyed, the paperwork is in order. You pay us, file the deed, and the property is yours, Mrs. Thornton. We don't want no check. We want one of them wire transfers down to our bank. That's a condition."

"I'm willing to do that. Would you like me to drive you to the bank? Your bank will have the money in an hour. Do you have a lawyer?" Fanny felt giddy. This was the way Sallie had done business during her day. A handshake, money changed hands, and that was the end of the deal. Obviously Ash had watched his mother conduct business over the years. What was good enough for Sallie was good enough for him.

"Don't need no lawyer. Hate lawyers. All they want is your money. They shuffle papers and charge two hundred dollars an hour. Then when they're done messing everything up they make you go to court in front of some dumb judge who don't know as much as I know. It's sinful."

Outside in the bleak sunshine, Fanny looked down at her

mulberry-colored coat. Clumps of cat hairs were everywhere. She sniffed, knowing the smell of cat urine would stay with her, even in the car. She couldn't help but marvel at how easy the whole thing was. Evidently Ash was right, doing business in person was the way to go.

Two hours later, Fanny ditched her coat in the nearest trash barrel, copies of the deeds to the properties secure in her purse. Jake, Polly, and Sage and Iris's unborn child's futures were secure.

It was two in the morning when Fanny, fresh from her shower, sat down to call Ash. "I did it, Ash. Eight million. I hope you know what you're doing. Eight million dollars is a lot of money. It's so stupid, neither one of us had a lawyer."

"Fanny, I talked to the guy a dozen times. He hates lawyers. I told him what to do, and he did it. Everything is legal. You filed the deeds, didn't you?"

"Of course I did."

"Then stop worrying. Did the guy really have twenty-seven cats?"

"More like 107. I smelled, Ash. I had to throw away my coat. I stood under the shower for an hour, and I can still smell cat. I'm tired and I'm going to bed."

"You did good, Fanny. I thank you. One day your grandchildren will thank you when they realize what we did for them. Sleep tight, Fanny."

"You too, Ash."

The date on the calendar said it was April 1. April Fool's Day. Fanny looked around at her family. Even Ash had come down off the mountain for the special event.

"Everything's ready, Mom," Sage said quietly. "The line to Japan is open, Aunt Billie is standing by. We're hooked up to the satellite. We'll be seeing Moss Coleman's plane take off at the same time they do. Dawn's just beginning to break over there. Aw, Mom, don't cry."

Ash reached for Fanny's hand. "I'm sorry I gave you such a hard time about that plane, Fanny. I want it to fly as much as you do. Honest to God I do."

"I know you do, Ash. I don't know what Billie will do if things go awry. It's been a battle every step of the way. Her children are estranged from her over this plane. It isn't right and it isn't fair."

"The test pilot is on his way," Sage whispered. "There he goes into the cockpit."

"He's Amelia's stepson, Lord Rand Nelson. His father was an RAF pilot during the war. Billie says he can fly the wings off a bird."

"God, this takes me back," Ash said. "There she goes! She's up. C'mon, baby, get that nose up. There you go! Jesus, I feel like I'm seeing history in the making."

"You are, Ash. It's so beautiful. Billie's saying something. No, no, she's just mouthing words, 'Rest easy, Moss. In a few minutes it will be history.' *Fanny, Fanny, we did it! Thank you, thank you. We couldn't have done it without you. Thank your whole family. We did it, Fanny!*"

Tears rolled down Fanny's cheeks. "Now Billie's son's death is not in vain. She did what she set out to do, and if she faltered, she picked herself up and continued. I don't know if I would have had the guts to do what she did."

Ash's voice was a mere whisper when he said, "You would have persevered, too, Fanny. And, you would have prevailed."

"Ash, that's one of the nicest things you've ever said to me. This calls for champagne!"

"I hear you, Mom!" Sage bellowed. "We should sing. Shouldn't we?"

"Whatever feels right, Sage," his father said.

"*Off we go into the wild blue yonder . . .*" The family joined in.

Everyone was off key, but no one cared.

PART THREE

1984–1985

PART TWO

19

"A penny for your thoughts, Fanny."

"Right now, Bess, they aren't worth that much. Simon's lawyer served me divorce papers early this morning. It's been ten months since that night when he came here and punched out Ash. Ten months, Bess!"

"Time has been going by so fast of late. My mother said that happens when you get older. She said she woke up one day and she was in her eighties." Bess laughed ruefully.

"I didn't think it would bother me, but it does. As the months went by I more or less assumed that . . . well, I don't know what I assumed. He's not simply filing for divorce; he's charging me with adultery and he wants a percentage share of Babylon. I own fifty-one percent and he's going to go after it."

"You're going to fight it, aren't you? I'm having such a hard time believing all this. Simon was . . . such a wonderful guy."

"Not according to Ash. To answer your question, yes, I'm going to fight him. I have to find a top-notch divorce lawyer. I have twenty days to answer these papers."

"Get a woman lawyer. They understand better than men. I've heard horror stories about women getting screwed in court. Some of them don't even get child support. You need a shark. Or a barracuda. Is there anything you want me to do?"

Fanny shrugged. "Is everything on target for Halloween?"

"Everything's been taken care of. Is Mr. Reed going to attend?"

"Don't look at me like that, Bess. I haven't seen or heard from him in months. He's a friend, nothing more."

"That's because you're still married. Things will change. I think the man really likes you. I think you like him, too. You had stars in your eyes last Christmas."

"It was the holidays. I always get stars in my eyes at Christmas."

"Listen, Fanny, why don't you and Billie want any fanfare when the rehab center opens next week? You know, the mayor, the ribbon cutting, all that stuff?"

"Just family. The center is a serious thing. The medical field has been alerted, Su Li, Sallie's young protégée, is in charge of all the medical stuff. She's got a terrific staff lined up, top-notch therapists, great nurses. We just want to ease into it without any fanfare. We thought it best for the patients. Patients with debilitating diseases don't want people gawking and staring at them and asking for interviews. It's important for the patients that things remain calm and serene. The first patients arrive the day after our dedication. We can accommodate a hundred. Keep your fingers crossed that we don't run out of money and that we can meet our payroll."

"They've been crossed since the day construction started. I drove by yesterday and it's beautiful. You and Billie did a wonderful job. Phone's ringing."

"I'll get it. Fanny Thornton, how can I help you this morning?"

"Mrs. Thornton, do you know who this is?"

Fanny immediately recognized the gruff, deep voice on the other end of the line. "Yes."

"Can you meet me at Sophie's Cafe in thirty minutes?"

"Why . . . yes, of course. I'll leave now."

"Who was that? You look like someone just stepped on your big toe."

"It's not important. I have to go out for a little while. Take over, okay?"

"Sure."

Fanny walked to the café, her thoughts in a turmoil. Her heart was beating too fast. It was broad daylight, what could possibly happen?

The moment Fanny closed the door behind her, the Open sign was switched to Closed and the green shades pulled down. A bowl of chicken noodle soup and a cup of coffee were placed in front of her.

Even sitting, the man dwarfed the room. "It's nice to see you again, Mrs. Thornton."

Fanny nodded. She tasted the soup. It was good. She waited.

"My . . . colleagues and I would like to help you. What you're doing out in the desert is a good thing. My side of the street would like to help. Anonymously of course."

"I don't understand." Fanny placed her soup spoon at the side of the bowl.

The man slid an envelope across the table. Fanny reached for it and opened it. Her gasp could be heard across the room. "This is . . . I don't know what to say."

"Thank you is good enough. If you are amenable, we've decided that we will donate one day's proceeds once a year. Look at it this way, Mrs. Thornton. My side of the street is giving to your side. How and what you do with the money is entirely up to you. We will never interfere. We did our own analysis of the situation and there is no way your center can stay in the black with just you and Mrs. Kingsley funding it. It's a worthwhile endeavor, and we'd like to be part of it. There are no strings of any kind."

"Then I accept. I just don't know how to handle this."

"Let your bankers take care of the details. They can talk to our bankers. We wish you every success."

"We aren't having a grand opening or anything like that," Fanny said, grappling for words. "You wouldn't happen to know a good divorce lawyer who's a woman would you?" God in heaven, did she just say that? Evidently she did because the man seemed to be having difficulty switching his mental gears. He shrugged.

"We understand the reasoning behind your decision. Enjoy your lunch, Mrs. Thornton."

"It's very good soup."

"Take some home."

"I might do that."

Fanny stared at the envelope in front of her. Five million dollars. *Five million dollars.* From the other side of the street. Suddenly she felt giddy, light-headed. She was about to leave when a paper bag was placed on the table. Chicken soup to go. She smiled all the way to the bank. She was still smiling when she returned to Babylon. She immediately placed a call to Billie Kingsley.

"You kept it, didn't you?"

"Billie, I did not walk, I *ran* to the bank. It was a cashier's check so the money is already in the rehab account. They're going to donate every year. Ash is never going to believe this."

"Is he coming for the dedication?"

"Yes, and I believe Sunny is coming, too. The sign is going up today. Chue's standing at the ready with his flowers and shrubbery. As soon as they walk away, he'll be planting and laying sod. When he's done, it will look like it's been there for years. I'm glad we decided on calling the center, The Sunrise Rehabilitation Center for your home in Texas and my mountain. It's like it was meant to be. Gotta go, see you on Sunday."

Fanny felt so good she danced a little jig. Her mood darkened immediately when her gaze dropped to the legal papers on the corner of her desk. "Guess what, Simon Thornton. I'll fight you for Babylon until hell freezes over, and then I'll fight you on the ice!"

Fanny tied the belt of the terry cloth robe. Her wet head swathed in a thick towel, she padded to the kitchen to make coffee and to feed Daisy. The doorbell rang at ten minutes past nine just as she was sitting down with her coffee and the morning paper. Daisy ran to the door, barking.

There was only one word to describe the woman standing in the doorway; spectacular.

"Mrs. Thornton?"

"Yes."

"I'm Clementine Fox. A mutual friend of ours said you were in need of an attorney and suggested I stop by."

Fanny wasn't about to ask which mutual friend. "Are you *the* Clementine Fox, better known as the Silver Fox?"

The woman smiled, each tooth a matched pearl. "That's one of my more flattering names. Everyone thinks my hair is dyed. It isn't. I was born with silver hair."

"Would you like some coffee?"

"I'd love some."

"Is the kitchen okay?"

"I love kitchens. As a child we lived in ours. My mother made the sweetest-smelling bread. I lived for the days she made bread and strawberry jam. You look puzzled. Did I come at a bad time?"

"No, not at all. I guess I'm just marveling at how fast people on the other side of the street do things."

The golden eyes beneath heavy lashes looked amused. "The telephone is a marvelous invention."

She wasn't just spectacular. She was exquisitely spectacular. She was lean and trim; obviously, she worked out. Fanny just knew there wasn't one extra ounce of body fat on this woman. She probably spoke seven foreign languages, too. She absolutely *reeked* of capability. The Chanel suit and purse said her bank account wasn't just healthy, it was robust.

"I have a problem," Fanny said.

Clementine crossed her legs, legs with no end. Fanny felt smug when she recognized the shoes on the attorney's feet. "I have all day. Talk to me."

Fanny talked.

Clementine listened, her pen flying over the yellow legal pad.

The moment Clementine capped her pen, Fanny said, "So, what do you think?"

"I think you married yourself one sorry son of a bitch. There's no way to know that going in, so you're excused. I know how to play the game, and I know the *name* of the game. Let me give it to you in clear, concise terms. The first rule in a divorce: if it looks like it's going to be the knock-down-drag-out kind, you fuck them before they fuck you. I know your husband's lawyer. Jason St. Clare studied law under the Devil."

Fanny winced. "Where did you study, Miss Fox?"

"Call me Clementine. From here on in I'm going to be your best friend. I was St. Clare's protégé."

Fanny smiled. "Not one cent from this casino. I mean that."

"I hear you." The long legs straightened themselves out. "I like what you did with this place. It looks like someone really lives here now."

She didn't mean to ask the question. It just rolled out of her mouth. "You've been here before?"

"Uh-huh. I think I was 960 on Ash's conquest list. That was okay," she trilled, "because he was 961 on my conquest list." Fanny burst into laughter. "You were already separated."

"That was a long time ago."

"You then married the brother! I would have thought you would have learned your lesson the first time around."

"Stupid is as stupid does."

Clementine held out her hand. Fanny shook it vigorously. She was in good hands, and she knew it.

"You won't hear from me until I have something concrete to tell you. It takes a while to wade through the bullshit. I don't expect Jason to dick around too much. He'll make a lot of noise for his client's benefit, then he'll lose his voice at just the right moment."

"Don't underestimate Simon the way I did."

"I'm duly warned. I want to be clear on something. Are we talking big bucks, whatever it takes, representation?"

"And more if necessary. Thanks for coming by, Clementine."

Clementine nodded. "Don't worry. You're paying me to do that. I can see myself out."

The moment the door closed behind her guest, Fanny dialed Ash at Sunrise. "Ash, it's Fanny."

"How's it going, Fanny?"

"Simon served divorce papers on me. He's charging me with adultery." Ash's hoot of laughter tickled Fanny. "He also wants a percentage share of Babylon."

"Not in this lifetime, baby."

"You wouldn't happen to know a good lawyer, would you?"

"Hell, I know hundreds of lawyers. All shapes, sizes, and colors. Some are good. Some are lousy."

"Anyone stand out in particular?"

"Can't think of anyone. If I do, I'll call you."

"How about old 960?"

Ash hooted again. "I could call her for you. Guess you already talked to her, huh?"

"Oh, yeah. She said you were 961 on *her* list."

"That's what she said all right. Listen, Fanny, she was good, but that thing you did last Christmas, that was the best."

"Thanks, Ash. That just makes my day. Back to business, Simon engaged an attorney here in Las Vegas, so that must mean he's somewhere close by."

"It wouldn't surprise me. Fanny, don't you let him get his stinking paws on my casino. You watch your back, too."

"Ash, you won't believe what happened yesterday. I feel like those people across the street are watching out for me. I can't shake the feeling."

"What happened? Don't tell me they're coming to your Halloween do?"

"How would I know? It's costume only. Listen to this—"

Ash whistled when Fanny finished her story. "That's great, Fanny."

"Did you convince Sunny to attend the dedication?"

"Yesterday she was planning on going. This morning she isn't. I still have time to work on her. The doctor was here yesterday. He is not pleased with her progress because there is no progress. He suggested she go into your center for two weeks. She said she'd think about it."

"At least she's thinking. How's Jake and Polly?"

"He's ready for preschool. Sunny doesn't want to hear about that. Polly is a treasure. She's starting to talk pretty good. When she doesn't have her thumb in her mouth. This whole situation is not good, Fanny. I think it's time for them to go down off this mountain."

"What about you, Ash?"

"Good days and bad days. There seems to be more bad of late."

"Is there anything I can do?"

"If there was, you know I'd ask. I don't want to leave the mountain, Fanny."

"I know. If you need me, call."

"Okay, Fanny. I'll see you on Sunday."

"Are you bringing the kids?"

"Yeah. Tyler's in town, did you know that?"

"No, I didn't. Where is he staying, do you know?"

"He didn't say. He's getting married over Christmas and he wants to take the kids. Sunny is throwing a fit. I think he plans to attend the dedication. Go easy on him, Fanny."

"Why should I do that, Ash?"

"Because I asked you to."

"Oh. All right."

"What are you dressing up as?"

"The wicked witch of something or other. *Nine hundred and sixty!*"

"It's a hell of a memory," Ash laughed as he hung up the phone.

Nine hundred and sixty. I don't think I had sex nine hundred and sixty times in my *whole* life. "I guess I'm a dud, Daisy."

"Blue skies, cotton-candy clouds, the sweet scent of sagebrush, what more could we want, Billie?"

"Fanny, it looks just like the architect's rendering. It really does look like a large Hansel and Gretel building nestled in the cottonwoods. It was a stroke of genius to use the same prairie pink brick we used to rebuild Sunbridge. It will weather beautifully. It looks so homey, so welcoming. God, Fanny, I hope Sunny feels the same way when she sees it."

"Chue did a magnificent job on the sod and the shrubbery. It looks like it's been here forever. The sign isn't too much is it?"

"Nope. It blends right in. The Sunrise Rehabilitation Center. I apologize for my family's lack of interest."

"Don't apologize. You're here, that's all that counts."

"Fanny, why don't our children have the same sense of family that you and I have?"

"I wish I knew. Time, progress, fast food, not enough money, who knows. It's what it is. I tell myself when they get older they'll feel as we do. Then I say, no, that won't happen because you and I had that feeling from the day we got married. Bess did, too. Perhaps it's our generation."

"Fanny, Thad said he'd fly us to Virginia tomorrow morning. If we get an early start we can visit Josh Coleman and fly back in the evening. I'd like to do it."

"Me too. More family. I wish there was a way for Sallie to know."

"She knows. She trusted you, depended on you to follow through. It took a while, but you found Josh. Too bad you could never find that guy Jake. By the way, do you still have his money?"

"I certainly do. That money has been around the block so many times I've lost count. I used it outright, paid it back, borrowed on it, paid it back at least a dozen different times. I put it all in a mutual fund that pays off handsomely. Here come the kids and Bess."

"Ash is parking. Oh, Fanny, Sunny is with him. I prayed she would come." She squeezed Fanny's hand. "Be cool, don't give her any reason to regret coming."

Fanny's breath exploded in a loud sigh.

Ash came up behind Fanny. "I don't know what to say, Fanny. It looks like it's been there for a hundred years. It's an oasis in the desert."

"Where are the kids, Ash?"

"Tyler came up to the mountain last night and took them back to town. He's coming today and will drop them off. There he is, he's parking the car. Jake didn't want to go with him. He wanted to stay with me. Can you beat that?"

Fanny looked around. "I guess we're all here. We're doing the dedication inside. One of the staff doctors is going to give a mini speech as we take the tour. He'll explain the different methods of therapy. He'll probably tell us more than we want to know. Tomorrow, Ash, all one hundred beds will be full. A month from now, the patients' families can come to visit for three days at a time. It's wonderful, isn't it?"

"Yes, Fanny, it is. Actually, it goes beyond wonderful. Billie's calling you."

Fanny took her place next to Billie, in front of the entire staff. She nudged Billie, who had tears in her eyes. "Fanny and I would like to dedicate this facility to the memory of my son, Riley Coleman, and—"

"And to my daughter, Sunny Thornton," Fanny said. She could barely make out her daughter's face through her tears. Fanny heard her, though, as she stumbled and shuffled forward to fall into her arms.

"We should be drinking this stuff instead of smashing it on the pillar," Ash roared.

"I have another bottle," Thad Kingsley roared back.

"Open it!" Ash said, his eyes on his ex-wife and daughter.

"What made you change your mind? Do you think you're up to the tour, Sunny?"

"I'm checking in, Mom. My bags are in the car. Dad brought me down yesterday, and I had the tour, compliments of Dr. Samuels. He told me all the rooms were booked except one—mine. I'm tired of fighting you, Dad, Tyler, Billie, and Sage, not to mention the kids and I include myself. I'm so tired, Mom. Whatever stamina I had is gone."

"Then we'll get it back."

"Dad needs you, Mom. The kids are too much for him, but he won't admit it. He loves the mountain. It's so strange, once he hated it. Will I ever be able to go back, Mom?"

"I think so, if you work real hard. Let's not think about that right now. Let's think about you getting settled here and what it's all going to mean to you."

"I'm not going to say I'm sorry, Mom."

"That's okay."

"This is some place. It kind of looks like elves and gnomes should live here. It's so *snug* if you know what I mean. It looks like it could be home. I guess it is home. I committed."

"That's the beginning of the battle, honey."

"Hi, Mom," Sage said, coming up behind her. Fanny whispered in his ear. His eyes wide, he marched off.

"What did you think of the pool and the whirlpool? The water exercises are supposed to be very good. Every hour of your day will be used up. You'll make friends here, Sunny."

"I know."

"You're allowed a pet. Actually, they want you to bond with a pet. That will be your one responsibility."

"How do you bond with goldfish?"

"No goldfish. I'm talking about four-legged animals. I guess I should have said it's mandatory. The animal will be with you at all times. It's going to work out just fine, Sunny. The key here is no stress."

"Tyler wants to take the kids to New York. I told him no. I can't do that to Dad. Tyler doesn't really care, and all you have to do is look at his girlfriend to know she doesn't want them. I have custody, Mom. I'm not giving that up. He can come here as often as he wants to see them. He's a doctor, and he's on call. His girlfriend works, so the kids would be with a stranger. Can you handle it for me?"

"If that's what you want."

"Mom, how long does Dad have?"

"I don't know, Sunny."

"You need to help him, Mom. He's like a real father these days. I wish . . . I wish so many things. Dad said you're getting a divorce."

"Yes."

"Too bad. Here comes Tyler. I don't want to talk to him. I'm going to walk to my room. Come say good-bye before you leave."

"I will, Sunny."

"Hello, Tyler."

"How are you, Fanny?"

"I'm well, thank you."

"This is wonderful. You have no idea how badly places like this are needed. I wish . . . They'll help Sunny. It's what it is, Fanny. We can't turn the clocks back."

"If I hear that phrase one more time, I'm going to scream. What happened to 'for better or worse'?"

"I'm not going to get into that, Fanny. It happened, it's over, and Sunny and I are moving on. I could ask you the same question, but I won't."

"You want the children?"

"Yes."

"No. I'll take them. I'll fight you, Tyler. Don't make me do that. The kids need to be here, close to Sunny. She's going to need them more than you. You're young. You'll have other children. They love the mountain. It's their home. I will not allow you to disrupt their lives."

"Is that another way of saying you'll throw the Thornton money in the ring with a slew of high-powered lawyers?"

"That's exactly what it means. We can work out a holiday schedule. I would never, ever, stop you from seeing your children. I think you owe Sunny a little more consideration. You don't have to make a decision today, Tyler."

"I'm not an ogre, Fanny."

"I hope not."

Tyler extended his hand. Fanny brushed it away before she hugged him. "We were family once, Tyler. Sallie adored you, as did

I. It seems like time is changing everything. Have a good life, Tyler."

"You make it sound so . . . terminal."

"That's because it is. You're going back to New York. Sunny is someone you used to know. You'll have other children, and these two little ones will become a memory. Your new life will take hold, and, before you know it, this part of your life will fade completely and it won't even be a memory. It's called life."

"I'll say good-bye, Fanny."

Fanny nodded as she walked away. "He's just someone I used to know, too," she muttered.

"Yo, Mom, wait up!" Sage called. Daisy barked as she raced across the carpeted floor. "Why'd you want all her gear? Oh, Jesus, Mom, you're giving up Daisy. You are, aren't you? You can't do that. You'll die without Daisy. I don't mean literally. How's Sunny going to take care of Daisy?"

"She needs the challenge. Don't make me cry, Sage, this is hard enough as it is. Bring all her stuff."

Sage's voice was gruff when he said. "Daisy only knows the penthouse and the mountain and that place you lived in California."

"See. She adapts. She likes Sunny. I'll come and visit."

Fanny leaned her forehead against the wall outside Sunny's room as she tried to choke back her tears She bit down on her lip until she tasted her own blood. *Love is putting the other person first. Remember that, Fanny Thornton.* She bent down to pick up Daisy.

"Sunny, it's me and Sage. Can we come in? I have something for you."

"You brought Daisy."

"Sort of. I'm giving Daisy to you."

Sunny started to cry as she bent down to pick up the little dog. "I can't take Daisy. You love Daisy. She's yours. Daisy loves you, too," Sunny said as she squeezed Daisy so hard she squealed.

Fanny tried to clear her throat. "She'll love you, too. It's all she knows how to do. Maybe you can teach her some new tricks. She's a tremendous responsibility. She gets her nails clipped every two weeks. She goes to the groomer once a week because she gets matted. You have to brush her every day. Once a week you have to clean her teeth so she doesn't get plaque. Dogs get a plaque buildup just like people. She sleeps with her blanket and her mouse. You have to walk her three or four times a day, and you have to play with her." She burst into tears as Sunny started to wail.

"That's it! That's it!" Sage bellowed as his arms circled his mother and sister. "Okay, that's enough now," he bellowed again. He handed out tissues from the dispenser on the dresser. "Everyone blow."

"What if she doesn't want to stay with me?"

"Daisy loves one-on-one attention. Let her sleep on the bed with you tonight. By morning she'll be fine. Call me if there's a problem." Sunny held on to Daisy, crushing the little dog to her chest. "We should leave now. Take her for a walk and give her a light supper because she's excited."

"Mom . . ."

Fanny kissed her daughter on the cheek. "Don't say anything. It's okay. You be a good girl for Sunny, Daisy. I'll see you next week."

Fanny ran down the hall, sobs choking her. She'd just given away the one being that loved her unconditionally. The one little creature who listened, never criticized, and only wanted to please.

She was outside, the wind in her face, running straight into Marcus Reed's outstretched arms.

20

Marcus Reed held Fanny a moment, aware that other eyes were on him. He drew in his breath moving her at arm's length. "Fanny, what's wrong?"

"Everything. Nothing. I didn't know you were coming today." Fanny blew her nose and wiped at her eyes. "You look terrible."

"That's because I feel terrible. I could lean up against this car, close my eyes and you wouldn't be able to wake me for three days. I don't think I've had six hours' sleep in the last week. Add jet lag on top of that, and it should give you a fairly accurate picture of the shape I'm in."

"Then what are you doing here?"

"I wanted to see the center. I wanted to congratulate you and Mrs. Kingsley. I wasn't sure anyone else would . . ."

"Notice?"

"In a manner of speaking. Now, what's wrong?"

Suddenly voices came from everywhere. Fanny heard snatches and bits of conversation and couldn't make any sense of it until Daisy ran to her and leaped into her arms. "Oh, no, Daisy, you have to stay here," Fanny sobbed.

"Mrs. Thornton, we can't allow Daisy to stay. I'm sorry if we didn't explain that to you. These canines are specially trained to work with our patients. They don't roll over to have their bellies scratched every five minutes the way Daisy does." In a soft whisper he said, "Giving Sunny your dog was the best thing you could have done. She understands your motives were sincere and that's what counts. We already have a dog for Sunny. Look!"

Sunny stood under the portico, a magnificent German shepherd at her side. Her arms flopped in the air. "His name is Zeus!" she shouted. The dog let out a deep belly woof. "The staff is trained to recognize the dog's distress," the attendant told Fanny. "He will not leave her side for any reason. You can take Daisy home, Mrs. Thornton."

Fanny blubbered, "She's all I have that is really mine." Only Marcus Reed heard the tearful words as Fanny cuddled the little dog, who was licking at her tears.

Fanny turned at the sound of Ash's chair approaching. A soft linen handkerchief was suddenly in her hands, compliments of Marcus Reed.

"I'm heading back to the mountain, Fanny. Jake and Polly want to say good-bye."

Fanny set Daisy on the ground so she could hug her grandchildren. "Ash, are you up to this?"

"You bet. Chue is sending up two of his granddaughters to help days. With Mitzi and Nellie, we got all the bases covered. Ash Thornton," Ash said, extending his hand to Marcus Reed.

"Marcus Reed."

Fanny watched both men. She didn't realize she was holding her breath until she saw Ash's imperceptible nod. Ash's opinion of Marcus was important to her.

"I'll walk you to the car. I want your promise, Ash, that you'll call me if there's any problem at all. I can be there in forty minutes."

Ash whispered, "Fanny, watch Jake buckle Polly into her seat. He's the best kid."

"What did you promise him?" Fanny whispered in return.

"That we would go fishing and I'd give him a cherry Popsicle if he caught a fish. I want you to know Chue now has *real* fish in the pond. We catch 'em and throw 'em back."

"Good luck." Fanny waved until the van was out of sight.

"Somehow I didn't think Mr. Thornton was the grandfatherly type," Marcus said.

"I didn't either for a long time. Jake and Polly adore him. Those children are his world right now. They're all he has left. In a way it's sad, and in another way it's quite wonderful. Oh, look, here come Iris and Sage with the baby. This is your chance to meet Lexie."

"I'll drop off Daisy's gear on the way home. It was a close call for a minute. I hate to say this, Mom, but Daisy can't hold a candle to Zeus," Sage said.

Fanny was oblivious to her son's words as she reached for baby Lexie. She rubbed her nose against the baby's nose until she squealed with laughter. "When can I baby-sit?"

"Anytime you want. We're due for a night out. A day out, a week out. I could use a month."

"Just call," Fanny said as she handed the baby over to Iris.

"And now to you, Mr. Reed. Thank you for coming. Tell me, what do you think?"

"I think it's wonderful. More places like this are needed."

"Wait till you hear this, Marcus. Yes, Billie and I funded this place, we built it and got it started. Smart businesswomen that we are, we didn't think beyond opening day. We did, but we just didn't think far enough ahead. And then the most marvelous thing happened. My *friends,* and I call them *friends,* with all due respect, gave me a check for five million dollars and promised more each year. It will cost more than that to keep this place operational, but it can be done. I feel . . . and Billie feels the same way that we are accepting accolades and aren't sharing the glory, for want of a better word. It's not right. It's still their side of the street and my side of the street. If the public knew, perhaps it could simply be called *the* street. I really have to do some serious thinking about this."

"Obviously your friends on the other side did all the thinking and want it to be this way. If they wanted publicity, they would have announced it on the six o'clock news. My advice would be to do nothing. Accept things the way they are. Are there any strings?"

"None."

"Then that's your answer."

"Where are you going now, Marcus?"

"Probably a hotel somewhere. If I knew where there was a secluded place with no telephones, no television sets, no radios, I'd snap it up in a second. I have two weeks off, and don't ask me how that happened. I feel like my head is empty, and I need to fill it back up. It's another way of saying I'm on overload."

"Are you in any condition to drive, Marcus?"

"As long as I don't close my eyes."

"I know where there's a place, Marcus. You can be there in an hour and a half. Here's the key," Fanny said, removing a solid brass key from her key ring. "It's a wonderful place nestled in a grove of cottonwoods. When you see it, you'll recognize the similarities to this center. This will probably sound idiotic to you, but when you drive up to it it's as though it holds out its arms to welcome you. Sallie left it to me as a sanctuary. I think you need it right now. I'll draw you a map. Chue maintains the grounds, and he keeps fresh supplies in the kitchen. I'll make sure he doesn't disturb you. I need to warn you, though, it's out in nowhere land. There are a lot of books on the shelves. Do you think you can handle the solitude?"

"God, yes. I accept. This is very kind of you, Fanny."

"It's a very good place to come to terms with one's life. If you get bored, you can build a tree house, since you're so handy with a hammer."

"Don't count on it, Fanny. Are things all right now between you and your daughter?"

"For now, I'm sure we'll work it out. All we can do is try."

"Have you heard from your son?"

"A postcard here and there. The last card was from Costa Rica. Birch joined the Peace Corps. He'll come back when he's ready."

Marcus settled himself in the car, Fanny's map in his hands. "And you, Fanny, how are you?"

"Last week I wasn't so good. This week . . . I think things are going to work out. I've learned to take it one day at a time. Simon served me with divorce papers last week. I read the papers and knew in my heart it was going to get ugly. I asked my friend from the other side of the street if he knew a good divorce attorney and the next day one showed up at my door. I can't shake this feeling that *they're* watching over me. I know that sounds crazy but it's how I feel. Her name is Clementine Fox."

"The Silver Fox?" Marcus whistled. "In that case, I'd say you're in good hands."

"I liked her."

"That's half the battle."

"You should see her, Marcus. She's gorgeous, and she has this air about her that she can do anything. I felt like a den mother compared to her. Anyway, when she walked out my door, I knew my affairs were in good hands. Go already. Your eyes are starting to close."

"Give me the tour some other day, okay?"

"When you come back from your R & R."

"It's a date. A real one. That means you get dressed up, I get dressed up, I ring your doorbell and I bring you back to your door where I kiss you good night."

"Yes, that's a date. Well . . . I . . ."

"Decide, Fanny, before I fall asleep."

"Okay. We have a date."

"Good-bye, Fanny. I'll see you in two weeks."

"Drive carefully, Marcus."

"The last person to tell me that was my mother. She said it because she cared. I hope you said it for the same reason. It's comforting to know someone worries about you."

"My middle name is worry." At Marcus's questioning look she said, "Yes, I care if you get there in one piece."

"Thank you for saying that, Fanny. Bye."

"Good-bye, Marcus."

Fanny turned around to see her daughter sitting under one of the cottonwoods. She walked over to her and sat down. "Wanna talk?"

"I guess so. Who was that guy?"

"He's a friend. A good friend. He's managed to get me through some tough times."

"Are you in love with him?"

"I don't think so. He's never even kissed me. I think, if the circumstances were right, I might be able to love him. He's a comfortable person to be with."

"Uncle Simon?"

"He served divorce papers on me last week. He wants part of Babylon. I won't give him any part of it."

"That's good. Dad talks to me a lot. He told me how it was, growing up with his brother. Everything isn't all black and all white. I think we all learned that. What I don't understand is, how could Grandma Sallie be so cruel to her firstborn son?"

"We can't change the past, Sunny. What you've done for your dad is remarkable. You gave him a reason to live. I will be forever grateful for that."

"I like it that you two get along these days. How did it happen?"

"There was no grand scheme or plan. Things just fell into place. We're different people today. I guess you could say we came to an understanding."

"Do you have any feelings for Uncle Simon?"

"They died when he refused to understand I had a commitment to my family. At first I tried to overlook it, then I realized it was too important to overlook. My eyes must have truly been full of stars for me not to see the obvious. Now when I think back, all the little signs were there. I chose to ignore them. Simon is a control person. If you're looking for a defense, the only one I can offer up is, I wanted to be loved. I wanted to believe someone could love me for me. Your dad . . . never loved me the way I wanted and needed to be loved. That's not to say he didn't care about me in his own way. He did. Simon gave me what I needed for a little while. Even then I think I must have subconsciously known that something wasn't right. I was afraid to leave his side for fear he wouldn't be there when I got back. That's why I . . . didn't do what you had every right to expect me to do. I was the loser, Sunny. I can never get those three years back again. I'm sorry I wasn't there for you and Jake. One of these days I hope you can forgive me. Not right now. Don't make promises unless you mean them."

"I worry about Tyler trying to take the kids."

"Put that worry right out of your mind. It will never happen. Tyler and I had a talk. He left here with a clear understanding of what would happen if he crosses the line."

"Mom, are you sure?"

"Look at me, Sunny. Do you think, even for one second, I would let someone come between you and your children? It will never happen in this lifetime."

Sunny let loose with a loud sigh. "Mom, Iris said something to me today. We were sort of talking about Dad and . . . the future. She said she would take Jake and Polly if . . . Dad found it to be too much. Sage agreed. Lexie will need a playmate later on when she gets older and Polly . . . Polly would do well with her. For those times when I have to be here. What do you think?"

"I think it's wonderful. Jake needs a male presence in his life, and Sage is the one to fill that spot. I adore Iris."

"Me too. Mom, about Daisy."

"Shhh, there's no need to talk about Daisy. It was my mistake."

"It was the single most wonderful thing you ever did for me. It's something only a mother would do."

"Sunny, there's nothing in this world I wouldn't do for you, for any of my children."

"Then you get Uncle Simon by the balls and when you got them in your hand, you squeeze!"

Fanny burst out laughing. "Clementine Fox will be doing the squeezing."

"The Silver Fox is representing you! Where'd you get her? More to the point, *how* did you get her?"

"The people on the other side of the street arranged it. She showed up at my door."

"No kidding."

"No kidding. I'll be out to see you next weekend."

"Sorry, Mom. Once a month. We both have to live with it. I'm psyched for this. I'm going to give one hundred percent. You aren't allowed to call either."

"Okay. If those are the rules, then those are the rules. Thad is going to fly Billie and me to Virginia tomorrow. We found Sallie's brother Josh. We're going to meet the rest of the family. I'll take pictures and show them to you when I get back. Billie brought the Coleman family albums, and I'm taking the Thornton albums. Your dad brought your albums down with you. I hope you don't mind."

"Are you kidding? I love showing off my kids."

"We'll say good-bye then. I'll be back on visiting day. C'mon, Daisy, we're going home."

Fanny climbed from the rental car, Billie behind her. "Do you think we should have called ahead?" Billie asked.

"No. Surprise is always best. Sallie would have just showed up, like she did when she went to Sunbridge to see Seth the first time. Too late now."

"This place looks as big as Sunbridge. All you can see is miles and miles of split-rail fencing. Raising Thoroughbreds must be big business."

"Oh, Billie, look at the arch! Look what it says."

"SUNSTAR Farm." Billie sucked in her breath. "Guess the Coleman children had a thing about the sun. Sunbridge, Sunrise, and now SunStar."

"I know the answer to that even though it wasn't a question," Fanny said. "Sallie told me there was a crack in the shack's roof and if she squinted really hard, she could see the stars at night. I would imagine Josh must have lain in the same cot in the same spot before Sallie came along."

"Seth told my mother the same story. He said he and Josh used to take turns looking up through the crack, trying to count the stars. It almost breaks your heart, doesn't it?"

"Yes. This is the last of the family. Finally, they're all present and accounted for. Ash will have so much to tell Sallie when he sees her."

"Fanny—"

"I'm just repeating Ash's words. He was real keen on this trip. He said when it's time for him to go, he doesn't want to go empty-handed. He's real worried about the Simon business and how he's going to explain that to his mother. I don't want to talk about this anymore. Do we have everything?"

"Six shopping bags, full to overflowing. In the car, everyone," Thad said.

Josh Coleman himself opened the door. His faded blue eyes were alert and curious. Fanny could see the resemblance to Sallie and Seth immediately. "Mr. Coleman, I'm Fanny Thornton, your sister Sallie's daughter-in-law. This is Billie Coleman Kingsley. Your brother Seth's daughter-in-law, and this is Senator Kingsley, Billie's husband. May we come in?"

His voice was deep, gruff and gentle at the same time. "Seth and Sallie? Lord have mercy. I tried for years to find them. Finally had to give up. Come in, come in."

The old man led them to a comfortable room filled with leather furniture, books, green plants, and four skylights overhead. He motioned for them to sit. He looked pointedly at the shopping bags. The denim-colored eyes were full of questions.

"We brought our family albums so you could see our families. I'd like to ask you something . . . well, actually, I think I want to tell you something. Did you name this farm SunStar because you and Seth used to look at the stars through the crack in the roof?"

"I purely did. Ma was partial to the sun. She loved flowers and couldn't understand why the posies wouldn't grow alongside the shack with all the sun we had. It was a long time ago." He paused. "Seth . . . Sallie . . . ?"

"Seth died in 1970 and Sallie in 1975. Peggy is still alive," Billie said.

"Sallie tried to find you for years and years," Fanny said. "She did find Seth, and our two families have been together ever since. This pretty much makes it complete."

"Did Sallie look like Ma?" the old man asked.

"She said she did. She had a beautiful voice and used to sing a lot."

"Don't have much time these days to do much of anything but think. Tell me about Seth." His eyes turned crafty when he asked, "Just how rich was he?"

Billie could almost feel Fanny start to bristle. "He was rich. He had two children, Amelia and Moss. The sun rose and set on Moss. He was a fighter pilot during the war. That's where he met Ash and Simon Thornton, Sallie's sons. If they hadn't met, we wouldn't be sitting here today talking to you. I'm sorry to say I have no fond recollections of your brother. He was never kind to me while he was alive. I don't think he was kind to his wife Jessica either, and he was absolutely brutal to my sister-in-law Amelia. I never forgave him for that. He thought women were worthless. I can't forgive him for that either. He did dote on my son Riley, but he ignored my two daughters as did Moss. Riley was killed flying a Coleman airplane." Billie's eyes filled with tears. "I wish there was something good and kind I could say about your brother, but there isn't. Like you, Seth did ask Sallie about your mother. She must have been a wonderful woman."

"She was plumb worn-out. She loved us, did her best. I was just a young'un, but I knew she sometimes didn't eat so there would be enough for us. Our pa, he drank and was always liquored-up. Where did Seth's money come from?" The faded eyes were full of greedy questions.

"Cattle ranching, aeronautics. Oil. During the war he *sold* his beef to the government. His sister Sallie *gave* the government chickens. That's another way of saying Seth was a taker and Sallie was a giver. I didn't like your brother, Mr. Coleman, and I never pretended I did. I wish it was otherwise."

"Truth is truth. Did he ever mention my name?"

"Not to me. Toward the end when Sallie came into our lives she told Seth she was searching for you. He didn't seem interested one way or the other. Also, I don't know if you're interested in this, but Sallie bought into Coleman Aviation. She owned fifty-one percent of the company. Sallie talked about you all the time. Fanny's in a better position to tell you about Sallie than I am."

Fanny blinked at the brittleness in Billie's voice. There was something wrong here. She cleared her throat. "I think you would have
loved Sallie, Mr. Coleman. I tend to think she was as kind, good, and
gentle as your mother. She was a simple person who required little
in the way of material things. I heard her say many times all she ever
wanted in life was a good dress for church on Sunday, to be warm
in the winter and cool in the summer, and to have enough food. She
educated herself. She told me when she came to Las Vegas she could
barely write her name. She brought a teacher to Nevada to educate
her and ended up marrying him. They had two sons. She wanted a
daughter desperately, but it wasn't meant to be. She spent years
searching for her family. I don't think she ever gave up. I promised
her I'd keep looking for you. You have five sisters, Mr. Coleman. I
don't know too much about Maggie and the others because they prefer their own quiet lives. Peggy, the oldest after Sallie, is married to
the former lieutenant governor of Nevada. Peggy told Sallie that
when your mother was dying, all she could talk about was Seth and
you. I think that broke Sallie's heart.

"Sallie brought Las Vegas to life. She used her money wisely and
built the sewage plant and a private power company. She built a
medical center, a college. The list of her good deeds is endless. Your
sister, Mr. Coleman, is a legend."

"Where'd she get all that money to begin with?"

Billie's eyes sparked. Fanny nodded imperceptibly. "She worked
hard for it, Mr. Coleman. Everything we've told you is in the albums,
all the pictures labeled along with dates. When you finish looking
through them you'll know Seth and Sallie's families.

"Why don't we let you look through the albums, and we'll walk
around outside if you don't mind?"

Thad motioned for Billie and Fanny to go outdoors. The old gentleman was already deeply engrossed in the albums.

"I imagine it must be beautiful here in the spring and summer
when things are green. It looks pretty barren right now. Let's go
down to the barns. I've never seen a Thoroughbred," Fanny said.

They walked around, shivering with the cold for close to two
hours, stopping once in the barn to warm up. Other than several
grooms, they didn't see anyone.

"I think we can go back now," Thad said.

They let themselves into the house and walked back to the room
where Josh Coleman was just closing the last album. "Would you be
of a mind to stay on a few days to meet the rest of my family?"

"We can't, Mr. Coleman, but we can leave the albums for you if you give us yours to show our families. We can visit another time. Your family will always be welcome at our homes anytime you want to visit," Fanny said.

"I can do that. It's good to know you have kin. I'm much obliged you took the time to come here. You'd make me proud if you'd have lunch with me. Got some good Virginia ham."

"We'd be pleased to have lunch with you," Thad said.

The all-too-short lunch was filled with reminiscences, real memories, and regrets.

"You're sure now there's nothing I can do for your families?"

Thad laughed. "Seth owned Coleman Aviation and Sunbridge grazes thousands and thousands of head of cattle. The family is self-sufficient. Sallie owned Las Vegas. She was the richest woman in the state. She searched for you and Seth because she wanted to help you both. It's kind of you to offer, though. Have you ever been to Las Vegas, Mr. Coleman?"

"Last year. Lost a poke, too. Went to that there fancy one that's one of the seven wonders of the world or something like that."

Fanny laughed. "In a manner of speaking, that's Sallie's casino. I'm sorry about your loss."

"We got us one of them Coleman airplanes. Now, don't that beat the dickens out of you?"

"I'd say so," Thad chuckled.

"I'm sorry about your boy, Miss Billie. It's not right a parent should bury a child. God acts in mysterious ways. I'm gettin' religion in my old age." He cackled, slapping his denim-clad leg with the palm of his hand to make his point. "I want to thank you for coming all this way. We'll talk again."

Thad filled the shopping bag with six different albums.

"What do you think of SunStar?" the old man asked. His voice turned crafty again when he said, "Did I do as well as Seth and Sallie?"

"Yes, sir, I think you did. It wouldn't have mattered to Sallie if you dug ditches for a living," Fanny said.

"I'm sorry to say it would have mattered to Seth," Billie said.

The old man cackled. "I knew the answer before I asked the question. I was testing you."

Fanny turned around. "Testing us for what?"

"Just testing. I test people all the time. Most times they don't measure up. You two, you measured up."

Fanny wasn't sure if she should be flattered or insulted. It looked to her like Billie was of the same opinion. In the end, both women shrugged.

There were no hugs, no embraces. Everyone shook hands with a promise to stay in touch.

The plane ride home was spent looking at the albums and speculating about this newest branch of the family.

"I think there's something out of kilter with that family. Don't ask me why I think that because I don't know," Billie said. "I didn't like him, that much I do know."

"I more or less feel the same way. Maybe it was something he said and we both picked up on it but didn't know what it meant. It's one of those things that come to you later on. I walked away with that kind of feeling."

"The people in the photographs look so, what's the word I'm looking for? Maybe austere? I didn't see one smile in any of the pictures. Kids always mug for the cameras at one time or another."

"It's not our problem, Billie. We followed through, we did what we thought we had to do. If there's going to be a next move, they have to make it. Let's agree on that."

"I agree. Now, tell me about Marcus Reed."

Marcus Reed stood back to view his handiwork. It was a tree house worthy of *Architectural Digest*. Maybe he should take pictures and send them to the magazine. Then again, maybe he shouldn't.

He sat down on the stump of an old tree. Two more days to go on his self-imposed vacation. All he'd done for the past twelve days was eat, sleep, read, and take long walks, commune with nature. His biggest accomplishment was the tree house. Using the materials at hand had been his ultimate challenge, but he now had a two-room tree house, completely open in the front, with a deck of sorts and a sturdy ladder leading to his haven in the tree. Tonight he might sit in the tree house and watch the stars. Maybe he could get a fix on the lights he thought he saw in the distance this past week.

Fanny had said no one knew about this place. To see lights, even at a distance, meant someone was close by. Someone who didn't belong here. Several times during the past days he'd thought he heard noises outside the house late at night, after he was in bed and the lights were out. He'd attributed the sounds to animals, but he slept with his revolver under his pillow.

He longed for a telephone, a newspaper. He realized all he had to do was get in his car and drive for ten miles and both would be within his grasp but if he did that, his solitude would be broken. He'd enjoyed every minute he'd spent in this secluded place Fanny called a sanctuary. It was that and more. He realized he was going to hate to leave. Maybe it was time for him to cut back on his workload, time to make a life for himself. He could put down some roots in Vegas, which would allow him to be near Fanny Thornton.

Two more days until his date with Fanny. Just the thought made him feel as giddy as a teenager.

Two more days.

Fanny listened to the message on her machine. "Fanny, it's Marcus. I'm at a gas station on the side of the road. I want to thank you for two of the best weeks of my life. I cleaned the house and locked up. I'll pick you up at eight this evening. We'll do the town, dinner, show, the whole bit."

Fanny looked at her watch. She had time to go to the beauty parlor and get the works. She might even have time for a leisurely bubble bath. What to wear? How did one act on a real date? She supposed it would be awkward at first, Marcus doing his best to put her at ease while she tried to fight off her nervousness. And when the evening ended, what would he expect? The kiss was a given. Nothing more. Kisses led to other things. One kiss should be all right. This wasn't an assignation, for heaven's sake. She could handle this. She enjoyed Marcus's company. They were friends.

Fanny looked at her watch again. Could she possibly be ready in five hours? She felt like she needed *days.* She called downstairs to the beauty shop to make an appointment and was told they could take her in an hour.

Fanny was tossing her wardrobe onto the bed, trying desperately to make a decision, when the phone rang. Her voice was light, cheerful sounding when she said, "Hello."

"It's Simon. I want to talk to you."

"I don't want to talk to you, Simon. If you have something to say, you need to say it to your lawyer, who will then say it to my lawyer. I don't want you calling me here. I'll get an unlisted number if you don't stop calling." Fanny hung up the phone. It rang almost immediately. She let it ring until the answering machine picked up. She quickly pressed the erase button. Then she took the phone off the hook.

The intercom in the foyer buzzed. "Mrs. Thornton, there's a message for you. Mr. Thornton wants you to call him at Sunrise."

Fanny called Ash. "Is Simon there with you?"

"No, why?"

"He just called here and I hung up on him. He called back. I took the phone off the hook. Is something wrong?"

"No. Jake wants to talk to you."

"How nice. Put him on."

"Grandma Fanny, will you take me Christmas shopping?"

"Of course. When would you like to go?"

Fanny waited as Jake negotiated the dates with his grandfather. "Saturday. I have money."

"How much do you have?"

"Seven nickels and two paper monies. Is that enough?"

"I think so."

"Pop Pop says you have plastic."

"He did, did he? Catch any fish lately?"

"One big one like my finger. Wanna talk to Pop Pop?"

"Okay."

"He wants to buy presents for everyone," Ash said. "You better start warming up the plastic, Fanny. How's it going?"

"Great. I have a date tonight. You know the kind, he's going to ring the doorbell and all that. We're doing the town."

"You like that guy, don't you?"

"Yes, I do. What did you think of him?"

"He looked like a worthy successor if we discount Simon."

"Ash!"

"Fanny, you asked me a question, and I gave you an answer. Tell the truth, you liked my answer, didn't you?"

"Sort of. Are you managing okay, Ash? Is there anything I can do?"

"Like what?"

"Like anything. You will call if you need me?"

"Fanny, you'll be the first one I call. What would you do if you didn't worry about everyone?"

"Probably get into some kind of trouble."

"There you go. Get into some trouble tonight. Forget about all of us and enjoy yourself."

"You mean that, don't you, Ash?"

"Hell yes. Hey, I looked through those albums from my new old uncle. You know what I noticed? No one fucking smiles in those pictures. Is that weird or what?"

"Maybe they're a serious family, unlike some families I know."

"I think I might like to meet them one of these days," Ash said.

"I'll see if I can arrange it. They have their own plane. A Coleman. How do you like that? So what are you doing with yourself to pass the time since Sunny's been gone?"

"I daydream. I fantasize. The usual. The kids take a lot of time. I spend a lot of time thinking about *that night.*"

"Oh yeah?"

"Yeah. You really fried my ass that night."

Fanny laughed.

"Listen, Fanny, I want to ask you a question. Billie sent a couple of sets of those dolls up here for Jake and Polly and Chue's kids. Sunny has the originals in glass cases. My question is, should Jake be playing with dolls?"

"Why not, Ash?"

"That's girl stuff. He does seem to like Bernie better than Blossom. He gets such a kick out of seeing the commercials on television. Soon as he sees it he runs for the dolls. You must be paying some big bucks for the airtime."

"What do you think of them, Ash?"

"They're pretty damn clever is what I think."

"Did you tell that to our daughter? If you didn't, maybe you should give some thought to calling her. She works sixteen hours a day, Ash. Compliments go a long way."

"Damn it, Fanny, why are you always right? I'll call her when we hang up. Just out of curiosity, how many did you sell?"

Fanny laughed. "At last count, a little over six million. Billie can give you the count right to the minute. She's on top of everything where those dolls are concerned. I told you, Ash, anything to do with kids sells."

"At forty bucks a pop!"

Fanny laughed. "Uh-huh. Do you know where we sell the most?"

"Where?"

"In the shops at the casino. The other casinos stock them, too, out of courtesy to me. Our customers want to take something home to the kids. We can't keep them on the shelves. Billie delivers twice a week. Right now we can't keep up with the demand."

"I'll be damned. And I thought decadence and opulence was where it was at."

"I keep telling you, Ash, everything comes back to family. People come here to this Fool's Paradise in the hopes of hitting it big. When that doesn't happen, they have to go back to their ordinary lives. The gifts they take back home reflect that wonderful, ordinary life. Say wonderful things to Billie, and if you really are concerned about Jake playing with dolls, ask her opinion. Gotta go."

"Bye, Fanny."

21

"Surprise! Surprise!"

Fanny whirled around, startled to hear Billie Kingsley's voice. "How . . . why . . . ? It doesn't matter. I'm just so glad you're here. What's the occasion as if we need one?"

"The occasion is . . . ta-da! I have here, right next to me, my granddaughter Sawyer, my grandson Riley, and this imperious gentleman is Riley's grandfather Shadaharu Hasegawa."

The old Japanese bowed low, his eyes merry. Uncertain if she was to bow, too, Fanny followed suit, then wrapped the old man in her arms. "It's so wonderful to finally meet you. Billie talks about you all the time. I'm honored that you have come to visit. Your grandson is very handsome," she whispered.

"Yes. A chip off the old rock. Did I say that right, Riley?"

"No, Grandfather, a chip off the old block."

"Such strange sayings. He is handsome like his grandfather. You see. It is better when you say exactly what you mean. You will show me around this magnificent establishment, Fanny-san."

"I would love to show you around just as soon as I kiss this lovely young woman and give your grandson a big hug.

"Sawyer, you look gorgeous. However did you sneak away from that wonderful husband of yours and those adorable twins?"

"It wasn't easy. Grandma said I needed a break, and she was right. Adam is so good with the girls. He dishes out lollipops and Popsicles hourly. You guys go ahead and do whatever you want. I'm going to put some money in the Thornton coffers."

"I do love to hear things like that. We'll meet up later."

"Welcome to Nevada, Riley," Fanny said, hugging the tall young man. "I'm delighted that we finally get to meet. Your grandmother talks about you nonstop."

Riley laughed. "It's good to be here. I think my grandfather is expecting to pull a lever and have a ton of money drop in his lap."

"You know what, that can be arranged," Fanny grinned. "However, it has to be our little secret."

"You got it."

"My wife is fixated with movie stars. Do you have any here?" the old Japanese asked.

"All shapes and sizes. I can get you autographs if you would like to take them to your wife."

"I would be too embarrassed to ask," the old gentleman said.

"I'll do it for you. What brings you to this part of the country, Mr. Hasegawa?"

"My grandson said it was time to visit. The young are always right. I must apologize for not visiting sooner. Thaddeus insisted I return with him from Japan. I find I cannot say no to Thaddeus. This is . . ."

Fanny smiled. "First-time visitors are usually speechless. At first glance it is rather decadent. After a while it becomes just another place, just another business."

"Operating costs must be enormous."

"Yes. How long will you be staying?"

"We will leave tomorrow for Texas, then I must return home. I have many daughters and a wife who depend on me. My grandson, as you must know, lives in Texas now."

"And that makes you sad."

"Very sad. He has been in my heart from the day he was born. It is right that he learns about his father's family and his other homeland. One day if the gods smile on this old man, he will return. Right now he's being torn between our ways, and this new life here in America."

"It's understandable. Young people need to find their own way and make their own mistakes. As parents and grandparents we must step aside. I think I know what you must be feeling."

"I could never live here or work here. How do you stand all the clamor?"

"I tune it out after a while."

"And how is your husband? Your past husband."

"He has good days and he has bad days. We take it one day at a time."

The old Japanese nodded. "And your daughter Sunny? Billie speaks of your family as though we are all entwined. I like that. My sense of family is very strong."

Fanny noticed Neal out of the corner of her eye. She offered a slight nod in his direction. "Would you like to try your luck, Mr. Hasegawa?"

"Is your establishment in the need of funds, Fanny-san?"

"No. No, I just wanted you to . . . try one of the machines. When I first arrived here many, many years ago, Mrs. Thornton gave me a silver dollar to play. She gave one to my friend, too. We each won a thousand dollars. It was a wonderful experience. I always like to give special guests a silver dollar to try their luck. Pick a machine, Mr. Hasegawa."

"If I lose your dollar?"

Fanny laughed. "Then I'll give you another one."

"I cannot refuse such an offer."

Fanny looked around the crowded casino as the old gentleman made his decision. She saw Simon weaving his way toward them. For one brief moment she thought her heart would explode right out of her chest. Like Moss Coleman, Simon held a deep hatred for all Japanese. There was going to be a scene and there was nothing she could do about it. Billie had said Riley's grandfather was a gentle man. He was never going to understand Simon Thornton.

Her heart gave another leap when Mr. Hasegawa made his choice and dropped in his dollar. She watched in slow motion as he pulled the lever. The delight in his eyes made Fanny smile as three sprigs of cherries danced across the front of the slot machine. The bells and whistles went off just as Simon shouldered his way toward the machine. Fanny sucked in her breath.

"Easy does it, Fanny," Thad said quietly.

"Grandfather, you won!" Riley said, pummeling the old man on the back. "Is it a jackpot?"

"Did I win a jackpot, Fanny-san?"

"I think you did, Mr. Hasegawa. Eleven hundred dollars! That's a hundred dollars more than I won that first time."

Fanny saw Simon's mouth open, knew he was going to say something vitriolic, knew he was going to embarrass and shame the old Japanese, and she was powerless to stop him. She worked her way around the small crowd, her hand stretching out to cover her husband's mouth, but she was too late; the ugly words spewed out just as Billie yanked at Simon's arm. Fanny's balled fist shot forward and upward, knocking Simon backward. Thad caught him by the shoulders as Simon shook his head to clear it.

"I saw that but I'm not sure I believe what I saw. Did you see that, Grandfather?" Riley asked. "Don't pay attention to people like that man."

"Yes, my grandson. I saw." To Fanny he said, "A magnificent uppercut. Is that the right expression, Thaddeus? Is the man a disgruntled employee?"

Her eyes burning with tears, Fanny said, "No, Mr. Hasegawa, that was my husband. I am so sorry. Things . . . I am so sorry." She fled then, Billie on her heels. Riley, Thad, and the old Japanese were left to pick up the winnings.

"This is not a good thing, Thaddeus," Mr. Hasegawa said. "The words do not matter. It is that fine woman who matters. We must do something."

"You can make it right, Grandfather," Riley said, his eyes sparkling. To Thad he said, "My grandfather can do *anything*. American women are so . . . forceful. Grandma Billie was going for a hammerlock."

"He sees these things in American films. My wife is as addicted to the films as he is. They truly are exceptional young women, are they not, Thaddeus?"

"They are without a doubt, two of a kind. They're both like tigers where family is concerned. Fanny reacted, and Billie followed suit. You are considered family, Shad."

"And I am honored. Later, you will show me exactly how she did that," the Japanese whispered.

"Trust me when I tell you Simon Thornton deserved that and more. We call it a one-two punch. Follow me, Shad, and I'll show you around. When the tour is completed, we'll head for the bar and one of those cigars you aren't allowed to have. And some sake."

"Aahh."

Fanny woke when Daisy woofed softly from the foot of the bed. She looked at the bedside clock. What would wake her at 4:10 in the morning? She climbed from the bed, slipped into her robe and slippers, and crept down the hall, Daisy at her side. In the moonlight filtering through the blinds, Fanny was able to see the old Japanese sitting in one of the red chairs, his head in his hands. She stood still, not knowing if she should make her presence known.

"Did I wake you, Fanny-san?"

"No, Mr. Hasegawa. Can I do anything for you? Can I make you some tea or coffee?"

"I think I would like some tea if it isn't too much trouble."

"It's no trouble. Would you like it in the kitchen or here in the living room?"

"The kitchen will be fine. My wife and I have our tea at breakfast in the kitchen before the girls can bombard us. My wife's favorite room in the whole house is the kitchen."

"Mine too. My next favorite things are the red chairs. I have two just like them at Sunrise. Mr. Hasegawa, are you awake for the day, or are you going to go back to sleep?"

"I rise early. Why do you ask?"

"Would you like to take a ride to Sunrise? It's only about forty-five minutes from here. I can show it to you as the sun is coming up. We can be back here in time for breakfast with your family."

"Yes. Shall we have the tea to go?"

"Absolutely. Just give me a minute to get dressed and we can be on our way."

"I feel like a conspirator," the old man said as he climbed into the Rover. He laughed when Daisy hopped onto his lap.

Fanny drove steadily, sipping her tea and making light conversation. As they approached Chue's house, she wasn't surprised to see him outdoors with his snowblower. She stopped the car. "Mr. Hasegawa, I'd like you to meet my very good friend, Chue. Chue and his family are part of my family. He's lived on the mountain as long as I have."

The old Japanese inclined his head. Chue bowed low. Fanny smiled as the two men chattered like magpies. Billie had told her the Japanese was fluent in seven languages. Obviously Chinese was one of them. She wondered what they were saying.

"He said you are a saint," Hasegawa said. Fanny burst out laughing. "He says he owes you his life. It's a wonderful thing the first Mrs. Thornton did and more wonderful that you followed in her footsteps. Loyalty today is something young people know little about."

Fanny drove on, her eyes looking toward the horizon. "This is

Sunrise, Mr. Hasegawa. My son Sage and his wife and daughter and my Sunny's two children will be moving here . . . soon. Ash and the children are in town this week. I can make us fresh tea. You need to talk, don't you? I can tell something is wrong. If it's not my business, don't be afraid to tell me. I'm a good listener, and I never betray a confidence."

"I know this, Fanny-san. Yes, we will talk in your kitchen over fresh tea. My grandson has told me of this place. He speaks lovingly, fondly of it because that is how Billie has spoken of it to him. He knows where the crooked path is, knows which cottonwood the birds nest in, the step that creaks, I believe he said it was the fourth one from the bottom. He knows about the fried egg sandwiches at midnight. He knows these same things about Sunbridge." His voice was so sad, Fanny felt like crying.

"There's more, isn't there, Mr. Hasegawa? It isn't just Riley."

"How do you know this?"

"I just know. It seems at times my life moves from one crisis to the next with barely a breath in between. I've gotten quite good at anticipating bad news and things that are going to affect my life in one way or another. I think it's a sixth sense most women have. Are you ill, Mr. Hasegawa?" Fanny felt her stomach muscles tighten with the words she'd just uttered.

"How did you know?" he asked.

"Well . . . for many years I worked with fabrics and designs. Your suit is . . . designed to . . . camouflage your weight loss, I suspect. The tailoring is impeccable. Are you, forgive me for this question, trying to keep your health a secret from your grandson?"

"Yes. I don't want him to feel he must return to Japan with me. I believe in my heart Riley desires to live in America. It was always his dream to come here and live among his father's people. When his mother died it became more important to him. Each of us must find our own way as you said. Riley will find his. I cannot put obstacles in his path for my own selfish desires."

"Will he forgive you when he finds out?"

"I do not know. I must continue on the path I have chosen."

"Is there anything I can do?" How anxious she sounded. As if there were really something she could do for one of the richest men in the world. She knew, though, that if this kind, gentle man asked her for a moonbeam, she'd try to find a way to get it for him.

The old Japanese smiled. "Two things, Fanny-san. When we walk through your gardens, I would like a cigar, and you will follow through on your promise for the film stars' autographs?"

Fanny clapped her hands in delight. "Ash has cigars here in the closet. I don't know where he got Cuban cigars, but he got them. Sometimes I think Ash can do things other people only dream of doing. I'm going to miss him terribly. My children will miss him so very much. I don't know if I'll be strong enough for them."

"You must pray for strength. I will pray for you also." The old man shifted his mental gears and said, "Tea in little bags. It is amazing to me that you do not die from this. Sugar in little packages, rice in bags you boil in water, fast food that gallops when you speak into a clown's mouth." He shook his head, his face full of utter disbelief.

"It's called convenience. That's what people want today. I do it myself if I'm running behind."

"When my grandson returned to Japan the last time, he asked for *flapjacks*. My household did not know what a flapjack was. Such scurrying, so many telephone calls to find this out. It was a mission."

Fanny laughed. "They're pancakes."

"I know that now. Gravy, grits, fried potatoes. My stomach rumbles at the mention of the words."

"So does mine. It's light now, would you like to see the sun come up over the mountain? It's beautiful. I'll get you your cigar. We even have sake, Mr. Hasegawa. After our walk we can have some if you're chilled."

"I will take it if it kills the taste of the tea. I am not allowed these things. I sneak them. Thaddeus brings me wonderful cigars. My daughters pretend not to know I smoke them in my garden. We play a game. They fuss and fret, especially my youngest daughter Sumi."

"Put this shearling jacket on, Mr. Hasegawa." The old man obliged. He puffed contentedly as they walked the perimeters of Sunrise. Fanny chatted nonstop, recalling little scenarios of her life, Sallie's life, her children's. The Japanese smiled indulgently.

"And this is the family cemetery. It's so peaceful and serene when the trees and flowers are in bloom. I used to come here often to rest and think. I always felt so comforted when I walked away. Have you seen the cemetery at Sunbridge?"

"Yes. I found it strange that a man would bury his horse next to where he was to rest in eternity."

"Yes." It was all Fanny could think of to say.

"I, too, have such a cemetery at my home. It is high on a cherry blossom hill. I go there often to think. The petals on the blossoms are so delicate and fragile they appear transparent. I find your mountain interesting. I cannot imagine living on a mountain."

"You're shivering. It's time to go back inside. It's a new day. For a long time I hated new days because I was afraid of what they would bring. Now, these new days are rushing by so fast I barely catch my breath and there's another new day in front of me."

"What can I do for you, Fanny-san?"

"Be my friend."

"That has already been done. My spirit meshed with yours the moment we met."

Fanny stopped on the path. "Do . . . you believe in . . . do you think that . . . sometimes I feel like Sallie is . . . there . . . you know, supervising, watching out for all of us . . . that kind of thing?"

"Do you believe it, Fanny-san?"

"Sometimes. I guess one has to keep an open mind until someone proves that it isn't so."

"A perfect answer."

Inside the warm kitchen Fanny boiled water a second time. She laced the tea generously with sake from Ash's liquor cabinet. She watched as the old man cupped the hot cup in both hands. He pretended to roll his eyes in delight.

They spoke then like old friends, of the past, of the present, of Fanny's dreams for the future.

"Thaddeus has shown me pictures of the center you and Billie-san dedicated to my son-in-law, Moss, and your daughter Sunny. He told me many things of this fine place. We drove by on our way to your casino. It wasn't visitors' day, so we could not go indoors. I will help."

"Oh, no, I can't let you do that. We're okay. We get some nice donations from the street. We have this foundation . . ."

"I know of this foundation. Much money is required. Thaddeus told me Billie-san sometimes loses sleep over expenditures. This is not good."

"It keeps us on our toes. It's more than kind of you to offer."

"Are you rejecting my offer, Fanny-san?"

"No. I just don't want you to feel obligated . . ."

"I feel no such thing. Your American newspapers say I am one of the three richest men in the world. They say my wealth is ninety billion dollars. Riley tells me it is so. It's amazing to me that he wants no part of it. He prefers to round up cattle and drill oil wells. My point, Fanny-san, is this—we are family. I would be honored if you would allow me to be part of your foundation."

"In that case, consider yourself a third party to the foundation."

The old Japanese whipped out a check and a gold pen from the inside pocket of his jacket. He signed it with a flourish and placed it in the center of the table.

"But, it's blank."

"You will fill it in."

"But . . . how much should I fill it in for?"

"How many centers do you wish to build?"

"I'd like to build one or two in every one of the states. Even I know that's unrealistic. It's a dream. Each center costs millions of dollars, Mr. Hasegawa. The upkeep is millions more."

"I understand. One, two, a dozen. Whatever you and Billie-san think is wise."

"But . . . that means the funds are *unlimited.*"

The old man nodded. A glorious smoke ring spiraled upward and seemed to circle his head. He puffed and smiled.

Fanny's heart thudded in her chest. How was it possible this man, who she'd only known for a matter of hours, would simply hand her a blank check whose account balance was unlimited?

"I don't know what to say, Mr. Hasegawa. Thank you seems inadequate."

"It is more than adequate. Would you and Billie-san be amenable to naming one of your centers after my daughter Otami?"

"Oh, yes, of course. We can have Riley dedicate it."

"Then our business is concluded. We must leave now. We are to breakfast with my grandson. More *flapjacks,* I suppose."

"What would you like for breakfast, Mr. Hasegawa?"

"Noodle soup."

"Well, you're in luck, sir. I know a place that makes the best chicken soup in Nevada. They give you so many noodles you can't eat them all. It's just a small café, nothing fancy. The truth is, it's a dump. Oilcloth on the tables and paper napkins. Big spoons. They serve crunchy bread with soft yellow butter. Are you interested?"

"I am most interested."

Fanny slipped on her coat. The last thing she did before leaving the kitchen was to take the box of cigars from the cupboard. She presented them with a flourish. "I think Ash would want you to have these. Mr. Hasegawa . . ."

The old man cupped Fanny's chin in his hand. "My family is your family. Your family is my family. Coleman, Thornton, Hasegawa."

"Oh, no, it doesn't work that way. You get top billing, Mr. Hasegawa. I insist. There is one more branch of this family that has just come into being. We'll talk about them on the way down the mountain."

"May I smoke one of these cigars in your vehicle?"

"Absolutely."

"And you won't tell anyone?"

"I absolutely will not tell anyone. You should give some thought to the smoke being on your clothes, though."

"I cannot be blamed if other people's smoke settles on me."

"No, you cannot. You are a fox, Mr. Hasegawa."

"That is a compliment, no?"

"That is a compliment, yes."

"We must stop at your friend's house. Ah, there he is. I wish to do something for Mr. Chue. What do you think he would like?"

"Perhaps a trip to his homeland with his family. Then again, maybe not. He doesn't like to leave the mountain."

"That is because you made him part of your family. I understand his thinking. We will offer it anyway. We must revise the family now. It should be Coleman, Thornton, Chue, and Hasegawa."

Fanny smiled. "Whatever you say."

Fanny watched and listened to the intense, long conversation. There were bows, inclined heads, more chatter, more bows. Hasegawa turned to Fanny. "He now understands we are one family. He says he will be delighted to visit his homeland. You will wait one little minute. He wishes me to meet his family, and he wants to show me his collection of yo-yos. A truly remarkable man. You do not mind, Fanny-san?"

"My time is your time, Mr. Hasegawa."

When the old Japanese returned thirty minutes later, he was laden with packages. "Rice cakes, honey cakes fresh from the oven, egg rolls, and this," he said holding up a sparkling golden yo-yo. "He gave me one lesson on how to work this strange contraption. He said it is very relaxing. I will test it later."

Fanny gasped. "That's Chue's favorite."

"I knew that. I did not wish to take it. He insisted. That is why I must master the technique he showed me. I wish to be worthy of such an important gift. He wishes me to have my picture taken and then sent to him. When I have mastered his technique. Do you think I can do this, Fanny-san?"

"I just happen to know somebody who has it down pat. Chue taught my grandson Jake how to do it. He's a whiz at it."

"I am much relieved. We must hurry now, Fanny-san. Riley grows impatient when I am late."

"When he gets to be our age, he'll be more patient. Why is it youth can't wait? Everything has to be done lickety-split."

"Someday they will ask the same thing of their children." His voice sounded weary to Fanny's ears.

In the underground garage, Fanny helped the old man from the Rover.

"I wish to thank you, Fanny-san, for an enjoyable morning. It is my wish that someday you come to Japan and see my home and my cherry blossom hill."

"The first time there is a lull in my life, I'll hop a plane. I'll ring your bell three long rings and one short one so you'll know it's me."

The Japanese chuckled. "Do not wait too long, Fanny-san."

"No, I won't wait too long. I think I can taste that noodle soup already. I don't think I ever had noodle soup for breakfast."

The Japanese chuckled again as he linked his arm with Fanny's.

"Ah, our family awaits," the old man said as he stepped from the elevator.

Everyone spoke at once. "Where were you? We were worried. We thought something happened."

"Something did happen. Fanny-san took me to the mountain. We had tea and sake and I had two cigars. We are now going out for noodle soup. Fanny-san says she knows a dump that serves the best noodle soup in the state of Nevada. They also have *flapjacks.*" Hasegawa wrinkled his nose to show what he thought of that menu item.

Fanny leaned closer to Billie. "You won't believe what I'm going to tell you," she whispered.

"Sure I will. Mr. Hasegawa gave you a blank check for the rehab centers. Unlimited funds. One of the buildings is to be dedicated to Otami. Later, one will bear his name."

"You know?"

"Fanny, how could I not know? He's making such a valiant effort for Riley's sake. Thad has known for some time. I love that old man. I really do. Did he tell you we're all one big family now?"

"Yes, and I think it's wonderful. He has this wonderful sense of family. He has all daughters. If ever a man deserved a son, it's Mr. Hasegawa."

"Riley is his son *and* his grandson. That's why he's so devastated that Riley wants to remain in Texas. He's giving me his grandson, Fanny. *Giving* him to me in every sense of the word. That tells you exactly who Shadaharu Hasegawa is."

"Our lives are richer because of him, and I don't mean monetarily."

"I know, Fanny, I know."

They filed into the elevator. "Noodle soup coming up," Thad said cheerfully. "You need to know, Shad, that I'm a chicken-fried steak man myself."

"Fanny-san said you will love this noodle soup. Afterward we will walk down the street and smoke our cigars like . . . butter and egg men."

Fanny and Billie smiled indulgently.

Their family.

22

Fanny pranced back and forth in front of the long mirror attached to the bathroom door, viewing herself from all angles. Daisy growled playfully as she circled her mistress's feet. "It's sexy, but not too sexy," Fanny said. "I like the slit up the side and I love the way this raw silk feels. No pearls tonight, Daisy. They're so . . . *debutantish* if you know what I mean. My diamond earrings and jewel pin will be just enough." Daisy barked again and started to race around the room, rolling in Fanny's discarded clothing. "I know you're trying to tell me something. You don't like the mess I created, huh? Well, I had to find just the right dress for this evening. None of that stuff on the floor seemed *quite* right."

The plum-colored sheath was a *Billie* original. The three-quarter sleeves were banded in rich heavy satin as was the neckline and the generous slit up the side, in a shade darker than the raw silk. It was an elegant, sophisticated dress, the kind Fanny rarely wore. Billie had dyed the silk shoes to match the satin on the dress to create an even, flowing line. The small evening bag was a creation in itself, made from the plum-colored raw silk attached to an intricate, antique gold chain. Fanny felt as elegant as she looked, and it had only taken five full hours to get to this point.

Fanny sprayed a delicious but naughty scent in the air, jiggling back and forth until she was satisfied the misty spray clung to her like a fine cobweb.

She was ready.

The doorbell chimed as she weaved her way through the piles of discarded clothing. Her heart started to thump in her chest when she saw Marcus's look of approval. It thumped harder when her own gaze registered his lean handsomeness.

Fanny smiled.

Marcus smiled.

Daisy chased her tail in a circle.

"Mrs. Thornton, you look exceptionally lovely this evening."

Fanny inclined her head to acknowledge the compliment. "And you, Mr. Reed, look quite dashing. Do they still use that term today?"

"Probably not, but who cares. I'll take any compliment I can get."

In the elevator, Fanny asked, "Where are we going or is it a surprise?"

"I think, Fanny, it's time for you to cross the street. I thought we'd go down the line—appetizers at one, main course at another, dessert at still another, coffee and after-dinner drinks farther down, and a show at the last casino on the block. I promise to have you home by midnight."

"What a wonderful idea. I should have done it sooner. I'm glad we're doing this, Marcus."

The word on the street spread faster than a brushfire; Fanny Thornton had crossed to the opposite side of the street. If there had been a red carpet, it would have been rolled out for her entrance into the casinos. She smiled, shook hands, and reveled in the attention she was receiving.

"Let's walk home, Marcus," Fanny said as they exited the last casino. "I had such a good time. Everyone was so gracious. They aren't at all like everyone says they are. I don't think it was enough of a thank-you though, do you?"

"More than enough. Tomorrow this whole town will know you crossed the street, if they don't know already. Crossing the street means you gave your seal of approval. In this town that's all important. It's what you feel, isn't it?"

"Yes. The owners have never bothered me. Yes, once they tried to put one over on Ash, but they . . . they reconsidered. I think it all has something to do with Sallie. I'm grateful that there have been no confrontations."

"Businessmen respect other businessmen. Just because you're a woman doesn't mean they won't or can't respect you."

"Do you think that respect has anything to do with light switches and flush handles?"

"To some degree. They know you aren't a flibbertigibbet. Is there such a word?" Marcus laughed.

"I think so, but don't ask me to spell it."

"We should do this again."

Never shy, Fanny said, "When?"

"Soon."

"Soon means different things to different people. I'll need time to get a new dress. I love any excuse to buy a new outfit. I'll require some notice, Marcus."

"Is a week long enough?"

"I'd like two weeks. That gives me two weeks to shop and think about the evening. You know what they say about anticipation."

"No, what do they say?"

"Ask someone else." Fanny felt flustered at his teasing look and proprietary hold on her arm.

"Okay, I will. I should be rewarded. I promised to have you home by midnight. It's a quarter to twelve and it looks like something exciting is happening inside your casino. I don't know if you picked up on it or not, but there seemed to be this same kind of excitement across the street all evening."

"Let's check it out."

"I'd say someone is winning big time," Marcus said.

Fanny was close behind Marcus as he shouldered his way to the blackjack table. Her eyes scanned the crowd for Neal. She waved, a frown building on her face as he made his way over to her. "What's happening?"

"That guy has hit every casino on the Strip tonight. The word went out about two hours ago. He's raked in more than two and a half million bucks up and down the Strip. He's hitting us big. He's no high roller either. I've never seen him before, and the other owners say the same thing. He's got a goddamn system. He hasn't done anything wrong so we can't turn him away."

"Does he have a name? I can't even see him?"

"He's a young guy with glasses, dressed well. I don't know this for a fact but one of the other owners said his name is Jeff Lassiter.

They got the name from his license plate when he parked his car. He's into us for four hundred grand, give or take a few thousand."

Fanny's face drained of all color. "I want to see him."

"He's very ordinary-looking. He reminds me of someone, but I can't think who it is. Follow me if you want a better look."

Fanny stared at the young man at the table. Lassiter's tie was askew, sweat beading his forehead as he looked at the cards in front of him. *Put a pair of navy whites on him and he'd look just like Ash at his age.* Fanny's mouth grew dry as a cheer went up from the crowd. Her gaze locked with Neal's.

"Change dealers, Fanny," Marcus whispered in her ear.

Fanny mouthed the words to Neal. He shook his head.

"We can't. When the shift changes, maybe, but not now. The crowd, not to mention Mr. Lassiter, won't allow it. I wonder what his exact take was at each of the other casinos?"

"Probably half a million at each place. He's into you for that right now. He looks to me like he's just starting to warm up. The guy's on a roll," Marcus said.

"The shift changes in three minutes. We'll know if he has a system when the new dealer comes on."

"I'll make some phone calls, Fanny."

"Thanks, Marcus."

The crowd cheered again when the dealer slid a pile of chips toward Jeff Lassiter.

Precisely at midnight, the new dealer approached the table. The crowd voiced its objections as the dealer made way for the new man to take his place.

"Sorry, ladies and gentlemen, my time is up. My family is waiting for me."

Lassiter squawked his disapproval. Fanny sensed that the young man didn't care one way or the other. He was voicing his opinion for the benefit of the crowd. That told her he indeed had a system.

"The house rules are four hours on and four hours off. The house reserves the right to change tables. We'll do that now."

The crowd once again voiced its displeasure. Lassiter smiled. Fanny felt a rush of fear.

"He took all five houses across the street for a half million each," Marcus said. "This is just my opinion, Fanny, but I think this is the casino he plans to hit really big. Keep watching his face, especially his eyes. He's not gambling. He's playing a game."

"Wait here, Marcus, I'll be right back."

Fanny threaded her way to the offices and called Ash. "Listen to me, Ash, I only have a few minutes. Your son, Jeffrey Lassiter, just hit all the casinos on the other side of the street for a half million each. He is now into us for seven hundred thousand and he's not stopping. The shift changed. Neal is changing tables. Tell me what to do."

"How do you know it's Jeff?"

"It's him, Ash. He looks exactly like you did when you were his age. You could never deny that young man in a court of law. It is your son. What should I do? Neal says he has a system. What the hell does that mean, Ash?"

"It means he has a fucking system is what it means. He's no gambler. He was always good with numbers according to his mother. As good as Simon . . . son of a fucking bitch, that's it!"

"What's *it*, Ash?"

"Simon."

"What does Simon have to do with this? Are you saying Simon knows about this boy?"

"Yeah, remember I told you I confessed to him in a weak moment. Back when things were okay between Simon and me."

"Ash, I don't want to hear this. You told me there was no such thing as a system."

"There isn't. Once in a while some guy comes up with something and it works for a little while. You can't beat the odds, Fanny."

"He's doing it. Maybe you should think about getting in your van and coming down here or else call him on the phone. You need to do something, Ash. It's going to be a very long night. What happens tomorrow night and the night after? Just tell me one thing, Ash. If Simon is behind this, is there any way, any way at all, that we can lose this place?"

"Jesus Christ, Fanny, you were married to the guy. You saw a side of him even I never saw or knew. The side I know says yes. What do you say? I'm coming down. The house rules say we can call a one-hour break. I had that initiated for just such a problem. Neal knows about it. Call the break in fifteen minutes. I'll be there before the time is up."

"Are you in any condition to drive?"

"I can drive, Fanny. I'll take care of this."

Fanny dropped her head into her hands. She felt like crying.

"What is it?" Marcus asked from the doorway.

"Jeffrey Lassiter is Ash's son. Ash thinks Simon and his son are . . . in this together. Simon's a whiz when it comes to numbers. Because you're good at numbers, does that mean you can beat the odds? Ash says no. I don't know. He said we can call a house break of an hour. He wants me to do it in fifteen minutes. He's on his way down the mountain. My God, I can't believe Simon hates us so much he would do this, if indeed he's behind it. This is all my fault."

"No, Fanny, this is not your fault. Your husband is a very troubled man who managed to hide it all these years. Some people can hide things like this all their lives and then some small thing, or sometimes some large event will happen and there's an explosion of emotion."

Fanny's voice was weary. "The young man isn't doing anything illegal. He's doing what everyone does who comes into the casino. He's gambling and he's winning. There's nothing we can do. Changing dealers, calling time out, those are just temporary solutions. He'll keep coming back if he has his own agenda, in this case, Simon's agenda. You should leave, Marcus. You said you had an early-morning flight and it's after midnight now. This isn't your problem."

"I can't leave you like this. Things can get ugly."

"We have security."

Marcus perched himself on the edge of the desk. "I was supposed to drop you off at your door and kiss you good night."

"I know. It was such a perfect, wonderful evening, and now . . ."

"Fanny, did you know about your husband's son?"

"I just found out recently. The kids don't know yet. How far will Simon go if he is behind this?"

"Fanny, I wish I had an answer for you. I don't. This is just a thought, but do you think perhaps your attorney made his attorney realize he has no grounds for a claim on Babylon? As I said, it's a thought. I think your fifteen minutes are up. I shudder to think what the young man has won in the past thirty minutes."

"Me too, Marcus."

He was so close Fanny could smell the scent of wine on his breath. She saw herself mirrored in his eyes and thought it strange. She felt deliciously warm as she felt herself drawn even closer and yet she had no memory of Marcus reaching out to her, had no memory of moving. She was there, in his arms, against his chest. The world as she knew it ceased to exist. She waited, knowing he was going to kiss her. It seemed to her in that one brief moment that she had waited for this moment all her life.

Fanny stepped back into reality when Marcus kissed her lightly on the mouth and murmured words she barely comprehended. "I'm not a man who starts something he can't finish. We have a lot of tomorrows, Fanny. Are we in agreement?"

Fanny nodded. Her tongue felt three sizes too big for her mouth and her lips still tingled from his touch. She felt Marcus's chin drop to the top of her head. He nuzzled her hair, murmuring words she couldn't hear or understand. It didn't matter. She felt his heart or was it her own? When he spoke again, she heard the words and she understood them clearly. "I think I'm falling in love with you, Fanny Thornton."

"Guess what, Marcus Reed, I think I'm already in love with you. I don't know how that happened either," Fanny said bluntly. "I think it was the fifty pairs of shoes."

Marcus threw back his head and laughed. "Our timing is incredible."

"It's the story of my life. You better get used to it. It seems I move from one crisis to another with hardly a breath in between. Right now I have crisis 466 to attend to. That's an arbitrary number I picked out of a hat."

Marcus squeezed her shoulders. "Things have a way of working out. I'm going to give this particular crisis my undivided attention, and I'll call you with any suggestions I come up with. It helps to be objective. You and your ex-husband are too close to the situation and you're dealing with emotions that are alien to you right now. I'm not hampered by such things. Come, Fanny, let's see how much more damage the young man has accomplished in the past twenty minutes. Remember something else, Fanny, you're losing other monies as well. By now I imagine play has stopped at the other tables and the slots. Everyone wants to watch a winner. Look at me, Fanny," Marcus said cupping her face in both his hands. "Nothing is so bad that it can't be fixed."

Once they were on the floor it was impossible to shoulder their way through the crowds of people surrounding the blackjack table. "Wait here, Fanny, I'll get your manager."

Fanny watched as Marcus plowed his way through the crowds, using his elbows and shoulders, smiling in apology as he forced the patrons to stand aside. From her position on the fringe of the crowd, she could hear the grumbles and the moans and groans as Neal called for the house break. Then he was at her side.

"Ash is on his way," she told him.

"That's a relief. Who the hell is that guy? He just walked in off the street, opened his tie, rolled up his sleeves, and started to play. He did the exact same thing at the other five casinos he hit. The kicker is he's playing a straight game. He shows no signs of tiring. He's not drinking either. He's alone, no one is with him. I can't be sure but he looks to me like he's ready to bet the whole bundle at one time. We're talking some serious money here."

"I know, Neal. Let's go into the bar. I think I see Ash. He must have flown down the mountain." She looked up to see Marcus, striding toward her.

"I'll say good-bye, Fanny," he said. "You're in good hands now."

No, I'm not. I want your hands. I want you, only you. She nodded as she watched Marcus walk away.

Ash's chair whirred to a stop. "Where is he?"

"Find the biggest crowd and that's where he'll be," Neal said. "Ash, he's playing a straight game. Don't open yourself to a lawsuit. He hit the whole street. He just likes Babylon the best. It's my opinion he's getting ready to play the wad he's won and call it a night. This guy is going to come back. Again and again."

"We'll see about that," Ash snarled. His chair whipped around as he headed down the center aisle to where a small, dark-haired woman stood waiting, her eyes filled with tears.

"This is how your son repays me? Would you mind telling me what the hell is going on here?"

"I don't know. Jeffrey leads his own life these days. You know he has his own apartment. How could I possibly know what he does every hour of the day. Someone called. I don't know who, and I came . . ."

"I suggest you go over to him and bring him here and I suggest you do it right now."

"Ash—"

"Now, Margaret."

"I'd like an explanation, Jeffrey," Ash said, his voice colder than chipped ice.

"I've been winning all night long. I guess it must be important for you to come down off your mountain."

"It's important. The Gaming Commission and the IRS will want to talk to you shortly. As a matter of fact, both gentlemen are on the way as we speak."

"The IRS?" Margaret Lassiter said in a squeaky voice. "Jeffrey, did you hear what Mr. Thornton just said?"

"Did I do something wrong, *Mister* Thornton?"

"I don't know. Did you? The Gaming Commission will decide. You did make one mistake though. You should have stayed on this side of the street."

"What's that supposed to mean?" Jeffrey blustered.

"My God, Jeffrey, did you win money over there, too?" Margaret Lassiter moaned.

"So what if I did."

"I don't think he'll pay attention to me, Margaret. Maybe you should explain what that means to him, to you, and to your lives. Not mine. Yours."

Margaret Lassiter led her son away as she spoke in low tones. Ash watched them, worms of fear crawling inside his stomach. He hadn't even brought Simon's name into the conversation yet. When they returned, Margaret was wringing her hands in frustration while Jeffrey's face exuded bravado.

Ash jumped right in. "I know that my brother Simon put you up to this. I want you to know it isn't going to work. I want you to tell him that for me. I can bar you from this casino, and I will do that. I'll explain the circumstances to the Gaming Commission and go on from there. Babylon is a privately owned casino. We make our own inside rules. What that means, Jeffrey, is, we answer only to ourselves, not Simon. Simon has no part in this casino."

"Yeah, well, how's it going to look to the other casino owners when you won't let me play here?"

"They're going to think I'm one hell of a smart man. They'd do exactly the same thing. You can't beat the odds. What that means is you are doing something you shouldn't be doing. I'm sure Simon promised you a bundle. What's going to be left of your bundle after the IRS takes theirs and Simon takes his? Less than you would get in the trust fund I set up for you and your mother. That's history now. You can take responsibility for that, too. We're finished. I'd like you to cash out now. They're waiting for you at the payout counter. One last thing. My side of the street, the other side of the street, it doesn't make a difference when something like this happens. We take care of our own and we protect what's ours. If I were you, I'd go back across the street and lose all that money you won. Do what you want. You are not welcome here any longer."

"Ash—"

"I don't want to hear it, Margaret. You and your son are on your own now. If nothing else, I did expect a certain amount of loyalty. I didn't expect my son to be so weak he would betray me for money. I'm sorry it turned out this way."

His shoulders quivering with anger, Ash wheeled his chair over to where Neal and Fanny waited. "Boot his fucking ass out the door. Mr. Lassiter is not welcome in this casino. I doubt if he'll be welcome anywhere else for that matter. He's cashing out. Make sure he leaves the building."

"Ash, this is going to hit the morning papers. It's not going to look very good for us."

"When it hits the morning papers, you won't recognize the scenario they play out. How many times do I have to tell you, this town takes care of its own? Take care of business, Neal," Ash said, jerking his head in the direction of the payout window.

"Ash, I'm sorry," Fanny said. "I didn't know what to do. Maybe I'm not suited for this business after all."

"Of course you are. You were trying to be fair because it was my son. I appreciate that. If it was anyone else, your instincts would have kicked in and you would have reacted to the situation in a forthright business manner. I think Simon thought this was going to be a snap, and he'd come out a winner. He's got to be over the edge, Fanny. For Simon to resort to something like this is so totally out of character I'm having trouble trying to comprehend it. Stay tuned for the next installment."

Fanny cringed at the bitterness in her ex-husband's voice. "Ash, he's young. Simon has . . . Simon can . . . charm the bees out of the trees, we both know that. God only knows what he promised the boy. A big windfall would seem like the pot of gold at the end of the rainbow to that kid. Don't be too hard on him."

"He didn't have to go along with it. I might not expect much in this life, but I damn well expect loyalty. Birch and Sage wouldn't have knuckled under to something like that. That's because *you*, not me, brought them up right, Fanny. I think I made it too easy for Jeff and his mother. This is all hindsight now. I'm going back up the mountain."

"Temptation is a terrible thing, Ash. Neither one of us can be certain Birch or Sage wouldn't have done the same thing. Where kids are concerned, you can't afford to bury your head in the sand. Cool off, assess the situation, call your son tomorrow and have a talk with him. Don't leave it like this, Ash."

"Good night, Fanny. Hey, how'd the big date go?"

Fanny snorted, a very unladylike sound. "You see me, do you see him? I guess you have your answer."

"He must be a hell of a patient man. Maybe you need to be more aggressive."

"Ash?"

"What?"

"Shut up."

"Testy, aren't we?"

"Yes, I am."

"Excitement's over. Call him up. The night's not over."

"I'm not looking for advice, Ash."

"It was for free, Fanny. You should never turn anything down that's free."

"Are you sure you're up to the trip home? It's late."

"If I stay, can we do that thing?"

"No."

"Then I'm leaving. I'll talk to you tomorrow. Call me in the morning and read me the paper."

"Okay. Good night, Ash. Drive carefully."

Ash slapped at his head. "Jesus, Fanny, I almost forgot. I got a letter from Birch today. I left in such a hurry I forgot to bring it with me."

"How is he? Is he all right? What'd he say?"

"I'll read it to you when you call me. It wasn't all that long. He did go on for one whole paragraph about how the chickens scratch on his tin roof at four in the morning. He said he hadn't had a bath in eight days. He sounds like he loves what he's doing."

"All I care about is that he's healthy and happy. Thanks for telling me. The night wasn't so bad after all."

"Do you really like that guy?"

"Yeah, I do, Ash."

"Do you like him better than you liked me and Simon?"

"Don't ask me questions like that, Ash. First of all, it's none of your business."

"I feel responsible for you, Fanny. You were my wife once."

"A fact that you conveniently forgot from time to time," Fanny snapped.

"C'mon, do you?"

"It's different, Ash. I'm not the young, crazy girl who fell in love with you. I'm not that needy woman who swallowed Simon's line.

I'm finally me. This new me sees and feels things differently. You do, too, Ash; you just won't admit it."

"I just don't want you to get snookered again. I'm not always going to be here to look out for you. I do, in my own way. I want you to know that."

"I do know that. I thought you didn't want to talk about stuff like this."

"I don't. You know, Fanny, you bring out the worst and the best in me."

"That's a compliment, isn't it?"

"Damn straight it is. Listen, Fanny, if Simon starts to call you, hang up on him. Don't give him a chance to say anything. If you talk to him, he'll feed on it. Promise me. Get an unlisted number. Do it tomorrow."

"All right, Ash. Give the kids a hug."

"Will do."

Fanny looked around the casino. Her new world.

Things were back to normal.

Good or bad?

Good, she decided as she made her way to the elevator.

23

As Fanny made her way down the grocery aisle, she had the strange feeling someone was watching her. The feeling had been with her from the moment she parked her car in the parking lot. She looked over her shoulder, certain she would see someone staring at her. Nerves. The episode at the blackjack tables last night had left her unnerved and today she was paying for it with the jitters.

Ash had been right. The morning paper had relegated the event to page four and one small paragraph. What it said basically was, young man wins big and loses big. So, Jeffrey had followed Ash's advice and crossed the street to return the money by losing. Babylon had taken the hit and things were back to normal.

Fanny scanned the list in her hand. Most of the items in her grocery cart were for Jake's visit on the weekend. They were going to make raisin-filled cookies, Jake's favorite. Peanut butter, jam, cherry Popsicles, cheese sticks, lollipops, and other goodies. The cart was almost full with her own purchases—vegetables, fruits, and a luscious-looking London broil.

Fanny looked over her shoulder again, then up and down the aisle. She tried to shake the uneasy feeling she'd had since entering the store. She saw him then as she reached for a box of cereal. She almost dropped the box. She swiveled around, her eyes wide, and struggled to take a deep breath and then another. Her knuckles gleamed white on the cart under the fluorescent lighting. Her instincts had been right: Simon had been watching her. How did he know she would go to the grocery store at this particular time of day? He couldn't know unless he'd been following her. *Don't panic, Fanny. Hold on to the cart and walk toward the front of the store, where the cashiers and manager are working.*

She could hear his cart behind her, hear the sound of his shoes on the tile floor. The fresh scent of citrus assailed her nostrils. Simon loved oranges, grapefruit, and lemons. She knew his cart was loaded with fruit. *Don't look over your shoulder. That's what he wants. Go to the checkout line. He won't do or say anything in front of other people. When you finish, ask to use the phone and have Security come to the market.*

She felt his touch on her shoulder. Once his touch had thrilled her. She recoiled and stepped to the side. "Hello, Simon."

"Fanny, imagine meeting you here."

"I wonder what the odds of that happening are." She was right. There were six grapefruit, a bag of oranges, and a bag of lemons in his cart. "I think you've been following me, and I'd like to know why. Don't do it again, or I'll apply for a restraining order."

"Don't flatter yourself, Fanny. I have as much right to shop in this market as you do. What am I doing wrong? Nothing."

He looked so normal in his white dress shirt open at the throat, the sleeves rolled to his elbows. His chinos were crisp and fresh. He was freshly shaven. She could smell his woodsy aftershave, a scent that had once made her dizzy with desire. He looked so damn normal. Until she looked at his eyes. The urge to bolt and run was so strong she yanked at the cart to put more distance between them.

Simon chuckled. "You're afraid of me, aren't you?"

"What do you want from me, Simon? Your plan didn't work last night, did it? That was a low-down dirty thing you did. I knew about Jeffrey. Ash told me. Nothing you do is going to work."

"I want Babylon. Give it to me, and I'll get out of your life. You can go back to sewing baby clothes."

"Not in this lifetime, Simon. Ash will never give it up to you."

"Ash isn't going to live forever."

"That's an ugly thing to say. Ash is your brother. He could very well fool us all and live another twenty years. If that doesn't happen, I'll make sure you never get a foothold."

Simon laughed. He sounded like she'd just told him a joke. She shuddered. Ash had told her not to talk to him, and here she was, babbling like some crazy person.

"You're just spinning your wheels, Fanny. I want it, and I'm going to get it."

"No. I won't let that happen. You just want it because of Ash. You said you hated this town, this casino. That was all a lie. I'm stupid, but Simon, you're even more stupid. If you had come here with me, I probably never would have caught on to you because I loved you so much. You couldn't come though, could you? Ash would have seen through you in the blink of an eye. That was your first mistake. Everything else you've tried has been a mistake, too. Your mother must be having a fit."

"Mom would want me to have Babylon."

"If that's true, Simon, why didn't she make provisions for you to have it?"

"Fanny, you're right, you are stupid. She didn't know I wanted it."

"It's the red and yellow lollipop. The rules changed, Simon. I'm not Sallie and this red lollipop is a billion-dollar industry. The only way you might have a shot at this is over my dead body, and even then the kids inherit, not you."

"Nobody lives forever," Simon said, then added, "I always liked the kids."

"This is going nowhere." Fanny shoved her cart at Simon's cart, making it spin out of the way. She literally ran down the rest of the aisle to the checkout counter. Ragged little puffs of air exploded from her mouth as she tossed her groceries onto the counter. She looked over her shoulder a dozen different times before she made her way to the parking lot. Simon was nowhere in sight.

It wasn't until she was back in the apartment with the door locked that Fanny drew a deep breath. Coffee in hand, she dialed the business office of the telephone company and was issued an unlisted number on the spot. She then called down to the office to tell Bess to call everyone and give them her new number. "It will go into effect at noon. Call the rehab center first. I have to call Ash, so I'll give him the number."

Fanny put away the groceries, her mind racing. Maybe she shouldn't call Ash. Maybe she should go up the mountain. Her sixth sense, the one that always kicked in when trouble loomed, was kicking in now. She didn't know how she knew, but she knew Simon was going to go up the mountain. She yanked the plug from the electric coffeepot, grabbed her purse and ran to the elevator. *Stupid, stupid, stupid. Call Ash, warn him. Have him take the kids to Chue's house.*

Fanny raced back into the apartment, dialed Ash's number, her foot tapping the floor as she waited to hear his voice. "Ash, it's Fanny. Send the kids down to Chue's. I'm on my way up the mountain. I think Simon is on his way as we speak. No, I'm not sure. It's my gut instinct. Just do it, Ash. Then go down to the studio and lock yourself in. I had special locks put on a long time ago. Your brother wants your billion-dollar yellow lollipop."

Fanny's eyes were everywhere as she barreled up the mountain at ninety miles an hour—directly ahead, in the scrub at the side of the road, in the trees, in the rearview mirror. It was all a blur until she reached Chue's house. She slowed, the car fishtailing in the middle of the road. "Block the road, and if Simon shows up, he'll have to make the rest of the way on foot. He'll leave his car. Push it over the mountain, Chue. I mean it, don't think twice. Then pile everyone into your truck and head for Babylon. Do you understand?"

"Yes, Fanny."

"Where's Ash?"

"In the studio."

"Okay." Fanny backed up the car and drove the rest of the way at a sedate eighty miles an hour. She skidded to a halt. She looped her purse around her neck as she ran from the car, the door hanging wide open. She was breathless when she reached the studio. "It's me, Ash. Open the door!"

"Fanny, what in the goddamn hell is going on? You damn near gave me heart failure."

"What do you think you would have felt if I hadn't called you and Simon got here before me? He cornered me in the supermarket. He's been following me, stalking me. Ash, he said . . . he said if Sallie had known he wanted Babylon, she would have given it to him. He *believes* that. He means to get it. Last night was just a game. It didn't mean a thing to him. He just wanted us to spin our wheels to show us what he can do if he wants to really get us going. I looked in his eyes, Ash. I couldn't see anything because there was nothing to see. He's gone."

"What makes you think he's coming here? Why would he come here?"

"For you. Think, Ash, he can't get the yellow lollipop unless you give it up. Sallie isn't here to take it from you. That means he has to step out of character and snatch it himself. Sallie isn't here to approve or disapprove of what he does."

"Fanny, I'm having trouble with this. Do you think he's going to push me off the mountain?"

"Yes, Ash, I do."

"You should have called the police."

"Get real. He hasn't done anything. It's like last night all over again. The police can't do a thing, and you and I both know it."

"Is it your intention for the two of us to hide out here in this studio *forever*? You must realize I have a slight disability here."

"We need to get out of here. I'm taking you back down the mountain. Chue is taking his family, Mitzi, Nellie, and the kids as soon as Simon shows up. He's coming, Ash. I know he is."

"Then why aren't we leaving?"

"Because we'll pass him on the road and he'll just turn around and race us back down. Who do you think is going to go over the side, the car in front or the car in back?"

"You're saying my brother wants to kill me. I don't want to believe that."

"You damn well better believe it, Ash. With me here he gets two for the price of one. He said no one lives forever. The Simon I spoke to in the grocery store is not the Simon either one of us knows. That Simon is gone. He looks so normal. He functions, and that's what boggles my mind. He was clean-shaven, he'd had a haircut, he was creased and pressed. He even *smelled* good. Listen, Ash, I don't want to die. I have things to do and places to go. I want to enjoy my children and grandchildren. I don't have a plan if that's your next question."

"What?"

"I can't anticipate him. You have to do that. You know him. He's in a place I've never been. You've been there. You lived in that place. What will he do? How far will he go to get what he wants? What's his Achilles' heel? Does he have a breaking point? I don't know those things. Look. I might be wrong. Maybe I didn't read him right."

"No, you're not wrong. Simon has no Achilles' heel. He has no breaking point. He's always been totally fearless. He will do whatever it takes to get what he wants. He used to hold his breath until he turned blue and passed out. Mom was scared out of her wits when he'd do that. She'd hold him and rock him and croon to him and then she'd give him what he wanted. It didn't matter what it was. If he'd wanted my skin, she would have ripped the hide right off my body. He has no conscience. I always thought everyone had a conscience of one kind or another. I never met anyone who didn't, except Simon."

"I hear a car, Ash."

Ash's face turned as white as the shirt he was wearing.

"I told Chue to block the road with his vehicles and when Simon got out to walk, he was to push his car over the mountain at which point he'll head for town. It's you and me, Ash."

"It's always been you and me, Fanny."

"To a degree. I'm your legs, tell me what to do. I know this mountain like the back of my hand. I can lure him away from here and that will give you time to get in the van and partway down the mountain. I'll meet you at some point. I'll tell him you went with Chue and the kids. I think he'll believe that. He'll think I came here to get you to safety because I still love you. He wants to believe that."

"Do you, Fanny?"

Fanny made no pretense of not understanding. "A small part of me will always love you, Ash. I would never deny that. If you care about me at all, you'll do what I said."

"All right, Fanny. I'd change my shoes if I were you."

"God, yes. I think I left my mountain boots here. Ah, here they are." Fanny kicked off her heels and pulled on the boots. Just then, there was a tremendous crashing sound.

"Jesus! What the hell was *that?*"

Fanny's face was grim. *"That* was Simon's car going over the mountain."

"Until just this moment I've been thinking this was all a bad dream."

"You aren't going to have much time, Ash. I have to go now."

"Fanny—"

"Shhh," Fanny said, placing her finger on his lips. "Be careful, Ash."

"You too, Fanny."

Fanny closed the door behind her and walked up to the house and then around to the back patio. She climbed on the picnic table so she could see the road leading onto the driveway. The moment she saw Simon set foot on the driveway she shouted. "I'm back here, Simon. What do you want?"

"Where's Ash?"

"The least you could do is say hello." She started to walk away, toward the top of the ravine where her children had played Tarzan light-years ago. She knew he was following her. She could hear the frozen grass crackling under his feet.

"Where's Ash?"

"He left with Chue and the kids. They pushed your car over the side. It exploded. If you stand here, where I am, you can see Chue's truck going down the mountain. You really didn't think I was going to let you get hold of Ash, did you? Simon, Simon, what a fool you are. He's mine, Simon. I love him. You know that though, don't you? I'll never let you hurt him. I only married you to get even with Ash for fooling around with other women. I made a fool out of you. You need to run to Mama, Simon, and tell her what nasty old Fanny did. Mama will make it right, won't she?" Fanny taunted as she inched closer to the edge.

Fanny saw something spark in Simon's eyes. She fumbled in her pocket, brought out one of the lollipops she'd bought for Jake. "I have the yellow one, Simon. I love yellow. Ash loves yellow, too. Here, you can have the red one. Red tastes nasty."

Fanny went over the side, slipping and sliding as Simon bent to pick up the red lollipop. She continued to taunt him as her eyes searched out the overgrown path. The moment she heard the sound of Ash's van engine turning over, her fist shot in the air. "Oh yeah."

Fanny ran along the crest, her boots digging into the slippery pine needles as sweat dripped down her body. She forged ahead. Simon close behind.

Fanny could hear Simon's ripe curses as his leather-soled shoes failed to gain traction on the pine needles. She ran, her breathing ragged, her eyes scanning the terrain for familiar signs. She'd played here with her children hundreds of times, maybe thousands. Where were the markings? She realized they'd been gone for years because of the elements. She had to go on memory now. She had to get away from the crest and the tree line. Go down, go down, and climb back later. He won't be able to follow you, her mind shrieked.

Her lungs ready to burst, Fanny started the climb, slid backward, and rolled down until her back smacked into a scraggly pine tree. The wind knocked out of her, her eyes smarting with pain, Fanny scrambled up the embankment on her hands and knees, only to be driven back by a violent gust of wind. She felt something cold and wet on her face. Snow. It seemed darker now in and among the trees. Where was Simon? She moved then when she heard brush cracking behind her.

Eventually Fanny reached higher ground. The trees were thicker, the old trail overgrown and barely discernible. She weaved her way to the right and then to the left, past small mountains of boulders, through deadfalls and thickets.

Overhead snow clouds were black and ominous. Fanny stared up at the top of the ridge, unsure if she had the strength to make it to the top. The stinging snow slapped her in the face. She was chilled to the bone, yet sweat dripped from her forehead. She scrambled, her hands digging into the tree roots and vines that hampered her climb. She felt a wet stickiness and knew her hands were raw and bleeding. A low branch whacked her across the face, stunning her for a second.

Simon was closer, his curses more distinguishable. *Move!* Her subconscious ordered. *Faster!*

Fanny toiled higher and higher. She felt her strength leaving her as she fought for handholds with her bleeding hands. She felt cold, so very cold. She knew her body heat was leaving her. He was closer and gaining. She stumbled when she saw a break in the trees. Black clouds scudded over the treetops. She stumbled and fell again. She didn't allow herself the luxury of stopping. She climbed on all fours until she saw another break in the line of trees. She had to be near the top. The air felt more fresh and wet. If only she could see through the snow squall.

Flat ground. The shoulder of the road? *Yessss. Thank you, God.* She was on her feet, running, shouting Ash's name. She heard it carried over the mountain to return to her own ears. She ran, the snow pelting her. She heard the horn, saw the lights, heard Ash's voice, and then the van was alongside her, the door sliding open. She used the last of her strength to climb in. The door slid shut.

"Go! Go!" she managed to gasp. "He was right behind me."

"Fanny . . ."

"I'm all right. Just go, Ash."

"I've been up and down this goddamn mountain five times blowing the horn and yelling until I got hoarse. Are you sure you're okay?"

"I'm alive. You're alive. That means we're okay. The kids are okay. When it comes right down to it, that's all that matters."

"You're right, Fanny. You're always right. Now what? Do we go to the police?"

"And what will we tell them? That I lured him down the mountain and he chased me? He's still my husband. You're my ex-husband. Forget it, Ash."

"We have to do something. That was a gutsy thing you did back there."

"Yeah, and it was also stupid. Want a red lollipop?"

"You got some?"

"A whole pocketful. That's how I got him over the edge. I taunted him with the yellow ones. The things I do for you, Ash." Fanny rolled over, the lollipop stuck in her mouth.

"What you have to do with these lollipops is work up a good spit. I guess I owe you my life. If I had a dollar for every time you bailed me out of a jam, I'd be rich, Fanny. Thank you hardly seems to cover it."

Fanny didn't hear him. She was sound asleep.

A fierce protectiveness he'd never experienced before shot through Ash. "I'm going to kill that son of a bitch" he said through clenched teeth, "for what he's done to you."

It was five o'clock before Chue and his family were settled in one of Babylon's luxurious suites. Iris had stopped by, while Fanny slept, to take Jake and Polly home with her. Ash sat in the living room, one ear tuned to Fanny's bedroom in case she woke. His brain whirred faster than the chair he scurried around in. He'd just gotten off the phone with the police chief, who told him the exact same thing Fanny had told him. Now what was he to do? Hire extra security guards to protect his family? Fanny would probably nix that idea the minute he brought it up. He could call Clementine Fox and apprise her of the day's events.

Ash was about to make the call when the phone rang. He picked it up on the first ring. It was Marcus Reed. "Fanny's sleeping, Marcus. She had a rough day. Do you want me to have her call you when she wakes up?"

"Is anything wrong?"

"There's a lot wrong here."

"Is Fanny all right?"

"Yes and no. She's going to be stiff and sore for a while, but she's okay. I might as well tell you what happened. Fanny herself will probably tell you when she calls you back."

"Fanny doesn't discuss her family with me, Ash. I'd like to hear what happened. Perhaps I can help."

Ash told him.

"It sounds to me like your brother views himself as a law unto himself. Sometimes the legal system is slow to act, Ash. My advice, and I realize you didn't ask for it, would be to let Fanny's attorney handle the matter."

"I guess we think alike then. I was going to call her, but your call interrupted me. I'll do it now. Shall I have Fanny return your call?"

"I would appreciate it. Watch over her."

"I guess you haven't realized that it's Fanny who does that watching over thing. I'll do my best."

Ash stared at the phone in his hand so long the operator came on to tell him to hang up. He lowered the receiver onto the cradle.

The clock on the television told him Clementine Fox was gone for the day. Tomorrow morning would be soon enough to make the call.

Fanny slept on. Ash called Iris to check on Jake and Polly and was told they were fine. With nothing to do, he made coffee and laced it liberally with brandy. He spent an hour watching the evening news and another hour watching two game shows. He was about to make himself a sandwich when Fanny limped into the living room.

"Do you feel like you look?"

"Worse."

"How about some coffee and a sandwich?"

"I'd like that."

Fanny lowered herself gingerly onto the couch. "I think I need to start exercising more. Muscles I didn't even know I had hurt. Did you check on the kids, Ash?"

"They're fine. Iris said they were stringing popcorn. I think what she meant was they would string it if there was any left. Jake loves the fluffies that pop first. He knows the difference. Marcus Reed called. He wants you to call him back."

"Did he leave a number?"

"No."

"Then how can I call him back?" Fanny asked wearily.

"I guess he was too upset and forgot to leave it. I told him what happened."

"I wish you hadn't done that, Ash. This is family stuff, and I don't make a habit of talking about family matters to anyone but Bess and Billie."

"I didn't know that, Fanny. I'm sorry."

"It's okay. He'll call back. If he doesn't, he doesn't."

"It doesn't sound to me like you're in love."

"Ash, Marcus Reed is the least of my problems right now. Your brother is front and center, and we need to decide what we're going to do."

"He's going to sulk for a while. He'll fall back and regroup and come up with some other devious scheme to get at me."

"You realize you can't go back to the mountain, don't you?"

"I know that, Fanny. I can get a room if you think I'll cramp your style."

"Don't be ridiculous. I'm glad for the company. We need to stick together. I think we should both get restraining orders in the morning."

"I agree. That won't stop Simon, though. You realize we're just going through motions to make ourselves feel better."

"I don't care. I want a restraining order on the record."

"Then that's what we'll do. More coffee?"

"Sure. Bring some ice cream."

"What are we going to do tonight, Fanny?"

"I don't know about you, but I'm going to soak in a hot tub and then I'm going back to bed. You can make breakfast. Don't worry about Daisy. She has a pad by the front door for emergencies."

"Alone again," Ash grumbled.

"How does it feel, Ash?"

"Pretty damn shitty. Fanny, thanks for today."

Fanny nodded. "You would have done the same for me, wouldn't you?"

"Yeah. Yeah, Fanny, I would have."

"See you in the morning."

"Okay."

Simon Thornton walked around the house, his hands stuffed in his pockets. The wind whistled and howled, sending chills up and down his spine. Ash probably had warm clothes and boots in the house. He knew he needed to change before his wet clothes froze to his back. He was covered with snow from head to toe, his wet hair plastered to his head in frozen layers. A hot shower would be good. He let himself into the house by the back door, turned on the kitchen light. Everything was neat and tidy, like Ash himself. He wandered around, looking at things, touching things, whistling to himself as he did so.

He made his way up the steps to his old room—Jake's room now. Toys were scattered everywhere. He closed the door and entered Ash's room. It was still Ash's room. All his stuff was here. His commendations, his pictures hanging on the wall, Ash's past. A picture of Ash and Fanny sat on the dresser. He looked at it with clinical interest. A picture of Jake holding his fishing pole was on the night table. He studied it for a long time.

Ash had five children and three grandchildren. He had none. Ash had a family. He didn't have one because he'd been sterile all his life. Ash had everything.

Simon opened the dresser drawers. Everything was neatly aligned. The best of everything. He rummaged through everything just the way he had when he was a boy. The closet beckoned. He did the same thing, jerking suits and jackets off the hangers and dropping them on the floor. He kicked at the line of shoes on the floor. He spent an hour going through Ash's personal things he kept on the top shelf. There wasn't one thing in the closet he wanted to take with him. He felt cheated, disappointed that Ash didn't have anything worth taking.

He rummaged some more, found a heavy jacket, some corduroy pants and a sweater. Pushed far back in the closet was a pair of shearling-lined boots. He was in good shape for the walk down the mountain.

He headed for Ash's bathroom where he showered, shaved, and dressed. He dropped his wet towel on the floor. Ash hated a mess.

In the kitchen he made himself a ham sandwich. He peeled an orange and ate it. He left the peels and bread crumbs on the counter. He took one last look around the house before he returned to the living room where he zipped up his jacket. He reached for Ash's knit cap on the hat rack and pulled it down over his wet head.

The last thing he did before leaving the house was to light a cigarette. Before he snapped the lighter shut, he held it to the hem of the lace curtains on the front window.

From time to time on his walk down the mountain he turned to look back at Sunrise, watching the flames dancing high in the sky.

He whistled all the way down the mountain, the wind carrying the sound high and wide.

24

Fanny woke, a feeling of panic squeezing her chest. She felt the puffiness in her face, the skin stretching beyond its boundaries near her right eye. She moved her bruised body to see the clock. Two o'-clock. What was it that woke her? Not Daisy; she was sleeping peacefully at the bottom of the bed. Ash? Not Ash. Daisy would be prancing around if something was wrong where her ex-husband was concerned. Was the television on? Was Ash having a sleepless night? She listened. The apartment was tomb quiet.

Maybe her body had all the sleep it could handle for one night. She struggled to get up, her muscles protesting each movement, no matter how slight. It was a monumental effort to fit her arms into her robe, but she did it. Her slippers were nowhere in sight. She padded barefoot into the kitchen, Daisy behind her. She was relieved to see the blank screen on the television. Ash must be sleeping.

Fanny measured coffee into the wire basket, put the lid back on the coffeepot. She pressed the red button. She hated smoking before she brushed her teeth, but she fired up a cigarette anyway. Daisy circled her feet, panting and wagging her tail.

"It's not morning. I'm off schedule." Fanny reached inside the refrigerator and unwrapped three slices of cheese. She broke it up into pieces and dropped them into the little dog's bowl. "Something's wrong, Daisy. I can feel it in my bones. Everything bad happens in the dark of night," she muttered.

Fanny was on her second cup of coffee when she heard Ash's chair. She looked up. Daisy was sitting in his lap. "Is something wrong, Fanny?"

Fanny poured him a cup of coffee. "I don't know. I feel like there is. I woke up and had this feeling of panic. I suppose I could have been dreaming, but if I was, I don't remember what the dream was about. Maybe my body just had enough sleep. That happens sometimes. If it was the kids, someone would have called."

"Jesus, Fanny, I took the receiver off the hook. I didn't want it ringing all night to wake you. I forgot to hang it back up." His chair backed up, circled and returned a moment later. "I'm sorry, Fanny."

"I do that too, Ash. If something was *really* wrong, there would have been a knock on the door. Daisy would have alerted us." Both Ash and Fanny stared at the phone on the kitchen wall.

"Fanny, call the switchboard. You have an unlisted phone number now."

"I forgot about that." Fanny pressed the zero for operator. "Have there been any calls for Mr. Thornton or me this evening? Thank you." She shook her head. "I told you, Ash, it's just a feeling. After yesterday, I'm entitled to feel a little strange."

"How about some breakfast?"

"Bacon and eggs?"

"Sounds good."

Fanny was placing the bacon strips in the fry pan when a loud knock could be heard. Daisy raced to the door, the hair on the back of her neck on end, her tail between her legs. Fanny turned off the stove, her eyes locked with Ash's. "It's someone strange, someone she doesn't know. Her tail isn't wagging."

"Ask who it is before you open the door," Ash said.

"I'm not an idiot. Who is it?" Fanny called.

"Pete Wilson, Mrs. Thornton. Neal is with me."

Fanny opened the door and stood aside. Ash backed up his chair. "What's wrong?"

"There's a fire on your mountain. Is anyone up there?"

"No, we all came down yesterday. The house is empty. Is it the house or the mountain?"

"Our main concern was that people might be in the house. Three of my men are slogging through the snow as we speak. When the call came in, we sent out a truck, but the roads were too treacherous. They had to turn around and come back. What do you people do when the weather turns bad up there?"

"Chue takes care of it. He's here in town with his family. He sands, salts, and uses the ashes from the fireplaces. Ash, what should we do? How can there be a fire if it's snowing?" Ash shot her a disgusted look.

"Is Birch's Land Rover still in the garage?"

"I think so."

"I'm sorry, Mr. Thornton. We can attempt it again, but I don't hold out much hope. It's been burning for some time now. My guess is it's the house. The trees are wet and covered with snow. The wind is pretty fierce, and for the flames to be as high as they are whatever it is that's burning has a good start on us."

"I'll get dressed," Fanny said, limping her way to her room.

"Thanks, Pete. Do what you can." This last was said over his shoulder as Ash maneuvered his chair down the hallway. Daisy barked until the door closed behind the two men.

Twenty minutes later, Fanny was behind the wheel of the Land Rover, Ash in the passenger seat.

"Don't worry about my chair. There's a spare in the garage. I alternate the chairs. Chue charges the one not in use. The chair isn't important, Fanny."

"*He* wouldn't . . ."

"Yeah he would. Now look, Fanny, take it easy. I know you know the mountain, but snow changes everything."

"I know, Ash. Talk to me."

"You look pretty ugly, Fanny. You're going to have a shiner for about ten days. I wouldn't let Marcus Reed see you right now."

"That's just what I need to hear. If you can't say something nice, shut up."

"I thought you wanted me to talk. It's probably arson. Houses don't just burn for no reason. Simon did this. How are we going to prove it? There was no one on the mountain. He could sue our asses off if we make our feelings known."

"He was there, Ash, we both saw him. All you have to do is look at me to know there was some kind of confrontation."

"Big fucking deal. His car is at the bottom of the mountain. How do we explain that? The son of a bitch is liable to go after Chue. The word 'lie' isn't even in Chue's vocabulary. What you should have done was have Chue push his car to the side and take his keys."

"I should have done a lot of things, Ash. What if he had a spare tucked in his wallet? I never said I was thinking clearly. All I knew was I had to get to you before he did. Should have, could have, would have. What the hell difference does it make now anyway?"

"I'm trying to think ahead," Ash said defensively. "He'll lie low now for a little while. When we were kids and he'd pull one of his more outrageous stunts, he'd hide out in his room for days until everyone calmed down. My mother would coax him to come out on an hourly basis. She'd buy him junk, make sure we had his favorite foods, that kind of thing. She'd just be so damn relieved that he finally came out and smiled at her, she wouldn't do a damn thing except to swat me saying I instigated whatever it was he did."

"Goddammit, Ash, he burned down my house."

"That's not how he sees it, and we aren't sure it's the house. Simon thinks the house is mine now because I've been living there the past few years. Don't you get it, Fanny? He thinks it's *mine.* He's going by what he sees and hears. He's not going by instinct now. I think that's good where we're concerned. He's bound to make a mistake soon."

"Soon?" Fanny screeched. "Soon can translate to a very long time. Soon could be tomorrow."

She concentrated on her driving. It got more and more difficult.

"Chue's house is safe," Ash said as they passed it. "We should be thankful for that."

"Oh, Ash, look, it's gone," Fanny wailed as she brought the Land Rover to a stop at the end of the driveway.

"I need my chair, Fanny."

Fanny motioned to the three firemen. One of them trotted off to return with Ash's spare wheelchair.

"It was too far gone when we got here, ma'am. We couldn't save it."

Fanny nodded, tears trickling down her cheeks. "Take the Rover back to town. Mr. Thornton and I can stay in one of the cottages or the studio. It's the only way you'll get off the mountain."

Fanny watched the Rover back up and start down the mountain.

"It was just a house, Fanny. Pete's right, it can be rebuilt."

"It was more than a house, Ash. It was your mother's home, your home, my home. I raised the kids here. They're going to be devastated. It's so senseless, so *insane.*" Fanny's shoulders started to shake. She dropped to the ground in the snow, tears streaming down her cheeks.

All Ash could do was stare at the ruins and at his wife.

"Sallie liked to open the windows and watch the curtains billow. Birch used to hide from Sage in that little cubbyhole under the steps. Sage never caught on, so I guess it really was a secret place. Billie used to line up her paper dolls and that small sewing machine Sallie gave her on the dining-room table. She used to make a regular parade, and she'd talk to the dolls."

"Fanny, don't do this to yourself."

"Sunny would run up and down the steps a hundred times a day. Either she was chasing the twins, or they were chasing her. Now she can barely walk. I must have taken a thousand pictures of the kids on the steps. For some reason they always wanted to pose on the steps. The paint's still on the living-room carpet where Sage spilled it. I don't know why I never replaced it."

"Fanny—"

"The cradles Sallie gave us were in the attic. All the things I saved from our kids that I wanted to give to our grandchildren are gone now. I put everything in boxes and labeled them. Sallie's things were in the attic, too. Even stuff from your dad that Sallie saved. All Jake and Polly's stuff is gone, Ash. We can't ever get it back. It's just a pile of dirty ashes.

"Simon took away my past, Ash. He took away all my memories."

Ash's hand reached out to Fanny. He slid from the chair to sit in the snow next to her. "You still have the memories, Fanny. He can never steal those from you." He put his arm around her shoulder. Fanny leaned her head against him, tears blinding her.

"I loved this place, Ash. Sunny did too. It was so right for her to live here with the kids. This mountain used to rock with sound when their friends came up from town. I can't believe it's gone."

"We'll rebuild it, Fanny."

"It won't be the same. It won't feel the same. It won't smell the same."

"I used to love coming here on the weekends. The house always smelled like cinnamon and spice and celery. It never smelled like that when we were growing up. I think I hated it then. Maybe it was Simon I hated and not the house at all. That goddamn safe is still standing. Part of the second floor looks to be intact. Is there anything in the safe, Fanny?"

"Yeah, all kinds of stuff."

"You'll have to take it out."

"I know. Oh, Ash, Polly and Lexie will never get to know this place." Fanny's shoulders shook with the force of her sobs. "How are we going to tell Jake the house is gone? Losing his mother for months at a time is bad enough. How, Ash?"

"We'll handle it. We're the old guard, Fanny. You can rebuild this for the next generation. It's what you put into it, Fanny, that made Sunrise what it was. The good feelings I have in regard to Sunrise are because of you, not because of my mother and the time I spent here as a kid. Sunrise is you, Fanny. Mom knew that. That's why she left the mountain to you. She knew in her heart you'd make it into what she could never do. She was right to do what she did by leaving it to you. My ass is freezing, Fanny. Let's go down to the studio and get warm. We can come back later. It's going to smolder for days, so there's nothing we can do right now. It's going to be light soon."

"All right, Ash," Fanny said struggling to her feet. She struggled again as she tugged and shoved Ash into his chair. "Do you think, Ash, if it hadn't snowed, the mountain would be gone?"

"Yes. And that you could never rebuild. It would take a hundred years for new trees to grow to this splendor."

"Then we need to be grateful for that."

Three days later, when the steep mountain road was cleared, the fire marshal gave Fanny permission to walk through the rubble. She watched as the arson squad left in their specially equipped van with all their high-tech equipment. She wondered if they would ever be able to prove what had happened.

"Fanny, why are you torturing yourself. We should leave and come back in the spring."

"You're right, Ash. I just want to walk through to see if there's at least one thing that didn't burn. I have to clear out the safe, too. Chue is lending me his pickup truck. I'll need all the space in the back. I just hope it will hold everything."

"Wait, just a minute. What the hell's in that safe that we need the back of the pickup to haul it?"

"Cotton Easter's gold."

"Cotton Easter's gold," Ash said, a stupid look on his face.

"Yeah. He left it to your mother. It scared her. She left it to me. It scared me, too."

"How . . . how much is there?"

"At least a ton. I don't know. The shelves are full of it."

"The shelves are full of it. Fanny, what the hell does that mean?"

"It means I have to move it. Unless you have a better idea."

"Well . . . are you sure you aren't exaggerating?"

"Ash, come see for yourself. You can watch me move it. I'll back up the truck and just throw it in the back. It's in sacks."

"And you never told me?"

"No, I never told anyone. I never considered it mine even though Sallie said it was. For some reason I thought your mother would have told Simon, but she didn't. I was the only one who knew. I think . . .

and this is just my opinion, Ash . . . but I think she knew . . . wanted me to use it for Babylon. It wasn't anything she said in words. It was a feeling she gave me. She told me I would know what to do with it. She was so wrong. We'll have to decide what to do."

Fanny worked the combination. When she heard the desired click, she pulled, shoved and used her backside to move the massive door. Ash stared at the contents, speechless for the first time in his life. Fanny started to lug the sacks to the back of the truck.

At the end of her seventeenth trip, Ash found his voice. "What's all that other stuff?"

"Stocks, bonds, deeds. Sallie's stuff."

"Sallie's stuff."

"Ash, stop repeating everything I say."

"What would you be saying if you were in my place?"

Fanny leaned on the end of the pickup and lit a cigarette. "Ash, I never wanted the responsibility of all this. I told you. I never thought of it as mine. It belongs to you and Simon." She told him about Jake then. "That money wasn't mine either. I borrowed on it a dozen times. Once I outright used it. I always paid it back. It's in a mutual fund collecting something like a 15 percent return per year."

"And you never told me that either?"

"Nope."

"What else haven't you told me?"

"I think that about clears my conscience. I'd give Jake's money back, but I don't know who to give it to."

"Try the boys across the street. I bet you all the gold in that truck if you march across the street and ask any one of those five owners if they remember a Jake and a large amount of money disappearing, they'll own up."

"How will I know if they're telling the truth?"

"Let them tell you the story. It's like fishing, you throw out the line with some good bait and you wait to see if it's snatched up."

"I can do that. It's a princely sum of money."

"I'll just bet it is. Fanny, you never cease to amaze me."

"I'm going to take that as a compliment."

Fanny went back to work. Ash was bug-eyed as he continued to watch her.

"That's the last of it," Fanny said a long time later. "I think my back is breaking. I want to . . . to walk through. It will only take me a few minutes. Do you mind, Ash?"

"Not at all."

"The heater is on in the truck. Get in. I'll take your chair back to the garage."

The fierce protectiveness Ash felt toward Fanny surfaced again. "You look like a tired old dog, Fanny. Let it go."

"I feel like a tired old dog. I can't let it go. I have to . . . I have to do this. There might be something. I want something. I need to . . . walk away knowing there's one small thing left. I don't expect you to understand. I understand, and that's all that is important. I won't be long."

Ash rolled his window up. He rolled it down minutes later when he heard Fanny's joyous shout.

"Ash! Ash! I found Sallie's old desk! One of the legs is burned through. It's burned and scarred all over, but it's here. I can't get it down, though. Her slate board is here too."

Ash could feel his shoulders start to crumple. Great heart-wrenching sobs shook his body. Of all the things in the world to be saved, his mother's desk. The desk where she had toiled to become the woman she was.

Fanny climbed into the truck. "It's okay, Ash. We can rebuild Sunrise now. We have something that belongs here. It's probably the most important thing of all. I'll have Chue get it down, and I'll find the best furniture refinisher there is to restore it. I could still see her initials in the corner where she scratched them. S.C. for Sallie Coleman. I don't feel so bad now."

Ash's voice was choked when he said, "Fanny, what if I don't live long enough to see it finished?"

"Don't even think such a thing, Ash Thornton. I give you my personal word you will not only see it finished, you will live here again. I never broke a promise to you, did I?"

"No, Fanny, you never did. That's good enough for me. I feel like singing. Do you feel like singing, Fanny?"

"I feel like singing, Ash."

"Off we go into the wild blue yonder . . ."

Please God, don't make me a liar. Let me keep my promise. "Climbing high, into the sky . . ."

"I must be getting old, Charlie," Ash said to the bartender. "The noise is really getting to me. I don't think I ever saw so many people in one place in my whole life."

"It's the Christmas season and Mrs. Thornton's decorations. It's

going to be like this till after New Year's. Guess that mountain of
yours is pretty quiet, eh. Can I get you something to drink, Mr.
Thornton?"

"A ginger ale will be fine," Ash said, craning his neck to see his
grandson being led off by Billie and Thad Kingsley. He relaxed as
he reached out to accept the soft drink.

"There was a lady in here earlier looking for you, Mr. Thornton.
A real looker. She reminded me of someone, but I can't put my finger on it. She asked for you specifically. She came in right after the
doors opened. Did she find you?"

Ash shrugged. "Did she have a name, Charlie?"

"No. I just told her you were here somewhere. She said she'd find
you. The night's still young." Ash shrugged again. He lit a cigarette
as he continued to make small talk with the bartender and the customers lined up at the bar.

An hour later when the noise and the smoke started to bother him,
Ash steered his chair away from the bar and out to the floor. His eyes
raked the crowds for a sign of Fanny and Billie. He turned again
when he felt a light touch to his shoulder.

"Mr. Thornton?"

Ash looked up. Charlie was right, she was a looker. If this was
the woman asking for him earlier. "I'm Ash Thornton. Is there something I can do for you?"

"Is there someplace we can go where it's a little more quiet?" Her
voice was soft, cultured, almost musical.

"Follow me. I think my office might be a little more quiet. Have
we met before?"

"No. We should have, but no, we never met."

Charlie was right, she reminded him of someone. He said so. The
woman laughed, the sound as musical as her speaking voice. Ash
opened the door to his office, the chair whirring through the oversize opening. He turned so that he was facing her. "I'm afraid you
have the advantage. You know me, but I don't know you. Can I order
you a drink from the bar?"

"No thank you. I'm Ruby Thornton. I'm your sister. Half sister,
actually. The shocked look on your face tells me you didn't know
about me."

"Whoa," Ash said holding up his hand, palm out. "You can't just
waltz in here and drop something like that on me."

"Why not? Because it's Christmas? Because my mother and father kept my birth a secret? I know everything there is to know

about you and Simon. You two were the princes living in the castle and I was the scullery maid living in a brothel. My mother kept scrapbooks on you and Simon. My mother was Red Ruby, my father was your father. Does that explain why I look so much like Simon?"

"Now, hold on here," Ash blustered.

"My mother and our father made a deal. I guess it was the same kind of deal you made with Margaret Lassiter. I know about Jeff. My mother was in a position to know everything there is to know about the people in this town. She left a detailed diary when she died. I might publish it someday. Do you find it amusing that your mother and my mother were . . . ladies of the night? As well as friends."

"My father would have told me about you. He never kept anything from me."

"Like you told him about Margaret Lassiter. He knew though. My mother told him. I think he was a little more comfortable with his secret after that."

"Spit it out, what do you want?"

"My share."

"Of what?"

"Everything. I think I'm entitled. A third of your parents' estate. I think that's fair. Your mother knew about me. They sent me to Boston to school. I came home summers when mother closed the . . . business. I was never permitted to come home on the holidays. One year my mother would visit me at Christmas and the next year it would be my father. It was the same with Easter and Thanksgiving. I wanted to know you and Simon so bad. I wanted to tell the world I had two big brothers, but I wasn't allowed to do that. I stayed on in Boston, got my master's and my Ph.D. Your mother didn't like that one little bit. Your mother was so beautiful compared to my own mother. I used to pretend she was my mother. I knew if she'd been my mother, she wouldn't have kept me hidden. I cried myself to sleep for many years."

"How old are you?"

The trilling laughter seemed to tickle the walls. Ash found himself shivering. "Does it matter? Here, this is what you probably want to see. Everything's in it, my birth certificate, your father's will, Mom's will. The contract Dad had with Mom. I inherited Thornton Chickens, did you know that?"

Ash cleared his throat. "No, I didn't know that."

"I want a third of everything in that old iron safe on the mountain."

"I'm afraid that's impossible. My mother left all that, including the mountain, to Fanny, my ex-wife. My father died first, leaving everything to my mother. She in turn made a new will and did what she wanted."

"My father made a later will. There's a copy of it in the envelope."

"Why are you coming forward now? Why do you want to rake up the past? Are you in this . . . scheme with Simon? It would be just like him to pull something like this."

"No, I haven't talked to Simon. I came to you because you were the older brother. My mother died last year. I've spent the year trying to decide what to do. I don't know if you'll understand this or not, but . . . I always wanted a real family. Everyone at school had nice normal families. I made one up. I had two handsome older brothers who were flying aces during the war. My mother was beautiful, warm, and gentle, and my father was a bookish professor who adored me. I told everyone they traveled all over the world and that's why they were never at school on visitors' day. He did, you know. Adore me, I mean. He used to send the most wonderful, creative presents, and he'd always sign the card, Love, Daddy. He was truly proud of my accomplishments. Much the way he was of yours."

Ash scanned the papers in his lap. She appeared to be telling the truth. A chill ran down his spine. Fanny said her life paralleled his mother's in so many ways. Now, here he was, experiencing the exact same thing. The chill seemed to settle around his lower extremities, causing a numb feeling in his legs. The urge to smash something was so great he gripped the arms of the wheelchair, his knuckles as white as the shirt he was wearing.

"Well?"

"Well what? I'll speak to my lawyer. I'm sure something can be worked out. If my mother wanted you to share in Thornton Enterprises, she would have done so. It was her decision, not mine and not Simon's. Dad . . . the lawyers can handle it. I think you'll have a fight on your hands."

"I'm prepared for that. Understand something, all of this"—Ruby said waving her hands about—"is through no fault of mine. Our father, your mother, my mother, they did this. You might not like it, but you are my family. I'd like to get to know my nieces and nephews. I'd like to believe they would want to meet an aunt if they knew they had one. My mother was a whore, your mother was a whore, and yet we shared the same father. This is not about money."

"The hell it isn't. Everything, when it comes down to the bottom line, is about money. I busted my ass for this casino, and I'm not about to give it up to you or anyone else, sister or not. You got Thornton Chickens? You didn't see me showing up on your doorstep making a claim. Another thing, whatever my father had came from my mother. He was a schoolteacher, and he didn't have a pot to piss in. My mother was the one with the money. There's no court in this land that will give you what's ours. And, it is ours, make no mistake. Have your attorney get in touch with Clementine Fox. She represents this family," Ash lied. Clem could find him a lawyer. Since she represented Fanny it would be a conflict of interest for her to step in where Ruby Thornton was concerned. Ash thought he saw a flicker of fear in the gray eyes at the mention of Clem's name. If it was fear, it was gone a second later.

"Oh, there is one other little thing," Ash said. "My mother pulled your mother out of the gutter. She set her up at the ranch. She did right by Red and we can prove it. This town takes care of its own."

"So I've heard. But I have the book. You know the book I'm talking about. All those upstanding citizens from here, there, and yonder. Does that fall under this town taking care of its own?"

"I wouldn't mess with that if I were you. Red was an honorable woman, and she would never have done what you just said. That red book was for her eyes only, and you damn well know it. You could ruin a lot of families if you do something foolish."

"Then those *families* aren't worth much, are they? The key word here is family, is that right?"

"That's right. I wish you had just walked in here and said you were my sister. I always wanted a sister. In his own way I think Simon did, too. This family has always been generous to a fault. We're all givers. I wasn't for a long time. I had to learn how to do that. We don't bow or bend to pressure and intimidation. You don't appear to be a stupid woman."

"I'm not. I just want what's mine."

"Well, lady, you're shit out of luck because you ain't gettin' one cent from this family."

"Ash . . . Mr. Thornton . . . please, I want you to understand where I'm coming from. You're my family. I have a right to be here. I have as much right to all of this," she said, waving her arms about, "as you do. Legally and morally."

"That's where you're wrong. You were right about Jeffrey Lassiter. Yes, he is my son. He doesn't bear my name, but I did take responsibility for him. I will never deny him in a court of law. My father . . . my father rubbed you under my mother's nose. That's the only way he could make up for her not loving him. My father used you. He didn't love your mother any more than I loved Margaret Lassiter. It never should have happened, but it did. I dealt with it. You have to deal with it, too."

"My case is different. Our father loved me. My mother loved him. I don't know if Philip loved her or not. There were times when I thought he did. I do know they were wonderful friends for many, many years. I think a jury and a court of law will make the right decision."

"I doubt it. There's not a person in this town who isn't aware of where my mother's money came from. My father, your father, had nothing to do with it. It was my mother's decision on how to divide her money at the end. She was more than generous in giving your mother a million-dollar company. As long as you own that company, you will never want for anything. It will support you and provide a very luxurious lifestyle. The ranch is yours, too, thanks to my mother. A jury will view you as a greedy bitch trying to put the bite on the Thorntons."

"I'm a Thornton, too."

"In this town you're from the other side of the tracks. I will not allow you to come in here and disturb our lives. For a woman as educated as you say you are, you must realize how foolish this is. What I'm trying to say without being cruel is you don't belong here. We have our lives; you have yours. If it's recognition you want, I'll tell the world I have a sister. That's as far as I'm willing to go."

"That isn't far enough."

"Let me ask you a question. Should you prevail, which you won't, then what? Do you honestly think any one of us will welcome you after a court case like the kind you're talking about? You said it wasn't about money. I guess that was a lie, right?"

"No, it isn't about money. Didn't you hear anything I said? How would you have liked to grow up like I did? If you were me, what would you do? Be honest?"

"Sit down, Miss Thornton, and let me tell you a story. I'm going to be so brutally honest with you you are going to run out of here in tears."

Ash talked and Ruby Thornton listened. When he finally wound down, Ruby offered him a lace-edged hanky. "All right, Mr. Thornton. You made your point."

"I want to know what that means."

"It means I'm going to walk away from here. It means I'm giving up any dream of belonging to a family, my family. It means I'm sorry we never got to know one another. To me you will always be the prince, and I'll always be the scullery maid. Obviously there was a lot my parents didn't share with me. My heart doesn't understand that you aren't the family I always wanted. I'm sorry your time has come. I want to believe we could have been friends had we been allowed to do so. I'm sorry I came here. I really am."

"I'm sorry, too. For the circumstances. I don't know if we could have been friends or not. I wasn't the same person back then that I am today. I'm sorry they messed up your life the same way they messed up mine and Simon's. Do you want me to tell the family about you or do you want to . . . what?"

"Let's pretend I never came here."

"Simon?"

"He doesn't sound like someone I'd ever want to know. You now, you're another story all together. I think I would have given you a run for your money. I'll be at the ranch if you . . . ever . . . you know."

"C'mere," Ash said motioning for her to drop to her knees. "Look at me, Ruby Thornton. You got the best of the deal. You may never believe it, but you did. Your mother and father loved you. They did what they thought was best for you. It was the best, unlike what our parents did to us. All things considered, you're the lucky one. You'll realize that when you think about this night in the days to come."

"Perhaps. Families aren't all black or white. I guess that's what makes them a family. I want you to know I adored Dad. I loved my mother, too. I used to count the hours and the minutes when it was time for them to visit me at school. I should be leaving. It's late and I've taken up enough of your time." Ruby stood and held out her hand.

Ash shook his head as he struggled to get out of his chair. He wrapped his arms around her before he gave her a kiss on the cheek. "Have a good life, Ruby Thornton, and don't have any regrets."

"Ash! I've been looking all over for you. Oh, I'm sorry, I didn't know you had company."

"She isn't company, Fanny. This is my sister, Ruby Thornton. Ruby, this is my ex-wife and my grandson Jake."

Fanny's jaw dropped as she held out her hand. Jake ran to his grandfather and climbed on his lap. "Santy Claus is wunnerful. He gave me this and this and this . . ."

"It's nice to meet you, Fanny. Good night everyone. Have a nice holiday."

When the door closed behind Ruby, Ash said, "She's my father's daughter. Red Ruby was her mother. Mom knew. We won't talk about this again. It's what it is and that's the end of it."

"I see."

Ash smiled. "No, you don't. That's okay, Fanny. She looks like both me and Simon, don't you think?"

"Ah, yes."

"So, is Jake ready to call it a night?"

"I don't know about him but I certainly am. You should take him up, Ash, unless you want me to do it."

"No, I'll do it. He'll probably be asleep before we get out of the elevator."

"Ash . . ."

"There isn't a problem, Fanny. Don't look for one, okay?"

"All right, Ash. I'll be up in a little while."

"Life goes on, Fanny."

"Yes, it does."

"Another year is almost gone," Fanny said to her ex-husband. "Tomorrow will be the first day of the new year. Are you looking forward to spending New Year's Eve with Sage and Iris?"

"I sure am. I wish you could come along."

"Ash, this is the busiest night of the year. I'll come by in the morning. Iris said she's making a brunch. I'm so excited that Sunny has a pass to leave the grounds. And, she's bringing a guest. I was hoping Birch would make it home, but I guess we need to be grateful for all the good things that have happened this past year. It doesn't pay to dwell on the bad."

"I gotta get going. Jake can tell time now, and I promised to be there by six. If he calls, tell him I'm on the way. Happy New Year, Fanny."

"Are you okay, Ash? You look a little flushed to me."

"It's the excitement of seeing Jake. He said he made me a present. That means it's something for him with my name on it. I'll see you tomorrow."

"Give everyone my love and kiss the kids for me."

"Will do."

Fanny rode the elevator down to the main floor. It wasn't her imagination. Ash was flushed, and his eyes were glassy. She called Iris from the phone on the bar to tell her to watch over Ash. Sage came on the phone. "Happy New Year, Mom."

"The same to you, Sage. Listen, I don't think your father is feeling all that well. It could be nothing. Then again, it could be something."

"I'll watch him, Mom. Bess and John are coming for brunch tomorrow, so we can have John give him a once-over."

"I'll see you tomorrow."

"Okay, Mom."

Fanny wandered into the Harem Lounge fifteen minutes before midnight. She sat down at one of the tables with a cup of coffee. Suddenly she wanted to cry. She had spent so many holidays alone. One more shouldn't make a difference, but it was. She could feel her eyes starting to burn.

"I seem to recall you sitting at this same exact table eons ago. Happy New Year, Fanny."

"Marcus! Oh, Marcus, it's so good to see you. I was just sitting here feeling sorry for myself. I was about ready to cry."

"No date of mine cries on New Year's Eve."

Fanny smiled. "Are we having a date? You didn't call."

"I have an excuse. I spent the last two days sitting in an airport in New York. They had a raging blizzard. All the flights were canceled and the phones were down. All I did was eat greasy food."

"I feel sorry for you, Marcus."

"No, you don't. Not even a little bit. I'm sorry I couldn't spend Christmas with you. Someday, Fanny, you and I should go to Australia. By the way, I have a whole week off. What kind of plans do you have and is it possible to break them?"

"I don't really have any plans. I do have one meeting with an architect and a contractor the day after New Year's. I'm free the rest of the week unless Ash gets sick. Would you like to go with me to brunch tomorrow at Sage and Iris's house?"

"I'd love to. Fanny, I am so sorry about your house on the mountain. Have there been any new developments where Simon is concerned?"

"No. The lawyers are still wrangling. Three minutes, Marcus! I have to get out to the floor." Marcus allowed his hand to be taken. They reached the main floor just as the customers started to chant the countdown.

"Three! Two! One! Happy New Year!" the boisterous crowd shouted.

Fanny lost herself in Marcus's arms as he kissed her. When he broke away, Fanny said, "Oh my, do that again."

Marcus pretended to take a great gulp of air before his lips found hers a second time. "I can do better without a crowd watching me."

"How do you think you'd do with just one little tiny dog in attendance?"

"Steam will ooze out from under your door."

"Uh-huh," was all Fanny could think of to say.

"When do you think you'll be going upstairs?" Fanny smiled at the way Marcus's eyes crinkled at the corners when he tried to be serious.

"How about right now?"

"You are a woman after my own heart. Do you remember what I told you about kissing?"

"That it leads to other things?"

"Uh-huh."

"I'm ready for those other things."

"Why are we still standing here then?"

"I thought you wanted to talk it to death."

"I don't, Fanny."

"Neither do I. Follow me, Mr. Reed."

"Lead the way, Miz Thornton."

She did.

Fanny rolled over, her naked body slick with sweat. She leaned up on one elbow. "I want you to know I have never been this satisfied in my entire life."

"Should I consider that a testimonial?"

"If I was in your place, I would." Fanny fell back against the pillows. "I'm surprised Ash never put mirrors on the ceiling. I wonder what that would be like, making love under a ceiling of mirrors. You'd be able to see *everything*. From every angle."

Marcus's fists pounded the mattress as he howled with laughter. "This is just an opinion mind you, but I would think both parties would be too busy to look. Stop and think about it. If you kept risking glances overhead everything would be out of sync."

"That's probably why Ash never did it."

"Do you always talk this much?" Marcus teased.

"Would you rather I did other things?"

"That's a topic worthy of discussion."

"Would you like me to expound on it?"

"Hell no. Show me."

Fanny shifted her body until she was on top of Marcus. Her hungry mouth searched for his, his fiery body heating up her flesh until she thought she would burst into flames.

They tore at each other, each of them seeking that which the other could surrender. There on the satin coverlet, they devoured each other with feverish lips and grasping fingers, just as they had done twice before.

Imperceptibly, Marcus's embrace tightened. Fanny smiled and stared into dark eyes that she later swore mirrored her soul. Once again hungry mouths searched, found, and conquered. He held her close, devouring her with his wet, slick body that glistened in the dim light on the nightstand. Gently he nuzzled her neck before he released her to the softness of the pillows.

"I can't think of anything more pleasurable than sleeping in your arms, Marcus. Why did we wait so long?" Fanny asked sleepily.

Marcus shifted his weight. "I guess we both had our reasons." His voice was as sleepy-sounding as Fanny's.

"Will you be here when I wake up?"

"A bomb couldn't get me out of here. Why do you ask?"

"Everyone leaves me. Sometimes I think I'm not meant to be loved. I don't want to feel that way with you."

"That's one thing you don't ever have to worry about. I want to marry you, Fanny. I want us to grow old together. I want to love you forever and ever and I want you to love me in the same way. Is it possible for that to happen?"

"Oh, yes. Yes, yes, yes. The first moment I'm free."

They slept, their arms wrapped tightly around each other, each secure in the knowledge they would awaken together.

Over coffee and toast in the morning Fanny and Marcus stared at one another, wonder in their eyes. "When will you be free?"

"Soon, I hope. When are you going to settle down here?"

"The exact moment you're free."

Elbows propped on the table, chin in her hands, Fanny said, "I love you, Marcus Reed."

Marcus propped his elbows on the table as he dropped his chin into his hands. "I love you, Fanny Thornton."

"This is a gambling town, so what do you think the odds are of us living happily ever after?"

"Very good."

"And if something goes awry with my divorce?"

"If that happens, we'll deal with it then. I have something for you. Before I give it to you, I want to explain what it means to me."

"Marcus, I'm not a person who expects or requires presents. I'm one of those card people, you know, the message is more important than the present."

"I understood that about you the first time I met you. Wait here. I'll be back in a minute." He was as good as his word, returning with a small box clutched in his hand. "This belonged to my mother. My father worked three jobs to pay for it. That was a long time ago. It cost $12.98. My mother wore it until the day she died. If you look closely, you can *almost* see the diamond. My three sisters didn't want it. They wanted those big solitaires. My father gave it to me. The box is tattered and torn. I don't think it came with the ring, but I'm not sure. When it's time for me to put a ring on your finger, will you be insulted if I gave you this one?"

"Oh, Marcus, not at all. You're wrong though. If I squint, I can see the diamond clearly. I'm honored that you want to give me this. I'll treasure it as much as your mother did."

Marcus stared at Fanny for a long time before he stuck the box back into his jacket pocket. He knew she meant every word she said.

"Happy New Year, Marcus."

"Happy New Year, Fanny."

25

Fanny picked up the phone on the third ring to hear Marcus Reed's excited voice. "I found Jake, Fanny! What I mean is I found out who he is and where he's from. I've been on this damn phone for almost four hours, but I now have substantial information."

"Is he alive? He can't be. Where? Can we go there?"

"His name was Jake Garrety and he died ten years ago. I know the cemetery in California where he's buried. He wasn't married, but he had a lot of female friends. They were all . . . ladies of the evening.

Two are in some kind of retirement village and three are in nursing homes. They're all in their late seventies. I have addresses if you want to visit."

"I do. What about those guys he traveled with?"

"They're all gone, Fanny. He was a courier. He always carried large sums of money and always used public transportation. I guess it was a cover. By the way, how is Ash?"

"He's doing nicely. He leaves the hospital today. It's a good thing we insisted he go in or he'd have pneumonia by now. I wish he wasn't so stubborn sometimes. John and Bess want him to stay a week with them, so John can monitor him hourly. John always takes the first week of the new year off. To get ready for the year ahead is how he explains it. Iris and Sage live around the block, so she can take the kids to see Ash every day. He lives for those kids."

"Any news from the architect or the contractor?"

"They'll be ready to start building in four weeks. They understand the . . . urgency. The contractor assured me everything would be done in four and a half months, maybe three. He has no other projects on hand, so there's every chance it will actually be finished by the middle of June. It has to be, Marcus, I promised Ash. Where are you calling me from?"

"In my car on my mobile phone. I've been looking for a house."

"How wonderful! Any luck?"

"One or two I'd like you to look at. When we get back from California. Any developments where Simon is concerned?"

"No, and I'm starting to get angry. I want it over. I called Clementine this morning, and she said he's holding tight. What he did, Marcus, was lend me money. I insisted on signing a note because I'm an honorable person. When I paid him back, he didn't give me back the notes. He's saying I still owe him millions of dollars. He handled my financial affairs, so I didn't question anything. He pulled some kind of deal with Sunny's Togs. I told him to sell the company and he said he did, but he didn't. Then he gave it back to me as a present. There were millions in that transaction alone. It's my own fault. I was so naively stupid I couldn't see straight where he was concerned. He's willing to forgive the debts if we turn over Babylon. Ash was right, Simon's as slick as they come. Clementine is looking for the paper trail. She'll find it because I paid him back. She said he's getting cocky and overconfident, and that leads to mistakes. He called the hospital several times to check on Ash. I guess he thought this was it. I'm having a hard time with this, Marcus. Let's talk about something else."

"When can you be ready to leave?"

"If we're driving, right now. If we're flying, one hour from now."

"We're driving. We can be in San Diego before dinner. I'll meet you in the front. Bring Daisy."

"She loves going in the car. I'm on my way downstairs right now." Fanny knew she had at least ten minutes. She used the time to call Ash, Bess, and Sage to tell them where she was going. She walked through the doors, Daisy in her arms, just as Marcus pulled his car to the curb.

"Marcus, I am so excited. At long last I can repay Jake's money. That money has been a burden on my back for so long. I have my checkbook with me."

"Fanny, the money didn't belong to Jake."

"Do you know who it did belong to?"

"Not exactly. You know what things were like here back then. It could have been anyone. It was such a large amount my thinking is it would have belonged to a *select* group."

"Can you be more specific?"

"No."

"Then the ladies of the evening get it. I think Jake would approve."

Marcus burst out laughing. "I second the decision. You know, I'm actually looking forward to this little adventure."

There was a lilt in Fanny's voice when she said, "Me too."

"There it is, Restful Palms. It would be nice if the owners had planted at least one palm tree," Marcus said.

"It's so shabby and dismal-looking," Fanny murmured. Daisy hopped from her arms to run to the door.

"Let's get to it," Marcus said. "According to my notes, Lola, Pearl, and Gertie are in residence. You ready, Fanny?"

"Yes."

The lobby was clean but shabby. The smell of Pine Sol and something Fanny couldn't define, assailed her nostrils. Daisy started to bark. The lobby chairs were covered in orange plastic. Tired-looking plants in need of water stood in the corners. Pictures of movie stars hung on the walls. Marcus marched up to the desk. "We'd like to see Lola, Pearl, and Gertie."

The receptionist allowed her jaw to drop. She recovered and said, "Who should I say is calling?"

"Jake Garrety's friends," Fanny chirped.

"Wait here."

"I'm not sitting in those orange chairs." Marcus guffawed.

"You think this is funny, don't you?" Fanny hissed.

"Yes I do."

Fanny perched on the edge of one of the orange chairs. Thirty minutes later she said, "What's taking them so long?"

"They're probably *getting ready.*" Marcus erupted into laughter again.

"For what?"

"God only knows. I hear footsteps."

Fanny wished for sunglasses. Daisy barked. Marcus sat down on one of the orange chairs.

They looked like triplets. Resplendent in various shades of satin with matching shoes, they teetered forward, their feather boas swinging in the breeze they created. Their sparse hair was frizzed and adorned with gaudy clips. Robin's egg blue eye shadow covered their wrinkly eyelids. Outrageous false eyelashes clung precariously to their own skimpy lashes. It was easy to tell their touch was less than steady with the way their rouge and bright red lipstick had been applied.

Marcus stared at the movie stars on the wall. Daisy continued to bark.

Fanny cleared her throat. "Ah, ladies, I'm Fanny Thornton, and this man is Marcus Reed. This is Daisy. She's my dog."

"We're charmed," Pearl, the one in the middle said.

"We purely are. Charmed," Lola said.

"Ladies, Marcus and I came here today to ask you if you'd . . . we'd like to do something nice for you in Jake's memory. We thought . . . if you aren't happy here we could get you a house with a garden and maybe a pet or two. A housekeeper of course and someone to mow the lawn, that kind of thing. We'd furnish it, too. Do you think you would like something like that?"

"You say you want to do this for us in Jake's memory?"

Fanny nodded. "New clothes, whatever you want."

"Did Jake ask you to do this for us? Did he name us in his will?"

"Ah . . . yes, in a manner of speaking. It . . . was left up to me."

"Forever and ever?" Lola asked, her eyes filling with tears.

Fanny's voice was soft and gentle when she said, "Forever and ever. If you have other friends here who would like to go with you, it's okay. We can get a big house with lots of bedrooms."

"And we won't have to worry about anything ever again?" Tears rolled down Lola's cheeks. "I'd like a yellow cat."

"A yellow cat's good."

"Can you get us a housekeeper who knows how to make corn bread? I love real corn bread. Will she cook what we tell her?"

"Absolutely," Fanny said.

The three women huddled, their whispers loud.

"We'd like a front porch. With screens."

"Okay. Anything else?"

"One of those big television sets so we can watch baseball games. A piano."

"You got it. Make a list. We'll be sure to get you everything you want. Here's my business card and my home phone number. I think this might take a month or so."

"We have a lot of time. Can we join the Literary Guild?"

"I'll enroll you myself. You can order as many books as you want."

"We accept," the three women said in unison.

Fanny held out her hand. The women pumped it vigorously. Everyone smiled, including Marcus. Daisy sniffed at the spike-heeled shoes.

"It was nice meeting you all." Marcus nodded as he too offered his hand.

"Where is Jake buried, do you know?" Pearl asked. "If it isn't too far, we'd like to maybe visit."

"I'll arrange it, ladies," Marcus said.

"We'll be in touch. Work on your lists and if anything else comes to you, call me and we'll take care of it."

The women nodded. "Any friend of Jake's is a friend of ours," the ladies said.

"You'll be hearing from us," Fanny said.

Fanny watched as the women teetered toward the door in their spike-heeled satin shoes. At the door they turned and flicked their boas. Fanny waved.

"We can do this, can't we, Marcus?"

"For you, Fanny, anything."

"It's kind of nice, isn't it? They went to so much effort to dress up for us. You know they don't get any visitors. Everyone's forgotten them. That's not right. They aren't giving up on life. I like that kind of spirit, and I don't care what they did for a living. All they want is recognition and attention. If it's in our power to give it to them, then we should do it. It's Jake's legacy. Marcus, I want to visit at some point in time when they're settled in."

"Anytime you want, Fanny."

"You're sweet to do this with me, Marcus."

"That's because I'm a sweet guy."

"That you are. I wish I had met you thirty years ago."

"Everything happens for a reason."

"I know. Sometimes I just want to know the why of it all."

"Let's finish taking care of business here so I can get you back home. I know you're worried about Ash."

"How do you know that?"

"I know, Fanny."

"And you don't mind? My concern for Ash doesn't bother you?"

"If you weren't concerned, it would bother me. He is the father of your children. Whatever came before, Fanny, isn't my business. Where your family is concerned, I will never interfere. I'll consider it an honor if you allow me to be part of it."

"Someone else said that to me once and it was a lie."

"I'm not Simon, Fanny."

"Thank God for that."

Clementine Fox and Fanny Thornton stepped from the elevator into the foyer of the law offices of St. Clare, Raddison, and Raddison. Subdued lighting, rich paneling, and marble floors greeted them.

The receptionist looked up as Clementine Fox sailed past her circular mahogany desk, Fanny in her wake. She looked like she was about to say something, then changed her mind as the Silver Fox, resplendent in floor-length sable, strode past her. She did manage to press Jason St. Clare's call button with the tip of her long manicured nail.

Both Simon and his attorney were standing when Clementine and Fanny walked into the office. Fanny inclined her head at the introduction. She did her best to avoid looking at Simon, who was smiling affably. Fanny felt her stomach muscles start to flutter. Simon looked like he was holding a straight flush. She wished she knew what kind of hand Clementine held.

This was an unexpected meeting she hadn't planned on. Clementine had called her at five minutes past nine and said the meeting was scheduled for ten-fifteen. "Consider it a belated Christmas present." Fanny took that to mean the Silver Fox held a hand of winning cards.

Fanny accepted a cup of coffee and lit a cigarette as the two attorneys exchanged pleasantries. They moved off to the far end of the table, their voices hushed.

"How are you, *Fanny?*"

"Does it matter, Simon? I don't understand why you're doing this. I was such a fool to think you were someone I wanted to spend the rest of my life with. You're worse than Ash ever was. If your mother is watching over you, she must be beside herself at what you're doing. When this divorce is final, Simon, I'm getting married."

Simon uncrossed his legs. He stared at Fanny for a long moment. "I always knew you'd go back to Ash. That's just like you, Fanny, to marry a dying man." He was agitated now, hunching and unhunching his shoulders.

Let him think what he wants to think. He's nervous now. He didn't expect me to say what I just said.

Clementine and Jason St. Clare sat down. Simon focused his gaze on his attorney's face. Fanny lit another cigarette as both lawyers opened their briefcases.

"I called this meeting, Mr. Thornton, so that we could have some face-to-face dialogue. Before things go any further, either you or Mrs. Thornton might wish to rethink your positions. I would like to say at this time, and Mr. St. Clare agrees with me, that it's very hard to hide things today with all the high-tech equipment at one's disposal. There's always a paper trail to be found. Subpoenas for Internal Revenue tax documents are standard fare these days. I've found, haven't you, Jason, that when a person is willing to pay out large sums of money to buy information that the term 'money talks and losers walk' is more than appropriate, especially in a situation like we have here in front of us. Does anyone have anything to say?"

Simon sat stone-faced. Fanny sipped at her cool coffee. She shrugged.

"Let's see what you got, Fox." St. Clare said.

"Everything I told you I had. My client does not owe your client one red cent. This is the proof. Mr. Thornton's friend and confidant . . . I believe his name was Malcolm something or other . . . found himself in need of a cabin cruiser which, by the way, sleeps six. He said he would give serious thought to naming his boat the *Silver Fox*. I found him to be a very nice man. Very *chatty*. Your buddy sold you out, Mr. Thornton, for sixty-five grand."

"Simon . . . why don't we go into one of the other offices and . . . *talk*."

When Fanny was alone with her attorney, Clementine said, "How badly do you want this divorce?"

"I don't want to be married to Simon one minute longer than I have to be. Does that answer your question?"

"Your husband wants one half of all your assets *and* Babylon. Those are his conditions to the divorce if we take away the debts he says you owe. That means half of your clothing business, half of everything you have in brokerage houses, and the bank."

"Fine. Not Babylon. Let him build his own damn casino. He has the money. I will not allow him to take Ash's casino."

"Then there's no divorce."

"Okay, no divorce. Draw up whatever papers are necessary and I'll sign them. I'm out of here, Clementine. I can't stand to be in the same room with Simon."

"Fanny, you don't understand. If there's no divorce, you don't pay him anything. Your husband doesn't care if there's a divorce or not. All he wants is the casino."

"I told him I was getting married when the divorce was final. He assumes I'm planning on marrying Ash. I didn't bother correcting him."

"I see," Clementine said. Her voice was thoughtful as she stared at Fanny. "Would you have any objection to my . . . planting a few seeds . . . of discomfort?"

"You can plant a whole garden for all I care. You know where to reach me."

Clementine finished packing her briefcase just as Simon and his attorney walked into the conference room. "No dice, gentlemen. Mrs. Thornton said she doesn't much care one way or the other if the divorce goes through. She's just so happy that her first husband's health has improved to the extent he's prepared to take over his duties at the casino. They're planning on living together in the penthouse. Can you imagine, Jason, being at death's door, staring at the great beyond, and then you get a cold and are hospitalized and boom, you get a clean bill of health? I guess The Emperor is going to reign again. That must make you very happy, Mr. Thornton, Ash being your brother and all."

"Don't answer that, Simon. She's baiting you. Enough, counselor."

"Ah, Jason, did I rain on your parade today? Look at it this way. Today it was just a little-bitty drizzle. Wait for the downpour. It's coming."

"What the hell is that supposed to mean, Clementine?"

"Jason, Jason, Jason, you don't really expect me to answer that now, do you? Wide-eyed wonder does not become you."

Clementine extended her hand in Simon's direction. "No hard feelings, Mr. Thornton, but you are one sorry son of a bitch." Palms flat on the conference table, Clementine leaned over, Jason St. Clare ogling her cleavage. "I'm gonna get you, Mr. Thornton. When I do, it will all be legal. That's a promise. Tell him, Jason, that I've never broken a promise in my life. And tell him what I hate more than anything in this world."

Jason St. Clare's voice was a low monotone when he said, "Miss Fox never broke a promise in her life. The one thing she hates in this life more than anything else is a man who tries to screw over a woman in a divorce case."

"And the bottom line, Jason."

St. Clare's voice dropped to an even more boring tone when he said, "Miss Fox has no scruples and no conscience."

"There you go. I knew you'd get it right. Good day, gentlemen."

The Silver Fox laughed all the way down in the elevator. She made one call on her car phone as she drove away. The message was short, concise: "He refuses to cooperate."

Fanny returned to the penthouse, her thoughts in a turmoil. What was Clementine Fox going to do or say? "You know what, Daisy, I don't even care."

Daisy leaped from her arms and raced to the front door. A second later the bell rang. "Come in," Fanny called.

"Hi, Mom. Long time no see." Billie wrapped her mother in her arms and gave her a great smacking kiss.

"And whose fault is that? You're in Hong Kong, Japan, New York, England. When are you ever here?"

"I call, though."

"Yes, you do. Would you like some coffee?"

"I would love some. How's Sunny doing? Sunday is visitors' day, so I'll be here to visit. Are you going?"

"Of course. She's doing wonderfully. She's made some friends, one in particular. Harry seems like a very nice man. The doctors told me they're good for each other. Why am I telling you this, you met him?"

"I liked him. He doesn't take any crap from Sunny. Dad told me she's really mellow these days. I'm so glad, Mom. I'm going with Iris when she takes the kids to the park in a little while. I brought some presents for the kids. Dad's looking a lot better, too."

"And what about you, Billie. Is there anyone special in your life?"

"Not right now. You know how fickle I am. As soon as some guy starts to get serious I get scared. I like my life just the way it is. That's just another way of saying the right man hasn't come along. How's your life, Mom?"

"Parts of it are good. Other parts aren't so good. That's life."

"When will your divorce be final?"

"Probably never." Fanny told her daughter about the morning events in the lawyer's offices.

"It's just so hard to believe that Uncle Simon could turn like that. Back when we were kids and he'd come to Sunrise, I used to see him stare at Dad when he thought no one was looking. His eyes were so strange. I was a kid, what did I know?"

"Have you heard from Birch?"

"Not since early October. He asked me to send some kid clothes to Costa Rica. I must have sent a ton of stuff. He sent a card saying it all arrived safely. That was the last I heard. We all write, long, wonderful letters. Maybe they make him feel bad and that's why he doesn't write. Sage writes pages and pages and sends pictures of Lexie. He misses Birch the most. He'll be back, Mom."

"I know that. I miss him."

"Well, that's my news. Gotta run or Jake will take a fit. Some fool bought him a kite and he wants to fly it. I was elected. I really love that kid."

"He's a precious little boy. Ash adores him."

"Is that strange or what? He's like Dad's shadow. Polly's a little priss. Lexie is a delight. Sage is so good with all three of them. Don't be surprised, Mom, if Sunny agrees to Iris and Sage adopting Polly and Jake."

"Honey, nothing surprises me these days. Tyler will have something to say. He is their father."

"Nope. He already gave his approval. He's another one that failed the test where I'm concerned. Simon and him. Guess nobody gets it all. I like your new fella, Mom," Billie teased.

"He is kind of nice."

"He's a lot nice. Dad said he was aces. Now, that has to mean something."

Fanny laughed. "They get along well."

"I think it's hilarious that Uncle Simon thinks you want to marry Dad again. This is one weird family."

"Weird but nice. Kiss the children for me."

"I will, Mom. I'll call."

"More than once every month, okay?"

"At least once a week. By the way, the business is going great guns."

"Thanks to you."

"Whatever."

The apartment was so quiet after Billie left that Fanny turned on the stereo. Daisy danced on her hind legs, barking vociferously.

"Okay, you deserve a nice walk in the park. I do too. Get your leash."

An hour later, Fanny unhooked Daisy's leash and sat down on a bench to smoke a cigarette. She watched, a smile on her face as Daisy chased a fat poodle who had no interest in running away. They tussled, barking at each other. Fanny felt like an indulgent mother as she watched the two dogs under the trees.

"Is this seat taken?" a voice behind her said.

Fanny shivered. "As a matter of fact it is, Simon. I'm calling the police. You're in direct violation of the restraining order. Get away from me."

"Fanny, it was so good once. Why can't we get that back? I'd like to try."

"Talk to my lawyer. It wasn't good. It was only good when you got what you wanted, when you wanted it. It took me a while to get my eyes open, but they're open now. I don't want you, and I don't want anything from you. I mean it, get away from me."

Fanny ran toward Daisy, scooped the little dog up in her arms, and ran from the park, her heart pumping faster than her legs.

The owner of the fat little poodle walked toward Simon. "I saw you bothering the lady."

"What's it to you?" Simon snarled.

"This is what it is to me. See this. It's my fist. Now, feel this." The man's fist shot forward into the middle of Simon's stomach. He looked around. Satisfied that no one seemed to be paying any attention, the man's fist shot upward. "Bother the lady or any other lady again and I'll blow out your kneecaps.

"Come to daddy, Cupcake." The fat poodle waddled over to her owner and waited patiently to have her leash hooked onto her collar.

Owner and dog walked away without a backward glance.

Simon rolled over on the ground as he massaged his jaw. He sat down on the bench trying to get his breath. He stared after the man, hatred spewing from his eyes, obscenities rolling off his lips.

26

"Well, Mrs. Thornton, what do you think?" the building contractor asked.

All Fanny could do was stare at her beloved Sunrise. "From this distance I can't tell the difference. It's hard to believe there was ever a fire."

"That man of yours, Chue, he was under our feet every single minute with his grass seed and plants. He worked from a *map!*"

"I know. That's how he was able to make things look the same. I don't know how to thank you, Mr. Wyler. You finished four months to the day."

"We had some unexpected help." Fanny shot him a questioning look, but the contractor didn't expand on his statement. "Are you having a dedication or family party?"

"No. Ash will be moving in tomorrow. The furniture is coming today, and my friends are coming up to help hang the curtains and things like that. I don't know what to say, Mr. Wyler."

"This has to be one of the prettiest spots in the world. My father used to tell me stories about Sallie Coleman and this mountain. I'm happy to have been a part of the restoration. Tell Ash I said hello. We miss him in town."

"I'll be sure to tell him, Mr. Wyler."

Fanny watched the contractor drive off in his pickup. She was alone now with her thoughts, even though Chue stood off in the distance, not wishing to intrude. She walked around the house, marveling at the neatly trimmed shrubbery, the flowers that looked as if they'd just bloomed. The patio furniture was new, the umbrella candy-striped. Clay pots full of geraniums added the final touch. Ash loved flowers. She hadn't known that until last year. There were so many things she hadn't known about Ash until last year. Her eyelids started to burn.

A sudden burst of anger raged through her. She kicked off her heels and ran around the house to the cemetery, where she banged on Sallie's tombstone with clenched fists. "Do you know what you did? Do you have any idea, Sallie?" she screamed. "You backed the wrong horse! Do you hear me, Sallie? Your son, the one you loved above all else burned down this house, and he's trying to steal Babylon! I believed you when you said he was wonderful. I believed all those lies because I couldn't imagine you would ever lie to me. You lied, Sallie! You damn well lied to me! Ash is dying, and you better have some answers when he gets there because he's got a list as long as that mountain road out there. Why did you do that to me, Sallie? You knew what Simon was all about. He wanted me because of Ash, and you set me up for that . . . evil, ugly person."

Fanny dropped to her knees, her hands still pounding the stone. "I'm turning out just like you. I can't marry Marcus because of Simon. It's you and Devin all over again. That's your legacy to me. If you loved me, Sallie, how could you have done that to me? How *dare* you do that to me!"

Chue's gentle hand on her shoulder caused Fanny to sob harder. "How . . . why, Chue? You lived here. You saw everything."

"Yes. I tried not to be involved in Miss Sallie's family. Come, let me clean your hands. We can talk in the kitchen. There is a first-aid kit the contractor left behind in the pantry. We will talk."

"You knew, Chue. Why didn't you say something?"

"It was not my place, Miss Fanny."

"Did Ash tell me the truth, Chue?"

"Ash was never a saint, Miss Fanny. He was a boy whose heart couldn't accept what was being done. He retaliated in the only way he knew how. As I said, he was no saint, nor was he a devil the way his brother was. I watched over Ash, as did Mr. Philip. Miss Sallie was blind to many things. You must let it go."

"Let it go! I would like nothing more, but I can't. We all know Simon burned this house down, but we can't accuse him because we didn't see him do it. He will not give me a divorce unless I turn the casino over to him. Ash is dying, Chue, he's coming home to the mountain to die. There's nothing I can do for him except to be here. How does one handle the fact that one knows one's only brother, one's flesh and blood, is waiting for him to die? How, Chue?"

"You and your God will give him the strength, Miss Fanny."

"Which one did you like the best?"

Chue grinned. "I did not much care for either one of the boys. I understood Ash's pain, so the things he did were understandable. He did not like his brother. I saw many things that wounded my heart. I could not interfere, Miss Fanny."

"I think I hate her, Chue. I really do. I think I hate her as much as I hate Simon."

"Perhaps for now. Later the pain will fade."

"It will never fade, Chue. My whole life is tied to this family, to Sallie and her sons. How can that fade?"

"You must make a new life. Somewhere else. A life free of the Thornton name."

"I'm not free to marry."

"Then you will live in sin," Chue said smartly. "Many people do this today."

"My family is here. The casino is here. Who will take care of things? I can't walk away from my family and my responsibilities. I did that once, and it proved to be a disaster."

"It is a heavy burden. I know you will make the proper decisions when the time is right. I brought a letter for you to read from your son."

"From Birch?"

"He writes to me quite often."

"He does! I never knew that, Chue. I don't think I should read your mail. What does he write about?"

"Everything and nothing. They are long letters. I have many should you want to read them."

"We only get postcards. I think it's wonderful, Chue, that Birch chose you to correspond with. Did you tell him of Ash's condition?"

"Yes. He will be home soon. You did not write, Miss Fanny?"

"I did, but Ash didn't want me to tell him how severe his condition is. He didn't want Birch to feel he had to come home because he's dying. I guess he's remembering when Sallie died and how . . . things were at that time."

"Time heals all wounds, Miss Fanny."

Fanny's voice was sad when she said, "Chue, time is not a magical elixir. All it does is dull the pain. Ash's pain has never gone away, and he's going to die taking it with him. Simon is living with his own demons every minute of the day. It started down below in that town and then carried up here to the mountain. It's as though my hands are tied. I can't change anything."

"Come, Miss Fanny, I hear cars on the road."

Fanny wiped at her eyes. "You've been a wonderful friend all these years, Chue. Your family has been more than kind to all us Thorntons."

"You are my family as much as my own flesh and blood."

"That's one of the nicest things anyone has ever said to me, Chue."

"You are nothing like Miss Sallie, Miss Fanny."

"Thank you for saying that too. Chue . . . do you think Sallie heard me? I wanted a sign. I wanted the earth to tremble, the skies to open. I wanted something."

"Something like *that*," Chue said pointing to the small cemetery where a dark cloud hovered overhead. "From here you can see that it is a gentle rain. Perhaps it is a cleansing rain."

Fanny ran to the cemetery. The huge cottonwood seemed to be bowing, its branches dripping with rain. Chue was right. It was a gentle rain washing her tears from Sallie's stone. She raised her eyes. "It's a start, Sallie, but you aren't off the hook." She was muttering. Something she rarely did. People in white coats locked you up when you talked to yourself or to clouds, the trees, and tombstones.

"Look, Miss Fanny."

Fanny turned to look in the direction Chue was pointing. The dark cloud overhead surged forward and scudded across the yard until it was over the house. She watched the rain pelt downward in a brief downpour. Fanny ran back to the house to stand on the patio. "You're christening it, aren't you?" she shouted. "It's not enough, Sallie! You need to make it right before Ash gets there."

Chue hugged his arms to his chest, his oblique eyes full of shock.

Thunder boomed overhead as a jagged streak of lightning ripped across the sky.

"You need to make it right! It's time. If you don't, I'll do it for you. You won't like that, Sallie. I want to know that you understand what I'm saying."

The rain came down harder, plastering Fanny's clothes to her body. She stared upward, the rain pelting her face. Lightning struck one of the beams from the old house that were piled high in the middle of the backyard. Fanny watched as the old wood smoked and sizzled. Her shoulders slumped. A good sign or a bad sign? Using every ounce of willpower she possessed, Fanny straightened her shoulders. Chue was looking at her as though she'd lost her mind. Maybe she had for a few minutes. What sane person talked to spirits and expected them to make things right in the earthly world?

"This person, that's who," Fanny shouted.

"The rain is over. The cloud is moving on. Very strange," the old Chinese murmured.

"Not at all, Chue." Fanny sloshed ahead of him as she made her way to the front of the house to greet Billie and Bess.

"We get rain squalls like that in Texas all the time. We even get them in Vermont," Billie said.

"That wasn't a squall. That was Sallie. We were having a . . . little discussion."

"I used to have some very intense conversations with Seth. Once or twice he made the earth move when I let him see my strength. I believe in stuff like that. So, Fanny, who won?" Billie asked, her voice upbeat.

"I think I did. I can't be sure."

"I always felt like that, too. We have the edge though. We're *alive!*"

"You're both crazy," Bess said, her eyes going from one to the other.

"Maybe," Billie said.

"There are worse things in life," Fanny said.

"Whatever. Here comes the furniture truck. We have all the curtains, linens, and dishes and stuff in the van that Ash was gracious enough to let us use. I say we get cracking and get this all done today so you can bring Ash up tomorrow. He told me he can't wait to get here. It worked out perfectly, Jake is finished with preschool and he has the summer off. Somebody up there is watching over you guys and it ain't Sallie Thornton."

"Let's not get into *that*," Fanny said. "Was Thad upset that you came, Billie?"

"Not for a minute. Thad understands everything about me. He knows how important family is to all of us. He's so busy right now. He encourages me to do things on my own, separate from *him* and separate from *us*. Thad is one of a kind. I love him so much sometimes my teeth hurt. I clench my teeth and say, I love him, I love him,

I love him. The first thing he always says is, what can I do? That's the kind of person Thad is."

"Whoever would have thought you would marry your husband's best friend. On the flip side of that coin, who would have thought I'd marry my ex-husband's brother? Maybe Bess is right, and we really are crazy."

"I was teasing, Fanny," Bess said.

"I'm going to iron the curtains, Billie is going to nail in the hooks and you, Bess, are going to hang the curtains. Did you bring an ironing board?"

"Yes. This is not a Mickey Mouse operation, Fanny Thornton."

"We need to switch up here. I see the furniture men need me, so someone else has to iron."

Billie and Bess grumbled good-naturedly as they moved off to the kitchen.

When the grandfather clock in the foyer chimed five times, Fanny dusted her hands dramatically. "Done!"

"It looks the same," Billie said, her voice full of awe.

"If you didn't know it wasn't the old house, you would think this place had been here forever. Ash will be so happy. Jake's room came out perfectly."

"It used to be Simon's room," Fanny said.

"Not anymore. There's not one iota of anything that says that was his room," Billie said.

"Do you want to see the schoolroom?"

"What happened to that iron monstrosity that took up a whole room?" Bess asked.

"I had the construction people push it over the mountain. They had to use cranes and bulldozers and all kinds of heavy equipment. We couldn't build the house around it, they couldn't get it down the road, so there was nothing else we could do. It's in a deep ravine. In two hundred years it might rust away to nothing. It's my mountain, so I guess it's okay."

"Ladies, your supper," Chue called from downstairs.

"Let's take our first ride in the elevator," Billie said.

"It works," the three women said in unison as they stepped from the elevator.

"Won ton soup, fried rice, spare ribs, chow mein, egg rolls, and fortune cookies." Chue unpacked the heavy picnic basket. "No cartons. We use bowls. My wife say you wash, give back. My sons and

I will have those old beams carried away by dark, Miss Fanny. There will be no sign of the fire at all. Mr. Ash will be most happy. The pond is stocked for Jake. You will tell him, please, that the fish are waiting for him."

"Thank you, Chue. I'll tell them. We should get here by ten tomorrow morning. Please come up and see Ash."

"I will do that, Miss Fanny. Good night, ladies."

It was seven o'clock when the women climbed into their cars for the ride down the mountain.

The following morning, Fanny drove Billie to the airport. "Fanny . . ."

"Shhh, I know what you're going to say. He's got a month, if he's lucky. He's dealing with it. I'm dealing with it. I'll call you, Billie. Go home to your husband and give him a big hug and kiss for me."

"I will, Fanny. If you need me . . . you know . . . sooner, call. Day or night. Thad can fly me here, so I don't have to mess around with reservations. I want your promise, Fanny."

"You have it."

"Do you really think you won that round up there, when you squared off with Sallie?"

"Yes, I do."

"Good for you. Love you, Fanny."

"Love you too, Billie."

"Are you comfortable, Ash?"

"Fanny, stop fussing. I'm okay. It's not a long ride. I didn't see my black canvas bag. Did you put it in the van?"

"Yes. Ash, you asked me that three times." Fanny slowed the van and pulled to the side of the road. She climbed in back, rummaging between the luggage. "Here it is, do you want to hold it? Do you have your life savings in here or what?" She handed the bag to Ash before she climbed behind the wheel.

"Ash, speaking of savings, we need to make a decision about all the stuff that was in your mother's safe. What do you want me to do with it?"

"Fanny, I don't give a good rat's ass what you do with it. Mom left it to you."

"It belongs to you and your brother."

"I don't want it. I sure as hell hope you aren't planning on giving it to him. You need to think ahead. Simon has no children, so unless he has some kind of airtight will, it will come back to our kids. He's got more money than he can spend in three lifetimes. Just keep it."

"I don't want it, Ash. I'm not feeling very kindly toward your mother's memory these days."

"You said there's a waiting list at the rehab center. Use it to add on or build another one."

"You wouldn't mind?"

"Hell no. Sunny's doing great. We went out to see her yesterday. I wanted to say good-bye. I think she's happier than I've ever seen her. We talked about the adoption. She cried, but she knows it's best. Sage and Iris will make sure the kids know she's their mother. It's going to work out, Fanny."

"I'm so glad you planted that first seed, Ash."

"You know, huh?"

"Of course I know."

"Then you know I don't want her to see me again until . . . it's over."

"Shut up, Ash, I don't want to talk about *that*."

"We have to talk about it."

"No, we don't. I'm here to take care of you. We aren't going to . . . dwell . . . talk about things. We'll pack each day with wonderful things."

"You know, Fanny, you're wonderful. You truly are. What wonderful things are you talking about? Once I start on those pills, it will be all I can do not to jump out of my skin. I'm going to turn mean and nasty because the pain will be unbearable. You'll wish you never signed on for this gig."

"I'm prepared, Ash."

"I think you are. I'm not. Therein lies the difference."

"I want you to remember one thing, Ash. God will never give you more than you can handle."

"Words are so easy to say, aren't they? They just roll off a person's lips and people react to those words. Stop the car for a minute, Fanny. Do you see that blue sky, those snowball clouds, those fragrant pine trees? I'm never going to see them again. I'm never going to ride up and down this mountain again. I'm not going to be able to take Jake fishing. All the things you do every single day of your life and take for granted will be gone for me. I won't be here. My heart will cease to beat. This chair will sit empty in the garage. I won't be able to count the stars with Jake. Most of all, Fanny, I won't be able to spit and snarl at you. I want so damn much to be able to leave this earth a man, so that when you think of me you'll have kind thoughts. I'm sorry for everything. At this point in time I know it probably doesn't mean anything. What it means to me is I finally got the guts to say it out loud. If it wasn't for you, Fanny, I'd probably be in a ditch somewhere. I owe everything to you. I didn't know that for a long time. It's eating at my soul, Fanny. I want to be what you want me to be, and I don't know how. I don't know how, Fanny."

Fanny climbed from her seat and dropped to her knees. She wrapped her arms around Ash. "Let's both cry now and get it over with. I just want you to be who you are. I don't care how you spit and snarl. I'll spit and snarl back. When the pain is bad, Ash, I'll give you enough pills to ease it. I know you have a stockpile. You will always be in my thoughts no matter where you are. You were right, there's a bond between us that can never be severed. I don't want you to worry about being a man now at this particular time. You came through when no one else cared enough or . . . You know what I'm saying. None of us will let Jake forget you. You'll always be a part of his life. I promise you that, Ash. Will you trust me with these last days of your life?"

They cried together, their arms entwined, their bodies shaking with their grief for each other. It was Ash who finally said, "Enough already. Let's get this show on the road. Jake will be up in a couple of hours. I want to get settled in. We're going fishing. Want to come along, Fanny?"

"I'd love to go. Should I pack up a picnic lunch?"

"Potato chips, Popsicles, gumdrops, and mallow cups."

"Ash Thornton! Is that what you give him for a snack?"

"Nah, that's the bait. Chue gives us homemade egg rolls and fortune cookies. You don't know the first thing about fishing, Fanny. Gumdrops are great bait when there's any left."

Fanny laughed.

"God Almighty! You really did do it, Fanny," Ash said thirty minutes later when she steered the van up the driveway. "It's perfect! It looks like it's been sitting here for hundreds of years. Too bad Simon can't see this. He'd piss his jockies."

"Wait till you see the inside. The furniture's the same, it's just not battered and worn. The elevator is a little bigger. The refrigerator is one of those super duper jobs that makes ice cubes. I got us one of those big screen television sets and the satellite dish brings in more channels than before. We get wonderful reception now. I had the men toss that ugly monster safe over the mountain."

"No shit! Bet that was a feat in itself. It's amazing. You'd never know there was a fire. You kept your promise, Fanny. I knew you would."

"How did you know, Ash?"

"Fanny Thornton always keeps her word. Is thanks sufficient?"

"It's sufficient. What do you want to see first?"

"Three green pills. Not one, not two, three. A shot of brandy to wash it down."

"Coming right up."

It took a full twenty minutes for the tightness to leave Ash's face. Fanny used the time to brew a pot of coffee and to carry the bags from the van inside. Ash still had the black canvas bag on his lap.

"Let's do the tour, Fanny."

"Yes, sir," Fanny said, saluting smartly. "Let me load the bags in the elevator first. I'll unpack your stuff as you make the rounds on the second floor."

She found him in the schoolroom, his eyes wet, his shoulders slumped. "I feel like this is where it all started. I actually feel it, Fanny. I wish I had the words to tell you how much I loved my mother and how I missed her when she died. My father, too. I didn't know how to handle it then, and I don't know how to handle it now."

"Let your emotions go, Ash. Say whatever you want. If there are no words, don't worry about it. If you want to cry, cry. Whatever you want to do is all right."

"I have a list. I keep it in my pocket at all times. A pencil, too. I'm taking it with me when I go."

"A list is good," Fanny said. "I'm going to get your room ready and hang up your clothes. You have time for a nap before Jake gets here if you want."

"I don't want to waste the pills. I'm feeling halfway decent now. I'll just sit here for a while."

Fanny busied herself first in Ash's room and then in her own room. She waited a full hour before she called out to Ash. "I'm ready to go downstairs. How about you?"

"Me too. Let's have some more coffee in the garden."

It was a companionable silence broken only by the sound of Iris's horn as she parked the car behind the van. Jake whooped his way to the backyard, shouting at the top of his lungs, "Pop Pop, I'm here. Let's go fishing!"

They all went fishing. Fanny said later that it was one of the nicest days of her life.

When it was time to go, Jake crawled on his grandfather's lap to smother him with hugs and kisses.

"I'll bring him up every morning until . . . and Sage will come up to get him around three," Iris said. "Ash won't be able to keep this up much longer."

"I know. I appreciate it, Iris. If it looks like it might be a bad day, I'll call you in the morning."

"If there's anything you want . . . if there's anything I can do . . . call me."

"Of course."

Three weeks to the day of Ash and Fanny's arrival at Sunrise, Ash took to his bed.

Two more days passed, with Ash slipping in and out of consciousness. The third day he woke, completely alert. "Fanny, I want to ask a favor of you."

"I know, you want me to talk dirty to you," she teased.

"Okay, but do me the favor first. Will you promise before I ask it?"

"Sure, Ash. You're making this sound so mysterious."

"I want you to call Simon and ask him to come up here. I know I don't have long so will you do it?"

"If that's what you want, Ash, of course I'll do it. I'll have to go through his attorney. I don't even know where he lives."

"Try, okay? Will you have the cook bring me some coffee?"

"Tea would be better, Ash."

"Coffee, Fanny."

"Coffee it is. My address book is in the kitchen. I'll make the calls from down there. Are you all right?"

"No, Fanny, I'm not."

"John Noble is coming up this morning."

"He shouldn't waste his time. Go, Fanny."

Her heart pounding, Fanny ran down the steps. "Take some coffee up to Mr. Thornton."

Fanny used up forty minutes until she heard Simon's voice on the other end of the wire. "Simon, it's Fanny. Ash wants you to come to Sunrise. I think he wants to make arrangements about Babylon where you're concerned," Fanny lied. "Can you leave now? I don't think he has much time."

"Really."

"Is that a yes or a no?"

"I'll have to think about it."

"I wouldn't think too long, Simon. The offer is only good as long as Ash is alive."

"What will we all do without Ash in our lives?"

"I don't know about you, Simon, but I'll grieve. What should I tell Ash?"

"Tell him I'm on my way."

"Thank you, Simon."

Fanny ran upstairs. "He said he's coming, Ash. Who knows if he'll actually show up. I lied to him, said you wanted to talk to him about Babylon. How was the coffee?"

"It wasn't a lie, Fanny. I do want to talk to him about Babylon. I spilled the coffee on the rug. I couldn't hold the cup."

"It doesn't matter, Ash. Stuff like that isn't important." Fanny stared at the gaunt-eyed man who had once been her husband. If there were a way to breathe her own life into his wasted body, she wouldn't think twice. She knew he was nearing the end, and he knew she was aware of the little time he had left.

Ash struggled for words. "I want to be cremated, Fanny."

"I know, Ash. Please, don't talk, save your strength. I'll keep telling you what time it is, so don't worry about that. Do you want to hold the clock?"

"No. There seems to be some kind of film over my right eye."

"It's a cataract."

"You aren't going to call everyone, are you? Will you let me die in peace?"

"Absolutely."

"Is he here yet?"

"Soon, Ash. I'll read yesterday's paper to you if you like. Maybe hearing my voice will help you stay awake."

"Read."

Fanny read for thirty minutes. She heard Daisy bark downstairs and knew what the bark meant: Simon Thornton had arrived.

"I think he's here, Ash. Are you sure you want to do this?" She was alarmed at his ashen skin and the perspiration dotting his brow. She knew if she touched his hands or face, they'd be cold and clammy.

"Fanny, can you prop me up just a little or else get me a few more pillows?"

Fanny struggled, her own forehead beading with sweat at the effort she expended to get Ash into a more upright position. She understood perfectly that Ash didn't want to be flat on his back with his brother towering over him.

Simon was debonair and arrogant when he walked up the steps ahead of Fanny. "Aren't you going to say anything about the house, Simon?"

"What is there to say? Did you do something different?"

"Yes, something," Fanny snarled.

"Ash, how's the world treating you. Not too good by the way you look."

"Fanny, close the door," Ash said.

"But, Ash . . ."

"Close the door, Fanny."

"I'll be right outside."

"Simon, stand at the bottom of the bed, right in the middle so I can see you. Among other things I have a cataract."

Simon moved to the foot of the bed. "So what made you change your mind? Guess you figured you were going to be seeing Mom and Dad and you wanted them to know you did the right thing, huh?"

"Yes. I'm going to do the right thing."

"You look like you plan on taking my picture. Wouldn't that be something if you did and you took it with you to show Mom."

"Why don't you smile, Simon? I'd like to remember that smile of yours when I move into eternity."

Ash's hands moved under the cover. The moment Simon threw his head back in laughter, Ash pulled the trigger of the gun he'd brought with him from town. Simon crumpled to the floor as Fanny rushed through the door.

"Ash! Oh my God!"

"Did I kill the son of a bitch?"

Fanny leaned down to feel for a pulse. Simon's wide-open eyes glared at her. She wanted to close the lids, but she couldn't make her hands move.

"He's dead, Ash. Why? Why did you do that?"

Ash grappled with his breathing. "For you, Fanny. He would never give you a moment's peace. In the end he'd do something terrible to you. I'm dying so it doesn't matter. He wanted to be first in everything. He'll get there before me. I gave him an edge, Fanny."

"Oh, Ash."

"You promised not to cry."

"I lied." She reached for his hands and held them tight. She tried not to look at the hole in the bedspread.

"You'll be okay now, Fanny. It was all I could do for you. Mom's going to be pretty mad."

"I don't think so. The day before we came up here Sallie and I had a confrontation. I won. It's going to be . . . it's going to be . . . okay when you get there. I promise, Ash."

"I can see her. Look. There's Pop behind her, and Devin. Where's my list, Fanny? I need my list. Quick, get it for me."

"Where is it, Ash?"

"Find it. I need the list."

Fanny stepped over her husband's body as she searched for the clothes Ash had worn last.

"Mom's holding out her hand, Fanny. She wants the *list.*"

"I have it! I found it, Ash!" She crumpled it into his hand. She heard him sigh with relief as she held his right hand.

"Let go, Fanny."

"No. No. I don't want you to go, Ash." She held his hand tighter.

"You have to let go of my hand, Fanny. It's time for me to go. Please, Fanny, let go."

"All right, Ash," Fanny sobbed. "Think about me sometime, okay?"

"Be happy, Fanny."

Fanny threw herself across the bed, her body shaking with sobs. What seemed like a long time later she felt gentle hands pulling her backward.

"John. Oh, John. I didn't think it was going to be like this. I didn't know I would care so much. He killed him for me, John. This is my fault. I swear to God I didn't know he had a gun. He brought this black bag with him from town. He was so concerned about it. It was heavy. I should have known. Somehow I should have known. That's why he asked for the coffee, so the cook could get the bag out of the closet for him. He couldn't ask me. The last thing he said was, be happy, Fanny. Oh, God, John, I feel like I want to lie down here and die, too. What are we going to do? As much as I detested Simon, he didn't deserve to die at his brother's hand."

"Ash must have thought so, Fanny. I know this will sound strange coming from me, since I'm a doctor, but if you stop to think about those two brothers you can understand Ash's thought processes. His condition, his concern for you, Simon's demands. That damn list he talked to me about last week."

"They're both dead, John. Does . . . do we . . . ?"

"I'll take care of it. What's he holding in his hand, Fanny?"

"*The* list. A list of all the . . . things Simon did and all the things . . . The grievances he planned to present to his mother when . . . *he got there.* I don't know. I never read it. I don't want to read it now. He said . . . he could see his mother and father and Devin. He said his mother was holding out her hand for the list. I know dying people always say things like that. Do you think he did see them?"

"I think Ash thought he saw them. I hope he did."

"He said he gave Simon the edge by letting him go first. Oh, God, John, how am I ever going to live with this?"

"One day at a time. Bess is on her way. I tried to get here sooner, but we had some emergency surgery earlier. Go downstairs, Fanny, and wait for Bess. Send Chue and his sons up."

Fanny did as John asked. There was nothing else for her to do.

Three hours after his death, Simon Thornton was buried in the Thornton cemetery by Chue and his children. Fanny, Bess, John, Chue, and his sons were the only mourners in attendance. John rushed through a prayer, his words garbled. No one seemed to mind. The moment they walked away, Chue and his sons began replacing the dirt. Fanny shuddered at the sound of the clumps of dirt hitting the pine box Chue had nailed together. By sundown the grave would look as though it had been there as long as the others.

John Noble signed Simon Thornton's death certificate under the watchful eye of his wife Bess. The cause of death was listed as cardiac arrest.

The following day, John Noble tendered his resignation to the Thornton Medical Center, citing the need to spend more time with his family as the reason for retiring from the medical profession.

It was the Thornton children, not Fanny, who decided to hold a memorial service for Ash Thornton at the small church called Saint Cotton Easter. It was a candlelight service because a delegation of casino owners had asked that Fanny darken the Big White Way for one hour. She agreed. Ash would have loved the tribute.

There were no stark headlines in the morning paper, out of consideration for the Thornton family. Page two carried a brief article with a small picture of Ash in his navy whites. Simon's obituary was on page seven, halfway down the page. There was no mention of how he died.

It was done. It was over. A large part of Fanny's life was gone forever, but life would go on.

Ash had said, don't be sad at my passing, be happy you still have what you have. She knew he was right.

"I *need* to grieve. Forgive me, Ash, for denying you your last request of me."

Fanny wept for the past.

27

Fanny hugged her children one last time.

"Do you have *any* idea of where you're going, Mom?" Sage asked.

Her voice was choked when she said, "Here, there, yonder. I'll call."

"We'll take good care of things, Fanny," Bess said. "John is just itching to help me at the casino. Think about it, if someone faints because they win too much money, we have a doctor on the premises. Take care of yourself, Fanny," Bess said.

"I will."

Sunny stepped forward. She hugged her mother. "I want to thank you, Mom, for everything. I'm sorry I was such a shit."

"It doesn't matter, honey. I'm so proud of you, Sunny. Promise me you'll keep up the good work."

"I promise, Mom. Jake wants to say something."

"Hi, big guy, catch any fish lately?"

"I got a big one yesterday. Are you going to see Pop Pop?"

"Not this trip, Jake. One of these days . . ."

"Okay. I miss him. I sent him a letter in a balloon."

Fanny cleared her throat. "Pop Pop loves to get letters."

"Don't get into any trouble, Mom," Billie said.

"I'll try not to."

"I'm going to hang around here for a while. I hate traveling."

"That's nice to know, Billie."

"No more hugs, no more kisses, no more *crying*," Sage bellowed. "We'll be here if you need us."

"I'll carry that thought with me. You know I love you all, more than I can ever say."

"Mom, will you go already!" Sage bellowed again. Fanny could see the tears in her son's eyes.

Fanny slipped the 4 by 4 into gear and left the underground garage. The time was 7:20 A.M. At the top of the ramp she was able to see a tall figure outlined in the early-morning sun. She pulled the Rover to the side and lowered the window. "You're up early, Marcus."

"I never went to bed. I've been sitting here on the curb all night. I wanted to say good-bye. Where are you going, Fanny?"

"I don't know."

"Are you coming back?"

"I don't know, Marcus."

"I love you, Fanny."

"I love you, too."

"I'll wait as long as it takes."

"I'll carry that thought with me. Will you watch over my family?"

"Fanny, the whole damn town watches over your family. I'll add my name to the list. Travel safely. Will you call or write?"

"I will when I need you the most."

Marcus nodded.

Fanny drove away. She didn't look back.

She had things to do, places to go.

Her first stop was Sunrise.

Chue watched from the gardens as Fanny climbed from the Rover, the ashes in her hand. He felt his heart thud in his chest when he saw Fanny go to the edge of the mountain. "You're free at last, Ash! You're one with the universe now." In a voice that was cracked and harsh she, who could never carry a tune, broke into song. *"Off we go into the wild blue yonder . . ."*

"Climbing high into the sky . . ." Chue sang, his arm going around her shoulder.

They finished the song, tears dripping down their cheeks.

"I saved a little," Fanny said, handing the urn to Chue. "Put them next to Sallie. Just a cross, Chue, nothing elaborate like what we did for Simon."

"Yes, Miss Fanny."

"Isn't it wonderful that Sage is moving his family here now? The children love the mountain. Everything happens for a reason. Ours not to reason why. Watch over my family. Someone told me earlier that many people watch over them. I didn't know that."

"Have no fear, Miss Fanny."

"I hope you put some real whoppers in that pond. Jake can't wait to get here."

"It is done, Miss Fanny."

"Good-bye, Chue."

"Good-bye, Miss Fanny."

Done.

Over.

Move on, Fanny.

It was eleven o'clock when Fanny parked her car in a neatly bordered driveway. A small box in her hand, she walked up the walkway to the door and rang the bell. Margaret Lassiter opened the door and held it wide for Fanny to enter.

"Mrs. Thornton, I'm so sorry about your husband and his brother. If there's anything Jeffrey or I can do, you only have to ask."

"I saw you and Jeffrey at the memorial service. It was nice of you to attend."

"We didn't want to intrude."

"Is Jeffrey home?"

"He's at work. He won't get home till around six."

"I wonder if you would give him this. It's . . . what it is . . . is Ash's aviator wings. I thought he might like to have them. Ash has . . . other wings now."

"Oh, Mrs. Thornton, I know Jeffrey will be so pleased. You have no idea how he's anguished over that episode at the casino. Are you sure you want to give *my son* his father's wings? You have boys of your own."

"I'm sure, Mrs. Lassiter. I have to go now. Thank you for seeing me."

"Good-bye, Mrs. Thornton."

Done.

Over.

Move on, Fanny.

Fanny looked at her watch the moment she turned off the engine. She'd made good time, the radio blaring for company. She took a long moment to commit the house nestled in the cottonwoods to memory. She looked at her watch again as she climbed from the car. She took one last walk around the property, marveling at the tree house Marcus had built.

A jackrabbit jumped from the bushes. Startled, Fanny backed up to the makeshift ladder leading to the tree house. She sat down on the third rung from the bottom. She stared at nothing, her thoughts whirling inside her head. She looked at her watch again. She had ten minutes. Time to get on with it.

Hands jammed in her pockets, Fanny walked to the center of the backyard, her head raised to the sun. "Hey, Sallie, listen up! In ten minutes this place is just going to be a memory. I'm breaking the chain. I don't want your legacy. Not anymore. This is the last link, Sallie. You hoped I'd bring your precious son Simon here. That was a mistake, Sallie. I will not allow myself to end up like you. Ash took care of that for me. Bet your hair is standing on end over that. All that stuff in your safe is gone. So is the damn safe. The first thing I did after Ash died was to throw your desk and blackboard down the mountain. I've got a regular junkyard down there. If there was a way to get rid of that cemetery, I'd do that, too. Private cemeteries are ob-scene. When I figure a way to get rid of it I'll do it. For now, it's what it is, a place. Nothing more. This house is the last link. Ooops, gotta go, I hear the machinery out on the road. I don't want any sign from you, Sallie. I don't think rain, thunder, and lightning are going to do it this time. Oh, yeah, one last thing. I'm taking back my maiden name. This is Fanny Logan signing off, Sallie." She offered up a sloppy salute before she walked to the front of the house.

"Mrs. Thornton?"

"Mr. Wyler. It's a beautiful day, isn't it?"

"Yes it is. This is the house?"

"Yes. It's pretty, isn't it?"

"Name your price. I'll buy it from you."

"I can't do that. You brought your wrecking ball. The house is made from quarry stone. Is your machinery strong enough?"

"Yes, Mrs. Thornton, it will do the job. You're sure now?"

"Yes, sir, I am."

"You want all the debris carried away to the quarry."

"Yes. Please, will you rake the grounds so nothing remains. The tree house, too."

"Okay, Mrs. Thornton, you're the boss."

"I'm not Mrs. Thornton anymore. I came here plain old Fanny Logan from Shamrock, Pennsylvania, and that's how I'm leaving. I know you don't understand. It's all right. Send your bill to the casino."

Daisy in her arms, Fanny watched as the heavy piece of machinery backed up, advanced and then backed up again. The massive iron ball swayed in the air. As far as Fanny could tell, there was no breeze anywhere. Her eyes didn't leave the ball for a second.

"Do it!"

The moment the ball hit the roof of the house, Fanny climbed into her car.

She didn't look back.

Done.

Over.

Move on, Fanny.

Fanny was exhausted by the time she drove the Rover down the long road that led to Josh Coleman's farm. It was late, almost eleven o'clock. The lights encouraged her to drive around the horseshoe-shaped driveway. Someone inside must have heard her engine. The front light under the overhang suddenly glowed a warm yellow. "Stay, Daisy, I won't be long."

Fanny walked up the four stone steps to the front door. Before she could ring the bell, the door opened. Josh Coleman stood in front of her, his face puzzled at this late visit. Fanny made no apologies.

"Mrs. Thornton, come in. Has something happened? Is something wrong?"

"I'm returning your family albums. I'd like mine back if you don't mind. I also brought you a letter from your nephew, Ash. He passed away two weeks ago on the same day his brother Simon died. There are only two Thornton men left in the family to carry on the name— my twin sons Birch and Sage."

"Was it important to you to bring these albums back to me at this time of night? I sense a certain anxiety in you."

"I dislike confrontations. I came here to tell you I think it's despicable what you and your brother did to that family you left behind in a tar paper shack. There are no excuses. Even if you had one, I don't want to hear it. A family, Mr. Coleman, is the most precious thing on this earth. When all else is gone, when everything else fails, family is the only thing that counts. I don't believe you looked very hard to find your family. You and Seth were already rich men when Sallie returned to that shack. You could have done the same thing. You could have gone back.

"The hatred she felt for what you did is what brings me here. Because of that deep hatred, she ruined her sons' lives and she tried to ruin mine. Today was the culmination of it all. My albums, please."

"Mrs. Thornton . . ."

"I'm no longer Mrs. Thornton. I'm Fanny Logan. My albums, please."

The old man inclined his head to the right where her albums were stacked neatly. Fanny picked them up and held them close to her chest. A sob tore at her throat. She felt herself being led to a chair. "I think you need to talk, Fanny Logan. I'm a good listener. If you want to cry, I have a whole pile of hankies."

A long time later Fanny stood, her hand extended. "I forgot about my dog. She's still in the car."

"Would you like to spend the night? It's a long drive to town."

"No thank you. It's late. Good night, Mr. Coleman."

"God willing I'll make my way to Nevada and Texas before the cold weather sets in. It's time for my clan to meet the others."

"Consider yourself damn lucky, Mr. Coleman, if any one of them opens their door to you."

"I'm not above begging and pleading," the old man said.

"Those are just words."

"You're wrong, Fanny Logan. Those are promises."

Done.

Over.

Move on, Fanny.

It was two o'clock in the morning when Fanny pulled into an all-night diner. She ordered food and carried it to the car, where she gobbled it down almost as fast as Daisy did. She sat in the parking lot for a long time, sipping her coffee and smoking cigarettes, Daisy cuddled in her lap.

At four-thirty she headed for Washington National Airport. She parked the car in long-term parking, wondering exactly what the words long-term meant. At five-thirty she was the first in line at the Delta checkin counter.

"Where to, ma'am?"

"Home. Shamrock, Pennsylvania. Two first-class tickets, one for me and one for my dog."

"Yes, ma'am. Your flight leaves in forty minutes. Gate Three."

Fanny walked across the concourse, her eyes searching for a phone booth. Daisy woofed softly when she placed her call.

"Marcus?"

"Fanny?"

"Fanny Logan, Marcus. I just wanted to tell you I love you. I also wanted to tell you I know where I'm going."

"Where, Fanny?"

"Home."

"Which home, Fanny?" Marcus asked gently.

"The only one that was ever really mine. Shamrock."

"Would you like some company? I mean besides Daisy."

"I would like that very much."

"Then hang up so I can get it all in gear. I can charter a plane. Will you wait for me at the airport in Pittsburgh?"

"Yes."

"How long will you wait?"

Fanny laughed. "Marcus Reed, me and my dog will wait as long as it takes. Didn't you hear what I said? I love you."

"You better be saying the same thing when I get off the plane. Hang up, Fanny."

"Marcus."

"Yes, Fanny?"

"I did everything I was supposed to do. I broke the last link."

"How do you feel?"

"I feel like I did in 1944 when I left Shamrock."

"Hot damn. Hang up, Fanny."

"Okay."

"You see, Daisy," she whispered, "something good did come of all of this."

She was going home. And when she got to that wonderful place called home, the man she had waited for all her life would join her.

Her world right side up, Fanny strode down the concourse to Gate Three on the last leg of her homeward journey.

Coming soon from Kensington Books

VEGAS SUNRISE

For a sample chapter of the next book in the
Thornton family's story, just turn the page . . .

1

At three-thirty in the afternoon, the loudspeaker in the offices of Babylon crackled to life. The decibel level remained high, but the customers continued to gamble. "This is a reminder, ladies and gentlemen, that Babylon will close its doors promptly at 6:00 P.M. and will not reopen until one minute past midnight. This announcement will be repeated six times during the next three hours."

"Oh, Marcus, do you really think it's going to be a surprise?" Fanny asked her husband. "What I mean is, Bess and John are smart. Don't you think they'll see through our little ruse to get them out of the casino?"

"No, I do not. Bess knows you never ask her to do anything unless it's important. She thinks she's going to the chicken ranch to coax Ruby Thornton, your—what is she, Fanny, your half sister-in-law?— to come to the casino? I think it's wonderful of you to want to include her in the family."

"She's part of this family even though Ash said she came in through the back door. She has Thornton blood, and that's good enough for me and the kids. The same goes for Ash's son. It's not right to deny Ruby or Jeff their rightful place. They're both fine people. I know it and so do my children."

"I hope it works out, Fanny."

"Of course it will work out. Why wouldn't it? Don't rain on my parade, Marcus."

"As if I would ever do that. Did the boy really agree to come in here and take over for Bess and John? I find that . . . amazing."

"I had to do some fast talking. His mother helped convince him. He's worked in the casino summers and holidays while he was in college. He knows the business and what he doesn't know, he'll learn. We signed a three-year contract with him two days ago. It has to work, Marcus, because I had no other options. If Birch were here, it would be different, but he isn't, so I did what I had to do. It's settled, so let's not talk about it. What am I going to do if Bess and John balk at their retirement present? Just because I think a year-long trip around the world is wonderful doesn't mean they will think so. Her children packed her bags and brought them over earlier. The limo is coming at midnight to take them to the airport. Everything is set unless she balks. She won't, will she, Marcus?" Fanny clenched and unclenched her hands as she paced around the office.

"Not a chance." Marcus's voice was airy, offhand. "She's going to love it. Stop fretting, Fanny. Let's check the dining room to see if your decorations are finished."

"Billie did it all. She even planned the menu, all of Bess and John's favorite foods. For five hundred people. She didn't even blink, Marcus. My daughter never ceases to amaze me. She said Bess and John weren't the only ones who were going to be surprised tonight. What do you think she meant by that?"

Marcus chuckled. "It's probably one of those inside Thornton family jokes. You love surprises. Guess you'll have to wait."

"Oh, honey, it's beautiful," Fanny exclaimed as Billie arrived, breathless, to check her handiwork. "We have to take pictures."

"The ice sculpture goes in the middle of the main table," Billie said. "There's a gizmo under the table that keeps it from melting. Sage hooked up the fountain. Chue brought the orchids earlier this afternoon. Aren't they gorgeous?"

"Only half as gorgeous as these tablecloths. Seed pearls sewn on linen, Billie?"

"I'm going to use them at our next trade show. I have a machine that does it. I wanted this to be really special. They're bringing the balloons at five o'clock. When Bess and John walk through the front door, they'll drop. From there on, it's fun, fun, fun. Our own private night. Bess's family and friends, the Colemans, all our workers and their families. Yes, Josh Coleman is coming from Virginia with his family. He called last night. We're going to have a full house. Think about it, Mom. Our blood family and our working family."

"It's like a dream," Fanny said. "I just hope Bess and John love it all. Marcus and I are going upstairs. We'll be down at five-thirty. Call me when Billie and Thad get here."

"I don't miss this place at all," Fanny said as she unlocked the door to the penthouse. "It's a shame it sits here empty. I offered Jeffrey the use of it, but he said he prefers to live at home. I don't think his mother is well, and he likes to look after her. I respect that in a son. Ash was proud of the boy even though he wouldn't admit it. I think he's going to do very well."

"Does that mean you like our little house better than these sumptuous surroundings?" Marcus asked.

"Marcus, I love our house. It reminds me of Sunrise. We have a front porch, a back porch, a garden for flowers and vegetables, a dog run, a gorgeous fireplace, a Jacuzzi. You to share it with. I couldn't ask for more. Retirement is . . . blissful."

Sage Thornton stood at the end of the jetway, his stomach muscles churning. He wondered if he was going to get sick.

He would have known his twin brother anywhere, even in profile. And then Birch turned. Air hissed from between Sage's lips. Sage stared at his father's image. Somewhere during his life, he'd seen this exact same scene. Probably sometime during his teens, when he picked up his father from the airport.

Even from this distance Birch looked lean and fit, with a bronze tint to his skin. A baseball cap that said Thornton Chickens was pushed back on his head. It was worn and frayed. A tee shirt that said Babylon across the middle, equally worn and frayed, faded blue jeans and scuffed hiking boots completed his outfit. A canvas carryall was slung over his shoulder. His eyes were bluer than sapphires against his tan. His teeth pearl white. At six-two, Birch could see over the heads of his fellow passengers. The moment he spotted Sage he dropped his bag and shouldered his way through the crowd of deplaning passengers.

They stood eyeball-to-eyeball as passengers milled about them. Sage's voice was choked when he said, "It's been a long time, Birch."

"Too long. The only thing I missed was you and Mom. C'mere, you big lug. Jesus, it's good to see you, Sage." His voice was just as choked as his brother's. "I knew you'd be the one to get married first and have a family. I want you to meet *my* wife."

Sage's jaw dropped. "You're married!"

"Yep, to the most wonderful girl in the world. We lived in a tent for three years, so that should give you some kind of an idea of what she's like. She's earthy, like Mom. She's standing over there because she wanted to give us a few minutes alone. You're gonna love her." Birch motioned for his wife to join them.

She was tall, like a showgirl, thin but well proportioned with blond hair faded almost white from the sun. Her eyes were dove gray, translucent against her honeyed tan. An eerie feeling washed through Sage when he met Celia's gaze. Somewhere within him an alarm sounded. He backed off a step and held out his hand once the introductions were made. He saw the puzzled look on Birch's face. His brother had expected him to hug his wife and welcome her into the family. Later he was going to have to think about this scene.

Celia reached for Sage's hand. "I feel like I know you. Birch spoke about you every single day."

Sage forced a laugh. "I hope it was good."

"Only wonderful things. I'm looking forward to meeting your family. We hung the pictures of you and your family in our tent. We used safety pins. Those pictures were the first thing we saw in the morning and the last thing we saw at night."

"I'm flattered. You could have written more, Birch."

"You know me. I was never a letter writer. You aren't either. Who's kidding who?"

"Okay, I'll give you that one. Do you have a lot of luggage?"

Birch and Celia burst out laughing. They pointed to their duffel bags. "This is it. I'm going to have to borrow some clothes or else show up in this attire. I'm assuming it's black tie."

"Yup. Big doings. Mom and Billie have been planning this for weeks. Probably months. Is this just a visit or are you staying?"

"We're here to stay. When you wrote that Bess and John were retiring I knew it was time to come back and run the casino. That's why I'm here. It's time."

Sage thought his stomach was going to lurch right out of his body.

"I figured we'd live in the penthouse if no one objected. How do you like living at Sunrise, Mr. Family Man?"

"I love it. Iris and the kids don't even want to come to town anymore. She says we're hermits. Maybe we are." He could feel the translucent eyes boring into his back.

"We have to buy something to wear, Birch," Celia said. "I didn't realize how awful we looked until I saw all these people so dressed up. Living in a Third World country is not conducive to fashion."

"It's not a problem, honey. We'll just go to one of the boutiques in the casino and get whatever we need."

"Just like that!"

"Uh-huh."

Sage concentrated on positioning the bags in the trunk of his car.

"God, I can't wait to take a shower. I'm going to stand under it until the water runs cold," Birch said.

"Sweetie, we have to shop. We don't want to embarrass your family."

"No, Celia, we don't have to shop. We call downstairs and they send the stuff up. We pick and choose and they take the rest back. You can do that while I'm standing under that nice hot shower."

Sage scrunched his big frame into the driver's seat. "Mom and Marcus are in the penthouse. I got you a room."

"A *room?*" Celia said.

"Actually it's a suite," Sage said. He wondered why his voice sounded so defensive.

"Guess you're going to have to wait a while to move into that fancy penthouse, honey," Birch said.

"It doesn't look the same, Birch. Mom redid it when she moved in. She hated all those mirrors, chrome and glass. It kind of looks like Sunrise now. She's got a set of those red chairs."

"What does Sunrise look like?" Celia asked from the backseat.

"Comfortable and worn. Green plants, bright colors. Home," Birch said.

"Oh," Celia said.

"You're gonna love it, honey."

"I'm sure I will."

"So, tell me about this party tonight. No, on second thought, tell me about the family. How's Mom?"

"Mom's great, happier than she's ever been. She has a wonderful life with Marcus. They live on the outskirts of town in a small house. They garden, they travel, they take the kids for days at a time. She really is happy. She and Dad made peace the last few years. There at the end he turned out to be quite a guy."

"If you call pumping a bullet into your brother quite a guy, I guess so."

"You weren't here, Birch. It was wrong, but it was right too in a cockamamie way. It's over, and I don't want to talk about it."

"Sure. I want you to know, Sage, I tried to get a plane out but it was the rainy season and I couldn't. I was sick over it. Hell, we couldn't even get to a phone for ten days. I figured it was just better to stay where I was at that point. I did grieve, Sage."

"We all did." Jesus, what was wrong with him. Why was he acting so . . . so stupid? This was Birch. This was his twin. This was his best friend sitting next to him, and he was acting like he had a burr in his jockies. He struggled with his emotions. "Sunny's doing great. She's in remission right now, and she's living permanently at the center. She has a whole new life. There aren't any words to tell you how I admire our sister. She's good with the kids, too, considering her limitations."

"I don't think I could ever give up my children for adoption," Celia said from the backseat.

Loyalty ringing in his voice, Birch said, "If Sage was your brother, you could. I bet Iris is a wonderful mother. She's like Mom, isn't she?"

"Yeah. Yeah, she is. Mom gave her all her recipes. She taught her to sew and do all those mothering things. She helped a lot with Dad at the end. Iris gets along with everyone. When the kids are older, she might want to go back to teaching at the university but then again, maybe she won't. Wait till you taste her strawberry-rhubarb pie. You can't tell the difference between hers and Mom's."

"Billie?"

"She's on top of the world. Three years in a row she was voted Woman of the Year by the textile industry. She managed to sell sixty-five million Bernie and Blossom dolls. They're still going strong. She's thinking of creating little brothers and sisters now. She's working on the prototypes. We'll test-market them in a few months."

"Guess that means the Thornton coffers are full, eh?"

Sage took that moment to look in the rearview mirror to check an eighteen-wheeler that was about to pass him. He felt his shoulders stiffen at the sight of Celia's glittering eyes.

A devil perched itself on Sage's shoulders. "You know Mom. She siphons the money out as soon as it comes in. It goes right to the rehab centers."

"How is the casino doing? Mom sent me a clipping from one of the newspapers that said Vegas expects to host 33,000,000 visitors this year and each one is expected to gamble $154.00. That's some very heavy money."

"You never showed me that article, Birch," Celia said.

"I didn't think you'd be interested, honey. I threw it away."

Sage risked a second glance in the rearview mirror. The glittering eyes looked hard and cold to him. He knew in his gut Celia was trying to calculate the amount of money in her head. He could feel a nerve start to twitch under his eye.

Birch, oblivious to his wife's petulant face, continued to ask questions. "Can we stop and see Sunny?"

"She's at the casino, Birch. Mom brought her and her friend Harry over early this morning. It was almost like old times except you were missing."

Celia leaned over the front seat. "In a wheelchair? Doesn't that create a problem?"

"No, honey. Dad was in a wheelchair. Everything at the casino is designed for the handicapped."

"She has her dog with her," Sage said. "So does Harry."

"In the casino! That's so . . . unprofessional," Celia said.

"They're trained," Sage said tightly. He didn't like this girl leaning over the seat, didn't like her warm breath wafting into his right ear, didn't like the soap and water smell of her. He didn't like her, *period*. Talk about instant reactions.

"Will you relax, Celia. Mom is closing the casino so it will be just friends and family. The dogs are special. The dogs enable Sunny to get out and about more. I think it's great."

Celia flopped back against the seat cushion.

"Where are you from, Celia?" Sage asked.

"A small town in Alabama. Population twelve hundred or so."

"Are you going back for a visit?"

"No."

"Celia's family is gone. There's nothing to go home to. In a manner of speaking she's an orphan. Was an orphan. Now she has me and our family. Right, honey?"

"We never talk about anything else. Morning, noon, and night. I feel like I know every single one of you, even the children."

The devil on Sage's shoulder moved slightly. "Didn't you *ever* talk about your family, Celia?"

"There wasn't anything to talk about. Your family is so much more . . . interesting."

And rich, Sage thought. "Do you want to go in the front door or up through the garage?"

"The garage. Neal would boot our asses right off the floor looking the way we look. What room are we in?"

"Dad's favorite room, 2711."

"What time should we be downstairs? Do you want me to hide and make a grand entrance? What's the drill here?"

"The party starts at six-thirty. Bess and John are coming in through the front door and everyone is going to yell, SURPRISE! Balloons will drop. Billie said you should weave your way around the crap tables and then we'll all yell, SURPRISE again at which point Mom will faint so be prepared to catch her. Nice meeting you, Celia.

Oh, by the way, we all kicked in to get Bess and John a year's trip around the world. Tap that trust fund, big brother."

"A year's trip around the world. That probably cost more than I could earn in a lifetime. What trust fund? Do you have a trust fund, Birch? Shame on you for not telling me. It was nice meeting you too, Sage."

Sage leaned against the wall. "This is not good," he muttered. He sat on the trunk of his car, his thoughts chaotic as he smoked three cigarettes, one after the other. Maybe he was having an off day. Maybe he didn't see what he thought he saw in the new Mrs. Thornton's eyes. *Keep your thoughts to yourself. Don't look for trouble,* an inner voice warned.

Sage walked over to the elevator. He shivered and didn't know why.

"Here they come! Here they come! Get ready!" Fanny cried, excitement ringing in her voice.

The great doors opened. Bess and John Noble walked onto the casino floor to the shouts of "SURPRISE!" Colored balloons rained downward.

Fanny ran to her friends of forty years and swept them into her arms. "Don't cry, Bess, I don't have any tissues. We wanted to do this for you. It hardly seems enough for all you've done for our family. We are giving you a trip around the world, a whole year, to do nothing but spend time with your husband. Please say you want it."

"I'm saying it for both of us," John said. "We were just talking about taking a trip last week. Nothing as grand as a trip around the world. We accept, don't we, Bess."

"Yes. Fanny . . ."

"Shhh, it's our pleasure. All the kids chipped in. Your kids packed your bags. I know they packed all the wrong things, so if you play the third machine from the left in aisle two you'll have enough money for a new wardrobe."

"Oh, Fanny . . . what a good, kind friend you are."

"Hey, I'm taking up too much time. The line behind me is getting longer and longer. Everyone wants to give you a kiss and a hug. Tonight you're Cinderella and your limo will be by the front door at exactly midnight. I'm going to miss you, so send lots and lots of postcards."

"Mom, look over there by the crap tables," Sage whispered in her ear.

"Is that Birch? No! It is!"

Sage stepped aside as his brother swept his mother into his arms, twirling her around and around until she was dizzy. "Oh, Birch, it's so good to see you. You look so handsome. Actually you look just the way your father looked when he wore his tux. This is such a wonderful surprise!"

"Mom, this is Celia, my wife."

"You're married, and you didn't tell anyone!"

"Mom, we're here to stay. I'd like to start to work on Monday if that's okay with you."

Sage, his wife next to him, watched as Birch drew Celia forward. He was in a perfect position to see his mother's raised eyebrows at the young woman's attire. He didn't think it was his imagination when he saw her shoulders tense.

Celia, dressed in a strapless, backless black sequined sheath of a dress with a slit up the side, stepped forward. Fanny reached for Celia's hands but didn't kiss or hug her. "I'm so pleased to meet you, Celia. Welcome to the family. How do you like Babylon?"

"It's . . . fantastic. I shopped all afternoon. Living in a tent and taking a shower under a waterfall is . . . this is just wonderful. I can't believe you *own* all of this."

"It is a bit startling at first. After a while, it's just a place of business."

Iris turned away to stare at the people surrounding Bess and John. "What would you do if I dressed like that, Sage? I feel like a Girl Scout leader compared to her. For someone who lived in a tent and showered under a waterfall she looks pretty good in those diamonds. I thought you said they only had raggedy stuff."

"She went shopping," Sage hissed. "Mom didn't hug her or kiss her the way she did you when she first met you."

"She's taking a wait-and-see attitude. Birch was shock enough. Coupling that with a new bride who looks like she belongs in the chorus line should give you your answer. What do you think of her?"

Sage evaded the question. "Birch is in love with her. It doesn't matter what anyone else thinks. She just got here. She's probably nervous, and by now she's aware that she isn't dressed right."

"Oh, she's dressed right. Those shoes she's wearing cost $800. I saw them in the shop last week. What you're seeing is who that young woman is. She's a lot younger than Birch, too. I don't think I'm going to like her."

Sage's sigh of relief was so loud, Iris shook his arm. "You don't like her either, do you? You were waiting for me to say it first. We need to give her a chance. First impressions are not always what they seem. Let's agree, Sage, to stand back and be fair. Okay?"

"Sure, honey. You don't look like a Girl Scout leader to me. That's a nifty dress you're wearing, and you look great."

"Aunt Billie made it for me. She made one for Sunny and Billie, too. Sunny's looking better than I've seen her look in a long time. I guess it's because she's happy."

"Guess so. I'm going to check on the kids. Lexie's probably wading in one of the pools by now."

"Marcus is watching them. They were picking flowers for Sunny in one of the hanging gardens."

"I'll check it out. It's my turn to kiss Bess and John. I'll see you later by the banquet table."

Sunny waved from across the room. Iris weaved her way toward her. She bent over to kiss her and Harry, whose chair was parked next to Sunny's, their dogs next to their respective chairs.

"There she is, one of my two favorite people in the whole world. Here comes the other one," Birch said as Billie came up behind Sunny's chair. Iris watched as Birch kissed and hugged his sisters before he introduced his new wife. She didn't know if she should laugh or cry at the expressions on Sunny and Billie's faces. The expression of distaste on her sister-in-law's face was so fleeting she thought she imagined it until Sunny, in her own inimitable way, let her know she'd seen it too.

"Harry and I were wondering if we dare head for the banquet table. We forgot our bibs." She looked pointedly at Celia when she said, "We drool and dribble our food at times. What would happen if you did that wearing such a fancy dress?" she asked Celia.

"I guess I'd have to get it cleaned." Celia looked pointedly at her husband, who was talking to Harry, Sunny's companion.

"The cleaners would ruin it," Billie said.

Celia made a little face. "I think I made the wrong choice when I picked out this dress. Birch has always said this was such a glittery, shimmering place, I thought it would be appropriate. I was wrong. I just itched to buy it. I lived in cutoff jeans and raggedy tee shirts for so long. I just didn't think. I hope I didn't offend anyone."

"Just my mother and me," Sunny said. Billie cleared her throat. Iris looked away.

"Did I miss something?" Birch asked.

"No. Sunny was just agreeing with me that I'm dressed all wrong. She said I probably offended your mother."

"See, I told you, but you wouldn't listen." Birch tweaked Celia's cheek before he walked over to Bess and John Noble.

"Are those diamonds real?" Sunny asked.

"No, but they're very good fakes. Birch insisted I get them. He said he wanted me to sparkle tonight. Guess they're wrong, too."

Sunny's voice was prim when she said, "We're not a showy family. Actually, we're all rather modest. Mom always said less is more if you know what I mean."

"Yes. Thank you for pointing it out to me."

"My pleasure," Sunny said.

"Excuse me. Birch is motioning for me to join him."

"Sunny, that was uncalled for," Billie said.

"Damn straight it was. I saw the expression on her face when she looked at me and Harry. It was distaste. Ask Iris if you don't believe me." Iris nodded, her face miserable.

"She's in a new environment. We're all strangers to her. So she dressed wrong, so what? All of us at one time or another either overdressed or underdressed. Don't create a problem, Sunny, where none exists. She's Birch's wife," Billie said.

Harry, silent until now, said, "I used to paint portraits. I was pretty good, too. The critics always said my eyes were the best. That's because they're the mirror of one's soul. That young woman has no soul. That's strictly my own opinion. Let's try the banquet table, Sunny. My hands are more steady than yours are today, so I'll hand you the food. We'll come back here to eat it out of the way, okay?"

"Sure. Will you guys watch our dogs?"

"Sure," Billie said.

"I admire Sunny so," Iris said, a catch in her voice.

Billie's voice was soft when she said, "Me too."

"Birch's timing was off. I think that's what this is all about. It would have been nice if he'd waited and made it a family thing so Celia could be the center of attention. However, I understand where he's coming from. Sage said he expects to start work on Monday. Did anyone tell him about Jeffrey? Sage said it wasn't his place to tell him. He also said Birch doesn't know how to play second banana. Does that mean there's going to be a problem, Billie?"

"Off the top of my head, I'd say yes. Let's not worry about that tonight. We're here to have a good time, so let's have a good time."

"Do I look dowdy and frumpy, Billie?"

"Absolutely not."

"Then why do I feel that way?"

"Because your quiet, peaceful world has been invaded by a smashing blond bombshell. I feel a little dowdy myself. I thought I looked pretty good when I left the house."

"So we're jealous is what you're saying."

"No, that's not what I'm saying. We're who we are, and Celia is who she is."

"Sage sees something we aren't seeing. He was so hyped about going to the airport to pick up Birch. He hasn't slept for three nights. That's how excited he was. When he got back, it was . . . sad. I felt so bad I wanted to cry for him. He had these wonderful plans, these great expectations, and suddenly a new wife on the scene wiped all those plans away. He knows there's going to be some kind of blowup when Birch finds out Jeff signed on to run Babylon."

"Everything will work itself out, Iris. Mom will step in and do what she always does, bring order and sense to everything."

"Not this time, Billie. Birch has a wife now, and she's going to have a voice in everything he says and does.

"There's Jeff now. He does look a lot like your dad. Ruby's really nice. I like her a lot. I'm glad your mom welcomed her into the family. She belongs. Right off, she wanted to know what she could do. She pitched right in. She looks so damn normal compared to . . . Celia. I thought you were bringing your boyfriend tonight."

"He had duty. Detectives are on call twenty-four hours a day. He might stop by later. It's not serious. We're good friends. I like him. He likes me. He doesn't just listen to me, Iris, he actually *hears* what I say. I like that in a man. I'm not about to get serious. I like being my own person, making my own decisions. It works for me. Being married and having kids works for you."

"What do you think works for Celia Thornton?"

"The Thornton money."

"I'm of the same opinion."

"Sunny's dribbling. Let's go clean her up."

"Me too," Iris said. "Billie, earlier Jake . . . what happened was Sunny was drinking a soda pop and she let the bottle slip. Jake . . . that little kid was so good about it. He wiped it up and said, 'Heck, Mom, I do that all the time.' Sunny's eyes filled up, and Jake wiped away her tears. He whispered to her for a long time. I guess he was giving her a pep talk because she started to laugh. He was grinning from ear to ear. He's really good with Harry, too. Ash made sure Jake understood his mother's limitations and his own as well. He really understands, Billie. Do you think as he gets older it will stay with him? Peer pressure is a terrible thing with kids. Every day I do my best to reinforce all that your dad taught him."

"Of course it will stay with him. That boy idolized his grandfather. Trust me, his teachings will stay with Jake. I appreciate you telling me this, Iris."

At ten minutes to midnight, Fanny asked for a drumroll. "Ladies and gentlemen, it's time for our guests of honor to make their way to the limo that is going to whisk them to the airport to begin the first leg of their journey. Let's all give them a big hand."

Bess and John ran to the door. Tears rolled down Bess's cheeks as she waved to everyone, her eyes searching for Fanny in the crowd.

"Have a good trip, old friend. Take lots of pictures and send a card every week."

"Fanny, this is the wrong time for me to be leaving. That girl spells trouble. I could feel it and I could smell it. My feeling has nothing to do with the outfit she's wearing either. John loved it. There's something about her that bothers me."

"Bess, don't worry. I have your itinerary. I'll call if there's a problem. Hey, old buddy, this is me. The me who has a crisis in her life at least twice a month. Go and have a wonderful time. They're blowing the horn for you."

"Come on, Fanny," Marcus said, taking her elbow. "Time to go upstairs. The doors are now open to the public. The party is over. I think it went very well. You see, you worried for nothing. Your family is headed for the Harem Lounge for a nightcap. They asked us to join them."

Fanny nodded. "Marcus, how am I going to tell Birch he has to work under his half brother?"

"You just tell him, Fanny. Are you thinking of going back on your word?"

"I would never do that."

"Then there's no other way except to be up front and open about it. You said Birch and Sage worked here together. Running this place is a full-time job for six people, never mind two. From what you said, this Birch is different from the Birch who went away a long time ago. He's older, wiser, more mature, and he has a wife now."

"I wonder if that's going to be a problem."

"Take a look," Marcus said. "I wonder what they're talking about."

Fanny looked into the lounge. Her children were seated at the bar. Celia was perched on one of the stools, a generous expanse of leg showing. To her right was Birch, who was talking to Sage. To her left, Jeffrey Lassiter. Celia swiveled her stool until she was facing Jeffrey.

Celia's voice was playful, coy when she said, "And who might you be?"

Jeffrey Lassiter smiled. "Me? I'm the illegitimate son who's going to own this casino someday."

YF

Michaels, Fern
Vegas heat

DATE DUE

JUN - 8 2009		
Stiles		

GAYLORD   #3523PI   Printed in USA